ANNUAL REVIEW OF
BIOPHYSICS AND
BIOMOLECULAR STRUCTURE

ANNUAL REVIEW OF BIOPHYSICS AND BIOMOLECULAR STRUCTURE

VOLUME 27, 1998

ROBERT M. STROUD, *Editor*
University of California, San Francisco

WAYNE L. HUBBELL, *Associate Editor*
University of California, Los Angeles

WILMA K. OLSON, *Associate Editor*
Rutgers, The State University of New Jersey

MICHAEL P. SHEETZ, *Associate Editor*
Duke University, Durham

http://annurev.org   science@annurev.org   650-493-4400

ANNUAL REVIEWS   4139 EL CAMINO WAY   P.O. BOX 10139   PALO ALTO, CALIFORNIA 94303-0139

ANNUAL REVIEWS
Palo Alto, California, USA

International Standard Serial Number: 1056-8700
International Standard Book Number: 0-8243-1827-7
Library of Congress Catalog Card Number: 79-188446

TYPESET BY TECHBOOKS, FAIRFAX, VA
PRINTED AND BOUND IN THE UNITED STATES OF AMERICA

PREFACE

NOVEL TECHNOLOGY, AND NEW HORIZONS IN SCIENCE   The old adage had it that one might best spend time looking for lost keys to the car under the street lamp because that was where the light shone. The synergy of advances in technology and science allows us to move away from the old street lamp in our search for the keys to biology. Biophysicists often play key roles in the intellectual process of inventing new technology, as they do in scientific discovery with their own hand on the wheel of technological advances. This year is marked by several breakthroughs that now remove the gap between organization at the cellular level and atomic structure. Fittingly, Max Perutz, the pioneer who first showed how the atomic structures of proteins could be determined, opens this volume.

Max Perutz and his colleagues focus on the mechanisms of hemoglobin. Max first found the way to determine the atomic structure of proteins by showing how addition of heavy metal ions to protein crystals could determine the essential phases of the diffracted x-ray intensities. Max's article, tracing the milestones, and the still outstanding issues with regard to hemoglobin, reminds us that understanding the mechanisms of any single protein is a profound lifelong goal.

Perutz's achievements were completely remarkable, so it is useful to recall the time when Max started his endeavors, as a postgraduate research student and a member of Peterhouse college, in Cambridge England, the institution he joined on October 1st. 1936. The science of x-ray crystallography was marked by the discoveries of Laue, and then of William Bragg and his son Lawrence. Max was fascinated by JD Bernal's demonstration, carried out with Dorothy Crowfoot Hodgkin in 1934, that protein crystals when maintained in a hydrated state, gave rich diffraction patterns that promised atomic resolution information. Their first crystals had been of pepsin. However, even the structure of sucrose had not yet been determined, and most structures of small molecules and minerals solved by crystallography were solved by trial and great ingenuity. How could one possibly approach the structure of a protein some 1500 times larger?

By 1937 Max had obtained some crystals of horse hemoglobin from Gilbert Adair, a professor of physiology at Cambridge, and Max quickly showed that

(*continued*)   v

they had rich diffraction patterns that promised atomic resolution information. Until this time, the problem for crystallographers of small molecules usually amounted to first matching intensities of the diffracted rays by intuition and trial, and then finally calculating the phases as refinement proceeded. In a sense Max recast the problem, as how to first extract the missing phases of diffracted rays and then to calculate the density map. After 16 years of diligent research, Max found in 1953 the solution that quickly became the formula for protein structure determination. He showed that addition of two mercury atoms to hemoglobin changed the diffraction pattern in a way that could be used first to determine the positions of the mercury atoms, and then to calculate the phases of the protein diffracted rays.

New horizons are made accessible by such rare and far reaching discoveries. Max's goal remains to understand the complex regulatory mechanisms of hemoglobin. Along the way, in 1945, he was joined by his first research student, the late John Kendrew who worked on sheep hemoglobin, and then switched to myoglobin. In 1947 the Medical Research Council made Perutz's group into the Medical Research Unit for Molecular Biology, then housed in an annex within the historic Cavendish Laboratories of Physics. In structural biology this was one of the most crucial developments in the history of the science, marrying insights from physics and chemistry, with the efforts to understand biology. In 1957 the first electron density maps of myoglobin were obtained. In 1959 the first atomic structure of any protein molecule was completed. In 1962, Max Perutz and John Kendrew were awarded the Nobel Prize for these landmark achievements. Max's discoveries are now taught in every university and in every medical school around the world. They are taught in every course in biochemistry and in protein crystallography. Max's perspective on the hemoglobin field illustrates many lessons. The problem of understanding the properties of proteins remains profound, and the solutions will be as enriching and novel, and surprising as they continue to be.

In the structural fields, 1997 marked the development of several mature technologies to critical transitions that eliminate the gap between cellular organelles, and atomic resolution structure and mechanism. The ability to analyze the structure of molecules by combining electron micrographic images of single molecules has closed the gap that used to exist between structures of cellular organelles and atomic structures. This field benefits from the unique developments in electron microscopes developed by Fujioshi in Japan, which has become the current mecca for electron microscopists throughout the world. Fujioshi and his collaborators have reported even higher atomic resolution structures of bacteriorhodopsin, and they continue to provide images that are the key to atomic resolution structures of neuroreceptors, nuclear pores, and tubulin.

A second technological milestone is the development of synchrotron technologies. The world's most powerful synchrotron, Spring-8, operates in Nishi-Harima, Japan. The second most powerful, the Advanced Photon Source in Argonne, Illinois, completed its first year of operations, and no less than 26 new synchrotron facilities are currently being developed. Using the emerging synchrotron technologies, Tim Richmond and his international group used the European Synchrotron Radiation Facility (ESRF) in Grenoble, France, to produce an atomic-resolution map of the nucleosome with DNA wound around the protein core. Rosenbusch and his team used the ESRF synchrotron source to determine the X-ray structure of bacteriorhodopsin, an integral membrane protein. The structure of the bluetongue virus, amazing in its complex association of over 1000 protein subunits was determined by Stuart and his colleagues at Oxford. The Advanced Light Source in Berkeley is now operational.

The power of NMR imaging, and in multi-dimensional NMR of the ability to study protein structure and dynamics, is illustrated in this volume. Advances in optical microscopy, including standing wave fluorescence and interference imaging, have dramatically increased the resolution attainable in the out of plane direction to 700 Å. The green fluorescent protein has illuminated cellular dynamics. Thus, the understanding of cellular dynamics at the level of atomic structure is finally within reach. Developments in technology continue to open new horizons in science, which make this volume of the *Annual Review of Biophysics and Biomolecular Structure* especially exciting.

ROBERT M. STROUD
EDITOR

Annual Review of Biophysics and Biomolecular Structure
Volume 27 (1998)

CONTENTS

    (continued)

RELATED ARTICLES FROM OTHER *ANNUAL REVIEWS*

From the *Annual Review of Cell and Developmental Biology*, Volume 14, 1998:

Biochemistry and Structure of p53, N. Pavletich Prions, C. Weissman
The Tight Junction: Morphology to Molecules, B. R. Stevenson, B. H. Keon
Cell Polarity and Adhesion, W. J. Nelson
The Mitotic Microtubule Complex, T. Salmon, K. Bloom
ER Signaling: Regulation of Unfolded Protein Response, P. Walter

From the *Annual Review of Physiology*, Volume 60, 1998:

The Physiological Basis of Diving to Depth: Birds and Mammals, G. L. Kooyman, P. J. Ponganis
Aquaporin-2 and 3: Representatives of Two Subgroups of the Aquaporin Family Colocalized in the Kidney Collecting Duct, S. Sasaki, K. Ishibashi, F. Marumo
The Luteinizing Hormone Receptor, M. L. Dufau
A View of SUR/$K_{IR}6.X$, K_{ATP} Channels, A. P. Babenko, L. Aguilar-Bryan, J. Bryan
CIC and CFTR Chloride Channel Gating, J. K. Foskett

From the *Annual Review of Physical Chemistry*, Volume 49, 1998:

Spectroscopy of Atoms and Molecules in Liquid He, J. P. Toennies, A. F. Vilesov
Nanocrystal Superlattices, C. P. Collier, T. Vossmeyer, J. R. Heath

Annu. Rev. Biophys. Biomol. Struct. 1998. 27:1–34

THE STEREOCHEMICAL MECHANISM OF THE COOPERATIVE EFFECTS IN HEMOGLOBIN REVISITED

M. F. Perutz
MRC Laboratory of Molecular Biology, Cambridge CB2 2QH, United Kingdom

A. J. Wilkinson, M. Paoli,[1] G. G. Dodson
Department of Chemistry, University of York, York YO1 5DD, United Kingdom;
e-mail: ajw@yorvic.ac.uk; m.paoli@massey.ac.nz; ggd@yorvic.york.ac.uk

KEY WORDS: allostery, reaction intermediates, heme tension

ABSTRACT

In 1970, Perutz tried to put the allosteric mechanism of hemoglobin, proposed by Monod, Wyman and Changeux in 1965, on a stereochemical basis. He interpreted their two-state model in terms of an equilibrium between two alternative structures, a tense one (T) with low oxygen affinity, constrained by salt-bridges between the C-termini of the four subunits, and a relaxed one (R) lacking these bridges. The equilibrium was thought to be governed primarily by the positions of the iron atoms relative to the porphyrin: out-of-plane in five-coordinated, high-spin deoxyhemoglobin, and in-plane in six-coordinated, low-spin oxyhemoglobin. The tension exercised by the salt-bridges in the T-structure was to be transmitted to the heme-linked histidines and to restrain the movement of the iron atoms into the porphyrin plane that is necessary for oxygen binding. At the β-hemes, the distal valine and histidine block the oxygen-combining site in the T-structure; its tension was thought to strengthen that blockage. Finally, Perutz attributed the linearity of proton release with early oxygen uptake to the sequential rupture of salt-bridges in the T-structure and to the accompanying drop in pKa of the weak bases that form part of them. Almost every feature of this mechanism has been disputed, but evidence that has come to light more than 25 years

---

[1]Present address: Department of Biochemistry, Massey University, Palmerston North, New Zealand.

1

1056-8700/98/0610-0001$08.00

later now shows it to have been substantially correct. That new evidence is reviewed below.

CONTENTS

INTRODUCTION AND OVERVIEW

In 1965, Monod, Wyman, and Changeux (MWC) proposed their famous theory of allostery. They postulated that cooperative effects arise in enzymes composed of several symmetrically arranged subunits that alternate between at least two structures, a tense one (T) and a relaxed one (R), which differ by the arrangement of the subunits and the number and strengths of the bonds between them. Metabolites unrelated to the enzymes' substrates control their reactions by altering the equilibrium between these alternative structures while symmetry is preserved. Recent thermodynamic evidence in favor of a metastable intermediate in the reaction of hemoglobin (Hb) with oxygen seemed to speak against the notion that two alternative structures were sufficient to account for the reaction's cooperativity, but this evidence has now been proved artifactual.

In 1970, emergence of the atomic structures of deoxy-(T) and oxyhemoglobin (R) brought the first structural test of the MWC theory. Hemoglobin is a tetramer in which the α and β subunits are disposed symmetrically about a central, water-filled cavity. Transition between the two structures consists in a rotation and translation of one $\alpha\beta$ dimer relative to the other. The additional bonds predicted by MWC were found to consist of C-terminal salt-bridges between the subunits in the T-structure. The regulator 2,3-diphosphoglycerate biased the

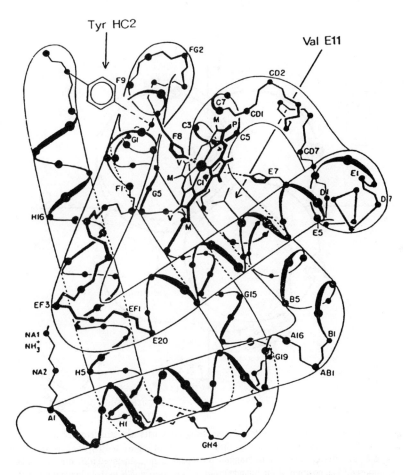

Figure 1   Secondary and tertiary structure of the hemoglobins showing α-carbons and coordination of the hemes. The diagram shows the proximal histidine F8 linked to the heme iron, the distal residues His E7 and Val E11, and also Tyr HC2, all of which are important in the mechanism of the mammalian hemoglobins. The numbers of residues in the different segments are the same in all mammals, but they vary in other vertebrates and especially in invertebrates. *M*, methyl side chain of the heme; *V*, vinyl side chain of the heme; *P*, propionate side chain of the heme.

allosteric equilibrium by binding to a stereochemically complementary site in the T-structure which is disrupted in the T → R transition (Figures 1–3). Perutz proposed that to initiate that transition "the oxygenation of Hb is accompanied by structural changes in the subunits, triggered by shifts of the iron atoms relative to the porphyrin and, in the β-subunits, also by the steric effects of oxygen itself." Steric hindrance by the distal residues in the β-subunits led to the prediction that the α-subunits have the higher oxygen affinity.

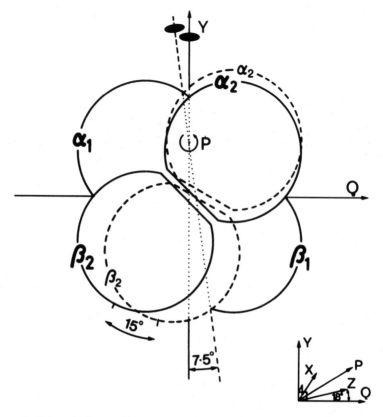

Figure 2 Schematic diagram illustrating the change in quaternary structure that accompanies ligation of hemoglobin. Ligation causes little movement of the α_1 and β_1 or of the α_2 and β_2 subunits relative to each other. In the diagram, the liganded and unliganded $\alpha_1\beta_1$ dimers have been superimposed. The position of the liganded $\alpha_2\beta_2$ dimer corresponds to that obtained by rotating the unliganded $\alpha_2\beta_2$ dimer about an axis P by an angle $\theta = 12$–15 degrees and shifting it along the axis P by 1 Å into the page (this axis is perpendicular to the dyad symmetry axes, marked Y, of both the liganded and unliganded molecules and to the picture plane). *Bold symbols* and *plain lines* in the diagram refer to deoxyhemoglobin; *light symbols* and *broken lines* to liganded hemoglobin.

In 1972, Perutz proposed that "heme-heme interaction, i.e. cooperativity, consists in a change of tension at the heme, brought about by a transition between two alternative structures of the globin." He attributed the low oxygen affinity of the T-structure to tension by the proximal histidines restraining the movement of the iron atom from its out-of-plane position in deoxy-Hb to its in-plane position in oxy-Hb. Spectroscopic evidence seemed to speak against that tension, but the recent structures of several ligated, low-spin Hbs have shown tension in the

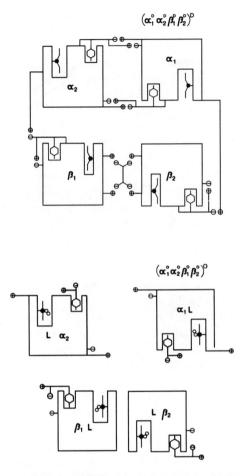

Figure 3 Diagrammatic sketch of closing of salt-bridges by C-terminal residues in deoxy (T) and opening in oxyhemoglobin (R). The molecule with the four negative charges between the β chains of the T structure represents diphosphoglycerate (34). The superscripts D and O stand for *deoxy* and *oxy*; L stands for *ligated*.

α-subunits to be strong enough to break the bond between the iron and the proximal histidine. In the β-subunits, on the other hand, steric hindrance to ligand binding by the distal residues is dominant. The absence of cooperativity in an Hb in which glycines have been substituted for the proximal histidines and their sidechains have been replaced by free imidazoles has proved the essential role of the iron-histidine bond in transmitting the movement of the iron to the globin. Comparison of the electron density maps of half- and fully-oxygenated Hbs in the T-structure has shown that ligand binding by one pair of heme-irons produces distinct stereochemical changes at the other pair, proving that some interaction between the hemes does take place even in the absence of an allosteric transition.

On the other hand, determination of the oxygen equilibrium curves of Hbs constrained in crystals or gels to maintain either the quaternary T or R structure has proved cooperativity within the T-structure to contribute no more than $\frac{1}{5}$ of the total free energy of cooperativity of oxygen binding. Cooperativity is absent in the R-structure. Oxygen equilibria of metal hybrids have shown that, as predicted, the oxygen affinity of the α-subunits is three times larger than that of the β-subunits.

In 1970, Perutz proposed the release of Bohr protons to be due to rupture of C-terminal salt-bridges. This has now been found to be true only for the chloride-independent part of the alkaline Bohr effect, while the chloride-dependent part is due to changes in charge compensation of cationic groups lining the central cavity. To account for the observed sequential release of Bohr protons with oxygen uptake by the T-structure, Perutz postulated that the C-terminal salt-bridges break sequentially, some of them breaking before the allosteric T $\rightarrow$ R transition, yet these bridges were found to remain intact in crystals of ligated Hbs in the T-structure. On the other hand, these crystals also lacked a Bohr effect. In Hbs maintained in the T-structure in gels, a Bohr effect has now been found, apparently because the molecules are less rigidly constrained, so that the salt-bridges are free to break. These gels also have a higher oxygen affinity than the crystals, close to that of Hb in solution.

Theory of Allostery

Allosteric proteins control and coordinate chemical events in the living cell. When Monod (23) conceived that idea he said that he had discovered the second secret of life. The first was the structure of DNA. The theory as published by Monod, Changeux, and Jacob was concerned chiefly with cooperativity and feedback inhibition of enzymes, such as the inhibition by isoleucine of threonine deaminase, the first enzyme in the pathway of the synthesis of isoleucine, and its activation by valine. Two years later the theory was formalized by Monod, Wyman, and Changeux, and is now generally referred to as the MWC theory (23, 24).

The MWC theory holds that cooperative substrate binding—and modification of enzymic activity by metabolites bearing no stereochemical relationship to either substrate or product—may arise in proteins with two or more structures in equilibrium. It predicts that such proteins are likely to be made up of several subunits symmetrically arranged, and that the structures would differ by the arrangement of the subunits and number and/or energy of the bonds between them. In one structure the subunits would be constrained by strong bonds that would resist the tertiary changes needed for substrate binding; they called this structure "T" for tense. In the other structure these constraints would be relaxed, and they called it "R." In the transition between them, the symmetry of the molecule would be conserved, so that the activity of all its subunits would be either equally low or equally high. The postulate of symmetry also seemed to have some aesthetic fascination for Monod, like Ptolemy's spheres, quite independent of its formal advantages. Koshland et al's sequential model did not invoke any restrictions: Each subunit is allowed to change its tertiary structure on substrate binding and thereby to affect the chemical activities of its neighbors (20). According to the MWC theory, allosteric enzymes would have the biological advantage that no direct interaction need occur between the substrate of the protein and the regulatory metabolite which controls its activity, because control would be due entirely to a change of structure induced in the protein when it binds its specific effector. The authors added the prophetic sentence: "More complete observations, once available, might justify the conclusion that allosteric transitions frequently involve alterations in quaternary structure."

Structure and Function of Hemoglobin

Hemoglobin (Hb) (MW = 64,500) is a tetramer made up of two α-chains and two β-chains, each containing 141 and 146 amino acid residues, respectively. Each chain carries one heme. The α-chains contain seven and the β-chains eight helical segments, interrupted by nonhelical ones. Each chain also carries short nonhelical segments at the N and C termini. As shown in Figure 1, the hemes are held in pockets formed by several helical and nonhelical segments; their Fe's are five-coordinated to N_ε of histidines F8, also known as proximal, and to the four porphyrin nitrogens (N_{porph}); the porphyrin is in van der Waals contact with another histidine on the distal side (E7) and also makes contact with 18 other amino acid side chains, most of which are nonpolar. The propionate side chains of the porphyrin protrude into the solvent and form hydrogen bonds with basic side chains of the globin. The ferrous heme irons combine reversibly with O_2 to form dioxygen complexes, and in the process change from high- to low-spin. The reaction is cooperative, with a free energy of cooperativity, under physiological conditions, of 3.6 kcal mol^{-1} (15 kJ mol^{-1}) heme^{-1}.

AV Hill first expressed the oxygen equilibrium of Hb mathematically in the equation named after him. If Y is the fractional saturation with oxygen and P_{50} the partial pressure of oxygen at 50% saturation, then

$$\frac{Y}{1-Y} = n \log\left(\frac{Po_2}{P_{50}}\right), \tag{1}$$

where n is known as Hill's coefficient and is normally 3.0. This equation holds only over the middle part of the sigmoid equilibrium curve, which was all that was known at the time (13). Adair later derived an exact equation with four association constants A_i, known as the Adair constants, which can be fitted to the equilibrium curve (2). If p is the partial pressure of oxygen,

$$A_1 = \frac{[\text{Hb}(O_2)]}{[\text{Hb}] \times p}, \quad A_2 = \frac{[\text{Hb}(O_2)_2]}{[\text{Hb}(O_2)] \times p},$$

etc, then

$$Y = \frac{\left(A_1 p + 2A_1 A_2 P^2 + 3A_1 A_2 A_3 p^3 + 4A_1 A_2 A_3 A_4 p^4\right)}{4\left(1 + A_1 p + A_1 A_2 p^2 + A_1 A_2 A_3 p^3 + A_1 A_2 A_3 A_4 p^4\right)}. \tag{2}$$

The oxygen affinity of mammalian Hbs is lowered by H^+, Cl^-, CO_2, and 2,3–D-diphosphoglycerate (DPG), all of which are present in the red cell. They are known collectively as allosteric effectors.

The cooperative binding of O_2 ensures uptake and release of O_2 over the comparatively narrow range of partial O_2 pressures that distinguishes the lungs ($pO_2 \sim 100$ mmHg) from the tissues ($pO_2 \sim 30\text{–}40$ mmHg). Hb binds one H^+ for every two O_2's released; this uptake biases the equilibrium of the reaction between CO_2 and H_2O in the direction of HCO_3^-, thus promoting the transport of CO_2 by the blood serum. Conversely, the protons released by the metabolic products, lactic and carbonic acids, facilitate the release of O_2 to the tissues.

In the hemoglobins of bony vertebrates the cooperative effects arise from an equilibrium between two alternative Hb structures, the oxy or R (relaxed) and deoxy or T (tense) structure. In the oxy structure the heme-irons are six-coordinated. This structure is the same regardless of the nature of the sixth heme ligand or the valency and spin-state of the iron. In the deoxy-structure the heme irons are five-coordinated, ferrous, and high spin. The O_2 affinity of the R structure is slightly larger than the average of free α- and β-subunits; that of the T structure is lower by the equivalent of the free energy of cooperativity. According to the MWC theory, the O_2 equilibrium of Hb can be described by the O_2 association constants K_T and K_R, usually expressed in mmHg^{-1}, and by the equilibrium constant $L_i = [T_i]/[R_i]$. Monod et al defined K_T and K_R as oxygen dissociation constants, but following Imai (15) we have defined them as association constants to give them the same dimensions as the Adair constants in Equation 2. L_i is the equilibrium constant with i oxygens or other heme ligands bound. Imai has shown empirically that $\log K_T/K_R = A - 0.25 \log L_0$, where A is a constant, which leaves K_T and K_R as the only independent variables. K_T varies over a wide range as a function of $[H^+]$, $[Cl^-]$, $[CO_2]$, and $[DPG]$; K_R varies as a function of $[H^+]$ below pH 7.0, but is little affected by the other ligands.

The T and R structures differ in the arrangement of the four subunits, referred to as the quaternary structure, and in the conformation of the subunits, referred to as the tertiary structure. The quaternary $R \leftrightarrow T$ transition consists of a rotation of the dimer $\alpha_1\beta_1$ relative to the dimer $\alpha_2\beta_2$ by 12–15° and a translation of one dimer relative to the other by 0.8 Å (Figure 2). The $\alpha\beta$ dimers move relative to each other at the symmetry-related contacts $\alpha_1\beta_2$ and $\alpha_2\beta_1$ and at the contacts $\alpha_1\alpha_2$ and $\beta_1\beta_2$; the contacts $\alpha_1\beta_1$ and $\alpha_2\beta_2$ remain rigid (3).

At the $\alpha_1\beta_2$ interface the nonhelical segment FGα_1 is in contact with helix Cβ_2, and helix Cα_1 with FGβ_2. During the R → T transition, the contact FGα_1-Cβ_2 acts as a ball and socket joint, while the contact Cα_1-FGβ_2 acts as a two-way switch that shifts Cα_1 relative to FGβ_2 by about 6 Å, like the knuckles of one hand moving over those of the other. Intermediate positions of the switch are blocked by steric hindrance which renders intermediates between T and R unstable (3). The gaps along the central cavity between α_1 and α_2 and between β_1 and β_2 narrow on transition from T to R. The shape of the $\alpha_1\beta_1$ and $\alpha_2\beta_2$ dimers is altered by changes in tertiary structure; for example, on oxygenation the distance between the α-carbons of residues FG1α_1 and β_1 shrinks from 45.3 to 41.3 Å. Janin & Wodak have shown that these changes make an $\alpha_1\beta_1$ dimer that has the tertiary oxy structure a misfit in the quaternary T structure and an $\alpha_1\beta_1$ dimer that has the tertiary deoxy structure a misfit in the quaternary R structure (58). This misfit has important consequences for the mechanism of cooperativity, which is discussed below.

EVIDENCE FOR STABLE INTERMEDIATES BETWEEN THE R- AND T-STRUCTURES

The Molecular Code for Cooperativity

Wyman introduced the concept of linkage (56). Hb dissociates into $\alpha\beta$ dimers, but the dissociation constant of the R-structure is higher by six orders of magnitude than that of the T-structure. According to Wyman, the fraction D of tetramers dissociated into dimers is related to Y, the fractional saturation with heme ligands by

$$\left[\frac{\partial Y}{\partial \ln D}\right]_Y = \left[\frac{\partial D}{\partial \ln Y}\right]_D.$$

Ackers and his associates have used that equation to predict the oxygen affinities of all possible intermediate states of ligation from the tetramer ↔ dimer dissociation constants of cyanomet-hybrids in which one or more α- or β-subunits containing $Fe^{3+}CN^-$ were combined with ferrous deoxy subunits (1). They prepared the ten microstates shown in Table 1 and reported that those were distinguished by three different tetramer-dimer dissociation constants, corresponding to free energies of −14.3 kcal for fully deoxyHb in the T-structure; −11.2 kcal for Hb with either any single deoxy subunit replaced by $Fe^{3+}CN^-$

Table 1 Cooperative free energies for the ten ligation microstates

Ligation microstate		Parent species	Assembly free energy	Cooperative free energy
[01]		None	−14.3	0
[11]		+	−11.3	3.0
[12]		+	−11.2	2.9
[21]		+	−11.3	3.0
[22]		+	−8.2	6.1
[23]		None	−8.4	5.9
[24]		None	−8.0	6.3
[31]		+	−8.0	6.3
[32]		+	−8.2	6.1
[41]		None	−8.3	6.0

or an $\alpha_1\beta_1$ or $\alpha_2\beta_2$ deoxy dimer replaced by an $Fe^{3+}CN^-$ dimer; and −8.2 kcal for all other hybrids and $Hb(Fe^{3+}CN^-)_4$ in the R-structure. Ackers therefore proposed a molecular code for cooperativity, with the R → T transition occurring, not randomly as successive hemes combine with oxygen, but requiring at least one heme to be liganded on each $\alpha\beta$-dimer.

Incompatibility with Free Energy of Cooperativity

These conclusions have recently been challenged. Edelstein investigated their likely consequences for the cooperativity of the reaction with oxygen (10). He assumed that Ackers' asymmetrically biliganded state has either the T-structure with the value of L_2 raised by a multiplying factor s or an intermediate structure H. This is proposed to be an asymmetric tetramer composed of an R-like (r) and a T-like (t) $\alpha\beta$ dimer with different affinities so that ligands preferentially occupy the two r sites. The stability of H is proposed to increase dramatically when a second oxygen binds to the same $\alpha\beta$ dimer (Figure 4). This would require the free energy states of the MWC theory on the left and right of Figure 5 to be supplemented by the ones in the center. The subscripts ir and jt stand for the number of oxygens combined with either the r-(oxy) or the t-(deoxy)-like $\alpha\beta$-dimer, the free energy of tetramer-dimer dissociation being low for the hybrids 1r and 2r and high for 1t and 2t.

Using the intermediate dissociation constant that corresponds to 11.2 kcal/mol, Edelstein calculated Hill's equation and the fraction of biliganded species

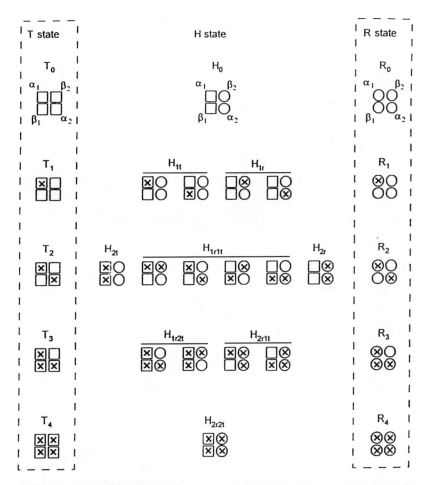

Figure 4 Quaternary T-states (*left*), quaternary R-states (*right*), and intermediate hybrid T-like quaternary H-states (*center*). *Squares*, subunits with t-like tertiary structures; *circles*, subunits with r-like tertiary structures; *crosses*, heme ligands; *subscripts i = 1–4*, number of heme ligands bound to r- or t-like subunits. (10, reproduced by permission).

on the basis of either of his models. Multiplication of L_2 by the required factor s reduced Hill's coefficient from 3.1 to 1.6; introduction of a third state H reduced it to 2.1. He concluded that "the reported hyperstability of the asymmetric biliganded cyanomet-hybrids is incompatible with the cooperativity of normal ferrous Hb, since it would introduce a marked anti-cooperative effect." Shibayama et al have pointed out that the observed Adair constants of successive oxygens in native Hb rise in the ratios of 1:2.8:14:160, while those calculated on the basis of the molecular code would rise in the ratios of 1:57:3:170 (49).

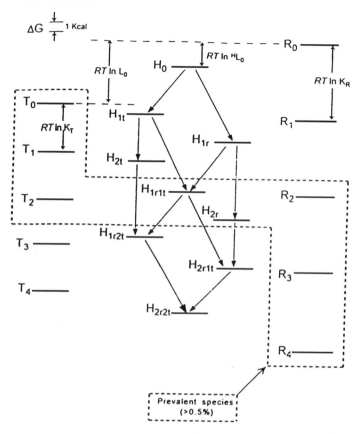

Figure 5 Energy diagram for the various T, H, and R forms. Each state is shown at a vertical height corresponding to its relative free energy. With respect to each R_i, the corresponding T_i is characterized by a relative stability defined by L_0c^i and each H form by $^HL_0c^i$ where $L_0 = [T_0]/[R_0]$, $^HL_0 = [H_0]/[R_0]$, $c = K_R/K_T$. The subscripts ir and jt indicate the number of ligands bound to the R-like and T-like sites, respectively. For the unliganded states, the vertical spacing defines RT ln L_0 and RT ln $^HL_0$, as indicated on the diagram. Each liganded form is displaced downward from the preceding form to reflect the energy of ligand binding, RT ln K_T and RT ln K_R for the T and R states, respectively, or the T-like and R-like subunits of the H state. The prevalent species (representing at least 0.5% of the molecular population during oxygenation) are indicated within the boxed area. (10, reproduced by permission).

Nickel porphyrins do not bind either oxygen or CO. Since the nickel atoms remain five-coordinated, they stabilize the T-structure. Shibayama et al found the average K_1s of the nickel-iron hybrids to be close to the first Adair constant of normal human hemoglobin, which suggested that permutations of such hybrids could serve as models of intermediates in the reactions of hemoglobins with ligands (48, 49).

They have investigated the experimental validity of the molecular code by determining the oxygen equilibria of Fe^{2+}–Ni^{2+} hybrids.

The Hill's coefficients of the hybrids varied as shown below.

Hybrid	Hill's coefficient
$[\alpha(Ni^{2+})\beta(Fe^{2+})]_2$	1.36
$[\alpha_1(Ni^{2+})\alpha_2(Fe^{2+})\beta_1(Ni^{2+})\beta_2(Fe^{2+})]$	1.41
$[\alpha_1(Fe^{2+})\alpha_2(Ni^{2+})\beta_1(Ni^{2+})\beta_2(Fe^{2+})]$	1.64
$[\alpha(Fe^{2+})\beta(Ni^{2+})]_2$	1.72

As expected from earlier studies of the relative affinities of the α- and β-subunits, $[\alpha(Fe^{2+})\beta(Ni^{2+})]_2$ had a threefold higher oxygen affinity than $[\alpha(Ni^{2+})\beta(Fe^{2+})]_2$. For this reason and because $[\alpha(Fe^{2+})\beta(Ni^{2+})]_2$ exhibits the greatest cooperativity, $[\alpha Fe^{2+}O_2\beta Fe^{2+}]_2$ must be the major intermediate at the second oxygenation step, rather than $[\alpha_1(Fe^{2+}O_2)\alpha_2(Fe^{2+})\beta_1(Fe^{2+}O_2)\beta_2(Fe^{2+})]$ as predicted by the molecular code.

Instability of Cyanomet Hybrids

The authors next investigated the stabilities of the asymmetric cyanomet hybrids. Ackers and his colleagues had prepared these by mixing equimolar quantities of normal human deoxyHb A and of the mutant cyanomet Hb C (Glu6β → Lys), recognizable electrophoretically by its extra four positive charges. They then incubated the mixture for 70 hours at pH7.4 and 21.5°C, because the equilibration of the two Hbs to a binomial distribution of deoxyHb A : $2[\alpha_1\beta_1$deoxyHbA $- \alpha_2\beta_2$ cyanometHb C] : cyanometHb C was governed by the extremely slow rate of dissociation of deoxyHb.

Shibayama and his colleagues found that in the course of this incubation exchange of electrons and evaporation of HCN led to an almost equimolar mixture of deoxyHb and *aquometHb*, instead of cyanometHb, in both Hbs A and C. The presence of 1 μM or 1 mM NaCN in the incubation mixture had been intended to prevent the conversion to aquometHb, but this precaution had failed, because HCN has a pK_a of 9, so that at pH7.4 HCN is the dominant species. HCN boils at 26°C; it has a sizable vapor pressure at pH7.4 and 21.5°C and therefore evaporated during the long incubation.

Having established the instability of the mixtures of deoxy- and cyanometHb used by Ackers and his colleagues, Shibayama et al mixed cyanometHb C with an equimolar quantity of oxyHb A instead. Because both dissociate rapidly into $\alpha\beta$ dimers, this mixture immediately produced a binomial distribution of

cyanometHb C : $2(\alpha_1\beta_1$cyanometHb C)$(\alpha_2\beta_2$HbO$_2$ A) : HbO$_2$ A.

The authors deoxygenated that mixture with pure N_2 for 25 min, and added an oxygen scavenging system. After another 10' incubation they quenched the mixture with $Na_2S_2O_4$, which converted all the Hbs, including cyanometHb, to undissociated tetrameric deoxyHb. Electrophoretic separation of the species under nitrogen showed that the fraction of cyanomet hybrid Hb had been reduced from the original 47% of the total Hb in the presence of oxygen to 8.6% in its absence (Figure 6). The cooperativity of the Hbs, due in part to the stereochemical misfit between low-spin six-coordinated cyanomet and high-spin deoxy-$\alpha\beta$ dimers, had made the hybrids disproportion. At longer incubation times disproportionation might have been complete, but fear of electron exchange made the authors keep that time short. Their experiment proved that the $\alpha_1\beta_1$ deoxy—$\alpha_2\beta_2$ cyanomet hybrid, and by implication also the $\alpha_1\beta_1$ deoxy—$\alpha_2\beta_2$ oxy intermediate, is extremely unstable and short-lived. On the other hand, the deoxy-aquomet hybrids produced inadvertently by the earlier workers had been stable, because aquomet, being high spin, easily switches

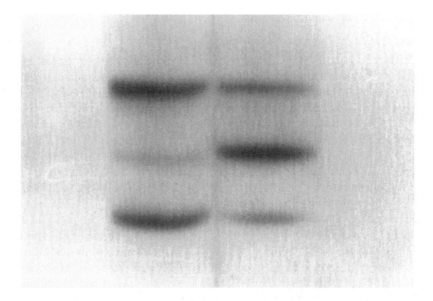

Figure 6 Distribution of hybrid Hbs after anaerobic isoelectric focusing in cylindrical gels. CyanometHb C was mixed with an equimolar amount of oxyHbA to obtain a distribution of HbC^+CN^- : $2[(HbC^+CN^-)(HbAO_2)]_2$: $HbAO_2$. It was then quenched with $Na_2S_2O_4$ + IHP. *Top bands*, HbC; *middle bands*, HbC-HbA hybrids; *lower bands*, HbA. *Right column*, HbC^+CN^- + HbO_2 quenched. The hybrid makes up 47% of the total Hb. *Left column*, same mixture deoxygenated with N_2 gas for 25', then incubated for 10' and finally quenched. Disproportionation has reduced the hybrid to 8.6% of the total Hb (50, reproduced by permission).

from the R to the T-structure, so that an aquomet $\alpha\beta$-dimer would readily fit onto a deoxy $\alpha\beta$-dimer, whereas a low-spin cyanomet $\alpha\beta$-dimer would be a misfit. This had given rise to the artifactual binomial distribution which led to the enunciation of the molecular code (48–50). Ackers et al have denied that electron exchange invalidates the molecular code (59), but Kiger et al have recently repeated the preparation of cyanomet hybrids under the conditions employed in Ackers' laboratory and have found the same electron exchange as Shibayama et al (60).

Jayaraman & Spiro (16) published UV resonance Raman spectra of the so-called third cooperative state of hemoglobin in the form of cyanomet hybrids prepared according to Ackers and his colleagues. These spectra will need reinterpretation in the light of the results of Shibayama et al.

A THIRD QUATERNARY STRUCTURE

In the absence of chemical evidence for a stable intermediate in the reaction of Hb with ligands, is there any crystallographic evidence for one? In the early fifties Perutz tried to trace the Fourier transform of Hb in the centrosymmetric projection of his crystals of horse metHb by recording the h0l reflections at various stages of swelling and shrinkage (33). He obtained one of his swelling stages in $(NH_4)_2SO_4$ solutions at pH5.5. When the first mercury derivative of this Hb was crystallized, a difference Patterson showed that the swelling of the crystals was accompanied by a contraction of the Hg-Hg distance from 33 Å to 27 Å (11). Some years later it became clear that this represented a quaternary structure different from both R and T, but it was pursued no further, because it lay well outside the physiological pH range.

Silva et al have recently reproduced this structure by crystallization of human HbCO from 16% polyethylene glycol of pH5.8 (53). It is related to T and R by a combined rotation and translation of the $\alpha_1\beta_1$ dimer relative to the $\alpha_2\beta_2$ dimer, but the directions and positions of the screw axes are different from those of the axis relating T to R (Figure 7). In the transition from T to R one $\alpha\beta$ dimer turns relative to the other by 13.2°; Janin and Wodak (57) have shown that in the T to R2 transition it turns by nearly 10° beyond R. The translation along the $\alpha_1\beta_2$ and $\alpha_2\beta_1$ contacts also goes beyond R. A similar quaternary structure was found in the abnormal human Hb Ypsilanti (AspG1β → Tyr) (54).

One might have thought that the T → R2 transition is responsible for the acid or reverse Bohr effect, with uptake of protons accompanying uptake of oxygen below pH6.0, but the R2 structure gives no indication of any ionizable groups likely to take up protons in the T → R2 transition. If the pK_a of the R ↔ R2 equilibrium did coincide with the transition from the alkaline to the acid Bohr effect, then 2% of HbO_2 would have the R2 structure at pH7.4, but its fraction

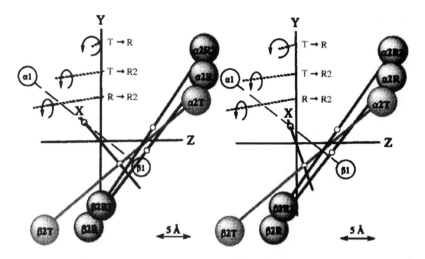

Figure 7 Stereoview of the movements of the $\alpha_2\beta_2$ dimers (*shaded circles*) relative to the $\alpha_1\beta_1$ dimer (*plain circles*) in going from T to R, from T to R2, and from R to R2. The screw axes are indicated by the *broken lines*. The *large circles* are at the centers of mass of the individual subunits, the *small circles* at the centers of mass of the $\alpha\beta$ dimers (53, reproduced by permission).

could rise significantly in hard-working muscle. Both Silva et al and Smith et al suggest that R2 might be an intermediate in the T $\rightarrow$ R transition, but Janin & Wodak have shown that its quaternary structure is far beyond R, rather than between T and R, which makes this unlikely.

Schumacher et al have published the structure of a human HbCO cross-linked prior to ligation between the amino groups of ValNA1β_1, LysEF6β_1, and LysEF6β_2 with a rotation angle of 8.5° from T towards R, suggestive of a short-lived intermediate (46). The C-terminal salt-bridges of the β-chains are broken as in R. The E-helices of the α-subunit are in their T-positions and their F-helices in the R-positions. The E and F helices of the β-subunits are between T and R and so are the distances of all four proximal histidines from the porphyrin planes. The oxygen affinity of this cross-linked Hb is also intermediate between T and R.

DOES THE T-STRUCTURE EXHIBIT COOPERATIVITY?

Reactions with Oxygen in Crystals and Gels

In the abnormal HbM Boston the distal histidines of the α-subunits are replaced by tyrosines that are linked to the ferric heme irons. The short Fe^+-O^- bond leads to rupture of their bonds with the proximal histidines and pulls the iron atoms to the distal side of the hemes. The abnormally large distance between the irons and these histidines gives the α-subunits an exaggerated, T-like tertiary structure that raises L so drastically that most of the molecules remain in the quaternary T-structure even when the normal β-subunits have taken up oxygen (41). The oxygen affinity is pH-independent and Hill's coefficient is 1.2. In Hb Iwate, which has similar properties, the proximal histidines of the α-subunits are replaced by tyrosines that are linked to the irons. In neither structure do the salt-bridges of the C-terminal histidines of the β-chains break when the β-hemes take up ligand (12). These two abnormal Hbs indicated more than 20 years ago that cooperativity is weak or absent without a change in quaternary structure.

This has now been firmly established by the elegant experiments of Mozzarelli, Eaton, and their colleagues who obtained accurate oxygen equilibrium curves of crystalline HbA immersed in concentrated solutions of polyethylene glycol (25, 42). When suspended in concentrated buffers, crystals of deoxyhemoglobin crack up on exposure to air, but in concentrated polyethylene glycol their T-structure remains intact. At pH6.0 their oxygen affinity was 14 times lower than that of Hb in solution, at pH9.0, 37 times lower, which implied that lattice forces constrained the T-structure and opposed the changes in tertiary structure that accompany oxygen uptake in solution. The oxygen affinity was essentially pH-independent, and Hill's coefficient was less than unity. The authors measured the equilibrium curves in light that was polarized along two mutually perpendicular crystal axes (Figure 8). From the known inclinations of the α- and β-hemes relative to these axes, the authors calculated their oxygen equilibrium constants to be 68–82 mmHg^{-1} and 239 mmHg-1, respectively, a fourfold difference, which Bettati et al later raised to a 4.6-fold one, larger than the threefold one generally found in solution (5). The difference is reduced in the presence of inositol hexaphosphate (IHP) (25). All these observations seemed to show that, contrary to Perutz's and consistent with a pure Monod mechanism, the C-terminal salt-bridges do not break on uptake of oxygen by the T-structure.

The authors also determined the structure and oxygen equilibria of crystals of human Hb lacking the C-terminal arginines of the α-chains (17). Despite the absence of the salt-bridges with which these arginines stabilize the T-structure, the atomic coordinates determined at 2.1 Å resolution were the same within error as those of deoxyHb A, except in the immediate vicinity of the deleted residues, but the temperature factors of the N-terminal residues and the EF-corners of the α-chains were higher than in HbA, showing that deletion of the arginines had loosened the structure. Oxygen binding was noncooperative, pH-independent between pH7.5 and 8.5, and exhibited a reverse Bohr effect of unknown origin at lower pH. Despite the preservation of the normal T-structure, the oxygen affinity of these crystals was 12–14 times higher than that of HbA crystals in the T-state, Hb Cowtown (His 146β-Leu) lacks the C-terminal salt-bridge connecting the imidazole of His 146β to the carboxylate of Asp 99β. Its crystal

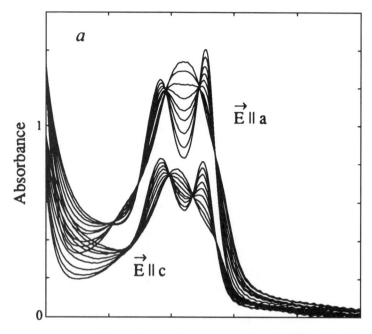

Figure 8 Optical absorption spectra of single crystals of human Hb suspended in 62% polyethyleneglycol of MW 8000 + 10 mM phosphate buffer at 15°C and pH 7.2 as a function of increasing pressure of O_2 in linearly polarized light. *Upper curves,* electric vector parallel to the crystallographic c-axis; *lower curves,* electric vector parallel to the crystallographic a-axis (42, reproduced by permission).

structure in the T-state is identical to that of HbA except in the immediate vicinity of the mutated residue. Bettati et al found crystals of Hb Cowtown maintained in the T-state to have an average of $P(O_2)_{50} = 44$ mm Hg^{-1} independent of pH, $[Cl^-]$ and the allosteric effector bezafibrate, and about 3.5 times lower than the average $P(O_2)_{50}$ of crystals of HbA in the T-state (66). The two results prove that rupture of salt-bridges raises the oxygen affinity of the T-structure even if it leaves it intact. In fact, experience has shown that rupture of any bond within the T-structure does so, presumably by relaxing the tension at the heme irons.

Shibayama and Saigo measured the oxygen equilibria of Hbs encapsulated in wet silica gels that were initially either aerated or oxygen-free (51). In both media the equilibria were noncooperative with Hill's coefficients below unity. In 100 mM equi 1 phosphate of pH7.0 and 20°C, the P_{50}s were 85 mmHg^{-1} in the oxygen-free and 0.16 mmHg^{-1} in the aerated gels, compared to 158 mm Hg^{-1} in the crystals, but close to $1/K_T = 71$ mm Hg^{-1} and $1/K_R = 0.4$ mm Hg^{-1} in 0.1 MCl^{-1} solutions at pH 7.4 and 25°C. These results proved again the absence of cooperativity without an allosteric transition, and they also showed that the oxygen affinity of the T-structure is greater in solution and in gels than in a crystal where it is constrained by lattice forces. The authors measured their equilibrium curves at only a single pH. Bettati & Mozzarelli have now repeated their experiments at several pHs and found that, dissolved in silica gels, Hb maintained in the T-structure exhibits a marked Bohr effect, inconsistent with a pure MWC mechanism and consistent with Perutz's rupture of salt-bridges with oxygen uptake by the T-structure (65).

TENSION AT THE LIGANDED HEMES IN THE T-STRUCTURE

Changes in Spin Equilibrium of the Irons

In transition metal complexes that are in a thermal equilibrium between alternative spin states, the average length of the metal-ligand bonds increases with the high spin fraction. Conversely, stretching of the bonds increases that fraction, compression reduces it. This property was exploited to gain a measure of the tension at the heme irons in the T-structure. Conveniently, the liganded derivatives of many fish Hbs can be switched from the R- to the T-structure simply by lowering the pH from 8.0 to 6.0 and adding IHP. In certain Hb derivatives, the ferric irons are in a thermal equilibrium between the spins of 5/2 and 1/2. Figure 9 shows the rise in paramagnetic susceptibility of nitrite metHb on switching from R to T. The shift in spin equilibrium is equivalent to a change in free energy of about 1 kcal/mol/heme, which represents the energy equivalent of the tension at the liganded hemes in the T-structure. In a postscript, Messana et al suggested that this comes mainly from the α-hemes and should therefore be doubled. The crystallographic results described below have confirmed this (30).

When Philo and Dreyer repeated the magnetic experiments with both human HbA and the abnormal human Hb Kansas in which the R-structure is destabilized by the rupture of a crucial hydrogen bond, they found no significant rise in the paramagnetic susceptibility of either Hb on switching their azide-met derivatives from R to T and concluded that this rise was a peculiarity shown only by fish Hbs (40). This seemed improbable in view of the extensive homology of the heme surrounds and subunit contacts in all vertebrate Hbs. When Perutz and Cowan repeated Philo and Dreyer's experiment, they confirmed their negative result with azide metHb, but found that human nitrite metHb exhibited the same rise in susceptibility as fish nitrite metHb (MF Perutz and J Cowan, unpublished information). A way out of the impasse came with the discovery that the antilipidemic drug bezafibrate and compounds modeled on it act as powerful allosteric effectors that do not compete with IHP because they bind

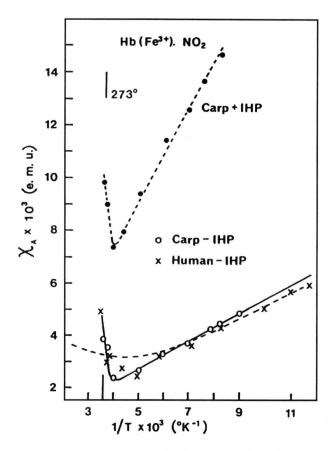

Figure 9 Temperature dependence of the paramagnetic susceptibilities of carp $Hb^+NO_2^-$ in the R-structure (*bottom*) and T-structure (*top*) and of human $Hb^+NO_2^-$ in the R-structure (22, reproduced by permission).

to different sites. This allowed Noble et al to switch several ferric derivatives of normal human Hb either partly or completely from R to T. They measured the rise in the high-spin fraction magnetometrically and also by visible and resonance Raman spectroscopy and found substantial rises, but they varied in different derivatives (27, 28).

Finally, Perutz found that the very strong allosteric effector L345 produced the same enhancement of the high spin bands in the visible absorption spectrum of human $Hb^+N_3^-$ as acid pH and IHP had done in fish (21). This proved that earlier negative results had been caused by failure to switch the structure of human Hb from R to T, rather than by any differences between the allosteric properties of human and fish Hbs.

A Theoretical Interpretation of the Spin Changes

Kelleher gave an elegant interpretation of the different responses to allosteric effectors by different Hb^+ derivatives (18). He pointed out that their influence on the spin equilibrium depends on their interaction with the $R \rightarrow T$ equilibrium, which is species-dependent, and on the interaction of the spin state with the $R \rightarrow T$ equilibrium, which is ligand-dependent. If α is the low-spin component, then the spin equilibrium constant is $K = \frac{\alpha}{1-\alpha}$. Taking the natural logarithm of both sides and differentiating gives

$$\frac{d\ln K}{d\alpha} = \frac{1}{\alpha} + \frac{1}{1-\alpha} = \frac{1}{\alpha - \alpha^2}. \tag{3}$$

Substituting $\ln K = \frac{\Delta G}{RT}$ gives

$$\frac{d\alpha}{d(\Delta G)} = -\frac{1}{RT}(\alpha - \alpha^2). \tag{4}$$

According to this equation, the rate of change of the low spin fraction α with the quantity of work done on the system, ΔG, at any one temperature is a nonlinear, quadratic function of α as shown in Figure 10. It is maximal at $\alpha = 0.5$ and declines towards zero at pure low or pure high spin. Therefore it takes the same amount of work, 500 cal/mol, to raise the high-spin fraction from 0.5 to 0.7 as it does to take it from 0.90 to 0.955. At 20°C $Hb^+NO_2^-$ is about 40%, and $Hb^+N_3^-$ 5 to 10% high spin. 240 cal/mol strain energy will raise $Hb^+NO_2^-$ to 50% but $Hb^+N_3^-$ to only either 7.5 or 14% high spin. This explains why IHP produced a fivefold larger spin change in $Hb^+NO_2^-$ than in $Hb^+N_3^-$. From the published changes in high- and low-spin absorption bands in the visible absorption spectrum of human $Hb^+N_3^-$, Kelleher calculated that the changes of free energy produced by addition of IHP alone, by IHP plus bezafibrate, or by L345 are

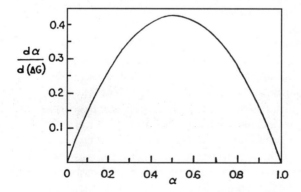

Figure 10   The instantaneous rate of change of the low-spin fraction, α, with work done on the Hb spin system $d(\Delta G)$, as a function of α at 20°C (18, reproduced by permission).

respectively 290, 440, or 970 cal/mol. The last figure agrees with the free-energy change found by Messana et al on switching carp $Hb^+N_3^-$ from R to T (22).

Structure of Ligated Hemoglobins in the T-State

The spin changes gave estimates of the changes in free energy at the heme iron but no indication of their distribution among the α- and β-hemes, nor of the accompanying stereochemical changes. Paoli et al have recently clarified these by X-ray analyses at high resolution of crystals of human Hb suspended in concentrated solutions of polyethylene glycol which maintained the T-structure intact on addition of a variety of heme ligands (31, 32).

In fully oxygenated Hb, the $Fe-N_\varepsilon$ bonds were stretched by 0.36 Å in the α and 0.13 Å in the β-subunits, compared to HbO_2 in the R structure. According to Pauling, changes in bond distance d are related to the bond number n, defined as the number of electrons shared in the bond. The length of a fractional bond $d(^1/_n)$ is related to that of a single bond by $d(^1/_n)-d(1) = \Delta d = -0.6 \log n$; stretching by 0.36 Å would reduce the bond number by a factor of 4; stretching by 0.13 Å would reduce it by a factor of 1.6 (9). The bond number is proportional to the bond energy (7), which is given by the enthalpy for the reaction of hemoglobin with oxygen: -14.2 ± 0.6 and -17.7 ± 0.6 kcal/mol O_2 for free α- and β-subunits, respectively. Stretching of the bonds by 0.36 Å or 0.13 Å would reduce these energies to 3.5 and 11 kcal/mol O_2, respectively. Reductions in bond energy by 10.7 and 6.7 kcal/mol O_2 at each of the α- and β-hemes amount to a total of 34.8 kcal/mol tetramer, much more than the free energy of cooperativity of 14 kcal/mol tetramer. This paradoxical result suggests that the apparent stretching of the $Fe-N_\varepsilon$ bonds conceals an unresolved superposition of six- and five-coordinated oxyhemes. In the α-subunits, combination with oxygen has moved the irons into the porphyrin plane, pulling the F-helix with it part of the way; in the β-subunits the porphyrins have moved towards the iron and the F-helix, thus making room for the oxygen as well as allowing the iron to come into the porphyrin plane.

Nagai et al found that the Fe-O stretching frequency at 570 nm remained unchanged on switching either carp Hb or the abnormal human Hb Kansas from the R- to the T-structure, and they argued that this is incompatible with tension in the ligated T-state (26). If our interpretation of the apparent stretching of the $Fe-N_\varepsilon$ bond is correct, then the single stretching frequency in the R-structure should be split into two in the T-structure, one identical to that in the R-structure and the other attributable to a five-coordinated oxyheme. According to Yonetani et al, the Fe-O bond in five-coordinated oxyheme is weaker by several orders of magnitude than the bond in six-coordinated oxyheme (T Yonetani et al, unpublished information). Therefore its stretching frequency should be lower but this has not been looked for. A similar interpretation may apply to the finding of the unchanged Fe-CO stretching frequency by Rousseau et al (44), but so far there is no crystal structure for Hb CO in the T-state.

The expected errors in the interatomic distances are for Deoxy T and Oxy T Hb 0.1–0.15 Å; for Deoxy R Hb 0.08–0.1 Å for Oxy R Hb 0.15–0.2 Å.

Figures 11 and 12 compare the heme geometries in the oxygenated T-state with those in the deoxy-T, oxy-R, and deoxy-R states. They show the different degrees of bending of the porphyrin and the changes in the length of the Fe-N$_\varepsilon$ bonds.

In the course of the T → R switch, the FG segment of each subunit moves relative to the C-helix of its neighbors at the $\alpha_1\beta_2$ and $\alpha_2\beta_1$ contacts. Figure 13 shows two of the accompanying switches in hydrogen bonding. In the oxygenated T-state, the hydrogen bonds that stabilize the deoxy T-structure are stretched, and the distances between atoms that are hydrogen-bonded in the oxy-R–structure have shrunk, showing that the stereochemical changes at the heme have been transmitted to the subunit contacts and have started the T → R transition (Table 2). In the deoxygenated R-state the directions of these changes have been reversed (55). In the oxygenated T-state, the essential C-terminal salt bridge between Lys C5α and His HC3β is stretched by 0.9 Å, suggesting that it is about to be broken (Table 2).

Structural comparison of the fully oxygenated T-state crystals with the earlier semi-oxygenated ones (α, oxy, and β, partly deoxy and partly aquomet) shows that the mean distance of the oxygenated α-irons from the plane of the porphyrin nitrogens has shrunk from 0.30 Å in the semi-oxy T-state to 0.05 Å in the fully oxy T-state. Their mean distance from the pyrrole plane has shrunk from 0.47 Å in semi-oxy to 0.11 Å in fully oxy. This shows that the transition from high to low spin iron in the β-hemes has made the iron move closer to the porphyrin plane in the α-hemes. Conversely, oxygenation of the α-hemes probably relieves steric hindrance by the distal histidines and valines at the β-hemes. Both effects are transmitted by stereochemical changes across the $\alpha_1\beta_2$ and $\alpha_2\beta_1$ interfaces (32).

Table 2 Stretching of the C-terminal salt bridge in the oxygenated T-state

α_1		β_2		DeoxyT[30] Å	Oxy T[30] Å	Deoxy R[55] Å	Oxy R[47] Å
Residue	Atom	Residue	Atom				
LysC5	N$_\zeta$	HisHC3	O$_\varepsilon$	2.3	3.2	13.7	14.6
LeuFG3	O	ArgC6	N$_\varepsilon$	3.0	3.8	4.3	4.0
ArgFG4	O	ArgC6	N$_\varepsilon$	3.2	3.6	4.4	4.3
AspG1	O$_{\delta 1}$	TrpC3	N$_\varepsilon$	2.8	3.5	3.6	3.7
AspG1	O$_{\delta 1}$	AsnG4	N$_\delta$	4.6	3.4	2.8	2.5
TyrC7	OH	AspG1	O$_{\delta 1}$	2.5	2.8	8.5	8.5

(a)

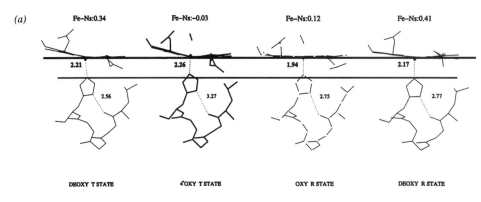

(b)

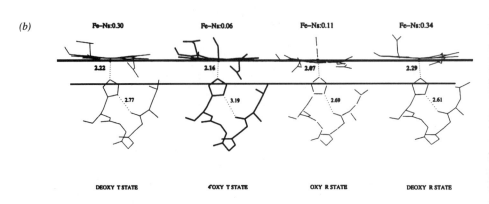

(c)

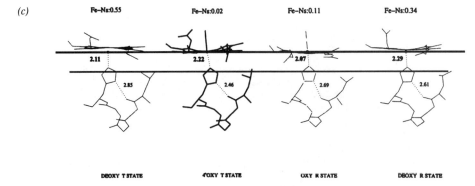

In Hb^+CN^- and Hb^+F^- in the T-structure, the $Fe-N_\varepsilon$-bonds are broken in the α-subunits and the irons have moved to the distal side. High-spin $Hb^+ H_2O$ is in equilibrium with low-spin Hb^+OH^-, with a pK_a of 8.1. X-ray analyses of crystals of metHb kept at different pHs showed the increase of the low-spin Hb^+OH^- fraction with rising pH to be accompanied by increasing fractions of five-coordinated heme in which the $Fe-N_\varepsilon$ was broken (30). Rupture of the $Fe-N_\varepsilon$ bonds in $Hb^+ CN^-$ has allowed the α-subunits to relax into an exaggerated T-like tertiary structure in the vicinity of the heme (Figure 12). At the β-hemes the $Fe-N_\varepsilon$ bonds have remained intact, but the distal residues have moved relative to the hemes to make room for the cyanide ion. The changes towards an R-like tertiary structure of the β-subunits are smaller than those accompanying oxygenation of all four hemes in the T-structure. It seems that an R-like tertiary structure of the α-subunits restrains the transition toward a T-like tertiary structure of the β-subunits, while an R-like tertiary structure of the α-subunits promotes it. This is clear evidence of stereochemical interaction between α- and β-subunits in the quaternary T-structure (31).

Reaction with Ligands of Hemoglobins Lacking the Iron-Histidine Bond

Barrick et al have tested the tension theory in yet a different way. They synthesized an Hb in which the proximal histidines of either the α- or the β-chains were replaced by glycines, and another Hb in which both proximal histidines were replaced by glycines (4). The synthesis and all subsequent steps were

←————————————————————————————————————

Figure 11 (a) Changes in α_1 heme geometry between different allosteric and ligation states. Four different Hb structures, deoxy T-state, fully oxy T-state[30], oxy R-state[47], and deoxy R-state[55], were superimposed on heme pyrroles 1 and 2 of the α_1 subunits. The least-square best-fit plane through the two pyrroles is shown by a *bold line* on the hemes. A line parallel to this plane through the N_ε atom of the proximal histidine of the deoxy T structure is also shown. The distance of the iron atom below the pyrrole plane is given (negative distances indicate that the iron is above the plane). Ligation shortens the $Fe-N_\varepsilon$ bond in the R-state, but not in the T-state. By contrast, the Leu F4 main-chain CO-His F8 $N\delta$ hydrogen-bond becomes stretched with ligation in the T-state, but not in the R-state. This behavior reflects the tension at the heme in the T-state and the absence of tension at the heme in the R-state. The α-subunit shows the same changes as α_1. (b, c) Changes in β_1 and β_2 heme geometry between different allosteric and ligation states. The structures shown are the same as in (a), but fitted on the β F-helix by least-squares. The best-fit line through the Fe atoms of the different structures is shown, and a line parallel to it through the C_δ atom of the proximal histidine of the deoxy T-state is also drawn. In contrast to the α hemes, the β hemes move as a whole towards the proximal histidine on oxygenation, β_1 by 0.24 Å and β_2 by 0.53 Å, but these movements are unequal owing to crystal contacts. The β_2 heme has become buckled and strained. As the β_2 heme is pressed down by the ligand, it pushes the proximal histidine down towards Leu F4. In contrast, the β_1 heme is not fully ligated and appears much less strained (30, reproduced by permission). The expected errors in the Fe-N distances are 0.05–0.08 Å; for the proximal F8 His $N\delta$-carbonyl O 0.1 Å.

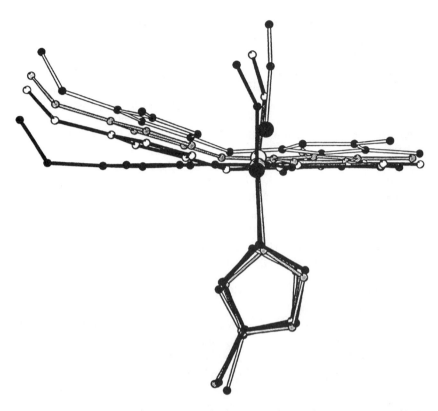

Figure 12 The α_1 heme and the proximal histidine of oxy R-state (*black*), oxy T-state (*black bonds and white atoms*), deoxy T-state (*light gray*), and cyanomet T-state (*white bonds and dark gray atoms*) hemoglobins viewed from the front of the heme pocket. The heme has been sectioned to reveal the iron atom positions more clearly. The comparison is based on a least-squares minimization superimposing the main chain atoms of residues F4-F8. The Fe-N$_\varepsilon$ bond in the cyanomet T-state heme is broken and the iron is 0.2 Å out of the plane of the nitrogens of its porphyrin toward the distal side. The diagram shows that oxygen binding to the α-heme in the T-quaternary structure causes structural adjustments in the direction of the R-state. In contrast, rupture of the Fe-N$_\varepsilon$ bond in Hb$^+$CN$^-$ leads to structural changes that are opposite in direction. As a result, the deoxy heme seen in this view lies midway between the T-state oxyheme and the T-state cyanomet heme.

carried out in the presence of 10 mM imidazole, which stabilized the mutant hemoglobins by effectively replacing the proximal histidines. Their linkage to the heme irons was proved by solution of the crystal structure of the mutant αH87G in the presence of imidazole. The authors measured equilibrium curves for the binding of oxygen and of n-butylisocyanide (Figure 14). Both the single mutant βH92G and the double mutant αH87G-βH92G show diminished cooperativity and raised oxygen affinity throughout; αH87G showed

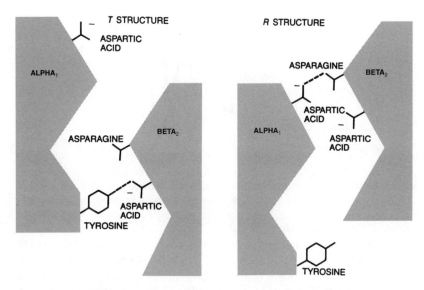

Figure 13   Changes in hydrogen bonds at the $\alpha_1\beta_1$ contact between the T and R structures.

a higher oxygen affinity than HbA at low partial pressures and a lower one than HbA at high partial pressures of oxygen. Because rapid oxidation of the heme irons made the oxygen equilibrium curves irreversible, the authors turned to n-butylisocyanide. All its equilibrium curves were hyperbolic rather than sigmoidal; allosteric effectors were ineffectual. The n-butyl-isocyanide curve of αH87G was biphasic, with microscopic dissociation constants $K_1 = 34$ μM and $K_2 = 225$ μM. K_2 was similar to the dissociation constant of the double mutant (αH87G–βH92G). In the single mutant (αH87G), the α-hemes have a high affinity because they have lost the constraints of the Fe-N$_\varepsilon$ bonds, while the wild-type β-hemes have a low one as in Hb Boston where the Fe-N$_\varepsilon$ bonds in α-subunits are broken; this biases the allosteric equilibrium toward T and inhibits cooperation with the β-hemes. These results have proved unequivocally that the Fe-N$_\varepsilon$ bonds are essential for cooperativity.

PROTONS AND CHLORIDE IONS

Origins of Alkaline Bohr Effect

Protons and chloride ions act as antagonists to oxygen despite their opposite charges. The influence of protons on the oxygen equilibrium is defined as $\frac{\partial \log(p50)}{\partial pH}$; it is -0.50 in $0.1 M Cl^-$ at pH 7.4. This is known as the alkaline Bohr

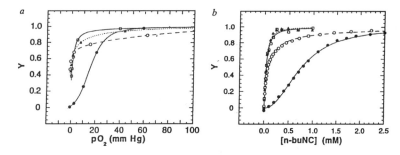

Figure 14 Binding of (*a*) oxygen and (*b*) n-butylisocyanide to Hbs with the proximal histidines replaced by glycines, in the presence of excess imidazole. Symbols: •, HbA; o, αH87G; ▲, βH92G; □, αH87G βH92G; Y, fractional saturation with ligand (4, reproduced by permission).

effect. It is reversed below pH 6.0. In the absence of chloride it is halved. The chloride-independent part of the alkaline Bohr effect was found to be due exclusively to a change in pK_a of His HC3β, which donates a hydrogen bond to Asp FG1β in the T-structure and accepts one from its own main-chain NH in the R structure (Figure 15) (38, 52). In 0.2 M NaCl, titration of the proton resonances of that histidine yielded pK_as of 7.1 in HbCO and of 8.0 in deoxyHb (19), but the pK_a of 7.1 in HbCO became controversial when another NMR study seemed to show that in bis tris/tris buffers with minimal Cl$^-$ it becomes as high as 7.9 (45). However, the resonance assigned to His HC3 in that study was later shown to belong to His FG4; its pK_a is abnormally high because it caps the carboxyl end of a helix (37). Discovery of the correct resonance for His HC3 has confirmed its original low pK_a (8).

The chloride-dependent part of the alkaline Bohr effect used to be attributed to Val NA1α and Lys EF6 β, because it was inhibited when the α-amino groups of the valines were carbamylated and the lysines were replaced by neutral residues. The presence of an inorganic anion linked to the α-amino group of the valine seemed to be corroborated by the presence of an (albeit weak) peak in a difference electron density map between native human Hb and Hb carbamylated at Val NA1α (29); on the other hand, there was no X-ray evidence of chloride-binding to Lys EF6β. Reports that the oxygen affinity of bovine Hb was more sensitive to Cl$^-$ than that of human Hb led to a new crystallographic search for Cl$^-$-binding sites, which proved entirely fruitless. Difference electron density maps of bovine deoxyHb crystals suspended in 50% polyethyleneglycol and buffered at pH 7.3 with either 50 mM Na phosphate $\pm$ 0.1 M NaCl or with 0.1 M HEPES buffer $\pm$ 0.1 M NaBr contained no significant peaks (36). When A Arnone repeated the same experiment with human deoxyHb he also drew a blank, showing that there are no specific halide binding sites in either bovine or human Hb (A Arnone, private communication). How then does chloride lower the oxygen affinity and contribute to the Bohr effect? The central, water-filled

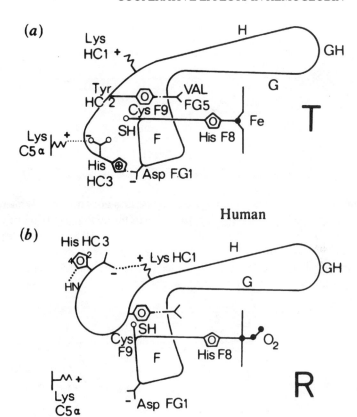

Figure 15 Contribution of HisHC3(146)β to the alkaline Bohr effect. The C-terminal salt-bridge between the imidazole of histidine HC3(146)β and aspartate FG1(94)β in the deoxyhemoglobin (T) structure raises the pK$_a$ of the imidazole to 8.0. In oxyhemoglobin (R), the α-carboxyl of histidine HC3(146)β forms a salt-bridge with lysine HC1(144)β; the imidazole of the histidine accepts a hydrogen bond from its own main chain NH, and as a consequence its pK drops to 7.1 or lower.

cavity of Hb is lined with an excess of positively charged ionizable groups (Table 3).

Bonaventura & Bonaventura suggested that their mutual repulsion increases the oxygen affinity by raising the free energy of the T-structure (6). Their neutralization by Cl$^-$ would therefore stabilize the T-structure and lower the oxygen affinity. On this basis, any amino acid substitutions that halved the excess positive charges should halve the chloride effect; complete neutralization of the excess should inhibit it and additional positive charges should enhance it. Charge changes on the outer surface of the molecule should have little or no effect. Figure 16 and Table 3 show that this is indeed the case (39), but they raise

Table 3 Polar residues lining the central cavity of human and bovine[a] hemoglobins

α-chains		β-chains	
Val NA1 (1)	+	Val NA1; Met in bovine	+
Asp G1 (95)	−	His NA2 (2) deleted in bovine	+
Lys G6 (99)	+	Lys EF6 (82)	+
His G10 (103)	+	Glu G3 (101)	−
Asp H9 (126)	−	Arg G6 (104)	+
		His 21 (143)	+

[a]Sequence numbers in bovine β are one less than in human Hbβ.

the question of why repulsion by the same residues does not equally increase the free energy of the R-structure, particularly as the central cavity narrows on transition from T to R. Electron density maps of human HbO_2 show no density for either Val NA1α or Lys EF6β, which suggests that they are mobile and that their charges are more effectively dissipated by hydration in the R-structure and therefore fail to contribute to the positive charges in the central cavity.

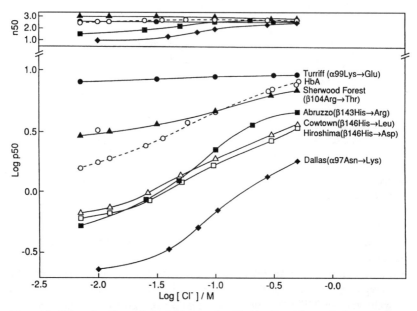

Figure 16 Effect of amino acid substitutions on the chloride effect. The graph shows the dependence of p(50) on [Cl⁻] at pH 7.4, 25°C and 60 μM heme. The replacements in Hbs Turriff, Sherwood Forest, Abruzzo, and Dallas are in the central cavity. Those in Cowtown and Hiroshima are on the surface; they exhibit the same chloride effect as HbA. Hb Hinsdale [Asn H17(139)β → Lys] exhibits the same enhanced chloride effect as Hb Dallas (39, reproduced by permission).

Do the Salt-Bridges Break in the T-Structure?

Where do the Bohr protons liberated by Hb in the T-state in silica gels come from? Their liberation must be due to rupture of salt-bridges induced by tertiary changes. The salt-bridges formed by His HC3β are external and could break without disruption of the quaternary T-structure. On the other hand, the central cavity cannot narrow without a T $\rightarrow$ R transition. In consequence, the chloride-independent part of the alkaline Bohr effect could be both tertiary- and quaternary-linked, while the chloride-dependent part must be quaternary-linked. Why did all crystal structures of ligated hemes show these salt-bridges to have remained intact and why did they also remain intact on oxygenation of the β-hemes in Hbs M Boston and Iwate? These crystals and the Hb Ms had much lower oxygen association constants than HbA under physiological conditions, showing that the T-structure was more constrained. The silica gel is the first medium capable of maintaining the T-structure without lowering the oxygen association constant abnormally. It seems that this property of the silica gel is essential for the normal rupture of the salt-bridges.

MONOD, KOSHLAND, OR "MONLAND"?

In Monod's mechanism, the microscopic equilibrium constants of the individual subunits within the quaternary T or R structures remain independent of the number of hemes that have taken up ligands. These ligands, and allosteric effectors, alter the ligand affinity solely by their influence on the allosteric equilibrium constant, L Koshland's mechanism, on the other hand, allows cooperativity without an allosteric transition. Because either mechanism is physically possible, there is no reason why nature should not use both, and this does indeed seem to be the case, as shown by the Bohr effect in gels, which requires rupture of hydrogen bonds in the T-structure. In the crystals of Rivetti et al, differences in the oxygen dissociation constants between the α- and β-subunits were compensated by a modest amount of cooperativity of oxygen binding to give a linear Hill plot with a Hill's coefficient of unity. Such compensation would require a ratio of K_R/K_T of about $1/3$, resulting in $\Delta G = -RT$ ln $\frac{K_R}{K_T}$ = 0.7 kcal/mol, or about a fifth of the total interaction energy. The stereochemical changes seen at the subunit boundaries on uptake of oxygen by crystals held in the T-structure (32) may be sufficient to transmit this amount of energy. However, the question of the presence and magnitude of cooperativity in the T-structure is of no physiological importance, because the oxygen equilibrium measured under physiological conditions and also the kinetics of the reactions of the hemoglobin with ligands can be accurately represented by the two-state MWC theory (64).

The variations of the oxygen equilibrium curve of hemoglobin with pH, ionic strength, and allosteric effectors can be described mathematically by a simplified MWC model with K_T and K_R as the only independent variables, but underlying that simple behavior is a subtle and complex molecular mechanism. This has now been unraveled in great detail by the endeavors of many investigators whose approaches cover the electromagnetic spectrum from gamma rays to microwaves, but some intriguing problems remain.

When crystal lattice forces inhibit the allosteric transition from T to R, ligand binding induces marked changes in heme geometry and tertiary structure of the globin within the quaternary T-structure, like the changes of a man flexing his muscles to lift a weight that is too heavy for him, but larger tertiary changes must take place within the T-structure in solution to account for the linearity of proton release with oxygen uptake. We can only guess what these are. The Bohr effect of mammalian hemoglobins has been satisfactorily explained, but its spectacular enhancement in teleost fish, which allows them to fill their swim bladders and their eyes with oxygen against large hydrostatic pressures, remains a mystery. Nor, for example, do we understand why the intrinsic oxygen affinity of ruminant Hbs without allosteric effectors is as low as that of primate hemoglobins with effectors, so that they can transport oxygen efficiently without them.

Visit the *Annual Reviews home page* at
http://www.AnnualReviews.org.

Literature Cited

1. Ackers GK, Hazzard JH. 1993. Transduction of binding energy into hemoglobin cooperativity. *Trends Biochem. Sci.* 18:385–90

2. Adair GS. 1925. The hemoglobin system. VI: The oxygen dissociation curve of hemoglobin. *J. Biol. Chem.* 63:529–45

3. Baldwin J, Chothia C. 1979. Haemoglobin: the structural changes related to ligand binding and its allosteric mechanism. *J. Mol. Biol.* 129:175–220

4. Barrick D, Ho NT, Simplaceanu V, Dahlquist FW, Ho C. 1997. A test of the role of the proximal histidines in the Perutz model for cooperativity in haemoglobin. *Nat. Struct. Biol.* 4:78–83

5. Bettati S, Mozzarelli A, Rossi GL, Tsuneshige A, Yonetani T, et al. 1996. Oxygen binding by single crystals of hemoglobin: the problem of cooperativity and inequivalence of alpha and beta subunits. *Proteins* 25:425–37

6. Bonaventura C, Bonaventura J. 1978. In *Biochemical and Clinical Aspects of Hemoglobin Abnormalities*, ed. WS Caughey, pp. 641–61. New York: Academic

7. Bürgi H-B, Dunitz JD. 1987. Fractional

bonds: relations among their lengths, strengths, and stretching force constants. *J. Am. Chem. Soc.* 109:2924–26

8. Busch MR, Mace JE, Ho NT, Ho C. 1991. Roles of the beta 146 histidyl residue in the molecular basis of the Bohr effect of hemoglobin: a proton nuclear magnetic resonance study. *Biochemistry* 30:1865–77

9. Dunitz JD. 1979. *X-Ray Analysis and the Structure of Organic Molecules*, p. 344. Ithaca, NY: Cornell Univ. Press

10. Edelstein SJ. 1996. An allosteric theory for hemoglobin incorporating asymmetric states to test the putative molecular code for cooperativity. *J. Mol. Biol.* 257:737–44

11. Green DW, Ingram VM, Perutz MF. 1954. The structure of haemoglobin. IV. Sign determination by the isomorphous replacement method. *Proc. R. Soc. London Ser. A* 225:287–307

12. Greer J. 1971. Three-dimensional structure of abnormal human haemoglobins M Hyde Park and M Iwate. *J. Mol. Biol.* 59:107–26

13. Hill AV. 1910. The possible effects of the aggregation of the molecules of haemoglobin on its dissociation curves. *J. Physiol.* 40:iv–vii

14. Huang S, Peterson ES, Ho C, Friedman JM. 1997. Quaternary structure-sensitive tyrosine interactions in hemoglobin: a UV resonance Raman study of the double mutant rHb (beta99Asp → Asn, alpha42Tyr → Asp). *Biochemistry* 36:6197–206

15. Imai K. 1982. *Allosteric Effects in Haemoglobin.* Cambridge: Cambridge Univ. Press

16. Jayaraman V, Spiro TG. 1995. Structure of a third cooperativity state of hemoglobin: ultraviolet resonance Raman spectroscopy of cyanomethemoglobin ligation microstates. *Biochemistry* 34:4511–15

17. Kavanaugh JS, Chafin DR, Arnone A, Mozzarelli, A, Rivetti C, et al. 1995. Structure and oxygen affinity of crystalline des-Arg141 alpha human hemoglobin A in the T state. *J. Mol. Biol.* 248:136–50

18. Kelleher MJ. 1993. The azido human methemoglobin controversy: Is there evidence for a quaternary structure-spin state linkage or not? *Acc. Chem. Research* 26: 154–59

19. Kilmartin JV, Breen JJ, Roberts GC, Ho C. 1973. Direct measurement of the pK values of an alkaline Bohr group in human hemoglobin. *Proc. Natl. Acad. Sci. USA* 70:1246–49

20. Koshland DE Jr, Nemethy G, Filmer D. 1966. Comparison of experimental binding data and theoretical models in proteins containing subunits. *Biochemistry* 5:365–85

21. Lalezari I, Lalezari P, Poyart C, Marden M, Kister J, et al. 1990. New effectors of human hemoglobin: structure and function. *Biochemistry* 29:1515–23

22. Messana C, Cerdonio M, Shenkin P, Noble RW, Fermi G, et al. 1978. Influence of quaternary structure of the globin on thermal spin equilibria in different methemoglobin derivatives. *Biochemistry* 17:3652–62

23. Monod J, Changeux J-P, Jacob F. 1963. Allosteric proteins and cellular control systems. *J. Mol. Biol.* 6:306–29

24. Monod J, Wyman J, Changeux J-P. 1965. On the nature of allosteric transitions: a plausible model. *J. Mol. Biol.* 12:88–118

25. Mozzarelli A, Rivetti C, Rossi GL, Eaton WA, Henry ER. 1997. Allosteric effectors do not alter the oxygen affinity of hemoglobin crystals. *Protein Sci.* 6:484–89

26. Nagai K, Kitagawa T, Morimoto H. 1980. Quaternary structures and low-frequency molecular vibrations of haems of deoxy and oxyhaemoglobin studied by resonance Raman scattering. *J. Mol. Biol.* 136:271–89

27. Noble RW, DeYoung A, Rousseau DL.

1989. Spin equilibrium in human methemoglobin: effects of inositol hexaphosphate and bezafibrate as measured by resonance Raman spectroscopy. *Biochemistry* 28:5293–97

28. Noble RW, DeYoung A, Vitale S, Cerdonio H, DiIorio E. 1989. Spin equilibrium in human methemoglobin: effects of inositol hexaphosphate and bezafibrate as measured by susceptometry and visible spectroscopy. *Biochemistry* 28:5288–92

29. O'Donnell S, Mandaro R, Schuster TM, Arnone A. 1979. X-ray diffraction and solution studies of specifically carbamylated human hemoglobin A: evidence for the location of a proton- and oxygen-linked chloride binding site at valine 1 alpha. *J. Biol. Chem.* 254:12204–8

30. Paoli M. 1996. *Structural studies on ligated T-state haemoglobins.* PhD thesis. York Univ., UK

31. Paoli M, Dodson G, Liddington RC, Wilkinson AJ. 1997. *J. Mol. Biol.* 271:161

32. Paoli M, Liddington R, Tame J, Wilkinson A, Dodson G. 1996. Crystal structure of T-state haemoglobin with oxygen bound at all four haems. *J. Mol. Biol.* 256:775–92

33. Perutz MF. 1954. The structure of haemoglobin. III: direct determination of the molecular transform. *Proc. R. Soc. London Ser. A* 225:264–86

34. Perutz MF. 1970. Stereochemistry of cooperative effects in haemoglobin. *Nature* 228:726–39

35. Perutz MF. 1972. Nature of heme–heme interaction. *Nature* 237:495–99

36. Perutz MF, Fermi G, Poyart C, Pagnier J, Kister J. 1993. A novel allosteric mechanism in haemoglobin: structure of bovine deoxyhaemoglobin, absence of specific chloride-binding sites and origin of the chloride-linked Bohr effect in bovine and human haemoglobin. *J. Mol. Biol.* 233:536–45

37. Perutz MF, Gronenborn AM, Clore GM, Fogg JH, Shih DT. 1985. The pKa values of two histidine residues in human haemoglobin, the Bohr effect, and the dipole moments of alpha-helices. *J. Mol. Biol.* 183:491–98

38. Perutz MF, Muirhead H, Mazzarella L, Crowther RA, Greer J, Kilmartin JV. 1969. Identification of residues responsible for the alkaline Bohr effect in haemoglobin. *Nature* 222:1240–43

39. Perutz MF, Shih DT, Williamson D. 1994. The chloride effect in human haemoglobin, a new kind of allosteric mechanism. *J. Mol. Biol.* 239:555–60

40. Philo JS, Dreyer U. 1985. Quaternary structure has little influence on spin states in

mixed-spin human methemoglobins. *Biochemistry* 24:2985–92

41. Pulsinelli PD, Perutz MF, Nagel RL. 1973. Structure of hemoglobin M Boston, a variant with a five-coordinated ferric heme. *Proc. Natl. Acad. Sci. USA* 70:3870–74

42. Rivetti C, Mozzarelli A, Rossi GL, Henry ER, Eaton WA. 1993. Oxygen binding by single crystals of hemoglobin. *Biochemistry* 32:2888–906

43. Rodgers KR, Su C, Subramaniam S, Spiro TG. 1992. Hemoglobin R → T structural dynamics from simultaneous monitoring of tyrosine and tryptophan time-resolved UV resonance Raman signals. *J. Am. Chem. Soc.* 114:3697–709

44. Rousseau DL, Tan SL, Ondrias MR, Ogawa S, Noble RW. 1984. Absence of cooperative energy at the heme in liganded hemoglobins. *Biochemistry* 23:2857–65

45. Russu IM, Ho NT, Ho C. 1980. Role of the beta 146 histidyl residue in the alkaline Bohr effect of hemoglobin. *Biochemistry* 19:1043–52

46. Schumacher MA, Dixon MM, Kluger R, Jones RT, Brennan RG. 1995. Allosteric transition intermediates modelled by crosslinked haemoglobins. *Nature* 375:84–87

47. Shaanan B. 1983. Structure of human oxyhaemoglobin at 2.1 Å resolution. *J. Mol. Biol.* 171:31–59

48. Shibayama N, Imai K, Morimoto H, Saigo S. 1993. Oxygen equilibrium properties of asymmetric nickel(II)-iron(II) hybrid hemoglobin. *Biochemistry* 32:8792–98

49. Shibayama N, Imai K, Morimoto H, Saigo S. 1995. Oxygen equilibrium properties of nickel(II)-iron(II) hybrid hemoglobins cross-linked between 82 beta 1 and 82 beta 2 lysyl residues by bis(3,5-dibromosalicyl)fumarate: determination of the first two-step microscopic Adair constants for human hemoglobin. *Biochemistry* 34:4773–80

50. Shibayama N, Morimoto H, Saigo S. 1997. Reexamination of the hyper thermodynamic stability of asymmetric cyanomet valency hybrid hemoglobin, (alpha+CN-beta+CN-) (alpha beta): no preferentially populating asymmetric hybrid at equilibrium. *Biochemistry* 36:4375–81

51. Shibayama N, Saigo S. 1995. Fixation of the quaternary structures of human adult haemoglobin by encapsulation in transparent porous silica gels. *J. Mol. Biol.* 251:203–9

52. Shih DT, Luisi BF, Miyazaki G, Perutz MF,

53. Nagai K. 1993. A mutagenic study of the allosteric linkage of His(HC3)146 beta in haemoglobin. *J. Mol. Biol.* 230:1291–96

53. Silva MM, Rogers PH, Arnone A. 1992. A third quaternary structure of human hemoglobin A at 1.7-Å resolution. *J. Biol. Chem.* 267:17248–56

54. Smith FR, Lattman EE, Carter CW Jr. 1991. The mutation beta 99 Asp-Tyr stabilizes Y, a new, composite quaternary state of human hemoglobin. *Proteins* 10:81–91

55. Wilson J, Phillips K, Luisi B. 1996. The crystal structure of horse deoxyhaemoglobin trapped in the high-affinity (R) state. *J. Mol. Biol.* 264:743–45

56. Wyman J Jr. 1964. Linked functions and reciprocal effects in hemoglobin: a second look. *Adv. Prot. Chem.* 19:223–86

57. Janin J, Wodak SJ. 1993. The quaternary structure of hemoglobin Ypsilanti. *Proteins* 15:1–4

58. Janin J, Wodak SJ. 1985. Reaction pathway for the quaternary structure change in hemoglobin. *Biopolymers* 24:509–526

59. Ackers GK, Perella M, Holt JM, Denisov I, Huang Y. 1997. Thermodynamic stability of the asymmetric doubly-ligated hemoglobin tetramer $(\alpha^{CN}\beta^{CN})$ $(\alpha\beta)$: methodological and mechanistic issues. *Biochemistry* 36:10822–10829

60. Kiger L, Marden MC, Poyart C. 1998. CO binding and valency exchange in asymmetric Hb hybrids. *Biochemistry.* In press

61. Smith FR, Ackers GK. 1985. Experimental resolution for cooperative free energies for the ten ligation states of human hemoglobin. *Proc. Natl. Acad. Sci. USA.* 82:5347–51

62. Ackers GK, Doyle ML, Myers D, Daugherty MA. 1992. Molecular code for cooperativity in hemoglobin. *Science* 225:54–63

63. Perutz MF, Fermi G, Shih T-b. 1984. Structure of deoxyhemoglobin Cowtown. *Proc. Natl. Acad. Sci. USA.* 81:4781–84

64. Henry ER, Jones CM, Hofrichter J, Eaton WR. 1997. Can a two-state MWC allosteric model explain hemoglobin kinetics. *Biochemistry* 36:6511–28

65. Bettati S, Mozzarelli A. 1998 T-State hemoglobin binds oxygen non-cooperatively with Bohr effect. *J. Biol. Chem.* 272: 32050–55

66. Bettati S, Mozarelli A, Perutz MF. 1998 Oxygen affinity of T-state hemoglobin Cowtown crystals. *J. Mol. Biol.* (Submitted)

Annu. Rev. Biophys. Biomol. Struct. 1998. 27:35–58

THE THREE-DIMENSIONAL STRUCTURE OF THE RIBOSOME AND ITS COMPONENTS

Peter B. Moore

Department of Chemistry, Yale University, New Haven, Connecticut 06520;
e-mail: moore@neutron.chem.yale.edu

KEY WORDS: rRNA, ribosomal proteins, ribonucleoproteins, NMR, crystallography

ABSTRACT

Exciting progress has been made in the last decade by those who use physical methods to study the structure of the ribosome and its components. The structures of 10 ribosomal proteins and three isolated ribosomal protein domains are known, and the conformations of a significant number of rRNA sequences have been determined. Electron microscopists have made major advances in the analysis of images of ribosomes, and microscopically derived ribosome models at resolutions approaching 10Å are likely quite soon. Furthermore, ribosome crystallographers are on the verge of phasing the diffraction patterns they have had for several years, and near-atomic resolution models for entire ribosomal subunits could emerge from this source at any time. The literature relevant to these developments is reviewed below.

CONTENTS

35

1056-8700/98/0610-0035$08.00

PERSPECTIVE AND OVERVIEW

The word "ribosome" was coined by Roberts in 1958 to describe a class of ribonucleoprotein particles that had been discovered in cytoplasm a few years earlier (69). Ribosomes were already the objects of intense scrutiny because of their involvement in protein synthesis (50), and large numbers of molecular biologists devoted themselves to ribosome-related problems until the late 1960s, when the coding problem was solved. The understanding of protein synthesis and ribosome function that emerged in that era has since required only modest adjustment.

Suffice it to say that the ribosome is a template-directed polymerase, similar in function to an RNA or a DNA polymerase. The most important functional differences between it and other polymerases are that it uses nucleic acid templates to direct the synthesis of proteins rather than other nucleic acids, and the chemistry it catalyzes consumes aminoacyl tRNA rather than nucleoside triphosphates. Protein sequences are determined by ribosome-mediated base-pairing interactions between tRNA anticodons and messenger RNA triplets, and the enzymatic activity that catalyzes peptide bond formation, peptidyl transferase, is intrinsic to the ribosome.

Given the importance of the ribosome in gene expression, the intimate involvement of RNA in all of its functions, and its formidable size, it is an exceedingly attractive target for structural biologists, as well as a tremendous challenge. Substantial progress has been made recently, and it is conceivable that the structure of the ribosome will be solved at atomic resolution in the next five years. The purpose of this article is to review what is known about the three-dimensional structure of the ribosome and its components. Readers interested in other aspects of the field should consult the volumes the ribosome community has produced at odd intervals, mostly in conjunction with its international symposia (e.g. 35, 52, 60, 101).

ORGANIZATION OF THE RIBOSOME

Subunit Structure

The molecular weights of ribosomal particles range from about 2.5×10^6, which is typical of bacterial ribosomes, to about 4.5×10^6 for the cytoplasmic ribosomes of eukaryotes, and the ratio of molecular weight of RNA to that of protein in all ribosomes is about 60:40. Ribosomes are 1:1 complexes of two nonequivalent ribonucleoprotein subunits, the larger being about twice the size of the smaller. The small subunit binds mRNA, and mediates the interactions between mRNA and tRNAs. The large subunit catalyzes peptide-bond formation, and is important in the factor-dependent steps of protein synthesis. During the initiation phase of protein synthesis, the two subunits behave independently, assembling into complete ribosomes only when elongation is about to begin (31).

Chemical Composition

The chemical composition of the ribosome is hard to define accurately because it copurifies with all the molecules with which it interacts during protein synthesis, as well as associating accidentally with substances released when cell compartments are disrupted. Furthermore, procedures that remove contaminants from ribosomes also deplete them of legitimate components. Thus ribosomes have the perverse property that the lower their content of contaminating substances, the lower their specific activity in protein synthesis in vitro.

In bacteria, small subunits contain a single copy of an RNA having a molecular weight of about 500,000 (16S rRNA). Large subunits contain a single RNA whose molecular weight is about 1,000,000 (23S rRNA), and one copy of a 40,000 molecular weight RNA (5S rRNA). With the exception of their 5S rRNAs, the rRNAs in the cytoplasmic ribosomes of the typical eukaryotes are bigger than their prokaryotic counterparts, and while their small subunits contain a single large rRNA (18S rRNA), their large subunits contain three: 5S rRNA, 5.8S rRNA, and 28S rRNA. 5.8S rRNA is homologous to the 5' end of bacterial 23S rRNA, and 28S rRNA is homologous to the rest (59). No one knows why the RNA in eukaryotic large subunits is subdivided, but the ribosomes of some protozoans offer far more extreme examples of the same phenomenon (e.g. 72).

Despite the purification problems alluded to above, by about 1975 the protein composition of the E. coli ribosome was understood in a general sense. Its small subunit contains single copies of each of 21 different proteins, and their average molecular weight is about 15,000. The 31 proteins in the large subunit of E. coli are about the same size (93). Large subunits contain single copies of every protein except the one called L7/L12, which is present in four copies. Eukaryotic ribosomes are qualitatively similar. They contain single copies of almost all the proteins found in them, but on average, eukaryotic ribosomal proteins are bigger than prokaryotic ribosomal proteins, and there are more of them (97). Ribosomal proteins are identified by an arbitrary numbering system (91, 94) about which all the reader need know is that small subunit proteins are designated SX, where S stands for "small subunit" and X is an integer. Large subunit proteins are designated L(arge)X.

The chemical composition of the ribosome has important structural implications. Macromolecular assemblies that contain single copies of most components *must* be asymmetric. It follows that each ribosome must have a single peptidyl transferase site, single sites for binding tRNA and mRNA, etc, and must therefore synthesize one polypeptide chain at a time, as the biochemical data have long indicated.

THE RIBOSOME AT LOW RESOLUTION

Shape

The asymmetry implied by the chemical composition of the ribosome is evident even in low resolution electron-microscopic images of negatively stained particles. Both subunits have distinctive shapes, and by about 1980 there was

Figure 1   The shapes of the ribosome and ribosomal subunits from *E. coli*. *Upper left*: 50S subunit. *Upper right*: 30S subunit. *Lower*: 70S ribosome. The models shown in these photographs were provided by James Lake (44).

a consensus that ribosomes resemble the objects shown in Figure 1 (44). The large subunit from *E. coli* is an irregular hemisphere, the "flat" face of which interacts with the small subunit. The projection extending form the right side of the particle's face in Figure 1, the "stalk," comprises L7/L12. Its middle projection, or "central protuberance," consists primarily of 5S rRNA and its associated proteins. The one on the left is composed primarily of L1. The small subunit is flatter and is divided into three domains. A relatively small "head" is joined to the "body" of the particle by a narrow neck, and the particle includes a "platform" that extends upwards from the body. While ribosomes from different kingdoms can be distinguished morphologically at this resolution, basically, they all look alike (45).

Quaternary Structure

Electron microscopy has also contributed to our understanding of the quaternary structure of the ribosome. The 52 ribosomal proteins in *E. coli* are so different in sequence that antibodies can be raised against them that do not cross-react between species (see below). Because almost all ribosomal proteins present epitopes on the surface of the ribosome, most antiribosomal protein antibodies bind to intact ribosomes (75). Furthermore, when these complexes are embedded in negative stain, their antibody components can be visualized (e.g. 87). Thus antibodies can be used as protein-specific stains to determine the positions of protein epitopes on the surface of the ribosome. By the mid 1980s, the positions of the surface epitopes of all the proteins in the *E. coli* small subunit had been mapped this way, as well as those of many large-subunit proteins (70, 77). 5S rRNA, some critical rRNA sequences, and a number of other important sites on the ribosome had also been located (e.g. 55, 66, 76).

The positions of ribosomal proteins were also determined by small-angle neutron scattering. The difference in neutron scattering between a protonated ribosome and a ribosome that contains two deuterated proteins in an otherwise protonated background is big enough to measure, and the distances between labeled proteins can be determined from difference signals of this kind (21, 38, 38a). Following demonstrations of the feasibility of this approach in the late 1970s—which depended on the reconstitutability of bacterial ribosomes and the ability of bacterial to grow in deuterated media (22, 46, 56)—a series of ever more complete partial maps of protein positions in the small ribosomal subunit from *E. coli* appeared, and the job was completed about 10 years later (9, 10). Figure 2 shows the result. Because the neutron map is reasonably consistent with the other data available at the time, it can be regarded as a summary of what was known about 30S quaternary structure as of 1990.

The distribution of protein in the *E. coli* 50S subunit was pursued the same way, but a complete map did not result. Only about 50 distances were measured, and seven proteins placed in three dimensions (53). Because the immunoelectron

Figure 2 The placement of proteins within the 30S subunit. Proteins are shown as spheres the volumes of which are proportional to molecular weight. Their placement was determined by neutron scattering (10). The protein array is superimposed on the outline of the 30S subunit in a manner that maximizes its overlap with epitope positions determined by immunoelectron microscopy. This figure was provided by Malcolm Capel.

microscopic information for the 50S subunit is also incomplete, our understanding of its quaternary organization is comparatively poor (78).

Investigation of ribosome structure by neutron scattering did not stop with the termination of the large subunit mapping project. New methods for extracting molecular shapes from SANS and SAXS data are being used today to study the shapes of the ribosomal subunits (80). Further, a major effort is under way to use dynamic nuclear polarization to generate contrast in ribosome samples. The feasibility of this approach has been demonstrated (54), and recent work indicates that information about the locations of single ribosomal components is likely to emerge (79).

rRNA STRUCTURE

Sequences and Secondary Structures

The first RNAs sequenced were tRNAs, and the secondary structures of these molecules were surmised from their sequences almost immediately, because the now-familiar cruciform structure of tRNAs maximizes their hydrogen bonding. The sequence of 5S rRNA from *E. coli*, which was the first non-tRNA RNA to be sequenced, was harder to interpret in this regard (7) because many different stem-loop structures can be proposed for it that have about the same number of base pairs (see 23). The now-familiar three-stem model for 5S rRNA (Figure 4) emerged from sequence comparisons done in the mid 1970s (26). The reasoning used is very powerful. Because homologous RNAs perform the same function, they must have the same structure. Therefore only the secondary structure that is compatible with all 5S sequences can be correct.

Six years later, the comparative, phylogenetic approach was applied to16S rRNA sequences with spectacular results (65). The input data were Noller's newly obtained sequence for *E. coli* 16S rRNA, and Woese's collection of oligonucleotide sequences derived from the 16S-like rRNAs of many species. A later, more refined version of their model is shown in Figure 3 (32). A similar model for 23S rRNA appeared shortly thereafter, which has also been refined over the years (64). These secondary structure models for 5S, 16S, and 23S rRNA have been tested by countless experiments; they are accurate descriptions of the secondary structures of these rRNAs, both in the ribosome and in solution (101).

The fact that the phylogenetic method works with rRNAs proves that the structures of rRNAs in all species are fundamentally alike, and provides compelling evidence that despite obvious differences in overall size, protein composition, and so on, the structures of the regions of the ribosome critical for function must be similar. Eukaryotic rRNAs are larger than their prokaryotic counterparts because they include "insertions" that lengthen stems and augment

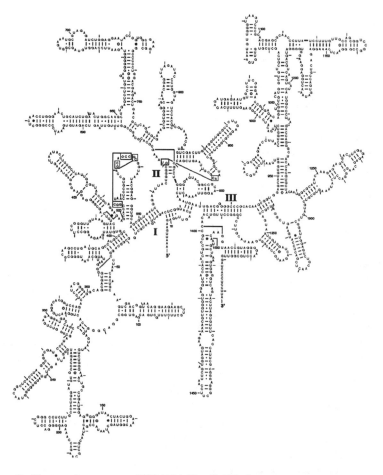

Figure 3 The secondary structure of 16S rRNA (*E. coli*). This diagram was prepared by Dr. Robin Gutell (32).

loops, but otherwise their secondary structures resemble those of prokaryotic rRNAs. Similarly, the rRNAs that are smaller than their regular prokaryotic homologues are smaller owing to block deletions in stems and loops that do not alter their overall organization. Observations like these helped make the hypothesis that RNA is responsible for everything important in ribosomes an article of faith in the field. (For supporting evidence see 63.)

rRNA Substructures

Current rRNA secondary structure models leave the secondary structure of a lot of rRNA unspecified. This does not mean that those sequences are unstructured,

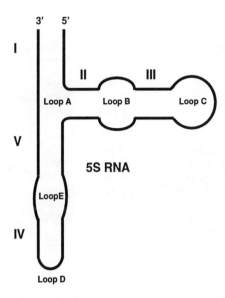

Figure 4   The secondary structure of 5S rRNA. This diagram was prepared by Anne Dallas.

however. When sequences are conserved, the sequence covariations used to prove the existence of base-base interactions cannot be observed. There are also instances where the variations seen are enigmatic, and so again no structure is specified. Furthermore, most stems include internal mismatches and terminal loops about which sequence comparisons are uninformative. In recent years, physical biochemists have begun studying the structures of oligonucleotides containing such sequences. Table 1 lists the ones whose three-dimensional structures are known.

Not surprisingly, the rRNA about which the most is known is 5S rRNA. The structure of the entire helix I, IV, V-half of *E. coli* 5S rRNA (Figure 4) has been determined crystallographically, and separate solution structures are available for its helix I and for its helix IV, V/loops D/E region, as well as an independent crystallographic structure for its loop E region (see Table 1). The structures of the helix I region of *Thermus flavus* 5S rRNA and the loop E region from *Xenopus laevis* have also been determined. As expected, except for wobble GUs, the helices in 5S rRNA are regular A-form helices. Further, the solution structure of the molecule closely resembles its crystal structure.

As is clearly evident in Figure 5, however, the structure of loop E is distinctly different in eubacteria and eukaryotes. The eukaryotic molecule contains a (GC)(GA)(AU) motif followed by a bulged G. Eubacterial loop Es have two similar (GC)(GA)(AU) motifs, arranged palindromically, with three non-Watson-Crick base pairs in between.

Table 1   rRNA motifs of known conformation

Structure	Species	Method	Reference
Tetraloops			
UUCG	generic	NMR	12
GNRA	generic	NMR, X-ray	11, 34, 42
CUUG	generic	NMR	43
5S rRNA			
Helix I	*Th. flavus*	X-ray	5
Helix I (1–11, 108–120)	*E. coli*	NMR	88
Loop E (69–81, 94–106)	*X. Laevis*	NMR	90
Loop E (70–81, 94–106)	*E. coli*	X-ray	13
Fragment 1 (1–11, 69–87, 89–120)	*E. coli*	X-ray	13
Loop D/E (69–106)	*E. coli*	NMR	12
16S-like rRNAs			
A-site (1404–1412, 1488–1497)	*E. coli*	NMR	25
23S-like rRNAs			
Sarcin/ricin loop (4316–4332)	rat	NMR	81
GTPase center (1090–1100)	*E. coli*	NMR	24, 40

Much less is known about the large rRNAs, both in absolute terms and in proportion to their sizes. Many of the loops that close their stem/loops are "tetraloops," i.e. loops that consist of four bases, and sequence comparison has revealed that certain sequences appear with unusually high frequency in tetraloops: UNCG, GNRA, and CUNG (84, 95). Structures are available for all three types. As expected, these specially favored tetraloops are stabilized by interactions that would be eliminated if their sequences were altered. Presumably the structures of these loops are the same everywhere they appear in nature.

The so-called GTPase center in 23S rRNAs, which binds thiostrepton and protein L11 and interacts with elongation factors, includes a hexaloop the conformation of which has been studied spectroscopically by two groups in two slightly different oligonucleotides. For reasons that are not understood, its conformation is different in the two oligonucleotides (24, 40). Nevertheless, both groups agree that this loop resembles the anticodon loops in tRNAs.

The longest totally conserved sequence in rRNAs occurs in a loop in 23S-like rRNAs, between A2654 and A2665 (*E. coli*). It is called the "sarcin/ricin loop" (SRL) because it is the target of the protein toxins ricin and sarcin, which catalyze the alteration of its covalent structure (19, 20). This modification inactivates ribosomes because it renders them unable to bind elongation factors properly, and once a sufficient number of ribosomes have been inactivated this

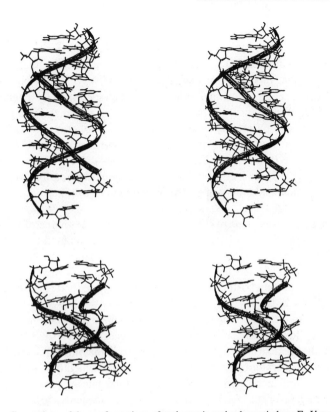

Figure 5 Comparison of the conformations of prokaryotic and eukaryotic loop E. *Upper*: stereo view of loop E from *E. coli* as determined by X-ray crystallography (13). *Lower*: *X. laevis* loop E determined by NMR (90). The two structures are aligned so that their (GA)(AU) motifs are oriented in the same way. The coordinates for eukaryotic loop E were supplied by Ignacio Tinoco.

way, cells die. Surprisingly, this molecule contains a bulged G motif similar to that found in loop E of eukaryotic 5S rRNA (Figure 5), and is capped by a GAGA tetraloop that has the standard GNRA tetraloop conformation.

Recently an extremely interesting structure was published of a complex between paromomycin, an aminoglycoside antibiotic that affects the fidelity of coding, and an oligonucleotide that corresponds to the A-site of 16S rRNA, where tRNA anticodons interact with mRNA codons (25). It provides a wealth of detail about the way aminoglycosides bind to ribosomes. It explains why bacteria are more sensitive to aminoglycosides than are eukaryotes, suggests the mechanism of many of the mutations that affect aminoglycoside sensitivity, and suggests the way mRNA binds to ribosomes.

Tertiary Structure Models

As soon as the first rRNA secondary structures models appeared, people began building three-dimensional models of the ribosome, which are effectively rRNA tertiary structure models. It is easy to understand why. The rRNA sites that interact with specific ribosomal proteins had been identified by a generation's worth of "bind-and-chew" experiments, chemical and enzymatic protection experiments, and by affinity labeling (e.g. 33). Furthermore, much was already known about the physical locations of proteins and the overall shape of the ribosome (see above). Finally, some RNA– RNA cross links had been identified (e.g. 17). It seemed obvious that it should be possible to produce a three-dimensional summary of this information that, with luck, might actually resemble the ribosome.

The problem was—and still remains—that no single source of experimental information comes close to providing enough information to place all the stems/loops in rRNA in three dimensions, let alone determine the positions of its "unstructured" connecting strands. Thus, to build any model at all, information about protein positions and protein binding sites had to be merged with data on RNA cross-linking, affinity-labeling, and the like, and assumptions made that had little experimental support. Mergers like this cannot be done in a rigorously logical way because each type of data speaks to a different aspect of the underlying structure (6). In recent years, the dominant contributors to the modeling literature have been Harvey's group, which has used molecular dynamics to find models compatible with all of the data available (18), Noller's group, which favors combining information on the sequences to which proteins bind with protein positions (62), and Brimacombe's group, which stresses the use of RNA–RNA and ligand–RNA cross-linking data (57).

The 30S subunit has gotten most of the attention both because it is smaller, and because the data are more complete. Some of the low-resolution conclusions reached are certainly correct. For example, the large 5′ domain of 16S rRNA (see Figure 3) forms the bulk of the body of the 30S subunit. The middle domain of 16S rRNA and its long 3′ terminal stem/loop form the lateral platform of the subunit, and its large 3′ domain is the subunit's head. The large domains of 23S rRNA can also be placed within the large subunit's shape with some confidence (6). The internal organization of these domains is more problematic, but here too there is some agreement, forced by the need for compatibility with the data on the placement of ribosomal proteins and protein binding sites. The significance of the differences between models, of which there are many, is hard to evaluate.

In the last two years, Brimacombe's group has started constraining its models by fitting RNA sequences into the (relatively) high-resolution electron density maps of the small subunit produced by electron microscopists (73) (see also below). This initiative may be premature because of limitations imposed by the low resolution of the images being interpreted. It is worth noting, however, that when and if higher resolution electron density maps of the ribosome are generated, they will be interpreted the same way: by fitting models of RNA and polypeptide sequences into electron density.

RIBOSOMAL PROTEINS

Primary Structures

Sequencing of ribosomal proteins began 30 years ago, when the first ones were purified, and has been under way ever since. Tremendous progress has been made, but the implications of this work are underappreciated both because of the field's fixation on rRNA and because the appearance of sequences has been so gradual. By 1984, sequences were available for the 52 ribosomal proteins from *E. coli* (92), and many have since been sequenced from other eubacterial and archaebacterial species (94). The project to sequence the 80 proteins from the rat ribosome is also virtually complete (97), and a flood of new ribosomal protein sequences is being delivered by the genome sequencing projects.

Several qualitative conclusions have emerged. First, there is little evidence for sequence homologies within the set of ribosomal proteins found in any organism (93). This is why antibodies can be raised that are specific for each member of such a set. Second, it is clear that homologies exist between species. Within kingdoms, almost all the ribosomal proteins in one species have homologues in another. In addition, there is convincing evidence for homologies between the ribosomal proteins from archaeal and eubacterial species. It is, however, harder to find the eukaryotic homologues of eubacterial ribosomal proteins without using their archaeal homologues as "intermediates," an observation that has interesting evolutionary implications (97). Third, there is intriguing evidence that at least some ribosomal proteins may have evolved from proteins that had different functions, or possibly vice-verse (96).

These observations demonstrate that the ancestral organism from which the three kingdoms diverged had ribosomes that included protein as well as RNA. They also imply that if modern ribosomal proteins evolved from a smaller set of ancestral ribosomal protein, as has been proposed in the past, they diverged so long ago that little or no trace remains in their sequences. Finally, because homologous proteins should have homologous functions, these data imply that the quaternary structures of ribosomes are conserved across kingdom boundaries also.

Tertiary Structures

Both because L7/L12 is acidic (most other ribosomal proteins are not), and because it easily washes off of ribosomes, L7/L12 (*E. coli*) was the first ribosomal protein to be purified and sequenced. Its C-terminal domain was also the first part of the ribosome to have its structure solved in three dimensions (48). Eight more crystal structures and four NMR structures have been reported for ribosomal proteins, or domains of ribosomal proteins, since 1980, most of them for proteins from thermophilic bacteria. The reason that thermophilic ribosomal proteins have been favored is that they are apparently more stable at room temperature than mesophilic ribosomal proteins in solution. Although the structures of individual ribosomal proteins tell us relatively little about ribosome function, comparisons within the set and between members of the set and nonribosomal proteins have become increasingly enlightening. Someday, useful information may be gained by building these structures into low-resolution ribosome models. Table 2 lists the structures available, and Figures 6 and 7 display their topologies.

Several conclusions have already emerged. First, the topologies of the C-terminal domain of L7/L12, the N-terminal domain of L9, L30, and S6 resemble that of the small nuclear RNP (snRNP) protein U1A, which binds to RNA through its exposed β sheet (67). Presumably these ribosomal proteins do the same. Second, no single topology dominates. Several α/β topologies are found in ribosomal proteins in addition to that found in L7/L12, and there are two examples of all-β proteins (L14 and S17) and one example of an all-α-helix domain (S15). Third, five of these proteins are probably bivalent RNA binders: L1, L6, L9, S5, and S8. All these proteins probably stabilize rRNA tertiary structure by fixing the positions of pairs of rRNA sequences. Because the two

Table 2 Three-dimensional structures of ribosomal proteins

Protein	Source	Domain organization	Method	Reference
L1	*T. therm.*	Two domains, both α/β	X-ray	61
L6	*B. stearo.*	Two domains, both α/β	X-ray	30
L7/L12	*E. coli*	C-term. domain only, α/β	X-ray	48
L9	*B. stearo.*	Two α/β domains + α linker	X-ray	36
L11	*B. stearo.*	C-term. domain only, α/β	NMR	51
L14	*B. stearo.*	β barrel, one domain	X-ray	16
L30	*E. coli*	One α/β domain	X-ray	89
S1-RM	*E. coli**	One β domain	NMR	8
S5	*B. stearo.*	Two α/β domains	X-ray	68
S6	*T. therm.*	One α/β domain	X-ray	49
S8	*T. therm.*	Two α/β domains	X-ray	15
S15	*T. therm.*	One α domain	NMR	3
S17	*B. stearo.*	One β barrel domain	NMR	41

*The S1-repeated motif (S1-RM) solved is that found in polynucleotide phosphylase (*E. coli*), not one of the six such motifs in S1, but there is every reason to believe that all such motifs are homologous.

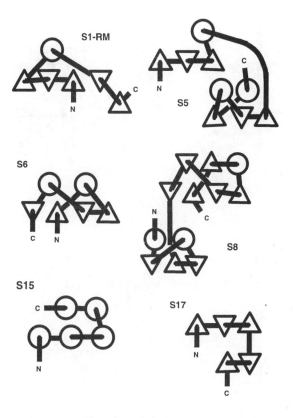

Figure 6   Topologies of 30S ribosomal proteins. Helices are shown as circles, and β-sheet is shown as triangles. *Upright triangle*: strand with N-terminus pointing toward the reader. *Inverted triangle*: strand with C-terminus pointing toward the reader. Every care has been taken to ensure that the topologies shown are accurate, but because the author derived some from nonstereo figures, their accuracy cannot be guaranteed.

domains of L6 have the same topology, it is likely to be the product of a gene duplication. It is less obvious how the others evolved. L9 is striking because the distance between its two globular domains is determined by a long α-helical spacer. Fourth, it has been discovered that the RNA-binding, C-terminal domain of L11 resembles the DNA-binding domains of homeodomain proteins, and evidence has been obtained that L11, like homeodomain proteins, binds to nucleic acids through its helix-turn-helix motif (98). These observations testify to the validity of the proposals made on the basis of sequence comparisons that at least some ribosomal proteins are homologous to proteins that have other

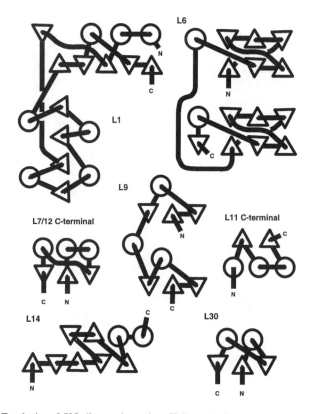

Figure 7 Topologies of 50S ribosomal proteins. Helices are shown as *circles*, and β-sheet is shown as *triangles*. *Upright triangle*: strand with N-terminus pointing toward the reader. *Inverted triangle*: strand with C-terminus pointing toward the reader. Every care has been taken to ensure that the topologies shown are accurate, but because the author derived some from nonstereo figures, their accuracy cannot be guaranteed.

functions in the cell. This concept is further supported by the discovery that other proteins—e.g. elongation factor EF-G—contain domains that resemble ribosomal proteins (1, 58).

It is clear that ribosomal proteins did not all evolve from the same ancestral protein; their tertiary topologies are too diverse for that. However, could it be, for example, that all proteins that include L7/L12-like domains share a common ancestor? Might it also be that the ribosomal versions of domains that occur in other proteins are the "closest living relatives" of the ancestors of those domains?

HIGH-RESOLUTION ELECTRON MICROSCOPY

About the time consensus was reached about the low-resolution shapes of the ribosome and its subunits, efforts got under way to analyze ribosome images quantitatively in three dimensions (e.g. 28). Over the next decade, as technical problems were solved, a stream of ever-more-accurate ribosome reconstructions appeared, all derived from the familiar negatively stained images. The farther along the enterprise got, the more irregular the appearance of both ribosomal subunits. The surface of the ribosome is far rougher than that of ordinary enzymes. It is full of crevices and invaginations big enough to swallow entire macromolecules of ordinary size, which is not surprising, given the size of the proteins and RNAs ribosomes interact with during protein synthesis.

Reconstructions done using micrographs of ribosome microcrystals led to an even more startling result; a hole runs through the middle of the 50S subunit, from its subunit interface all the way to its "back" (99). Because the hole starts near the peptidyl transferase site and ends about where nascent polypeptides first emerge from the ribosome (4), it is possible that nascent polypeptides work their way through it as they elongate.

The resolution of negative-stained images is limited to 20–30Å by the grain size of the stain. Their interpretation is complicated by the tendency of macromolecules to bind heavy metals specifically and thus to become positively as well as negatively stained. Thus the development of methods for visualizing ribosomes embedded in vitreous ice was a huge advance. It eliminated the need for staining, and also avoided specimen dehydration (27). The payoff came in mid 1995, when two groups announced independent 20–25Å resolution reconstructions of the ribosome derived from the merger of thousands of low-dose images obtained from samples of this kind (29, 73). To understand the magnitude of the advance, the reader need only compare Figure 1 with Figure 8. A 38Å resolution image of the eukaryotic ribosome was also reported (86), as well as a reconstruction at similar resolution of the small subunit of *E. coli* documenting small differences between activated and inactivated subunits (47).

Early in 1996, the Frank group reported images of ribosomes with tRNAs bound (2). The particles in question had tRNAs bound simultaneously to their A, P, and E sites, and while the resolution was not high enough to determine the orientations of the tRNAs unambiguously, it is now clear where tRNAs bind to the ribosome. A year later, van Heel and colleagues published images of ribosomes with 2 tRNAs bound, in both the pretranslocational and post-translocational states (74). The positions found for tRNAs by van Heel et al fall inside the tRNA envelope defined by Frank and his colleagues. However,

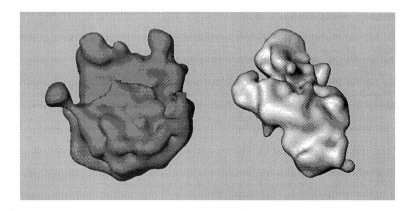

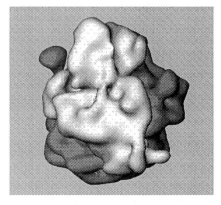

Figure 8 Surface views of the *E. coli* ribosome and its subunits at 23 D resolution. The images shown were obtained by cryoelectron microscopy (29) using methods described in detail by Zhu and coworkers (100). The views used were chosen to approximate those in Figure 1. They were produced by Yanhong Li and Joachim Frank.

the two groups do not agree about the orientations of tRNAs in the A, P, and E sites. This is not surprising given the resolution of the images available, and there is every reason to believe that interpretations will converge when higher resolution images become available.

In the next few years, electron microscopists are certain to reap a tremendous harvest of information about the structure of the ribosome and the complexes it forms during protein synthesis. Some feel that electron microscopy can produce 10Å-resolution images. If so, reliable near-atomic resolution models of the ribosome are likely to result.

RIBOSOME CRYSTALLOGRAPHY

The progress made by the electron microscopists challenges the long-held belief that crystallography will be the source of high-resolution explanations for ribosomal phenomena. The first ribosome crystals were obtained by Yonath and coworkers about 1979, and she and her colleagues have been the principal champions of ribosome crystallography ever since. They discovered ways of preparing crystals that diffract to high resolution (85), and developed methods for obtaining high resolution data from them (37). What they have not been able to do so far is find a way to phase their ribosomal diffraction patterns. Yonath's group has concentrated much of its effort on the introduction of heavy metal cluster compounds into ribosome crystals, and believe they have had some success in obtaining isomorphous derivatives this way (71, 82, 83), but nothing of use to the rest of the community has emerged as yet. However, the stalemate that has existed in this area for a number of years could be broken at any time. Once the first good derivative is obtained, our understanding of the ribosomal architecture and protein synthesis will be instantly transformed.

ACKNOWLEDGMENTS

I offer my thanks to those who provided the figures that appear in this review: Dr. Malcolm Capel, Ms. Anne Dallas, Dr. Joachim Frank, Dr. Robin Gutell, Dr. James Lake, Ms. Yanhong Li, and Dr. Ignacio Tinoco, Jr. Their contributions are also acknowledged in the figure legends. This work was supported by a grant from the NIH (GM 54216).

NOTE ADDED IN PROOF

Several relevant papers have appeared since this review was written, among them the following:

rRNA Substructures   The conformation of the tetraloop that caps the 3′-most stem/loop in eukaryotic 18S rRNA has been determined by NMR (7a), as has the conformation of the conserved loop in 23S-like rRNAs that interacts with the CCA end of tRNAs (67a). In addition, we now have a structure for the region of 16S rRNA that binds ribosomal protein S8 (43a).

rRNA Tertiary Structure Models   A detailed model for the 30S subunit based on fitting RNA sequences into EM-based electron density maps has appeared (57a–c).

Protein Tertiary Structures   Crystal structures have been reported for S7 from *T. thermophilus* (90a), and for S7 from *B. stearothermophilus* (39).

Literature Cited

1. Aevarsson A, Brazhnikov E, Garber M, Zheltonorova J, Chirgadze Y, et al. 1994. Three-dimensional structure of the ribosomal translocase: elongation factor G from *Thermus thermophilus. EMBO J.* 13:3669–77

2. Agrawal RK, Penczek P, Grassucci RA, Li Y, Leith A, et al. 1996. Direct visualization of A-, P-, and E-site transfer RNAs in the *Escherichia coli* ribosome. *Science* 271:1000–2

3. Berglund H, Rak A, Serganov A, Garber M, Hard T. 1997. Solution structure of the ribosomal RNA binding protein S15 from *Thermus thermophilus. Nat. Struct. Biol.* 4:20–23

4. Bernabeu C, Lake JA. 1982. Nascent polypeptide chains emerge from the exit domain of the large ribosomal subunit: immune mapping of the nascent chain. *Proc. Natl. Acad. Sci. USA* 79:3111–15

5. Betzel C, Lorenz S, Fuerste JP, Bald R, Zhang M, et al. 1994. Crystal structure of domain A of *Thermus flavus* 5S rRNA and the contribution of water to its structure. *FEBS Lett.* 351:159–64

6. Brimacombe R. 1995. The structure of ribosomal RNA: a three-dimensional jigsaw puzzle. (Review). *Eur J. Biochem.* 230:365–83

7. Brownlee GG, Sanger F, Barrell BG. 1968. The sequence of 5S ribosomal ribonucleic acid. *J. Mol. Biol.* 34:379–412

7a. Butcher SE, Dieckmann T, Feigon J. 1997. Solution structure of the conserved 16S-like ribosomal RNA UGAA tetraloop. *J. Mol. Biol.* 268:348–58

8. Bycroft M, Hubbard TJP, Proctor M, Freund SMV, Murzin AG. 1997. The solution structure of the S1 RNA binding domain: a member of an ancient nucleic acid-binding fold. *Cell* 88:235–42

9. Capel MS, Engelman DM, Freeborn BR, Kjeldgaard M, Langer JA, et al. 1987. A complete mapping of the proteins in the small ribosomal subunit of *E. coli. Science* 238:1403–6

10. Capel MS, Kjeldgaard M, Engelman DM, Moore PB. 1988. The positions of S2, S13, S16, S17, S19, and S21 in the 30S ribosomal subunit of *Escherichia coli. J. Mol. Biol.* 200:65–87

11. Cate J, Gooding AR, Podell E, Zhou K, Golden BL, et al. 1996. Crystal structure of a group I ribozyme domain: principles of RNA packing. *Science* 273:1678–85

12. Cheong C, Varani G, Tinoco I. 1990. Solution structure of an unusually stable RNA hairpin, 5'GGAC(UUCG)GUCC. *Nature* 346:680–82

13. Correll CC, Freeborn B, Moore PB, Steitz TA. 1998. Metals, motifs and recognition in the crystal structure of a 5S rRNA domain. *Cell.* In press

14. Dallas AD, Moore PB. 1998. The solution structure of the loop E/loop D region of *E. coli* 5S rRNA. *Structure.* In press

15. Davies C, Ramakrishnan V, White SW. 1996. Structural evidence for specific S8-RNA and S8-protein interactions with the 30S ribosomal subunit: ribosomal protein S8 from *Bacillus stearothermophilus* at 1.9 C resolution. *Structure* 4:1093–1105

16. Davies C, White SW, Ramakrishnan V. 1996. The crystal structure of ribosomal protein L14 reveals an important organizational component of the translational apparatus. *Structure* 4:55–66

17. Dokudovskaya S, Dontsova O, Shpanchenko O, Bogdanov A, Brimacombe R. 1996. Loop IV of 5S ribosomal RNA has contacts both to domain II and to domain V of the 23S RNA. *RNA* 2:146–52

18. Easterwood TR, Harvey SC. 1995. Modeling the structure of the ribosome. *Biochem. Cell Biol.* 73:751–56

19. Endo Y, Mitsui M, Motizuki M, Tsurugi K. 1987. The mechanism of action of ricin and related toxic lectins on eukaryotic ribosomes. The site and the characteristics of the modification in 28S ribosomal RNA caused by the toxins. *J. Biol. Chem.* 262:5908–12

20. Endo Y, Wool IG. 1982. The site of action of alpha sarcin on eukaryotic ribosomes. *J. Biol. Chem.* 257:9054–60

21. Engelman DM, Moore PB. 1972. A new method for the determination of biological quaternary structure by neutron scattering. *Proc. Natl. Acad. Sci. USA* 69:1997–99

22. Engelman DM, Moore PB, Schoenborn BP. 1975. Neutron scattering measurements of separation and shape of proteins in 30S ribosomal subunit of *Escherichia coli*: S2–S5, S5–S8, S3–S7. *Proc. Natl.*

Acad. Sci. USA 72:3888–92

23. Erdmann VA. 1976. Structure and function of 5S and 5.8S RNA. *Prog. Nucleic Acids Res. Mol. Biol.* 18:45–90

24. Fountain MA, Serra MJ, Krugh TR, Turner D. 1996. Structural features of a six-nucleotide RNA hairpin loop found in ribosomal RNA. *Biochemistry* 35:6539–48

25. Fourmy D, Recht MI, Blanchard SC, Puglisi JD. 1996. Structure of the A site of *Escherichia coli* 16S ribosomal RNA complexed with an aminoglycoside antibiotic. *Science* 274:1367–71

26. Fox GE, Woese CR. 1975. 5-S RNA secondary structure. *Nature* 256:505–7

27. Frank J, Penczek P, Grassuci R, Srivastava S. 1991. Three-dimensional reconstruction of the 70S *Escherichia coli* ribosome in ice: the distribution of ribosomal RNA. *J. Cell Biol.* 115:597–605

28. Frank J, Verschoor A, Boublik M. 1981. Computer averaging of electron micrographs of 40S ribosomal subunits. *Science* 214:1353–55

29. Frank J, Zhu J, Penczek P, Li Y, Srivastava S, et al. 1995. A model for protein synthesis based on cryo-electron microscopy of the *E. coli* ribosome. *Nature* 376:441–44

30. Golden BL, Ramakrishnan V, White SW. 1993. Ribosomal protein L6: structural evidence of gene duplication from a primitive RNA binding protein. *EMBO J.* 12:4901–8

31. Grunberg-Manago M. 1980. Initiation of protein synthesis as seen in 1979. In *Ribosomes: Structure, Function and Genetics*, ed. G Chambliss, GR Craven, J Davies, K Davis, L Kahan, et al, pp. 445–77. Baltimore: Univ. Park Press

32. Gutell RR. 1996. Comparative sequence analysis and the structure of 16S and 23S rRNA. In *Ribosomal RNA: Structure, Evolution, Processing and Function in Protein Biosynthesis*, ed. A Dahlberg, R Zimmerman, pp. 111–28. Boca Raton, FL: CRC

33. Heilek GM, Noller HF. 1996. Site-directed hydroxyl radical probing of the rRNA neighborhood of ribosomal protein S5. *Science* 272:1659–62

34. Heus HA, Pardi A. 1991. Structural features that give rise to the unusual stability of RNA hairpins containing GNRA loops. *Science* 253:191–94

35. Hill WE, Dahlberg A, Garrett RA, Moore PB, Schlessinger D, et al, eds. 1990. *The Ribosome: Structure, Function, and Evolution.* Washington, DC: Am. Soc. Microbiol.

36. Hoffman DW, Davies C, Gerchman SE, Kycia JH, Porter SJ, et al. 1994. Crystal structure of prokaryotic ribosomal protein L9: a bilobed RNA binding protein. *EMBO J.* 13:205–12

37. Hope H, Frolow F, von Bohlen K, Makowski I, Kratky C, et al. 1989. Cryocrystallography of ribosomal particles. *Acta Cryst.* B45:190–99

38. Hoppe W. 1972. The label triangulation method and the mixed isomorphous replacement principle. *J. Mol. Biol.* 78:581–85

38a. Hoppe W. 1972. A new X-ray method for the determination of the quaternary structure of protein complexes. *Isr. J. Chem.* 10:321–33

39. Hosaka H, Nakagawa A, Tanaka I, Harada N, Sano K, et al. 1997. Ribosomal protein S7: a new RNA-binding motif with structural similarities to a DNA architectural factor. *Structure* 5:1199–208

40. Huang SG, Wang YX, Draper DE. 1996. Structure of a hexanucleotide RNA hairpin loop conserved in ribosomal RNAs. *J. Mol. Biol.* 258:308–21

41. Jaishree TN, Ramakrishnan V, White SW. 1996. Solution structure of prokaryotic ribosomal protein S17 by high-resolution NMR spectroscopy. *Biochemistry* 35:2845–53

42. Jucker FM, Heus HA, Yip PF, Moors EHM, Pardi A. 1996. A network of heterogeneous hydrogen bonds in GNRA tetraloops. *J. Mol. Biol.* 264:968–80

43. Jucker FM, Pardi A. 1995. Solution structure of the CUUG hairpin loop: a novel RNA tetraloop motif. *Biochemistry* 34:14416–27

43a. Kalurachchi K, Uma K, Zimmermann RA, Nikonowicz EP. 1997. Structural features of the binding site for ribosomal protein S8 in *Escherichia coli* 16S rRNA defined using NMR spectroscopy. *Proc. Natl. Acad. Sci. USA* 94:2139–44

44. Lake JA. 1976. Ribosome structure determined by electron microscopy of *Escherichia coli* small subunits, large subunits and monomeric ribosomes. *J. Mol. Biol.* 105:131–59

45. Lake JA, Henderson E, Clark MW, Matheson AT. 1982. Mapping evolution to ribosome structure-intralineage constancy and interlineage variation. *Proc. Natl. Acad. Sci. USA* 79:5948–52

46. Langer JA, Engelman DM, Moore PB. 1978. Neutron-scattering studies of the ribosome of *Escherichia coli*: a provisional map of the locations of proteins S3, S4, S5, S7, S8, and S9 in the 30S subunit. *J. Mol. Biol.* 119:463–85

56   MOORE

47. Lata KR, Agrawal RK, Penczek P, Grassucci R, Zhen J, et al. 1996. Three-dimensional reconstruction of the *Escherichia coli* 30S ribosomal subunit in ice. *J. Mol. Biol.* 262:43–52
48. Leijonmarck M, Eriksson S, Liljas A. 1980. Crystal structure of a ribosomal component at 2.6 C resolution. *Nature* 286:824–26
49. Lindahl M, Svensson LA, Sedelnikov SE, Eliseikina IA, Fomenkova NP, et al. 1994. Crystal structure of the ribosomal protein S6 from *Thermus thermophilus*. *EMBO J.* 13:1249–54
50. Littlefield JW, Keller EB, Gross J, Zamecnik PC. 1955. Studies on cytoplasmic ribonucleoprotein particles from the liver of the rat. *J. Biol. Chem.* 217:111–24
51. Markus MA, Hinch AP, Huang S, Draper DE, Torchia DE. 1997. High-resolution structure of a ribosomal protein L11-C76, a helical protein with a flexible loop that becomes structured upon binding to RNA. *Nat. Struct. Biol.* 4:70–77
52. Matheson AT, Davies JE, Dennis PP, Hill WE. 1995. Frontiers in translation. *Biochem. Cell Biol.* 73:739–1227
53. May RP, Nowotny V, Nowotny P, Voss H, Nierhaus KH. 1992. Inter-protein distances within the large subunit from *Escherichia coli* ribosomes. *EMBO J.* 11:373–78
54. Meerwinch W, Olah G, Schink HJ, Stuhrmann HB, Wagner R, et al. 1991. Nuclear-spin order and excitation of inner shell electrons in macromolecular structure research—an application to the large subunit of the *Escherichia coli* ribosome. *J. Appl. Cryst.* 24:493–500
55. Montesanoroditis L, Glitz DG. 1994. Tracing the path of messenger RNA on the *Escherichia coli* small ribosomal subunit. Immune electron microscopy using defined oligodeoxynucleotide analogs of mRNA. *J. Biol. Chem.* 269:6458–70
56. Moore PB, Langer JA, Schoenborn BP, Engelman DM. 1977. Triangulation of proteins in the 30S ribosomal subunit of *Escherichia coli*. *J. Mol. Biol.* 112:199–234
57. Mueller F, Doring T, Erdemir T, Greuner B, Junke N, et al. 1995. Getting closer to an understanding of the three-dimensional structure of ribosomal RNA. *Biochem. Cell Biol.* 73:767–73
57a. Mueller F, Brimacombe R. 1997. A new model for the three-dimensional folding of *Escherichia coli* 16S ribosomal RNA, I: Fitting the RNA to a 3D electron microscopic map at 20 Å. *J. Mol. Biol.* 271:524–44
57b. Mueller F, Brimacombe R. 1997. A new model for the three-dimensional folding of *Escherichia coli* 16S ribosomal RNA, II: The RNA-protein interaction data. *J. Mol. Biol.* 271:545–65
57c. Mueller F, Stark H, van Heel M, Rinke-Appel J, Brimacombe R. 1997. A new model for the three-dimensional folding of *Escherichia coli* 16S ribosomal RNA, III: the topography of the functional center. *J. Mol. Biol.* 271:566–87
58. Murzin AG. 1995. A ribosomal protein module in EF-G and DNA gyrase. *Nat. Struct. Biol.* 2:25–26
59. Nazar RN. 1980. A 5.8S rRNA-like sequence in prokaryotic 23S rRNA. *FEBS Lett.* 119:212–14
60. Nierhaus KH, Franceschi F, Subramanian AR, Erdmann VA, Wittmann-Liebold B, eds. 1993. *The Translational Apparatus.* New York: Plenum
61. Nikonov S, Nevskaya N, Eliseikina I, Fomenkova N, Nikulin A, et al. 1996. Crystal structure of the RNA binding ribosomal protein L1 from *Thermus thermophilus*. *EMBO J.* 15:1350–59
62. Noller HF, Green R, Heilek G, Hoffarth V, Huttenhofer A, et al. 1995. Structure and function of ribosomal RNA. *Biochem. Cell Biol.* 73:997–1009
63. Noller HF, Hoffarth V, Zimniak L. 1992. Unusual resistance of peptidyl transferase to protein extraction procedures. *Science* 256:1416–19
64. Noller HF, Kop J, Wheaton V, Brosius J, Gutell RR, et al. 1981. Secondary structure model for 23S ribosomal RNA. *Nucleic Acids Res.* 9:6167–89
65. Noller HF, Woese CR. 1981. Secondary structure of 16S ribosomal RNA. *Science* 212:403–11
66. Oakes MI, Scheinman A, Atha T, Shankweiler G, Lake JA. 1990. Ribosome structure: three-dimensional locations of rRNA and proteins. In *The Ribosome: Structure, Function & Evolution*, ed. WE Hill, AE Dahlberg, RA Garrett, PB Moore, D Schlessinger, et al, pp. 180–93. Washington, DC: Am. Soc. Microbiol.
67. Oubridge C, Ito N, Evans PR, Teo C-H, Nagai K. 1994. Crystal structure at 1.92 C resolution of the RNA-binding domain of the U1A spliceosome protein complexed with an RNA hairpin. *Nature* 372:432–38
67a. Puglisi EV, Green R, Noller HF, Puglisi JD. 1997. Structure of a conserved RNA component of the peptidyl transferase centre. *Nat. Struct. Biol.* 4:775–78
68. Ramakrishnan V, White SW. 1992. The structure of ribosomal protein S5 reveals

sites of interaction with 16S rRNA. *Nature* 358:768–71

69. Roberts RB. 1958. *Microsomal Particles and Protein Synthesis.* New York: Pergamon

70. Scheinman A, Atha T, Aguinaldo AM, Kahan L, Shankweiler G, et al. 1992. Mapping the three-dimensional locations of ribosomal RNA and proteins. *Biochimie* 74:307–17

71. Schlunzen F, Hansen HAS, Thygesen J, Bennett WS, Volkmann N, et al. 1995. A milestone in ribosomal crystallography: the construction of preliminary electron density maps at intermediate resolution. *Biochem. Cell Biol.* 73:739–49

72. Schnare MN, Gray MW. 1990. Sixteen discrete RNA components in the cytoplasmic ribosome of *Euglena gracilis. J. Mol. Biol.* 215:73–83

73. Stark H, Mueller F, Orlova EV, Dube P, et al. 1995. The 70S *Escherichia coli* ribosome at 23 C resolution: fitting the ribosomal RNA. *Structure* 3:815–21

74. Stark H, Orlova EV, Rinke-Appel J, Junke N, Mueller F, et al. 1997. Arrangement of tRNAs in pre- and posttranslocational ribosomes revealed by electron cryomicroscopy. *Cell* 88:19–28

75. Stöffler G. 1974. Structure and function of the *Escherichia coli* ribosome: immunochemical analysis. In *Ribosomes,* ed. M Nomura, A Tissieres, P Lengyel, pp. 618–67. Cold Spring Harbor, NY: Cold Spring Harbor Lab.

76. Stöffler G, Stffler-Meilicke M. 1984. Immunoelectron microscopy of ribosomes. *Annu. Rev. Biophys. Bioengin.* 13:303–30

77. Stöffler G, Stffler-Meilicke M. 1986. Immuno electron microscopy on *Escherichia coli* ribosomes. In *Structure, Function, and Genetics of Ribosomes,* ed. B Hardesty, G Kramer, pp. 28–46. New York: Springer-Verlag

78. Stöffler-Meilicke M, Stffler G. 1990. Topography of the ribosomal proteins from *Escherichia coli* within the intact subunits as determined by immunoelectron microscopy and protein-protein cross-linking. In *The Ribosome: Structure, Function & Evolution,* ed. WE Hill, A Dahlberg, RA Garrett, PB Moore, D Schlessinger, et al, pp. 123–33. Washington, DC: Am. Soc. Microbiol.

79. Stuhrmann HB, Nierhaus KH. 1996. The determination of the in situ structure by nuclear spin contrast variation. In *Neutrons in Biology,* ed. BP Schoenborn, R Knott, pp. 397–413. New York: Plenum

80. Svergun DI, Koch MHJ, Skov-Pedersen J,

Serdyuk IN. 1996. Structural model of the 50S subunit of *E. coli* ribosomes from solution scattering. In *Neutrons in Biology,* ed. BP Schoenborn, RB Knott, pp.175–90. New York: Plenum

81. Szewczak AA, Moore PB. 1995. The sarcin/ricin loop, a modular RNA. *J. Mol. Biol.* 247:81–98

82. Thygesen J, Krumbholz S, Levin I, Zaytzev-Bashan A, Harms J, et al. 1996. Ribosomal crystallography: from crystal growth to initial phasing. *J. Cryst. Growth* 168:308–23

83. Thygesen J, Weinstein S, Franceschi F, Yonath A. 1996. The suitability of multimetal clusters for phasing in crystallography of large macromolecular assemblies. *Structure* 4:513–18

84. Tuerk C, Gauss P, Thermes C, Groebe DR, Gayle M, et al. 1988. CUUCGG hairpins; extraordinarily stable RNA secondary structures associated with various biochemical processes. *Proc. Natl. Acad. Sci. USA* 85:1364–68

85. van Bohlen K, Makowski I, Hansen HAS, Bartels H, Berkovitch-Yellin Z, et al. 1991. Characterization and preliminary attempts for derivitization of crystals of large ribosomal subunits from *Haloarcula marismortui* diffracting to 3 C resolution. *J. Mol. Biol.* 222:11–15

86. Verschoor A, Srivastava S, Grassucci R, Frank J. 1996. Native 3D structure of eukaryotic 80S ribosome: morphological homology with the *E. coli* 70S ribosome. *J. Cell Biol.* 133:495–505

87. Wabl MR. 1974. Electron microscopic localization of two proteins on the surface of the 50S ribosomal subunit of *Escherichia coli* using specific antibody markers. *J. Mol. Biol.* 84:241–47

88. White SA, Nilges M, Huang A, Brunger AT, Moore PB. 1992. NMR analysis of Helix I from the 5S RNA of *Escherichia coli. Biochemistry* 31:1610–20

89. Wilson KS, Appelt K, Badger J, Tanaka I, White SW. 1986. Crystal structure of a prokaryotic ribosomal protein. *Proc. Natl. Acad. Sci. USA* 83:7251–55

90. Wimberly B, Varani G, Tinoco I Jr. 1993. The conformation of loop E of eukaryotic 5S ribosomal RNA. *Biochemistry* 32:1078–87

90a. Wimberly BT, White SW, Ramakrishnan V. 1997. The structure of ribosomal protein S7 at 1.9 Å resolution reveals a beta-hairpin motif that binds double-stranded nucleic acids. *Structure* 5:1187–98

91. Wittmann HG, Stöffler G, Hundennach I, Kurland CG, Randall-Hazelbauer L,

et al. 1971. Correlation of 30S ribosomal proteins of *Escherichia coli* isolated
in different laboratories. *Mol. Gen. Genet.*
111:327–33

92. Wittmann-Liebold B. 1984. Primary
structures of *Escherichia coli* ribosomal
proteins. *Adv. Prot. Chem.* 36:56–78

93. Wittmann-Liebold B. 1986. Ribosomal
proteins: their structure and evolution. In
*Structure, Function, and Genetics of Ri-
bosomes,* ed. B Hardesty, G Kramer, pp.
326–61. New York: Springer-Verlag

94. Wittmann-Liebold B, Kopke AKE, Arndt
E, Kromer W, Hatakeyama T, et al. 1990.
Sequence comparison and evolution of ribosomal proteins and their genes. In *The
Ribosome: Structure, Function, & Genetics,* ed. WE Hill, A Dahlberg, RA Garrett, PB Moore, D Schlessinger, et al, pp.
598–616. Washington, DC: Am. Soc. Microbiol.

95. Woese CR, Winker S, Gutell RR. 1990.
Architecture of ribosomal RNA: con-
straints on the sequence of "tetra-loops."
Proc. Natl. Acad. Sci. USA 87:8467–71

96. Wool I. 1996. Extraribosomal functions of
ribosomal proteins. *Trends Biochem. Sci.*
21:164–65

97. Wool IG, Chan Y-L, Gluck A. 1995.
Structure and evolution of mammalian
ribosomal proteins. *Biochem. Cell Biol.*
73:933–47

98. Xing Y, Guha Thakurta D, Draper DE.
1997. The RNA binding domain of ribosomal protein L11 is structurally similar
to homeodomains. *Nat. Struct. Biol.* 4:24–
27

99. Yonath A, Leonard KR, Wittmann HG.
1987. A tunnel in the large ribosomal subunit revealed by three-dimensional image
reconstruction. *Science* 236:813–16

100. Zhu J, Penczek PA, Schroeder R, Frank J.
1997. Three-dimensional reconstruction
with contrast transfer function correction
from energy-filtered cryoelectron micrographs: procedure and application to the
70S *Escherichia coli* ribosome. *J. Struct.
Biol.* In press

101. Zimmermann RA, Dahlberg AE, eds.
1996. *Ribosomal RNA: Structure, Evolution, Processing, and Function in Protein
Biosynthesis.* Boca Raton, FL: CRC

Annu. Rev. Biophys. Biomol. Struct. 1998. 27:59–75

SIGNALING COMPLEXES:
Biophysical Constraints on
Intracellular Communication

Dennis Bray

Department of Zoology, Downing Street, University of Cambridge CB2 3EJ,
United Kingdom; e-mail: d.bray@zoo.cam.ac.uk

KEY WORDS: diffusion, membrane proteins, receptors, membrane domains

ABSTRACT

This review surveys the kinds of protein complex that participate in cell communication and identifies, where possible, general principles by which they form and act. It also advances the notion that biophysical constraints imposed by macromolecular crowding and diffusion have had a controlling influence on the evolution of cell signaling pathways. Complexes associated with the bacterial aspartate receptor, with eucaryotic tyrosine kinase receptors, with T-cell receptors, and with focal contacts are examined together with proteins that serve as adaptors, anchors, and scaffolds for signaling complexes. The importance of diffusion in controlling the numbers and locations of signaling complexes is discussed, as is the special role played by membranes in signaling pathways.

CONTENTS

59

1056-8700/98/0610-0059$08.00

Perspectives and Overview

One of the most important unifying principles to have emerged from the past decade of cell signaling research concerns the physical location of the proteins involved. It now appears that many of the protein kinases, protein phosphatases, transmembrane receptors, and so on, that carry and process messages inside a living cell are associated with compact clusters of molecules attached to cell membranes or the cytoskeleton. These clusters, variously termed signaling complexes, signal cassettes, signaling modules, signalosomes, or transducisomes, operate as computational units. Each receives one or more inputs and generates one or more specific outputs.

Signaling complexes are important conceptually because they provide an intermediate level of organization analogous to the integrated circuits used in the construction of large electronic circuits. There is an exciting possibility that they could help us make sense of the seemingly impenetrable jungle of molecular interactions that characterizes even the simplest forms of cellular communication.

My purpose in writing this short review is to survey the kinds of protein complexes that participate in cell communication and to identify, where possible, general principles by which they form and act. I would also like to advance the notion that biophysical constraints that result from macromolecular crowding, rates of diffusion, and the energy-cost of information have an important and perhaps controlling influence on the design of cell signaling pathways. Why do cells use protein complexes? Why are these always associated with membranes or the cytoskeleton? Why do many receptor complexes form when active and dissociate when inactive? Answers to these questions may be more easily found in the biophysics of the participating molecules than in the chemical details of the transformations they undergo.

Tar Complex: Solid-State Circuitry

To set the stage, it is helpful to examine one signaling complex in detail. The cluster of proteins associated with the chemotactic receptor of coliform bacteria, here called the *Tar* complex, is particularly well understood and illustrates many features found also in larger eucaryotic complexes [reviewed in (48)]. The Tar complex is built around a dimeric transmembrane receptor (Tar) that has an extracellular binding site for aspartate (34). The receptor is multifunctional and monitors not only (*a*) the concentration of aspartate in the surrounding fluid, but also (*b*) the concentration of maltose, through a specific interaction with the maltose binding protein, (*c*) repellents, such as nickel ions, (*d*) ambient pH, and (*e*) ambient temperature. On its cytoplasmic domain, Tar is associated with a cluster of "Che" (for chemotaxis) proteins and, together with these proteins, generates a signal that is sent to the flagellar motors (Figure 1). The magnitude

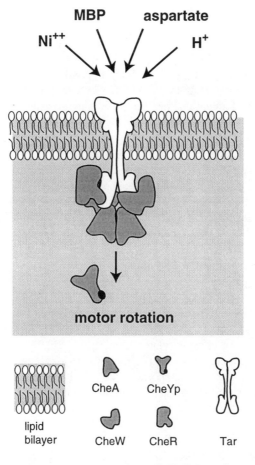

Figure 1   The core Tar complex. Two other proteins, CheY, CheB, are known to associate with the complex transiently, and there is some evidence that CheZ may also bind.

of the signal depends on the size of the various inputs to the Tar molecule or, more precisely, the rate of change thereof.

Proteins associated with the Tar complex include the autophosphorylating protein kinase CheA, the transducing protein CheW, the methylating enzyme CheR, and perhaps the protein phosphatase CheZ (17, 18, 33, 44). A small, highly charged protein CheY associates transiently with the Tar complex and is phosphorylated at a rate that depends on the level of activity of that complex. The phosphorylated product CheYp then diffuses to the flagellar motor where it interacts with the switch complex, changes the direction of rotation of the motor, and thereby modifies the swimming behavior of the cell. A second cytosolic protein, CheB, which also interacts transiently with the Tar complex, removes the methyl groups added by CheR at a rate that depends on the level of stimulation.

The mechanism of action of the Tar complex is best understood in its response to aspartate, which acts as an attractant. Aspartate molecules bind to the extracellular domain, one per Tar dimer, and are believed to favor the formation of coiled-coils between subunits by changing the relative orientation of the monomers (6, 49).

This conformational change is propagated through the membrane to the cytoplasmic domain where it is thought to cause a matching change in the CheA molecule, decreasing the rate of its autophosphorylation and hence modulating the level of CheYp. The rate of autophosphorylation is also influenced by the level of methylation of Tar at four sites on each receptor monomer (eight sites in the dimer). In this way, CheR and CheB provide an adaptation mechanism to the chemotactic response.

We see therefore that the Tar complex operates like a self-contained, solid-state processing unit. It receives environmental stimuli through its extracellular domain and information on the current state of the cell by methylation of its cytoplasmic domain. These inputs are integrated within the complex so as to produce a certain rate of phosphorylation of CheA and hence a specific rate of formation of the phosphorylated species, CheYp. From a physiological standpoint, the Tar complex greatly simplifies the aspartate pathway, reducing it to a single freely diffusing species (CheYp), a protein complex concerned with the stimulus (the Tar complex), and a second protein complex concerned with the behavioral response (the flagellar motor).

PDGF Receptor Complex: Assembly on Demand

Receptor-associated complexes also function in eucaryotic signaling pathways, as in the family of receptors activated by growth-factors and cytokines and characterized by having a tyrosine kinase in their cytoplasmic domain (13, 32). In contrast to the Tar complex just described, the protein aggregates associated with tyrosine kinase receptors are not tightly bound and form only transiently, when the receptor is bound to its cognate ligand. For example, the receptor for platelet-derived growth factor (PDGF) exists as a single transmembrane protein diffusing freely in the lipid bilayer. When it encounters a molecule of PDGF in the extracellular milieu, the receptor associates laterally with a second (presumably unoccupied) receptor to form a dimer. As the two receptor tails make contact, their kinase domains become active and phosphorylate each other at multiple sites.

Phosphorylation then triggers the assembly of an intracellular signaling complex on the receptor tail (38). Six newly phosphorylated tyrosines serve as

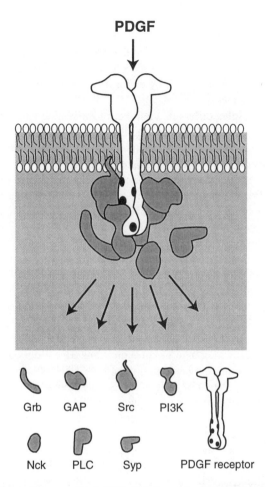

Figure 2   Signaling complex associated with the PDGF receptor. *Black patches* on the cytoplasmic domain of the receptor indicate the tyrosine phosphates to which signaling proteins bind. Note that it is not known at present how many signaling proteins are bound to any individual activated receptor at one time.

binding sites for six different intracellular signaling molecules (Figure 2). These include Src, a tyrosine kinase of broad specificity; GAP, a protein that activates small G proteins; PLC-γ, an enzyme that hydrolyzes the inositol phospholipid PIP_2; and the regulatory subunit of PI_3 kinase. These and other proteins cluster onto the active dimerized receptor, becoming themselves activated. The complex then broadcasts signals along multiple routes to many destinations inside the cell, activating and coordinating the numerous biochemical changes needed to trigger a complex response such as cell proliferation. To terminate the activation of the receptor, the cell contains protein tyrosine phosphatases, which remove the phosphates that were added in response to the extracellular signals. Cells can also dispose of activated receptors in a more brutal way: bringing them into the interior of the cell by endocytosis and then destroying them by digestion in lysosomes.

The PDGF complex differs in a number of interesting and instructive ways from the Tar complex. To begin with, activation with PDGF requires a sequence of reactions (receptor clustering, tyrosine phosphorylation; binding of multiple signaling molecules) each of which takes time. Its response is therefore expected to be slower than the propagated conformational change of a pre-formed Tar complex. Presumably the action of a growth factor on a eucaryotic cell does not require the subsecond response of a swimming bacterium. Secondly, not every PDGF receptor carries a signaling complex on its cytoplasmic domain, only those receptors that have become activated by the binding of cognate ligand. Hence the cell can make large numbers of receptor molecules, thereby casting its net as wide as possible to catch diffusing PDGF molecules, without having to make an equally large number of copies of each of the many proteins in the signaling complex. The Tar complex, by contrast, not only must be ready to react quickly, but there is a real possibility that all or nearly all of the receptors on the cell will be occupied at the same time. The ability to respond to gradients of aspartate over a wide range of concentrations (five orders of magnitude, it is claimed) means that the bacterium must be ready to distinguish, say, 90% receptor occupancy from 95% occupancy. So all receptors must come equipped with their intracellular signaling baggage.

A third difference concerns the outputs of the two complexes. The Tar complex has only two outputs—phosphorylated CheY and phosphorylated CheB—both of which are dedicated to the same specialized response of the cell (motor switching). Moreover, there are other signaling complexes in bacteria not so far mentioned, such as the serine receptor and the ribose receptor, that also influence the same pool of phosphorylated species. The circuitry is one of multiple controlling elements converging onto a single process, like arrows to a bull's-eye. The PDGF receptor complex, by contrast, produces multiple outputs. Each PDGF molecule that arrives on its receptor fires a starburst of effects, activating protein kinases, phosphoinositide cascades, G-protein cascades, and so on. The circuitry here is highly divergent, with effects spreading throughout the cell and regulating many different processes related to the cell cycle.

We mentioned above that the PDGF receptor holds its protein acolytes with a weaker grasp than the Tar receptor, and it seems probable that any single PDGF receptor will have less than a full complement of signaling proteins. Exactly how many proteins are bound at any instant, and to what extent they interact with each other, are questions that are not resolved at present, and the answer may differ between different tyrosine kinase receptors. But in general, it seems clear that such receptor complexes have the potential for many cooperative and hierarchical interactions (21). Moreover, different tyrosine kinase receptors can also come together in a variety of heterodimers on the cell surface, each of which can stabilize a discrete receptor complex and thereby transmit a distinct biological signal to the cell (39).

Adaptors, Anchors, and Scaffolds

The formation of clusters of proteins around a tyrosine kinase receptor depends on conserved binding motifs known as Src-homology domains, SH2 and SH3. These compact regions, which are found in many different proteins, bind to salient structural features of receptor molecules (37, 38). SH2 domains bind phosphorylated tyrosines in the context of particular amino acid sequences, with different SH2 domains showing slightly different specificities. The SH3 domain (which is entirely unrelated structurally) binds sequences rich in proline residues. Other binding domains involved in signaling include pleckstrin homology (PH) domains (45); phosphotyrosine-binding (PTB) domains (51); and PDZ domains, originally found in postsynaptic density proteins (26). These and other binding domains enable proteins to be put together, like Lego bricks, in multiple combinations. In fact, there are proteins, such as Grb2 and Nck that have no enzymatic activity themselves but simply contain multiple SH2 and SH3 domains (16, 31). These proteins serve as connectors or adaptors that allow additional proteins to be recruited to a signaling complex. For example, Grb2 provides a link (via yet another intermediate protein) between the activated receptor and the important Ras proteins—small GTP-containing proteins that have a controlling influence on cell proliferation and cell differentiation. The fact that proteins such as Grb2 and Nck have evolved solely for the purpose of making protein clusters underscores the importance of the latter in the transmission of signals.

A related function is served by anchoring proteins that serve as attachment sites for protein kinases and protein phosphatases (14, 15, 24, 36). These attach their cognate enzyme to particular locations in the cell such as the nuclear membrane, the Golgi, or the actin cytoskeleton, often showing a preference for particular isoforms of the enzymes. In some cases a single anchoring protein binds multiple signaling molecules. For example, the protein AKAP79, which is enriched in postsynaptic densities, has the ability to bind protein kinase A (stimulated by cyclic AMP), protein kinase C (stimulated by Ca^{2+}-calmodulin), and PP-2B (a protein phosphatase stimulated by Ca^{2+} ions and phospholipids) (14). The implication is that AKAP79 might act as a template or scaffold that nucleates formation of a signaling complex.

One of the clearest examples of a scaffold protein emerged in a study of the visual system of *Drosophila* (50). The rhabdomeres of this organism contain a highly organized signaling complex, which includes the principal light-activated ion channels. One of the proteins of this complex, called InaD, is made primarily of five PDZ domains. Mutations in this protein lead to a dramatically reorganized subcellular distribution of signaling molecules lacking the signaling complex. This and other evidence suggests that InaD acts as a scaffold for the highly ordered visual-transduction complex.

Another scaffold protein may be present in yeasts, in a signal pathway activated by pheromones during mating (14, 30). Experiments based on the yeast two-hybrid system suggest that a protein called Ste5 (the name derives from the *ste*rile phenotype of mutants lacking this protein) provides attachment sites for a series of serine/threonine kinases in a phosphorylation cascade, perhaps binding them in the same sequence as the reactions of the cascade.

The strategy of bringing various enzymes involved in the same reaction sequence together in a multienzyme complex is of course a familiar one, widely employed by cells. Since the product of one enzyme can be passed directly to the next enzyme, and so on to the final product, diffusion rates need not be limiting even when the concentration of substrate in the cell as a whole is very low (52). Multienzyme complexes are very common in cells and involved in nearly all aspects of metabolism, including the central genetic processes of DNA, RNA, and protein synthesis. It is tempting to speculate that this same principle is used in cell signaling.

Focal Contacts: Giant Signaling Complexes?

The size of many signaling complexes cannot be defined precisely. Some proteins bind tightly, others weakly, and yet others have a casual liaison solely for the purpose of catalysis. The PDGF receptor complex mentioned above is in some ways more like a "swarm" or "penumbra" of proteins than a rigidly defined, static structure. At the other extreme are complexes that grow in size beyond that of a simple molecular assembly. Even the humble Tar complex has been found to associate, for reasons that are presently unclear, with other chemotaxis receptors to form a large cluster or patch on the surface of the bacterial cell (29). IgE receptors on mast cells aggregate when they bind antigen (23), and T lymphocytes recognize their target cells by means of an even larger protein complex comprised of multiple receptors and accessory proteins (5, 41). Each T-cell receptor in the latter complex mediates a discrete contact with the target cell and activates a distinct set of signaling events involving tyrosine phosphorylation and SH2 regulated pathways. Together, these different receptors provide an intricate fail-safe mechanism, requiring the antigen fragment and the correct MHC molecules to be presented on the target cell, and other surface determinants to be absent, before the T cell is activated.

Other signaling complexes grow to such an extent that they reach a size visible in the light microscope, thereby becoming candidates for organelle status. Do we call kinetochores, adherens junctions, and synaptic endplates, signaling complexes? Probably not, but they certainly share some of the same properties.

Consider focal contacts: regions of attachment that form on the lower surface of a fibroblast in tissue culture. These are sites at which clusters of integrin molecules and associated proteins form links across the plasma membrane, from matrix molecules on the outside of the cell to actin filaments on the inside (25). For years, focal contacts were thought of as sites of mechanical anchorage of the cell. But abundant evidence now indicates that they also have a crucial function in cell communication. Formation of focal contacts tells the cell that it has adhered to a suitable substratum, so it can now divide, or grow, or differentiate (2). In reciprocal fashion, the physiological state of the cell, as displayed in the activity of a variety of protein kinases, has a controlling influence over the formation of focal adhesions (54).

From a structural standpoint, focal contacts are assemblies built from hundreds of thousands of protein molecules. More than 20 different types of protein have been identified in this complex, including integrins, actin-binding proteins, and several protein kinases (Figure 3). One of the latter, focal adhesion kinase (FAK), is an enzyme with a remarkably wide range of functions. FAK binds to structural components of the focal contact such as integrins as well as the tyrosine kinase Src and the adaptor protein Grb2. It also phosphorylates tyrosines in various proteins in the focal contact, including itself, thereby causing other proteins with SH2 domains to cluster in this region. The complex then generates signals that travel out from the focal contact to reach targets in the cytoplasm and nucleus. We see, therefore, that even though a focal contact is a large cytoskeletal-based structure, it also has some characteristics of a signaling complex. It receives multiple inputs from components of the extracellular matrix, mechanical tension, and phosphorylation signals, integrates them, and then produces multiple outputs that influence the growth and division of the cell as well as its state of differentiation.

Making the Complex: Macromolecular Crowding

Most of the information we have about intracellular signaling pathways comes from biochemistry. The enzymatic properties of isolated proteins, their ability to serve as substrates for kinases or methylating enzymes, and their binding affinity for ligands: These are the raw data on which the signal pathways portrayed in books and research papers are based. But chemical changes are only half the

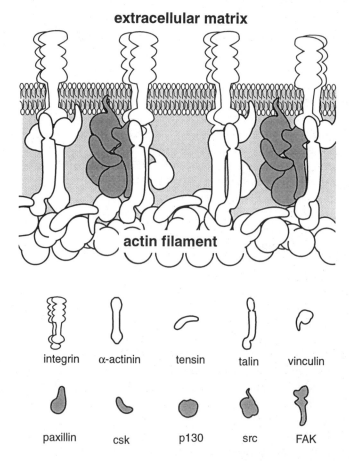

extracellular matrix

actin filament

integrin   α-actinin   tensin   talin   vinculin

paxillin   csk   p130   src   FAK

Figure 3   Schematic section of a focal adhesion (representing about 30–40 nm of a structure that might be several microns in diameter). Structural proteins such as integrin and actin are shown in *white* whereas proteins mainly concerned with signaling are shaded *gray*. Shapes and sizes are approximate, and many proteins have been omitted for clarity. Similarly, the locations of proteins in the focal contact are not known with any precision, and signaling proteins may not be clustered in the fashion shown here.

story. Unless we consider also the spatial location of molecules in the cell, their diffusion rates, and other biophysical parameters, our understanding will be incomplete.

A case in point is macromolecular crowding. Intracellular reactions do not take place in a dilute solution such as biochemists use to assay enzymes but in a concentrated slurry of molecules. The concentration of proteins in the cytosol of a living cells is comparable to that of some protein crystals (10, 19). This high concentration of proteins and other macromolecules leads to a competition for water and has a major influence on the rate at which molecules diffuse in the cell (35, 55). It also changes the tendency of protein to associate with each other—the basis on which signaling complexes are built. Whether they are comparatively stable structures, such as a Tar complex or a focal adhesion, or short-lived, such as a PDGF receptor complex, the formation of a signaling complex requires a sequence of binding steps in which protein molecules come together in a diffusion-limited interaction governed by the law of mass action. Both experiment and theory show that the crowded conditions in the interior of cells strongly favor associations between macromolecules, often increasing the binding affinity by an order of magnitude or more (53).

If signaling complexes are made by multiple diffusion-limited binding associations, how are their numbers in the cell controlled? Recent theoretical work suggests that some proteins in a complex, such as the anchoring proteins mentioned above, might have a key role to play in this regard. Computer-based analysis of model complexes with different topologies reveals that certain proteins in a complex, typically those forming a link between two or more other proteins, inhibit complex formation if they are present in high concentrations (9). Under these conditions, the linking protein drives the formation of small, incomplete aggregates at the expense of the complete complex—an effect analogous to the familiar inhibition of antibody-antigen precipitation in the precipitin test.

An effect of this kind is thought to occur in the case of the Tar complex when CheW is expressed at high levels (8, 42). It is also the basis of suppression of dynactin, a multimeric complex involved in movement along microtubules (12). Evidently the number of bridging molecules made by a cell will control the quantity of the complete complex in the cell. Other proteins in the complex can be changed in amount over a wide range of values without affecting the quantity of the final signaling complex.

Why Signaling Complexes?

The biochemical steps by which living cells integrate, codify, and transduce extracellular stimuli all require molecules to come into physical contact. It is easy to see, therefore, why clusters of molecules in permanent association with each other would be well suited to perform such reactions. Solid-state computations should be more rapid, more efficient, and more noise-free than systems of diffusing molecules in which each encounter is subject to the chaotic fluctuations of thermal energy. Of course, as just mentioned, each complex will have to be constructed by diffusion-limited encounters of its constituent molecules. But, once made, the complex could work repeatedly, processing signals rapidly and accurately without further need for diffusion. Later modifications to the assembly reflecting the current state of the cell (as in the methylation of Tar receptors described above) could be made without requiring the complex to be disassembled.

A recent estimate of the cost of transmitting information in an insect eye underscores this conclusion. Taking an ion channel as a benchmark, an individual protein can switch conformational states 10^4 to 10^6 times per second (22). If operated as a digital switch, driven by ATP hydrolysis, a single protein might therefore transmit at least 10^4 bits per second at a cost of 1 ATP per bit. In the real world of insect vision, however, experiments show that a blowfly photoreceptor cell transmits information at one tenth the rate and a million times the unit cost of a single ion channel (11). This huge difference emphasizes that the major expense is not in registering information as conformational change. The costs are incurred when information is distributed, integrated, and processed within and between systems. Limiting factors will be Brownian motion, the uncertainty of molecular collisions, and the inefficiency of diffusion as a means to carry signals.

Why Diffusion?

If molecular encounters between freely diffusing single protein molecules are so unreliable and costly, why use diffusion at all? The answer seems to lie in the extensive interconnections that characterize communication within living cells. Most extracellular stimuli do not pass in a linear chain of cause and effect from one receptor in the plasma membrane to one target molecule in the nucleus or cytoplasm. If they did, then they could be propagated most effectively as a chain of conformational changes along a protein filament. Indeed, some of the signals that travel from one end to another of nerve axons—carried as action potentials or, perhaps, as motor proteins moving along microtubules—have this one-dimensional advantage. However, the vast majority of signals in cells spread as a rapidly diverging influence from membrane-associated receptors to multiple chemically distinct targets in the cell, often at widely separate spatial locations. Sometimes the divergence amplifies a signal, whereas in others it controls different processes in the cell, a form of molecular cross-talk. But the machinery of the divergent influence in every case involves at least one molecule that diffuses as a free element.

The essential function of diffusion in signal transduction is displayed in the wide variety of signal-transduction transducers—from hormonal and synaptic systems to the receptor cells of vision and olfaction—that utilize G proteins (20, 28). The capture of a photon of light, or a molecule of odorant, hormone, or neurotransmitter, is conveyed to effector molecules (phosphodiesterase, adenylate cyclase, potassium channel, or phospholipase C) through the intermediate activation of a GTP-binding protein freely diffusing in association with the plasma membrane. We could easily imagine a situation in which each receptor was stably associated with one effector molecule and did not need a G protein to connect the two. In this hypothetical receptor complex, the activation step would indeed be faster and more efficient. But it would also be much smaller, since one photon or stimulant molecule would change the activity of at most one effector molecule rather than, as in the actual situation, many thousands. The cell therefore pays a price in time and consumption of ATP molecules for a huge reward in sensitivity.

Smart Membranes

Diffusion is essential to allow messages to spread widely through the cell but, at the same time, interactions based on diffusion are inefficient, error-prone, and costly in energetic terms. These conflicting constraints will determine the physical form of the signaling species and their location in the cell. I have argued that they provide partial justification, at least, for the existence of signaling complexes. Do they also tell us why these complexes, and the reactions that lead from them, are so often located on the membrane?

At first sight it seems obvious that diffusion in two dimensions would be a more effective way to send a message than diffusion in three dimensions. It is far easier for a molecule to find a distant target by random walking in a plane—in fact, it is guaranteed to find such a target given enough time. A molecule diffusing in an unbounded free solution, by contrast, might never arrive: its probability of eventual capture being the ratio of the target size divided by its distance (4). Unfortunately for this argument, particle diffusion is much slower in a membrane: A small protein might have a diffusion coefficient of about 5×10^{-7} cm^2 sec^{-1} in free solution, whereas in a lipid bilayer, a protein of similar size would have a diffusion coefficient of perhaps 5×10^{-9} cm^2 sec^{-1} (3, 40). Because of this factor of two orders of magnitude, most calculations of the time taken for signals to travel a micron in a living cell indicate that the best route is through the cytosol.

What membranes do provide is a discrete compartment in which molecules that relay and process messages can be sequestered. Receptors and ion channels have to be in the membrane, since they interact with the outside world. It makes sense, therefore, to put the molecules that interact with these receptors in the same place ... and the molecules that interact with these molecules, and so on. As intracellular signaling pathways evolved into systems of increasing complexity, it would have been advantageous to put newly appearing molecular species, wherever possible, in (or close) to the membrane. In present-day cells, many if not most signals are carried by proteins that are embedded in the membrane or loosely associated with it through hydrophobic or other interactions. There are even proteins that normally reside in the cytosol but move to the membrane in order to participate in signaling response—the protein recoverin in the vertebrate rod outer segment being an excellent example (1).

It is likely, in fact, that cells exploit the principle of compartmentalization to an even greater degree. There is increasing evidence that individual proteins and protein complexes do not roam freely over the entire surface of the cell but are constrained to move within specific subcompartments. How is this regionalization achieved? One basis is the formation of domains of different lipid composition, especially rafts enriched in sphingolipids and cholesterol [it has been observed that many proteins involved in cell signaling partition into these glycolipid-enriched domains (47)]. Another way is to use cytoskeletal proteins underlying the plasma membrane to delineate small compartments (46). Single-particle tracking and manipulations with laser-based optical traps reveal that most proteins are confined to domains of $0.1-1 \mu m^2$ (27). Given this evidence of regionalization, we can suppose that many proteins concerned with the transmission and processing of signals are sequestered into the membrane. There they will be held in close proximity to their reaction partners so that, when diffusion occurs, it will be constrained and channeled so as to obtain maximum speed and efficiency (43). According to this viewpoint, the plasma membrane acts as the "sensory cortex" of the cell: the place that receives environmental signals and processes them using protein-based computational machinery (7).

Analogy to Signaling in the Nervous System

The most effective design for a signaling pathway appears to be a combination of signaling complexes and freely diffusing molecules, associated where possible with membranes. But in this case, how do we select which molecules are to be part of the complexes and which freely diffusing? An analogy to the nervous system might suggest an answer here.

Many regions of the nervous system of vertebrates and invertebrates show a modular organization—vertebrate brain regions, invertebrate ganglia, cortical columns, canonical microcircuits (e.g. cortex, hippocampus, cerebellum, retina), all display this feature. Communication within any one of these modules is made possible by multiple short axons and dendrites, whereas messages that pass between one module and another are carried by long axons running in tracts that extend across the brain or down the spinal cord. In the first case, the computational elements are in close proximity and signals pass from one to the other with minimal delay. In the second case, the signaling elements are far apart and the messages (even though they travel in one dimension, as action potentials) take an appreciable time to pass from one to the other.

In some respects, therefore, the microanatomy of signaling pathways in a living cell is like the architecture of the brain. There are modular regions in which precise, rapid, stereotyped computations are performed by local circuitry and carried by conformation changes and protein modifications. And there are communication channels that allow the results of local computations to be sent to often multiple distant targets, usually by diffusion. Evidently, during evolution, it has become advantageous to group together molecules that perform a specific task and that have to be active at the same time. Signaling complexes might therefore represent abstractions of the cell's environment, such as the current state of chemotactic stimulating activity, or the presence of a suitable extracellular matrix. They could, as suggested at the beginning of this review, provide elements at an intermediate level of complexity that will eventually help us decipher the signaling code used by living cells.

ACKNOWLEDGMENTS

Many thanks to Graeme Mitchison, Bill Gullick, Mike Berridge, Bob Bourret, Howard Berg, Mark Nelson, David Morgan, Matthew Levin, Carl Morton-Firth, and Simon Laughlin for their comments and suggestions.

> Visit the *Annual Reviews home page* at
> http://www.AnnualReviews.org.

Literature Cited

1. Ames JB, Ishima R, Tanaka T, Gordon JI, Stryer L, Ikura M. 1997. Molecular mechanics of calcium-myristoyl switches. *Nature* 398:198–202
2. Ben-Ze'ev A. 1997. Cytoskeletal and adhesion proteins as tumor suppressors. *Curr. Opin. Cell Biol.* 9:99–108
3. Berg HC. 1993. *Random Walks in Biology*, p. 152. Princeton, NJ: Princeton Univ. Press
4. Berg HC, Purcell EM. 1977. Physics of chemoreception. *Biophys. J.* 20:193–219
5. Berridge MJ. 1997. Lymphocyte activation in health and disease. *Crit. Rev. Immunol.* 17:155–78
6. Biemann H-P, Koshland DE. 1994. Aspartate receptors of *Escherichia coli* and *Salmonella typhimurium* bind ligand with negative and half-of-the-sites cooperativity. *Biochemistry* 33:629–34
7. Bray D. 1995. Protein molecules as computational elements in living cells. *Nature* 376:307–12
8. Bray D, Bourret RB. 1995. Computer analysis of the binding reactions leading to a transmembrane receptor-linked multiprotein complex involved in bacterial chemotaxis. *Mol. Biol. Cell* 6:1367–80
9. Bray D, Lay SW. 1997. Computer-based analysis of the binding steps in protein complex formation. *Proc. Natl. Acad. Sci. USA.* In press
10. Clegg JS. 1984. Properties and metabolism of the aqueous cytoplasm and its boundaries. *Am. J. Physiol.* 246:R133–51
11. de Ruyter van Stevenick RR, Laughlin SB. 1997. The rate of information-transfer at graded-potential synapses. *Nature* 379:642–45
12. Escheverri CJ, Paschal BM, Vaughan KT, Vallee RB. 1996. Molecular characterisation of the 50-kD subunit of dynactin reveals function for the complex in chromosome alignment and spindle organization during mitosis. *J. Cell Biol.* 132:617–33
13. Fantl WJ, Johnson DE, Williams LT. 1993. Signalling by receptor tyrosine kinases. *Annu. Rev. Biochem.* 62:453–81
14. Faux MC, Scott JD. 1996. Molecular glue: kinase anchoring and scaffolding proteins. *Cell* 85:9–12
15. Faux MC, Scott JD. 1996. More on target with phosphorylation: conferring specificity by location. *Trends Biochem. Sci.* 21:312–15
16. Galisteo ML, Chernoff J, Su YC, Skolnik EY, Schlessinger J. 1996. The adapter protein Nck links receptor tyrosine kinases with the serine-threonine kinase Pak1. *J. Biol. Chem.* 271:20997–21000

17. Gegner JA, Dahlquist FW. 1991. Signal transduction in bacteria: CheW forms a reversible complex with the protein kinase CheA. *Proc. Natl. Acad. Sci. USA* 88:750–54
18. Gegner JA, Graham DR, Roth AF, Dahlquist FW. 1992. Assembly of an MCP receptor, CheW, and kinase CheA complex in the bacterial chemotaxis signal transduction pathway. *Cell* 70:975–82
19. Goodsell DS. 1991. Inside a living cell. *Trends Biochem. Sci.* 16:203–6
20. Hepler JR, Gilman AG. 1992. G proteins. *Trends Biochem. Sci.* 17:383–87
21. Herbst R, Shearman MS, Jallal B, Schlessinger J, Ullrich A. 1995. Formation of signal transfer-complexes between stem-cell and platelet-derived growth-factor receptors and SH2 domain proteins. *Biochemistry* 34:5971–79
22. Hille B. 1992. *Ionic Channels of Excitable Membranes.* Sunderland, MA: Sinauer Assoc.
23. Holowka D, Baird B. 1996. Antigen-mediated IgE receptor aggregation and signaling. A window on cell surface structure and dynamics. *Annu. Rev. Biophys. Biomol. Struct.* 25:79–112
24. Hubbard MJ, Cohen P. 1993. On target with a new mechanism for the regulation of protein phosphorylation. *Trends Biochem. Sci.* 18:172–77
25. Jockusch BM, Bubeck P, Giehl K, Kroemker M, Moschner J, et al. 1995. The molecular architecture of focal adhesions. *Annu. Rev. Cell Dev. Biol.* 11:379–416
26. Kornau HC, Schenker LT, Kennedy MB, Seeburg PH. 1995. Domain interaction between NMDA receptor subunits and the postynaptic density protein PSD-95. *Science* 269:1737–40
27. Kusumi A, Sako Y. 1996. Cell surface organization by the membrane skeleton. *Curr. Opin. Cell Biol.* 8:566–74
28. Lamb TD, Pugh N. 1992. G-protein cascades: gain and kinetics. *Trends Neurosci.* 15:291–98
29. Maddock JR, Shapiro L. 1993. Polar location of the chemoreceptor complex in the *Escherichia coli* cell. *Science* 259:1717–23
30. Marcus S, Polverino A, Barr M, Wigler M. 1994. Complexes between STE5 and components of the pheromone-responsive mitogen-activated protein kinase module. *Proc. Natl. Acad. Sci. USA* 91:7762–66
31. Margolis B. 1994. The Grb family of SH2 domain proteins. *Prog. Biophys. Mol. Biol.* 62:223–44
32. Marshall CJ. 1996. Specificity of receptor tyrosine kinase signaling: Transient versus sustained extracellular signal-regulated kinase activation. *Cell* 80:179–85
33. McNally DF, Matsumura P. 1991. Bacterial chemotaxis signaling complexes: formation of a CheA/CheW complex enhances autophosphorylation and affinity for CheY. *Proc. Natl. Acad. Sci. USA* 88:6269–73
34. Milligan DL, Koshland DE Jr. 1988. Site-directed cross-linking. Establishing the dimeric structure of the aspartate receptor of bacterial chemotaxis. *J. Biol. Chem.* 263:6268–75
35. Minton AF. 1992. Confinement as a determinant of macromolecular structure and reactivity. *Biophys. J.* 63:1090–1100
36. Mochly-Rosen D. 1995. Localization of protein kinases by anchoring proteins: a theme in signal transduction. *Science* 268:247–51
37. Morton CJ, Campbell ID. 1994. Molecular "Velcro". *Curr. Biol.* 4:615–17
38. Pawson T, Schlessinger J. 1993. SH2 and SH3 domains. *Curr. Biol.* 3:434–42
39. Pinkas-Kramarski R, Alroy I, Yarden Y. 1997. ErbB receptors and EGF-like ligands cell lineage determination and oncogenesis through combinatorial signaling. *J. Mammary Gland Biol. Neoplas.* 2:97–107
40. Pugh EN, Lamb TD. 1993. Amplification and kinetics of the activation steps in phototransduction. *Biochim. Biophys. Acta* 1141:111–49
41. Qian D, Weiss A. 1997. T-cell antigen receptor signal transduction. *Curr. Opin. Cell Biol.* 9:205–12
42. Sanders DA, Mendez B, Koshland DE. 1989. Role of CheW protein in bacterial chemotaxis: overexpression is equivalent to absence. *J. Bacteriol.* 171:6271–74
43. Saxton MJ. 1995. Single-particle tracking: effects of corrals. *Biophys. J.* 69:389–98
44. Schuster SC, Swanson RV, Alex LA, Bourret RB, Simon MI. 1993. Assembly and function of a quaternary signal transduction complex monitored by surface plasmon resonance. *Nature* 365:343–46
45. Shaw G. 1996. The pleckstrin homology domain: an intriguing multifunctional protein module. *BioEssays* 18:35–46
46. Sheetz MP. 1993. Glycoprotein motility and dynamic domains in fluid plasma membranes. *Annu. Rev. Biophys. Biomol. Struct.* 22:417–31
47. Simons K, Ikonen E. 1997. Functional rafts in cell membranes. *Nature* 387:569–72
48. Stock JB, Surette MG. 1996. In *Chemotaxis*, ed. FC Neidhardt, pp. 1103–29. Washington, DC: Am. Soc. Microbiol.
49. Surette MG, Stock JB. 1997. Role of α-helical coiled-coil interactions in receptor

dimerization, signaling, and adaptation during bacterial chemotaxis. *J. Biol. Chem.* 271:17966–73

50. Tsunoda S, Sierralta J, Sun Y, Bodner R, Suzuki E, et al. 1997. A multivalent PDZ-domain protein assembled signalling complexes in a G-protein–coupled cascade. *Nature* 388:243–49

51. van der Greer P, Pawson T. 1995. The PTB domain: a new protein module implicated in signal transduction. *Trends Biochem. Sci.* 20:277–80

52. West IC. 1997. Molecular and physicochemical aspects. In *Channelling in Intermediary Metabolism*, ed. L Agius, HSA Sherratt, pp. 13–39. London: Portland Press

53. Wilf J, Minton AP. 1981. Evidence for protein self-association induced by excluded volume myoglobin in the presence of globular proteins. *Biochim. Biophys. Acta* 670:316–22

54. Yamada KM, Geiger B. 1997. Molecular interactions in cell adhesion complexes. *Curr. Opin. Cell Biol.* 9:76–85

55. Zimmerman SB, Minton AP. 1994. Macromolecular crowding: biochemical, biophysical, and physiological consequences. *Annu. Rev. Biophys. Biomol. Struct.* 22:27–65

Annu. Rev. Biophys. Biomol. Struct. 1998. 27:77–103

SPATIO-TEMPORAL RESOLUTION OF EXOCYTOSIS FROM INDIVIDUAL CELLS

Eric R. Travis and R. Mark Wightman

Department of Chemistry, University of North Carolina at Chapel Hill, Chapel Hill, North Carolina 27599-3290; e-mail: etravis@email.unc.edu; rmw@unc.edu

KEY WORDS: microelectrodes, amperometry, patch-clamp, capacitance measurements, cyclic voltammetry

ABSTRACT

Biophysical events involved in late stages of exocytosis occur at highly localized areas of cells on millisecond and submillisecond time scales. Thus, methodologies with high spatio-temporal resolution are required to achieve measurements at individual secretory cells. Much has been learned about the mechanisms and kinetics of vesicular release through analysis with the carbon fiber microelectrode techniques amperometry and cyclic voltammetry. Coupling of these techniques with other methods such as patch-clamp continues to reveal details of the secretion process. It is now clear that extrusion of the vesicular contents is a more complex process than previously believed. Vesicle-cell fusion, revealed by cell capacitance measurements, is temporally dissociated from secretion measured amperometrically. The stability imparted by interaction and association of vesicle contents at rest results in a rate-limiting extrusion process after full fusion. Furthermore, the presence of partial fusion events and the occurrence of nonquantized release have been revealed with electrochemical tools.

CONTENTS

1056-8700/98/0610-0077$08.00

PERSPECTIVES AND OVERVIEW

Many different types of cells communicate extracellularly through the triggered secretion of small molecules. A major method by which these molecules are secreted is exocytosis, the regulated process by which a membrane-bound vesicle in the cytoplasm fuses with the plasma membrane via a Ca^{2+}-dependent mechanism. This leads to the extrusion of the intravesicular contents, including the chemical messengers, into the extracellular space (2). There has been much interest in elucidating the biochemical and biophysical mechanisms of exocytosis as it is the fundamental mode of chemical communication among neurons. Accordingly, several single-cell techniques have emerged that allow detailed investigation into individual steps of exocytosis with increasingly high spatio-temporal resolution. These findings serve to increase the understanding of this important process with detail that is unavailable through studies using cell populations or intact tissues.

Early electrophysiological studies of end plate potentials at the frog neuromuscular junction showed that neurotransmission resulted in quantized packets of information reaching the postsynaptic membrane (22, 24). These and other discoveries led to formulation of the quantal hypothesis (47), which asserts that chemical transmitters are stored and released in predetermined unit amounts that are independent of the event initiating release. A large body of evidence (23) suggests that the unit is the secretory vesicle, the contents of which are released following exocytosis. Functional evidence for exocytosis from secretory cells came when the contents of vesicles from the adrenal medulla were found to be secreted in an "all-or-none" fashion and in proportions stoichiometrically equivalent to their storage ratios in the vesicles (79, 80).

The advancement of these concepts required techniques to provide spatial and temporal information at the level of individual cells and single vesicles. In the late 1970s and early 1980s, the advent of the patch-clamp technique (60) greatly advanced the study of dynamic biophysical processes at single cells. Similarly, optical and electron microscopic techniques allowed exocytosis to be observed in some cells at the single-vesicle level. The adaptation to the single-cell level of voltammetric microelectrode techniques, originally developed to monitor secretion from populations of nerve terminals in intact tissue (1), provided the first direct chemical measurement of the release of packets of chemical messengers from individual vesicles during exocytosis (86).

Owing to the small size of individual secretory vesicles (25–500 nm), the relatively small number of molecules released (5,000–10^6), and the rapidity at which vesicular content is extruded (0.1-100 ms), sensitive techniques of chemical analysis with high signal-to-noise ratios and high spatio-temporal resolution are required to achieve a fundamental understanding of secretion accompanying exocytosis. Electrochemical techniques with carbon-fiber microelectrodes provide this capability. We review this topic and some other techniques that have been developed and applied to the study of exocytosis at the single-cell level. In particular, patch-clamp techniques are capable of resolving exocytosis of individual vesicles and can be used simultaneously with the electrochemical methods.

Because several technical papers and reviews exist on high-resolution membrane capacitance measurements (25, 30, 48, 55), we placed primary emphasis in this review on the spatio-temporal resolution of electrochemical methods employing microelectrodes.

EXAMINING EXOCYTOSIS AT THE SINGLE-CELL LEVEL

Imaging Techniques

The unparalleled spatial resolution of electron microscopy has made it a much-used tool in the ultrastructural analysis of exocytosis from individual cells. Several researchers have provided electron micrographs with a snapshot view of vesicle exocytosis in a diverse set of preparations (see 31 for review). Appropriately stimulated and fixed endocrine and mast cells sometimes produce electron micrographs with characteristic omega shapes that appear to arise from partially opened vesicles that have fused with the plasma membrane surface. Vesicle-cell membrane fusion events also have been closely examined through freeze-fracture analysis of rapidly frozen secretory cells (13). Tannic acid fixation is an electron microscopic method especially useful for imaging exocytosed vesicle cores (53). However, because of the transient nature of vesicle release, capturing and quantifying exocytosis by electron microscopy remains a challenge. Furthermore, possible image artifacts can arise as a result of chemical fixation or quick-freezing, leading to results that are difficult to interpret.

Examination of the time course of morphological changes that accompany exocytosis by traditional light microscopy is best suited to cells with unusually large vesicles. One example is the goblet cell, from which mucin, the primary component of mucus, is secreted by an exocytotic process (78). Similarly, peritoneal mast cells of the mutant beige mouse have a few (1–10) large (1–5 μm in diameter) secretory granules, making them an ideal model system for quantitative light microscopic observations of exocytosis (52, 95). Studies at these cells have shown that exocytosis is a multistage process that appears to proceed in a series of finite steps. Unfortunately, the diffraction limit precludes quantitative real-time microscopy studies with visible light of secretory cells with smaller vesicles (76).

Exocytosis has also been observed with fluorescent microscopic techniques. For molecules without intrinsic fluorescence, immunofluorescence techniques allow qualitative analysis of morphological changes and movements of proteins associated with exocytosis. For example, the enzyme dopamine β-hydroxylase (DBH) is a major membrane protein in chromaffin cell secretory vesicles. Because it appears on the cell surface during exocytosis, the sites of exocytosis can be visualized following attachment of fluorescently tagged DBH antibodies (61, 69). The presence of fluorescent spots on the cell surface spatially resolves areas of exocytosis, but temporal information is lost since cell fixation must be used.

Real-time observation of exocytotic events and subsequent endocytosis (retrieval of vesicles from the cell membrane) can be accomplished using fluorescent markers such as the styryl dye FM1-43 (6) that selectively labels membrane surfaces. With this dye in the extracellular solution, addition of vesicle membrane to the cell surface during exocytosis results in an increase in cell-surface fluorescence. In addition, capacitance measurements (see below) have been combined with FM1-43 fluorescence to allow simultaneous time-resolved measurement of exocytosis and endocytosis (3a, 70).

In another approach, total internal reflection microscopy has been used to observe the dynamics of intracellular vesicles during evoked release. Loading of chromaffin vesicles with acridine orange, a dye that only fluoresces in acidic environments, provides a marker that disappears when exocytosis occurs (72). A similar application of evanescent-wave microscopy involves fusion of green fluorescent protein (GFP) to known secreted peptides of PC12 cells (42a). GFP fluorescence near the plasma membrane thus provides a marker for time-resolved microscopy of transport, docking, and exocytosis of secretory vesicles.

While the techniques described above indicate that exocytosis has occurred, direct optical detection of secretion is only possible if the secreted substance has native fluorescence. Such is the case for 5-hydroxytryptamine (5-HT), whose exocytosis from mast cells has been examined (45). As illustrated for measurements of 5-HT storage in RBL cells (46), three photon techniques appear to hold even more promise in this regard because of the use of lower-energy input photons, which cause less damage to the cell.

Cell-Membrane Capacitance Techniques

In whole-cell recording mode, the patch-clamp method (29, 60) constitutes a very sensitive way of measuring changes in cell membrane capacitance (28, 55). The cell's plasma membrane serves as an electrical capacitor whose capacitance is proportional to cell surface area (~ 1 $\mu F/cm^2$). The whole cell capacitance can readily be measured with AC impedance techniques. Because incorporation of vesicle membrane into the plasma membrane during exocytosis leads to an increase in cell surface area, fusion of individual secretory vesicles leads to step-like increases in cell membrane capacitance (25, 55). Following exocytosis, subsequent membrane retrieval by endocytosis leads to capacitance decreases. With millisecond temporal resolution, cell membrane capacitance measurements provide detailed information on the time course of vesicular membrane fusion events. Whole-cell patch-clamp techniques have been of particular importance in examining and characterizing exocytotic fusion pores (8, 49–51, 71) and synaptic membrane events (48, 81). However, the method cannot provide chemical or kinetic information about molecules released from the vesicle following complete opening of fusion pores. In addition, signal-to-noise issues in measuring capacitance steps less than one fF make the technique best suited for cells with vesicles larger than 200 nm in diameter.

Another caveat is that cell membrane capacitance recordings are based on the assumption that the cell can be modeled as a simple electrical equivalent circuit. Because changes in the equivalent circuit unrelated to fusion events may occur, increases in capacitance that are not resolved as steps should be confirmed by an independent technique (57). Nonetheless, the patch-clamp technique is a powerful research tool that is readily coupled to several complementary methods of analysis for resolving exocytosis from single cells.

Electrochemical Techniques

Several important secreted chemical messengers are easily oxidized. When the oxidation is done at the surface of an electrode, the oxidation current can be measured to provide information on the quantity and type of molecule available at the electrode tip. The indoleamine 5-HT and the catecholamines dopamine, epinephrine, and norepinephrine are among the most easily oxidized chemical messengers at common electrode materials. Other candidates for this approach are histamine and peptides containing a tryptophan or tyrosine residue. During the 1980s, voltammetric microelectrodes (85, 88) were developed with dimensions similar to those of cells. These electrodes were shown to be useful for detection of neurotransmitters in brain tissue (1), and thus it was a logical extension of this work to examine chemical events at single cells.

Amperometry and cyclic voltammetry are the two primary techniques that have been used to monitor exocytosis from single cells noninvasively. In amperometry, the electrode potential is held constant, whereas in cyclic voltammetry it is periodically scanned in a triangular waveform. The advantage of amperometry is that it provides exquisite time resolution. However, it provides no information on the chemical nature of the species detected. Cyclic voltammetry, while having lower temporal resolution, provides a current-voltage curve whose characteristics depend on the particular molecule present at the electrode surface. It is an especially valuable technique for identifying electroactive chemical entities in preliminary studies of release from previously uncharacterized secretory cells. Thus, the two techniques of amperometry and cyclic voltammetry provide complementary information and should both be used in studies of exocytosis at single cells.

In single-cell electrochemical experiments, the microelectrode is generally fabricated from a carbon fiber (2.5-5 μm radius). It is placed in a pulled glass capillary or other suitable insulating material (39). Best results are obtained with a beveled tip that has an elliptical sensor surface with overall dimensions dictated by the size of the fiber employed. The tip surface area should be of the same size as the target region of the cell that is to be examined. A minimal surface area is advantageous because the double layer capacitance of the electrode tip ($\sim$40 μF/cm^2) is the major noise generator in these experiments (33). The sensing area of microelectrodes and its associated double-layer capacitance also sets the time constant for these measurements. For normal physiological buffers, this is in the microsecond time domain. The microelectrodes generate current in the pico- to nanoampere range, depending upon the type of experiment. Thus, low-noise current-measuring devices such as patch-clamp amplifiers are normally employed (18).

Experiments with cells are performed on the stage of an inverted microscope. The microelectrodes are mounted on an appropriate x-y-z micromanipulator and positioned adjacent to a single cell in a cell culture dish (Figure 1). With their spatial and temporal attributes, voltammetric microelectrodes are ideally suited for highly resolved measurements of exocytosis from individual cells. A reference electrode is also placed into the physiological buffer solution and a glass micropipette positioned near the cell is used to administer solutions of stimulatory agents via pressure ejection. With its sensor surface placed directly

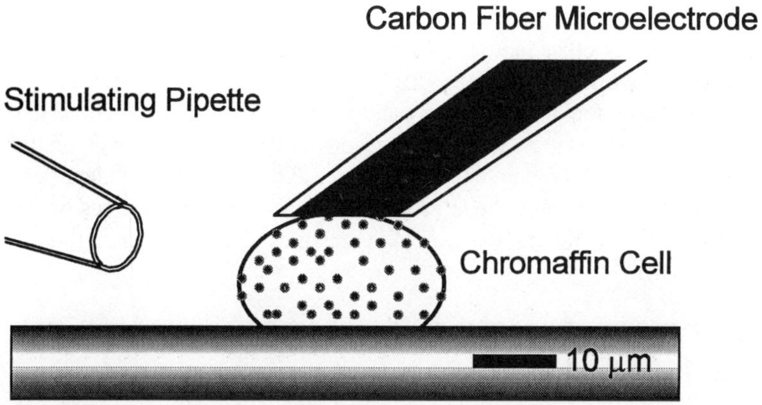

Carbon Fiber Microelectrode

Stimulating Pipette

Chromaffin Cell

10 μm

Figure 1 Cartoon of typical cell-microelectrode arrangement for electrochemical measurement of exocytosis. The beveled tip of a glass-encased carbon fiber microelectrode is placed in direct contact with the surface of a single chromaffin cell adhering to a culture plate. A nearby pressure ejection micropipette is used to administer nL volumes of stimulating solutions directly onto the cell.

adjacent to a single secretory cell, a microelectrode detects the electroactive contents of exocytotically released vesicles.

The first demonstration that microelectrodes allow detection of secretion from single cells was at bovine adrenal medullary chromaffin cells (43, 44). In vivo, the primary functions of chromaffin cells are the uptake, storage, and secretion of the catecholamine hormones epinephrine and norepinephrine. Because of biochemical and functional similarities to neurons, this primary cell preparation has often been employed as a model system for exocytosis (10). Each chromaffin cell contains approximately 150 fmol of catecholamine, distributed among some 30,000 vesicles. Although individual exocytotic events were not observed initially, it was clear that secretion could be detected with carbon fiber microelectrodes.

Improvements in spatial resolution of the measurements allowed demonstration of the electrochemical measurement of time-resolved current spikes from single, stimulated chromaffin cells in culture (86). These spikes were shown to be due to electrooxidation of catecholamine molecules released from single vesicles (86). Spikes occurred only when the cell was stimulated, were dependent on extracellular Ca^{2+} (37), and originated from spatially restricted locations on the cell surface. In contrast, ascorbate efflux from chromaffin cells is observed as a broad envelope rather than a spike because ascorbate is predominantly cytoplasmic, not vesicular (12). Taken together, these measurements provided the first direct chemical evidence for exocytosis and confirmed its quantal nature. Electrochemical techniques using microelectrodes have since been adopted by other laboratories and utilized for high-resolution measurements of exocytosis from several different cell types (reviewed herein).

Besides providing much spatially and temporally resolved chemical and kinetic information, electrochemistry is readily coupled to other single-cell techniques such as patch-clamp and fluorescence. Disadvantages of electrochemical methods are that only the exocytotic steps following vesicle fusion can be directly observed and that the secreted molecules must be electroactive.

EXOCYTOSIS MEASUREMENTS WITH CYCLIC VOLTAMMETRY

Background-Subtracted Fast-Scan Cyclic Voltammetry

The technique of cyclic voltammetry has been used by electrochemists for many years to identify the electrochemical properties of molecules (4). In its adaptation for use in exocytotic measurements, relatively fast scan rates are employed to maintain the millisecond time resolution necessary to monitor the dynamics of single-vesicle release. For example, in the detection of catecholamines the electrode potential (versus a sodium-saturated calomel reference electrode) is periodically scanned in a triangle waveform from a rest potential of -0.4 V to $+1.1$ V and back to -0.4 V at 800 V/s. The rapid voltage sweep results in significant capacitive and other surface-associated currents. Thus, digital background subtraction is used to reveal the Faradaic current corresponding to the concentration of the solution phase species of interest (5). Fortunately, these background currents at carbon fiber electrodes are stable, allowing subtraction of a voltammogram recorded just prior to exposure to electroactive species from one obtained in the presence of the species of interest. The resulting background-subtracted fast-scan cyclic voltammograms contain considerable information. The positions of the current peaks for oxidation and reduction aid in identification of the detected species (5). The amplitude of the current is directly proportional to the local concentration of the detected species, and the technique has nanomolar limits of detection (11). With the parameters given above, each scan takes 3.75 ms to complete and is repeated every 16.7 ms, allowing time for reestablishment of the original concentration profile between scans.

The time delay between cyclic voltammograms and the optimum cell-electrode spacing are dictated by consideration of the molecular events that occur during an individual cyclic voltammogram. During a single voltage sweep, the concentration of oxidizable species immediately next to the electrode is depleted by the electrolysis process. If the duration of the electrolysis (t) is 1 ms, then the distance perturbed by the electrolysis, the diffusion layer (x), is given by $x = (Dt)^{1/2}$, where D is the diffusion coefficient of the electrolyzed species (typically 6×10^{-6} cm^2 s^{-1}), and x is calculated to be less than 1 μm. The time between scans is made sufficiently long relative to the electrolysis time to allow the diffusion layer to relax to a shape dictated by the cell secretion process. If the cell-electrode spacing is greater than that of the diffusion layer, the current measured will be directly proportional to the average concentration, both at the cell surface and in a calibration solution, unlike the output in amperometry (see below).

Chemical Identification of Secreted Molecules

The first use of cyclic voltammetry at single cells was to identify the source of the electrochemical currents measured during secretion at chromaffin cells. Background-subtracted fast-scan cyclic voltammetry (FSCV) confirmed the identity of secreted catecholamines (Figure 2). The potentials at which oxidation

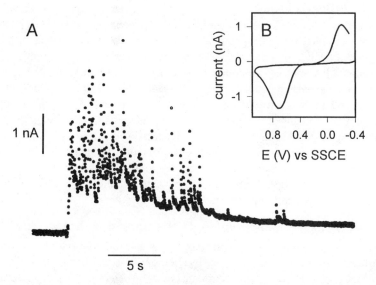

Figure 2 Cyclic voltammetric detection of catecholamine secretion. (*A*) Concentration spikes observed by FSCV (800 V/s) from an individual chromaffin cell stimulated to release by K$^+$ depolarization. The oxidative current (integrated over a 100 mV potential window) is sampled in each successive voltammogram (16.7 ms intervals) to generate a trace that monitors temporal changes in secreted species concentration. (*B*) Background-subtracted cyclic voltammogram obtained from a single concentration spike in (*A*). This characteristic current-voltage curve confirms that the species secreted during the single-vesicle event is a catecholamine.

and reduction peaks are found, as well as the separation of the peaks, chemically fingerprint different classes of compounds, in this case revealing catecholamines. The time course of exocytosis during cyclic voltammetric recording can be monitored by sampling the catecholamine oxidation current (around +0.6 V) in each successive scan. Therefore, with 16.7 ms time resolution, exocytosis from stimulated chromaffin cells can be detected as a series of concentration spikes. Each individual spike corresponds to the electrooxidation of the catecholamines from a single vesicle to their corresponding o-quinones. Some exocytotic spikes observed with FSCV and amperometry have a small amplitude pre-spike feature commonly termed the foot (19, 36). This feature is believed to correspond to the flux of free vesicular catecholamine through a narrow fusion pore (49–51) prior to full release of vesicle contents. FSCV allows this foot feature to be chemically confirmed as a change in catecholamine concentration (87).

Detection of Epinephrine and Norepinephrine Secretion from Chromaffin Cells

Chromaffin cells are known to secrete both epinephrine and norepinephrine. When examined over the potential range outlined above, the background-subtracted cyclic voltammograms of these compounds are indistinguishable. A cyclic voltammetric technique has been developed to differentiate between vesicular epinephrine and norepinephrine secretion (62) that takes advantage of a second, more positive oxidation wave for epinephrine. When the potential scan limits are changed to 0.0 and +1.425 V, the secondary amine on the side chain of epinephrine can be oxidized. This does not occur for norepinephrine, a primary amine. This approach was used to demonstrate that most chromaffin cells release either epinephrine or norepinephrine, but not both. A small fraction of cells (20%) was found to release both catecholamines, but each vesicular event was comprised of one catecholamine or the other.

Detection of Histamine and 5-HT Secretion from Mast Cells

FSCV has also been used to characterize vesicular release from rat peritoneal mast cells. Mast cells are stimulated by allergens to secrete histamine and 5-HT via exocytosis. Both of these compounds can be detected with low detection limits by FSCV at 800 V/s when the carbon electrode is activated with an electrochemical pretreatment (62a). The voltammetric waves for histamine and 5-HT are sufficiently resolved so that the concentration of each can be determined simultaneously during release from individual vesicles by monitoring the oxidative current at different potential windows in the same voltammogram (Figure 3). Unlike epinephrine and norepinephrine secretion from chromaffin cells, temporally resolved concentration spikes for each compound did occur

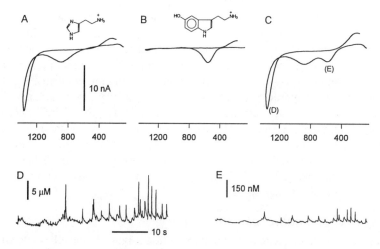

Figure 3 Detection of histamine and 5-HT corelease with FSCV. Background-subtracted voltam-mograms of (*A*) histamine, (*B*) 5-HT, and (*C*) a mixture of both compounds at 800 V/s. (*D* and *E*) Demonstration of simultaneous FSCV measurement of histamine and 5-HT secreted from indi-vidual mast cells. The current from successive voltammograms (16.7 ms apart) was monitored at +1.41 V for detection of histamine (*D*) and +0.55 V for 5-HT (*E*), revealing that these two com-pounds are released from the same individual vesicles. (62b, by permission of the Electrochemical Society.)

at the same time, providing the first direct measurements of corelease of any chemical messengers from single vesicles.

EXOCYTOSIS MEASUREMENTS WITH AMPEROMETRY

Comparison of Amperometry and Cyclic Voltammetry

In amperometry, a microelectrode is held at a constant potential sufficient to oxidize or reduce an analyte of interest and the resulting electrochemical current is monitored with time. Although amperometry boasts superior time resolu-tion, both amperometry and FSCV have sufficient temporal resolution to ob-serve individual exocytotic spikes. A major difference between amperometry and FSCV is the concentration profiles they establish (4). Unlike the transient, small concentration profiles that occur with FSCV, the profiles in amperometry can extend far into solution. However, amperometry is normally done with the electrode directly in contact with the cell. In this case, the diffusion layer is the separation between the two, and thus very steep gradients are generated. Indeed, the gradient during amperometry is sufficiently steep that it can promote release of molecules from vesicles that have fused with the plasma membrane under conditions where release measured by cyclic voltammetry is halted (36). In contrast, catecholamines are transiently oxidized, then rapidly reduced, to their original form during a cyclic voltammogram with minimal perturbation of the secretion process. This difference in concentration gradients, i.e., the consumption of material by the electrode in amperometry, also causes amperometric spikes to be much narrower than those measured by FSCV (87). Because the concentration gradient at a cell and in a calibration solution are different in amperometry, concentration units are not used for calibration of the currents. Rather, advantage is taken of the basic law of electrolysis, Faraday's law. This states that the charge (time integral of the current) is directly proportional to the number of molecules electrolyzed.

Temporal Resolution of Amperometry

Amperometry has excellent temporal resolution (Figure 4) and allows detailed real-time analysis of the kinetic processes involved in extrusion of vesicular content into the extracellular space. The width at half height ($t_{1/2}$) of an exocytotic current spike is often used to evaluate the time course of an individual secretion event. Despite being quite rapid, amperometric current spikes measured at chromaffin cells are broader (mean $t_{1/2} > 5$ ms) than would be predicted for diffusion from an instantaneous point source (68, 84). This is the case even with the electrode in direct physical contact with the cell membrane where diffusional broadening can play only a minimal role (87). Thus, it appears that there are one or more rate-limiting kinetic steps in the extrusion of vesicular contents following vesicle-cell fusion. The excellent temporal resolution of amperometry has therefore been employed to resolve independent late stages of exocytosis (67) and to examine effects of different extracellular parameters on the extent and time course of vesicular release (see Characteristics of Exocytotic Current Spikes below).

Spatial Resolution of Amperometry

Owing to their small physical dimensions, microelectrodes enable spatially resolved measurements of exocytosis from well-defined regions of a single cell. With a microelectrode pressed firmly against the outer surface of an individual cell, losses due to diffusional mass transport are minimized, and the area of the cell analyzed is determined by the electroactive surface of the microelectrode. Carbon fiber microelectrodes normally employed for single-cell analysis have tips with radii of ~5 μm, making them similar in size to many isolated cells in culture. To further improve spatial resolution, however, carbon electrodes with tip radii of ~1 μm can be fabricated by flame-etching a carbon fiber and insulating its sides with poly(oxyphenylene) (38, 73). Experiments in which

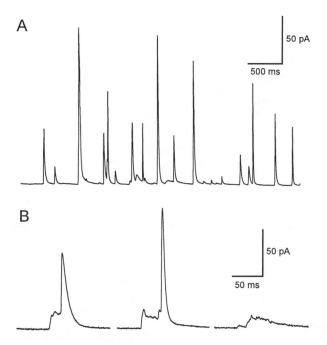

Figure 4 Single-vesicle release observed by microelectrode amperometry. (*A*) Amperometric current trace showing temporally resolved exocytotic spikes from a stimulated chromaffin cell. Each current spike corresponds to oxidation of the catecholamine contents of a single vesicle at a carbon fiber microelectrode held at +0.65 V. (*B*) The spike-shaped oxidative current features (*left* and *center*) are preceded by "feet" that correspond to flux of catecholamine through a fusion pore. The smaller feature on the *right* is a flickering foot (without an accompanying spike), which is believed to represent transient release of vesicular catecholamine through a fusion pore of fluctuating diameter.

two flame-etched carbon fiber microelectrodes were used to electrochemically map zones of exocytosis (Figure 5) revealed information about the localization of release sites on the surface of individual chromaffin cells in culture (69).

Quantitative Analysis with Amperometry

Another advantage of amperometry is in the area of quantitative analysis of released content when the electrode is placed in contact with the cell surface (26). For each spike, the integral of the current with respect to time yields the measured charge. The charge (Q) in coulombs is related to the number of moles of material detected (N) by Faraday's law, $Q = nFN$, where n is the number of electrons involved in the electrochemical reaction ($n = 2$ for catecholamines)

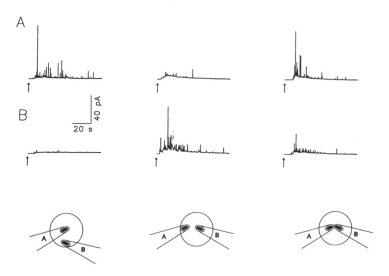

Figure 5 Spatially resolved measurements by amperometry at chromaffin cells. The current traces in panels (*A*) and (*B*) show results of simultaneous amperometric measurements with two flame-etched carbon fiber microelectrodes (labeled *A* and *B* in the lower panel cartoon) positioned at a single cell. Stimulation with nicotine (*arrows*) only causes significant numbers of coincident spikes (i.e. events detected at both electrodes) in the rightmost arrangement where the insulating layers of the electrode tips are touching. (69, by permission.)

and F is Faraday's constant (96,485 C/equivalent). Using amperometry, the contents of very small vesicles can be quantified. Recently, for example, amperometry was applied to detect release of synaptic vesicles from cultured leech neurons that contained about 4,700 5-HT molecules (9).

The mean quantity for an exocytotic event at chromaffin cells is $\sim$2 million catecholamine molecules, but the histograms of Q values are broadly spread in a skewed, non-Gaussian distribution (26). Thus, unlike the expectation from quantal analysis of postsynaptic potentials, the packets of secreted substances are surprisingly nonuniform. To model this, a uniform concentration in each spherical vesicle has been assumed. Then, the amount that reaches the electrode during an event will be proportional to the volume (radius cubed) of the source vesicle. Vesicle radii in most cells show a Gaussian distribution. Therefore, the cube root of the charge ($Q^{1/3}$) should have a similar distribution. Indeed, $Q^{1/3}$ histograms were found to be Gaussian with a relative standard deviation similar to that for the respective vesicle radii for four different cell types—mast cells, pheochromocytoma (PC12) cells, pancreatic β-cells, and chromaffin cells (26).

CHARACTERISTICS OF EXOCYTOTIC CURRENT SPIKES

Much has been learned about the mechanisms of vesicular release through analysis of individual exocytotic current spikes. These transient features reveal amount secreted and time course of release for the final steps in exocytosis.

The first electrochemically observable event in exocytosis from several different secretory cell types is flux of transmitter through a fusion pore. A fusion pore (49–51) is a narrow aqueous channel that connects the lumen of a fusing secretory vesicle with the extracellular space. Transmitter that is not bound in the intravesicular matrix may leak through the fusion pore to create a feature in the current trace known as the foot (19, 87). Upon expansion of the fusion pore, there is a rapid flux of transmitter out of the exposed intravesicular matrix. This generally leads to a sharp current transient with a shape characterized by a fast but not instantaneous rise to a peak amplitude and a more gradual decay to baseline (67). Current spikes have been electrochemically observed from several different cells often used as models for synaptic vesicle exocytosis.

Mast Cells

Early patch-clamp investigations into membrane capacitance suggested that fusion of the large secretory vesicles of beige mouse mast cells may occur transiently (3). That is, the cell membrane capacitance may increase permanently from complete fusion or it may immediately undergo a subsequent decrease corresponding to reversible opening and closing of a fusion pore. Alvarez de Toledo et al (3) therefore combined patch-clamp measurements of fusion pore opening with amperometric detection of 5-HT release to show that significant release of secretory products occurs during transient fusion. An amperometric foot preceding a spike was observed only with a fluctuating capacitance trace. Stand-alone feet were observed electrochemically with capacitance flickers that did not result in a permanent capacitance increase. With this combination of complementary techniques, it was also determined that the onset of spikes without feet was considerably delayed from the onset of capacitance signals in beige mouse mast cells.

Even when capacitance traces reveal complete opening of the fusion pore, release of the interior contents does not occur instantaneously. The observed slowing appears to be a result of the tight association of the costored vesicular components. In mast cell granules, histamine and 5-HT are contained in and tightly associated with a heparin-sulfate proteoglycan matrix. This intragranular complex exhibits properties similar to an ion exchange material (59, 77). Isolated matrices of beige mouse secretory granules remain intact in acidic histamine solutions and behave as smart polymer gels that contract and expand in response to applied voltage (54). In addition, these granule matrices have been optically observed to shrink in the presence of divalent cations but swell in the presence of monovalent cations (21).

Electrochemical experiments were devised to test the hypothesis that granule matrix dissociation is a rate-limiting step in the release of molecules from mast cell granules following fusion with the plasma membrane (63). Earlier optical microscopy studies at mast cells with large vesicles provided support for this view. For example, electrical events associated with membrane fusion invariably precede swelling of beige mouse mast cell secretory granules (52, 95). Examination of individual exocytotic events at rat peritoneal mast cells (700 nm granule diameter) with amperometry revealed that, on average, spikes became taller, narrower, and had larger overall areas at physiological temperature (37°C) compared with room temperature (21°C) (63). The reduction in $t_{1/2}$ shows that molecules are being released from the granule at a faster rate at 37°C, consistent with an accelerated matrix dissociation rate. The increase in area (Q) is extremely surprising because it demonstrates that not all of the vesicle contents are released at the lower temperature as a result of their association with the granular matrix. In a FSCV study, exposure to Zn^{2+} was found to decrease spike frequency and increase mean $t_{1/2}$ (63). These effects are attributed to crosslinking of negative charges and concomitant tightening of the granule matrix by the divalent cation Zn^{2+}. Indeed, all of the electrochemical evidence supports the view that ionic forces play a central role in the release of histamine and 5-HT from mast cell granules (64).

Chromaffin Cells

Spikes measured at chromaffin cells are also wider than expected for a diffusion-controlled process (68, 84). This temporal broadening appears to have the same source as in mast cells—a rate-limiting dissociation of the vesicular matrix following vesicle-cell fusion (63, 67). In chromaffin cells, the catecholamines are stored in vesicles at a high concentration (0.55 M) along with other components including Ca^{2+}, ATP, and the acidic protein chromogranin A (32, 89). Similar to those of mast cells, several of the components in chromaffin cell vesicles are known to associate (Figure 6). Chromogranin A, which has a high percentage of aspartate and glutamate residues, can play an important role in reducing osmotic pressure in the vesicle by interacting with Ca^{2+} and catecholamines. The remarkably high concentration of soluble molecules (>750 mM) sequestered in the vesicular matrix leads to a considerable osmotic gradient upon vesicle-cell fusion and exposure of the vesicle contents to isotonic (315 mOsm) extracellular solution. As revealed by amperometry, reduction of the osmotic gradient through the use of hypertonic extracellular solutions (630 mOsm) greatly reduces the frequency of Ba^{2+}-induced current spikes and causes lower amounts

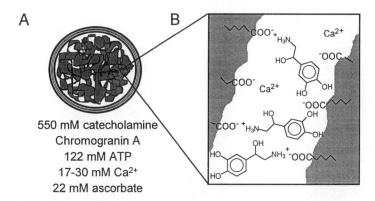

Figure 6 Association of vesicle contents in chromaffin cells. (*A*) Cartoon of a single membrane-bound chromaffin vesicle accompanied by list of major intravesicular constituents and their concentrations. (*B*) Schematic representation of possible interactions and associations of molecules within the intravesicular storage matrix of a chromaffin cell vesicle.

of catecholamine to be secreted per event (7). Conversely, hypotonic solutions (200 mOsm) cause an increase in the number of spikes and average amount secreted per spike (67).

When a chromaffin cell's external osmolarity was raised even higher (970 mOsm), very few spike-shaped events were observed in response to exposure of the cell to Ba^{2+} (7). However, numerous small-amplitude events were observed in the current records that appear to be feet without accompanying spikes. These features have been observed under isotonic conditions as well (94) and sometimes flicker, suggesting that they are the result of catecholamine flux through a fusion pore of fluctuating diameter. Interestingly, when a Ba^{2+}-stimulated cell in hypertonic media is transiently exposed to isotonic solution, spike-shaped events reappear (7). Elimination of the normal osmotic gradient in 970 mOsm solutions appears to allow only unbound vesicular catecholamine to be released from fused vesicles and detected at the electrode. However, when the normal osmotic gradient is restored, the vesicular matrix is able to unravel and release its sequestered contents to produce spikes.

Water entry into the vesicular matrix following fusion therefore appears to be an important driving force for dissociation and release of intravesicular content. Several studies involving changes in a cell's extracellular environment show that factors other than osmotic pressure are important in the dissociative process. In high pH solution, for example, more catecholamine molecules are released from a vesicle than at a physiological pH (36). Thus, an increase in the pH gradient between the vesicle interior (pH 5.5) and extracellular solution drives matrix expansion and release of contents. Similar to the situation for mast cells, an increase in temperature promotes release of more molecules per spike at a faster rate (63, 83). External ionic composition has also been shown to affect quantal size and kinetics of release (35). However, ionic forces do not appear to be as important in release from chromaffin cells as they are in release from mast cells.

Peptide-Releasing cells

PANCREATIC β-CELLS Kennedy et al (41) have developed an amperometric method for detecting secretion of the peptide hormone insulin from rat and human pancreatic β-cells. Under physiological conditions, insulin oxidizes too slowly at common electrode materials to be readily detected electrochemically. Thus, a carbon fiber microelectrode is modified with an electrodeposited ruthenium oxide and cyanoruthenate film to catalyze the oxidation of insulin disulfides. Such an electrode held at +0.85 V and placed 1 μm from a single β-cell stimulated with tolbutamide, K^+, or glucose detects current spikes believed to represent exocytosis of single insulin-containing vesicles (34, 41). Liquid chromatography of releasates from islets of Langerhans showed that the primary secreted substance that can be detected by the electrode is insulin (34). These measurements represent the first direct detection of single exocytotic events at β-cells. Amperometry with chemically modified microelectrodes therefore provides improvements in temporal and spatial resolution for insulin measurements that may lead to a better understanding of insulin secretion and the pathology of diabetes.

Insulin is likely stored in β-cell vesicles at pH 5.5-6.0 as a crystalline hexamer zinc complex. Kennedy's group (40) used the modified electrodes to examine insulin secretion at different extracellular pHs and found that spikes with an average content of 1.6 amol and $t_{1/2}$ of ~40 ms were detected at pH 7.4, whereas no spikes were detected at pH 6.4. As a control, β-cells were loaded with 5-HT, which accumulates in the β-cell vesicles in a readily releasable form. Vesicular release of 5-HT was detected at both pHs of interest.

Thus, it appears that vesicle fusion and opening can occur at pH 6.4. However, similar to the case in chromaffin cells, a pH gradient is necessary to drive release of β-cell vesicular contents following fusion. Furthermore, the fact that insulin spikes were found to be much wider than 5-HT spikes points to dissolution and dissociation of the Zn-insulin precipitates as rate-limiting steps in exocytosis of free insulin. Thus, as for mast and chromaffin cells, secretion of insulin from β-cells is limited by dissociation of the intravesicular components, but the experiments with 5-HT reveal another intravesicular compartment.

In a separate study, Zhou & Misler (93) coupled patch-clamp and amperometry to study stimulus-secretion coupling in β-cells loaded with 5-HT. The amperometric spikes obtained were of relatively low amplitude (~6 pA) and short duration ($t_{1/2} \sim 6$ ms). The presence of these spikes (representing detection of $\sim$100,000 5-HT molecules) was used to correlate secretion with cell electrical activity. In this way, dynamic information regarding the coupling of stimulation and vesicular release was obtained in real time.

PITUITARY MELANOTROPHS   Amperometry at a carbon fiber microelectrode has also been used to detect peptide hormones secreted from single melanotrophs of the intermediate lobe of the rat pituitary gland (58). In this application, electrochemical detection depends on oxidation of tryptophan and tyrosine residues in peptides secreted from the melanotrophs. Upon mechanical stimulation or stimulation with K^+, time-resolved ($t_{1/2} = 36$ ms) Ca^{2+}-dependent current spikes were observed. FSCV was used to confirm that the substance being detected was a small tryptophan or tyrosine-containing peptide, most likely α-melanocyte stimulating hormone.

Cells with Small Vesicles

PC12 CELLS   Rat pheochromocytoma (PC12) cells synthesize, store, and release catecholamines in a manner similar to sympathetic ganglion neurons. Ewing's group (16) used amperometry with microelectrodes to make the first direct observations of quantal release from PC12 cells. These cells, which have a mean vesicle radius of 75 nm, were found to yield Ca^{2+}-dependent spikes of, on average, 190 zmol (114,300 molecules) of catecholamine with a $t_{1/2}$ of 9.3 ms. Measurements of vesicles of this size support the plausibility of amperometrically measuring release of neuronal synaptic vesicles. The spatial resolution of amperometry at microelectrodes has further allowed a comparison between sites of exocytosis on differentiated and nondifferentiated PC12 cells (91). Cells treated with nerve growth factor (NGF) released catecholamines primarily from varicosities along their neurites and not from the cell body. These results provide possible evidence for relocation of exocytotic sites. Finally, amperometry has been used to determine the latency between stimulation and secretion for several different types of stimulation of PC12 cells (90).

SYMPATHETIC GANGLION NEURONS   Zhou & Misler (92) have reported that amperometry is also capable of detecting stimulated quantal release of catecholamines from developing superior cervical ganglion (SCG) neurons maintained in culture. Varicosities located along axons of these neurons contain 30-90 nm diameter vesicles. As measured with a polyethylene-insulated carbon fiber microelectrode, K^+ and black widow spider venom evoked small amplitude (2-20 pA) spikes of short duration (0.5-2 ms) corresponding to vesicular release of catecholamine. Zhou & Misler estimated from median spike charge that $\sim$30,000 catecholamine molecules were released per quantum.

LEECH NEURONS   Bruns & Jahn (9) characterized the release of 5-HT from isolated Retzius cells of the leech *Hirudo medicinalis*. Taking full advantage of the sensitivity and temporal resolution of real-time amperometry, two types of action potential-evoked 5-HT spikes were observed. These spike categories are believed to correspond to Ca^{2+}-dependent exocytosis of small clear synaptic vesicles (SSV) and large dense-core synaptic vesicles (LDCV). Electron microscopy confirmed the presence of SSV close to the plasma membrane and LDCV in more remote areas of the cytoplasm of Retzius cells. The amperometric spikes attributed to small vesicles had a $t_{1/2}$ of 600 μs and corresponded to detection of only about 4,700 5-HT molecules. In contrast, putative LDCV spikes had a $t_{1/2} < 4$ ms and had charges indicating release of about 80,000 5-HT molecules. SSV spikes were found to occur more rapidly and frequently than LDCV spikes following a single-action potential stimulus. Foot signals were often found to precede the LDCV spikes but not the SSV spikes. The rapid time course observed for the SSV spikes (submillisecond) points out the possibility that total release of synaptic vesicular content could take place through an undilated fusion pore without ever proceeding through full fusion. However, the nature of fusion pores associated with small synaptic vesicles remains unknown as feet on SSV spikes could be present but at signal amplitudes unable to be resolved from the instrumental noise level of amperometry (66).

GIANT DOPAMINE NEURONS   The pond snail *Planorbis corneus* has a fully developed dopamine neuron, and its cell body can be quite easily exposed. Although the studies described above in differentiated cells showed that release occurs at terminals, Ewing's group (14) showed that quantal release can also occur from the cell body. Intracellular and extracellular stimulation of these cells was found to elicit exocytotic catecholamine spikes measured with a carbon fiber microelectrode. Analysis of interspike intervals revealed the occurrence of distinct bursting patterns caused by an as-yet unknown mechanism (15). Average spike area indicated that about 818,000 molecules were being detected per exocytotic event. In addition to FSCV, capillary electrophoresis sampling and separation of released material following stimulation was utilized to positively identify the released substance as dopamine. For these cells, a bimodal distribution of $Q^{1/3}$ raises the possibility of two distinct classes of vesicles or release mechanisms (14).

The cell bodies of these cells are sufficiently large (70 μm) that they remain functional when a 1 μm carbon fiber microelectrode or small injection pipette is inserted into them. Thus, the unique opportunity is afforded to study the intracellular processing that occurs for neurotransmitters (74). For example, this preparation was used to examine the reverse transport of dopamine via its uptake carrier, an alternative to exocytosis as a mode of chemical secretion.

Common Features of Secretory Spikes

Several common features concerning release during exocytosis can be observed in all cells examined to date that have relatively large vesicles (>100 nm diameter). First, the vesicle contents are not free, but exist in an associated form that helps maintain them in a stored state. As a consequence of this storage and the time required for dissociation, release at the single vesicle level tends to be prolonged. In the case of very large vesicles such as those in goblet cells and beige mouse mast cells, microscopic observation can be used to observe the relatively slow swelling of the vesicular matrix that occurs after the actual vesicle-cell fusion event. Recent studies of mast cell granular matrices with approximately 500 nm diameter by atomic force microscopy show that matrix properties are similar to those of an ion exchange gel (59). The amperometric measurements at a variety of cell types described above are consistent with this view, and all reveal that secretion from individual vesicles is much more prolonged than simple diffusion out of a spherical compartment.

A second common observation is that secretion occurs in a step-wise fashion. The initial event observed is the foot, which may then progress into the full secretory event (Figure 7). However, multiple reports show that secretion can

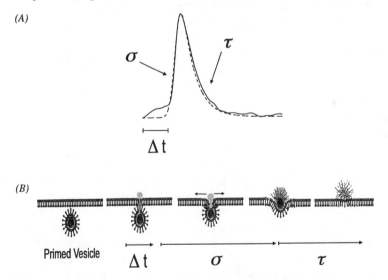

Figure 7 Temporally resolved independent stages of exocytotic secretion. (*A*) A single exocytotic current spike (*solid line*) with an exponentially modified Gaussian function (*dashed line*) superimposed. (*B*) Cartoon depicting stages of exocytosis. In response to stimulation, a vesicle fuses with the plasma membrane. Flux of catecholamine molecules through the narrow fusion pore gives rise to a foot (Δt). Next, expansion of the fusion pore leads to a Gaussian flux from the vesicle with a time constant σ. Retardation of release by the matrix dissociation rate is reflected in the parameter τ. (67, by permission.)

occur without full fusion, as would be expected for the case where an initially formed fusion pore does not lead to complete incorporation of the vesicle membrane into the plasma membrane. A third common finding is that the secretory packets are not quantized in the tight fashion expected from electrophysiological studies. The broad distribution observed seems to be due to several factors. Secretion without full fusion obviously will lead to a nonquantized event. In addition, the broad range of vesicular volumes leads to a broad range of contents. In the specific cases of giant dopamine neurons and leech neurons, two distinct distributions of vesicles are apparent. Finally, nonquantized events can occur when the associated resting vesicular contents do not fully unravel during a full fusion event. At the present time, insufficient data exist to know whether these characteristics are operant at cells with smaller vesicles such as neurons, although this is suspected to be the case (64).

USE OF SINGLE-CELL TECHNIQUES TO STUDY OVERALL RELEASE PROCESS

Carbon fiber microelectrodes provide considerable information on individual secretory events. Additionally, because they are normally located external to the cell, these electrodes can be combined with several other biophysical techniques to address a variety of questions concerning the overall process of exocytosis. Following are several examples illustrating applications of high-resolution measurements to gain detailed information about relationships among some of the complex events that comprise the overall process of exocytosis.

Stimulus-Secretion Coupling

With the ability to monitor events from the onset of cell stimulation to final release of vesicular contents, the powerful combination of patch-clamp measurements and amperometry has the potential to provide information about important intermediate biochemical and biophysical steps in exocytosis. At chromaffin cells, for instance, Chow et al (19) found that the onset of amperometric spikes was delayed an average of 50 ms from the time of a voltage-clamp depolarizing stimulus. Such latency is not observed in neuronal synapses (<1 ms delay), implying possible differences from neuroendocrine cells in the molecular mechanisms through which a stimulus leads to vesicle release or perhaps differences in spatial aspects of coupling. Chow et al (17) combined capacitance and amperometric measurements to further examine this delay and determined with Ca^{2+} buffering that the most important mechanism responsible for the delayed secretion is the time needed for the trigger molecule Ca^{2+} to reach the chromaffin cell fusion machinery. Similar measurements have also been made that incorporate flash photolysis of caged Ca^{2+} compounds (56) to gain temporally resolved information on the complex steps (82) between stimulus and secretion.

It has long been known that exocytosis is closely associated with an increase in intracellular Ca^{2+} concentration (23). A combination of microelectrode amperometry and epifluorescence measurements has allowed correlation of catecholamine release and cytosolic free Ca^{2+} from single chromaffin cells in real time (27). Through use of the fluorescent Ca^{2+} probe fura-2 and different stimulation protocols, it was found that exocytosis could be induced in a single cell by an increase in cytosolic Ca^{2+} as a result of entry of extracellular Ca^{2+} or release of internal Ca^{2+} stores. In an application with improved spatial resolution, pulsed-laser imaging was used in conjunction with flame-etched carbon fiber microelectrodes and patch-clamp to map sites of Ca^{2+} entry and catecholamine release (65). The fluorescent Ca^{2+} indicator rhod-2 was transiently excited by laser to produce snapshot images of changes in intracellular Ca^{2+} concentration in single patch-clamped chromaffin cells. Amperometry was used simultaneously to detect catecholamine spikes from spatially localized areas on a cell. With this combination of analytical approaches, sites of Ca^{2+} entry and zones of catecholamine release on single chromaffin cells were found to be colocalized.

Modulation of Release

Amperometric measurements of release have also been shown to be useful for examining the extent and duration of secretion induced by specific pharmacological agents. For example, Wakade and coworkers (20) found significant differences in the time course of release at the single cell level when induced by nicotine and muscarine. Koh & Hille (42) used microelectrode amperometry to evaluate neuromodulation of norepinephrine release from isolated superior cervical ganglion neurons. Norepinephrine secretion was quantitated by integrating current traces of release evoked by K^+ and electrical stimulation in the presence of numerous pharmacological agents including α_2-adrenergic and muscarinic agonists. Secretion envelopes with superimposed spikes were thus compared to reveal that secretion is inhibited presynaptically at sympathetic ganglion neurons by a wide range of neurotransmitters in ways that parallel modulation of N-type Ca^{2+} channels.

CONCLUSIONS

In less than a decade, carbon fiber microelectrodes have been shown to be important tools for examining the exocytotic process at individual cells. Both cyclic voltammetry and amperometry can be used to resolve secretory spikes arising from single vesicle-cell fusion events at a variety of cell types and from a wide range of vesicle sizes. The results from such investigations have revealed that the extrusion of the vesicular contents is a more complex process than previously believed and that the stability imparted to the resting vesicle by the interaction of its contents results in a rate-limiting extrusion process after full fusion. Furthermore, the presence of partial fusion events and the occurrence of nonquantized release have been revealed with these tools. High-resolution electrochemical techniques with carbon fiber microelectrodes will undoubtedly play an important role in the future in the quest to unravel the complex process of exocytosis.

ACKNOWLEDGMENT

This research was supported by the Office of Naval Research.

Visit the *Annual Reviews* home page at
http://www.AnnualReviews.org.

Literature Cited

1. Adams RN. 1990. In vivo electrochemical measurements in the CNS. *Prog. Neurobiol.* 35:297
2. Almers W. 1990. Exocytosis. *Annu. Rev. Physiol.* 52:607
3. Alvarez de Toledo G, Fernandez-Chacon R, Fernandez JM. 1993. Release of secretory products during transient vesicle fusion. *Nature* 363:554
3a. Angleson JK, Betz WJ. 1997. Monitoring secretion in real time: capacitance, amperometry and fluorescence compared. *Trends Neurosci.* 20:281
4. Bard AJ, Faulkner LR. 1980. *Electrochemical Methods.* New York: Wiley. 718 pp.
5. Baur JE, Kristensen EW, May LJ, Wiedemann DJ, Wightman RM. 1988. Fast-scan voltammetry of biogenic amines. *Anal. Chem.* 60:1268
6. Betz WJ, Mao F, Smith CB. 1996. Imaging exocytosis and endocytosis. *Curr. Opin. Neurobiol.* 6:365
7. Borges R, Travis ER, Hochstetler SE, Wightman RM. 1997. Effects of external osmotic pressure on vesicular secretion from bovine adrenal medullary cells. *J. Biol. Chem.* 272:8325
8. Breckenridge LJ, Almers W. 1987. Currents through the fusion pore that forms during exocytosis of a secretory vesicle. *Nature* 328:814
9. Bruns D, Jahn R. 1995. Real-time measurement of transmitter release from single synaptic vesicles. *Nature* 377:62
10. Burgoyne RD. 1991. Control of exocyto-

sis in adrenal chromaffin cells. *Biochim. Biophys. Acta* 1071:174
11. Cahill PS, Walker QD, Finnegan JM, Mickelson GE, Travis ER, Wightman RM. 1996. Microelectrodes for the measurement of catecholamines in biological systems. *Anal. Chem.* 68:3180
12. Cahill PS, Wightman RM. 1995. Simultaneous amperometric measurement of ascorbate and catecholamine secretion from individual bovine adrenal medullary cells. *Anal. Chem.* 67:2599
13. Chandler DE. 1991. Membrane fusion as seen in rapidly frozen secretory cells. *Ann. NY Acad. Sci.* 635:234
14. Chen G, Gavin PF, Luo G, Ewing AG. 1995. Observation and quantitation of exocytosis from the cell body of a fully developed neuron in *Planorbis corneus. J. Neurosci.* 15:7747
15. Chen G, Gutman DA, Zerby SE, Ewing AG. 1996. Electrochemical monitoring of bursting exocytotic events from the giant dopamine neuron of *Planorbis corneus. Brain Res.* 733:119
16. Chen TK, Luo G, Ewing AG. 1994. Amperometric monitoring of stimulated catecholamine release from rat pheochromocytoma (PC12) cells at the zeptomole level. *Anal. Chem.* 66:3031
17. Chow RH, Klingauf J, Heinemann C, Zucker RS, Neher E. 1996. Mechanisms determining the time course of secretion in neuroendocrine cells. *Neuron* 16:369
18. Chow RH, von Ruden L. 1995. Elec-

trochemical detection of secretion from single cells. In *Single-Channel Recording*, ed. B Sakmann, E Neher, 11:245. New York: Plenum. 2nd ed.

19. Chow RH, von Ruden L, Neher E. 1992. Delay in vesicle fusion revealed by electrochemical monitoring of single secretory events in adrenal chromaffin cells. *Nature* 356:60

20. Chowdhury PS, Guo X, Wakade TD, Przywara DA, Wakade AR. 1994. Exocytosis from a single rat chromaffin cell by cholinergic and peptidergic neurotransmitters. *Neuroscience* 59:1

21. Curran MJ, Brodwick MS. 1991. Ionic control of the size of the vesicle matrix of beige mouse mast cells. *J. Gen. Physiol.* 98:771

22. del Castillo J, Katz B. 1954. Quantal components of the end-plate potential. *J. Physiol.* 124:560

23. Douglas WW. 1968. Stimulus-secretion coupling: the concept and clues from chromaffin and other cells. *Br. J. Pharm.* 34:451

24. Fatt P, Katz B. 1952. Spontaneous subthreshold activity at motor nerve endings. *J. Physiol.* 117:109

25. Fernandez JM, Neher E, Gomperts BD. 1984. Capacitance measurements reveal stepwise fusion events in degranulating mast cells. *Nature* 312:453

26. Finnegan JM, Pihel K, Cahill PS, Huang L, Zerby SE, et al. 1996. Vesicular quantal size measured by amperometry at chromaffin, mast, pheochromocytoma, and pancreatic β-cells. *J. Neurochem.* 66:1914

27. Finnegan JM, Wightman RM. 1995. Correlation of real-time catecholamine release and cytosolic Ca²⁺ at single bovine chromaffin cells. *J. Biol. Chem.* 270:5353

28. Gillis K. 1995. Techniques for membrane capacitance measurements. In *Single-Channel Recording*, ed. B Sakmann, E Neher, 7:155. New York: Plenum. 2nd ed.

29. Hamill OP, Marty A, Neher E, Sakmann B, Sigworth FJ. 1981. Improved patch-clamp techniques for high resolution current recording from cells and cell-free membrane patches. *Pflügers. Arch.* 391:85

30. Henkel AW, Almers W. 1996. Fast steps in exocytosis and endocytosis studied by capacitance measurements in endocrine cells. *Curr. Opin. Neurobiol.* 6:350

31. Heuser JE. 1989. Review of electron microscopic evidence favouring vesicle exocytosis as the structural basis for quantal release during synaptic transmission. *Q. J. Exp. Physiol.* 74:1051

32. Holz RW, Senter RA. 1986. Effects of osmolality and ionic strength on secretion from adrenal chromaffin cells permeabilized with digitonin. *J. Neurochem.* 46:1835

33. Howell JO, Kuhr WG, Ensman RE, Wightman RM. 1986. Background subtraction for rapid scan voltammetry. *J. Electroanal. Chem.* 209:77

34. Huang L, Shen H, Atkinson MA, Kennedy RT. 1995. Detection of exocytosis at individual pancreatic β-cells by amperometry at a chemically modified microelectrode. *Proc. Natl. Acad. Sci. USA* 92:9608

35. Jankowski JA, Finnegan JM, Wightman RM. 1994. Extracellular ionic composition alters kinetics of vesicular release of catecholamines and quantal size during exocytosis at adrenal medullary cells. *J. Neurochem.* 63:1739

36. Jankowski JA, Schroeder TJ, Ciolkowski EL, Wightman RM. 1993. Temporal characteristics of quantal secretion of catecholamines from adrenal medullary cells. *J. Biol. Chem.* 268:14694

37. Jankowski JA, Schroeder TJ, Holz RW, Wightman RM. 1992. Quantal secretion of catecholamines measured from individual bovine adrenal medullary cells permeabilized with digitonin. *J. Biol. Chem.* 267:18329

38. Kawagoe KT, Jankowski JA, Wightman RM. 1991. Etched carbon-fiber electrodes as amperometric detectors of catecholamine secretion from isolated biological cells. *Anal. Chem.* 63:1589

39. Kawagoe KT, Zimmerman JB, Wightman RM. 1993. Principles of voltammetry and microelectrode surface states. *J. Neurosci. Meth.* 48:225

40. Kennedy RT, Huang L, Aspinwall CA. 1996. Extracellular pH is required for rapid release of insulin from Zn-insulin precipitates in β-cell secretory vesicles during exocytosis. *J. Am. Chem. Soc.* 118:1795

41. Kennedy RT, Huang L, Atkinson MA, Dush P. 1993. Amperometric monitoring of chemical secretions from individual pancreatic β-cells. *Anal. Chem.* 65:1882

42. Koh D-S, Hille B. 1997. Modulation by neurotransmitters of catecholamine secretion from sympathetic ganglion neurons detected by amperometry. *Proc. Natl. Acad. Sci. USA* 94:1506

42a. Lang T, Wacker I, Steyer J, Kaether C, Wunderlich I, et al. 1997. Ca²⁺-triggered peptide secretion in single cells imaged with green fluorescent protein and evanescent-wave microscopy. *Neuron* 18: 857

43. Leszczyszyn DJ, Jankowski JA, Viveros OH, Diliberto EJ Jr, Near JA, Wightman RM. 1990. Nicotinic receptor-mediated catecholamine secretion from individual chromaffin cells: chemical evidence for exocytosis. *J. Biol. Chem.* 265:14736

44. Leszczyszyn DJ, Jankowski JA, Viveros OH, Diliberto EJ Jr., Near JA, Wightman RM. 1991. Secretion of catecholamines from individual adrenal medullary chromaffin cells. *J. Neurochem.* 56:1855

45. Lillard SJ, Yeung ES, McCloskey MA. 1996. Monitoring exocytosis and release from individual mast cells by capillary electrophoresis with laser-induced native fluorescence detection. *Anal. Chem.* 68:2897.

46. Maiti S, Shear JB, Williams RM, Zipfel WR, Webb WW. 1997. Measuring serotonin distribution in live cells with three-photon excitation. *Science* 275:530

47. Martin AR. 1966. Quantal nature of synaptic transmission. *Physiol. Rev.* 46:51

48. Matthews G. 1996. Synaptic exocytosis and endocytosis: capacitance measurements. *Curr. Opin. Neurobiol.* 6:358

49. Monck JR, Fernandez JM. 1992. The exocytotic fusion pore. *J. Cell Biol.* 119:1395

50. Monck JR, Fernandez JM. 1994. The exocytotic fusion pore and neurotransmitter release. *Neuron* 12:707

51. Monck JR, Fernandez JM. 1996. The fusion pore and mechanisms of biological membrane fusion. *Curr. Opin. Cell Biol.* 8:524

52. Monck JR, Oberhauser AF, Alvarez de Toledo G, Fernandez, JM. 1991. Is swelling of the secretory granule matrix the force that dilates the exocytotic fusion pore? *Biophys. J.* 59:39

53. Morris JF, Pow DV. 1988. Capturing and quantifying the exocytotic event. *J. Exp. Biol.* 139:81

54. Nanavati C, Fernandez JM. 1993. The secretory granule matrix: a fast-acting smart polymer. *Science* 259:963

55. Neher E, Marty A. 1982. Discrete changes of cell membrane capacitance observed under conditions of enhanced secretion in bovine adrenal chromaffin cells. *Proc. Natl. Acad. Sci. USA* 79:6712

56. Neher E, Zucker RS. 1993. Multiple calcium-dependent processes related to secretion in bovine chromaffin cells. *Neuron* 10:21

57. Oberhauser AF, Robinson IM, Fernandez JM. 1996. Simultaneous capacitance and amperometric measurements of exocytosis: a comparison. *Biophys. J.* 71:1131

58. Paras CD, Kennedy RT. 1995. Electrochemical detection of exocytosis at single rat melanotrophs. *Anal. Chem.* 67:3633

59. Parpura V, Fernandez JM. 1996. Atomic force microscopy study of the secretory granule lumen. *Biophys. J.* 71:2356

60. Penner R. 1995. A practical guide to patch clamping. In *Single-Channel Recording*, ed. B Sakmann, E Neher, 1:3. New York: Plenum. 2nd ed.

61. Phillips JH, Burridge K, Wilson SP, Kirshner N. 1983. Visualization of the exocytosis/endocytosis secretory cycle in cultured adrenal chromaffin cells. *J. Cell Biol.* 97:1906

62a. Pihel K, Hsieh S, Jorgenson JW, Wightman RM. 1995. Electrochemical detection of histamine and 5-hydroxytryptamine at isolated mast cells. *Anal. Chem.* 67:4514

63. Pihel K, Schroeder TJ, Wightman RM. 1994. Rapid and selective cyclic voltammetric measurements of epinephrine and norepinephrine as a method to measure secretion from single bovine adrenal medullary cells. *Anal. Chem.* 66:4532

64. Pihel K, Travis ER, Borges R, Wightman RM. 1996. Exocytotic release from individual granules exhibits similar properties at mast and chromaffin cells. *Biophys. J.* 71:1633

65. Rahamimoff R, Fernandez JM. 1997. Pre- and postfusion regulation of transmitter release. *Neuron* 18:17

66. Robinson IM, Finnegan JM, Monck JR, Wightman RM, Fernandez JM. 1995. Colocalization of calcium entry and exocytotic release sites in adrenal chromaffin cells. *Proc. Natl. Acad. Sci. USA* 92:2474

67. Robinson IM, Yamada M, Carrion-Vazquez M, Lennon VA, Fernandez JM. 1996. Specialized release zones in chromaffin cells examined with pulsed-laser imaging. *Cell Calcium* 20:181

68. Schroeder TJ, Borges R, Finnegan JM, Pihel K, Amatore C, Wightman RM. 1996. Temporally resolved, independent stages of individual exocytotic secretion events. *Biophys. J.* 70:1061

69. Schroeder TJ, Jankowski JA, Kawagoe KT, Wightman RM, Lefrou C, Amatore C. 1992. Analysis of diffusional broadening of vesicular packets of catecholamines released from biological cells during exocytosis. *Anal. Chem.* 64:3077

70. Schroeder TJ, Jankowski JA, Senyshyn J, Holz RW, Wightman RM. 1994. Zones of exocytotic release on bovine adrenal medullary cells in culture. *J. Biol. Chem.* 269:17215

71. Smith CB, Betz WJ. 1996. Simultaneous independent measurement of endocytosis and exocytosis. *Nature* 380:531

72. Spruce AE, Breckenridge LJ, Lee AK, Almers W. 1990. Properties of the fusion pore that forms during exocytosis of a mast cell secretory vesicle. *Neuron* 4: 643

73. Steyer JA, Horstmann H, Almers W. 1997. Transport, docking and exocytosis of single secretory granules in live chromaffin cells. *Nature* 388:474

74. Strein TG, Ewing AG. 1992. Characterization of submicron-sized carbon electrodes insulated with a phenol-allylphenol copolymer. *Anal. Chem.* 64:1368

75. Sulzer D, Chen TK, Lau YY, Kristensen H, Rayport S, Ewing A. 1995. Amphetamine redistributes dopamine from synaptic vesicles to cytosol and promotes reverse transport. *J. Neurosci.* 15: 4102

76. Deleted in proof

77. Terakawa S, Manivannan S, Kumakura K. 1993. Evidence against the swelling hypothesis for initiation of exocytosis in terminals of chromaffin cell processes. *J. Physiol.* 87:209

78. Uvnas B, Aborg C-H. 1989. Role of ion exchange in release of biogenic amines. *News Phys. Sci.* 4:68

79. Verdugo P. 1990. Goblet cells secretion and mucogenesis. *Annu. Rev. Physiol.* 52: 157

80. Viveros OH. 1975. Mechanism of secretion of catecholamines from adrenal medulla. In *Handbook of Physiology, Section 7: Endocrinology VI*, ed. H Blaschko, G Sayers, AD Smith, 27:389. Washington, DC: Am. Physiol. Soc.

81. Viveros OH, Arqueros L, Kirshner N. 1969. Quantal secretion from adrenal medulla: all-or-none release of storage vesicle content. *Science* 165:911

82. von Gersdorff H, Matthews G. 1994. Dynamics of synaptic vesicle fusion and membrane retrieval in synaptic terminals. *Nature* 367:735

83. von Ruden L, Neher E. 1993. A Ca-dependent early step in the release of catecholamines from adrenal chromaffin cells. *Science* 262:1061

84. Walker A, Glavinovic MI, Trifaro J-M. 1996. Temperature dependence of release of vesicular content in bovine chromaffin cells. *Pflügers Arch.* 432:885

85. Walker A, Glavinovic MI, Trifaro J-M. 1996. Time course of release of content of single vesicles in bovine chromaffin cells. *Pflügers Arch.* 431:729

86. Wightman RM. 1981. Microvoltammetric electrodes. *Anal. Chem.* 53:1125A

86b. Wightman RM, Hochstetler S, Michael D, Travis E. 1996. Chemical communication. *Interface* 5:22

87. Wightman RM, Jankowski JA, Kennedy RT, Kawagoe KT, Schroeder TJ, et al. 1991. Temporally resolved catecholamine spikes correspond to single vesicle release from individual chromaffin cells. *Proc. Natl. Acad. Sci. USA* 88:10754

88. Wightman RM, Schroeder TJ, Finnegan JM, Ciolkowski EL, Pihel K. 1995. Time course of release of catecholamines from individual vesicles during exocytosis at adrenal medullary cells. *Biophys. J.* 68:383

89. Wightman RM, Wipf DO. 1989. Voltammetry at ultramicroelectrodes. In *Electroanalytical Chemistry: A Series of Advances*, ed. AJ Bard, 15:267. New York: Dekker

90. Winkler H, Smith AD. 1975. The chromaffin granule and the storage of catecholamines. In *Handbook of Physiology, Section 7, Endocrinology VI*, ed. H Blaschko, G Sayers, AD Smith, 23:321. Washington, DC: Am. Physiol. Soc.

91. Zerby SE, Ewing AG. 1996. The latency of exocytosis varies with the mechanism of stimulated release in PC12 cells. *J. Neurochem.* 66:651

92. Zerby SE, Ewing AG. 1996. Electrochemical monitoring of individual exocytotic events from the varicosities of differentiated PC12 cells. *Brain Res.* 712:1

93. Zhou Z, Misler S. 1995. Amperometric detection of stimulus-induced quantal release of catecholamines from cultured superior cervical ganglion neurons. *Proc. Natl. Acad. Sci. USA* 92:6938

94. Zhou Z, Misler S. 1996. Amperometric detection of quantal secretion from patch-clamped rat pancreatic β-cells. *J. Biol. Chem.* 270:270

95. Zhou Z, Misler S, Chow RH. 1996. Rapid fluctuations in transmitter release from single vesicles in bovine adrenal chromaffin cells. *Biophys. J.* 70:1543

96. Zimmerberg J, Curran M, Cohen FS, Brodwick M. 1987. Simultaneous electrical and optical measurements show that membrane fusion precedes secretory granule swelling during exocytosis of beige mouse mast cells. *Proc. Natl. Acad. Sci. USA* 84:1585

Annu. Rev. Biophys. Biomol. Struct. 1998. 27:105–31

MINOR GROOVE-BINDING ARCHITECTURAL PROTEINS: Structure, Function, and DNA Recognition[1]

Carole A. Bewley, Angela M. Gronenborn, G. Marius Clore
Laboratory of Chemical Physics, Building 5, National Institute of Diabetes and Digestive and Kidney Diseases, National Institutes of Health, Bethesda, MD 20892-520; e-mail: clore@vger.niddk.nih.gov

KEY WORDS: TATA box binding protein, HMG-box proteins, integration host factor, HMG I(Y), DNA bending

---

ABSTRACT

To date, high-resolution structures have been solved for five different architectural proteins complexed to their DNA target sites. These include TATA-box–binding protein, integration host factor (IHF), high mobility group I(Y)[HMG I(Y)], and the HMG-box–containing proteins SRY and LEF-1. Each of these proteins interacts with DNA exclusively through minor groove contacts and alters DNA conformation. This paper reviews the structural features of these complexes and the roles they play in facilitating assembly of higher-order protein–DNA complexes and discusses elements that contribute to sequence-specific recognition and conformational changes.

CONTENTS

105

INTRODUCTION

A recurring theme of events that control transcription, recombination, and replication is the involvement of multiprotein-DNA complexes. The intricate architecture of these complexes relies not only on sequence-specific protein-DNA interactions, but also on the interaction of multiple proteins whose DNA binding sites may be quite distant from one another. Thus, the formation of such higher-order structures usually requires that the conformation of the DNA template be bent or distorted in order to bring the requisite proteins into close proximity. In large part this task is accomplished by architectural proteins that typically lack the potential to activate transcription or carry out recombination on their own, but instead induce conformational changes in the DNA, thereby facilitating the assembly and enhancing the overall stability and activity of the multiprotein-DNA complexes.

Many DNA-binding proteins possessing disparate functions have been shown to bend their DNA recognition sites (28, 44, 45). A distinction can be made, however, between those proteins whose primary, if not sole, function is to bend DNA, and those proteins that happen to bend DNA in the process of carrying out their distinct primary functions. The first group we refer to as architectural proteins in the strictest sense, while the second group could include any other relevant DNA-binding proteins such as transcriptional activators or repressors. High resolution three-dimensional structures for five different architectural proteins complexed to their cognate DNA sites have been solved to date and include (*a*) TATA-binding protein (TBP) (23–26, 34), (*b*) the male sex determining factor SRY (59), (*c*) lymphoid enhancer-binding factor 1 (LEF-1) (30), (*d*) integration host factor (IHF) (39), and (*e*) high mobility group I(Y) [HMG I(Y)] (21). All five of these architectural proteins interact exclusively with the minor groove of DNA.

Although the deficiency of chemical features presented by the minor groove is typically considered to be insufficient for specific recognition, all of these minor groove-binding proteins bind with high affinity and varying degrees of sequence specificity. Moreover, they exhibit very different global folds (Figure 1) and use different strategies, or combinations of strategies, for recognition and binding. Accordingly, these proteins also remodel the DNA conformation in distinct

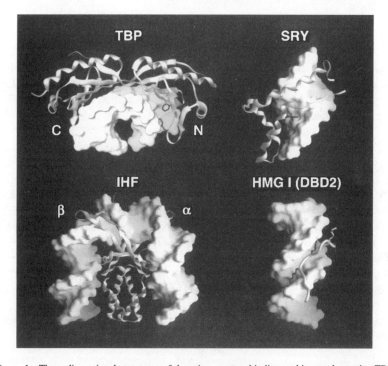

Figure 1   Three-dimensional structures of the minor-groove binding architectural proteins TBP, SRY, IHF, and HMG I in complex with their DNA targets. The DNA is represented as a surface and the protein as a ribbon. Where visible, sidechains key to modulating the DNA conformation are shown as *black rods*. These include Phe99 and Phe116 in the N-terminal domain of yTBP, Ile13 in SRY, and Arg10 and Arg12 of DNA-binding domain 2 of HMG I. The C- and N-terminal subunits of TBP and the α and β arms of IHF are labelled. Figures were produced with GRASP (32).

ways. The structures and functions of these minor groove binding architectural factors are reviewed below, and structural and chemical elements contributing to sequence-specific minor groove recognition are discussed.

STRUCTURE AND FUNCTION OF MINOR GROOVE-BINDING ARCHITECTURAL FACTORS

TATA-Box Binding Protein TBP

In eukaryotes, initiation of transcription of messenger, ribosomal, small nuclear, and transfer RNAs by any of the three RNA polymerases requires the TATA-box binding-protein (TBP) (19). In the case of class II nuclear genes in higher organisms, activation of transcription depends on the formation of a functional preinitiation complex (PIC), comprising RNA polymerase II (polII) and a host of other general initiation factors (such as TFIIA, -B, -D, -E, -F, -I, -J), about the TATA element of core promoter sequences (3, 41, 43). TBP mediates PIC assembly because recognition of the TATA element by TBP is considered to be the nucleating event in complex formation. On its own, TBP cannot substitute for the accurate control of transcription provided by TFIID and larger transcription initiation complexes (20, 37), but it does recognize the TATA element, thereby initiating basal transcription (2).

The first view of a minor groove-binding architectural protein at work came in 1993 when two separate crystal structures of TBP complexed to TATA-box–containing oligonucleotides were solved by the groups of Sigler and Burley (25, 26): Sigler and coworkers solved the structure of yeast TBP bound to a 29-nucleotide DNA hairpin whose stem contains a 12-bp helix that encompasses the TATA box sequence 5'-TATATAAA-3' from the yeast CYC1(-52) promoter, while Burley and coworkers solved the structure of TBP 2 from *Arabidopsis thaliana* bound to the TATA element of the adenovirus major late promoter (AdMLP) which contains the central binding sequence 5'-TATAAAAG-3' (Table 1). Despite the differences in the protein sequences and their cognate

Table 1   Protein sources and DNA sequences used for structural studies of minor groove-binding architectural proteins

Protein source	DNA[a]	Reference
TBP *Arabidopsis thaliana*	5'**GCTATA**AAAG**GGCA**3' 3'**CGATATT**TTC**CCGT**5'	24, 25
TBP yeast	5'**GTATATAAA** ACGG$^{\text{G}}_{\text{T}}$ 3'**CATATATTT** TGCG$_{\text{G}}$	26
TBP human	5'**CTGCTATA**AAA**GGCTG**3' 3'**GACGATATT**TTC**CGAG**5'	34
TBP human	5'**CGTATATATA**CG3' 3'**GCATATATAT**GC5'	23
SRY human	5'**GCACAAAC**3' 3'**CGTGTTTG**5'	59
LEF-1 human	5'**C**ACCC**TTTGAAG**CTC3' 3'**G**TGGG**AAACTTC**GAG5'	30
IHF *Escherichia coli*	5'**GGCC**AAAAAAAGCAT TGCT**TATCAA**TTTGTTGCACC3' 3'**CCGG**TTTTTTTCGTAACGAA**TAGTT**AAACAACGTGG5'	39
HMG I(Y) human	5'**GGG**AAAATTCC**TC**3' 3'**CCC**TTTAAGG**AG**5'	21

[a]Consensus sequences are shown in bold; required sequences such as A-tracts or AT-rich DNA are underlined. The sequences used in the TBP structures are aligned with respect to the 8 bp TATA elements.

DNA-binding sites, the primary structural features of these two protein-DNA complexes are nearly identical. Protein-DNA interactions for both complexes are summarized in Figure 2a, and numbering for the yeast TBP-TATA box complex is used in the text below unless otherwise specified.

TBP is composed of two separate domains, an amino-terminal domain that varies considerably in both length and sequence, and a 180-amino acid carboxy-terminal domain that is highly conserved. It has been shown that the amino-terminal domain is unnecessary for the initiation of transcription, and accordingly the carboxy-terminal domain has been shown to be sufficient for high affinity binding to TATA-box elements, as well as for initiating basal transcription (7). The carboxy-terminal domain of TBP is composed of two subunits, α and β, which contain 89 and 90 amino acids, respectively, and flank a highly basic region referred to as the basic repeat. Although the two subunits of the carboxy-terminal region display only 30% sequence identity, they are nearly identical structurally, and thus give rise to the strong intramolecular pseudo-symmetry of TBP (Figures 1, 3b); both crystal structures were solved using constructs of this carboxy-terminal domain bound to the TATA-box-containing promoter sequence. TBP is best described as having a saddle-like structure where each subunit of TBP consists of a five-stranded, curved antiparallel β-sheet and two α-helices, one long and one short. The central eight strands of the curved β-sheet form the concave underside of the saddle which interacts extensively with the distorted minor groove of the TATA-element, and the β-turns between the outermost antiparallel β-strands appear as stirrups of the saddle. The longer α-helix is located above and approximately orthogonal to the β-sheet, and together with the shorter helix provides a scaffold for the back, or convex side, of the β-sheet. As for the oligonucleotide, the central eight base-pairs that contain the TATA element are underwound and bent by $\sim80°$ toward the major groove, presenting a wide concave surface with complementary curvature to the underside of the protein (Figures 1, 3b). To either side of the TATA element, the DNA returns to B-form as it leaves the region of TBP binding.

Typically, transcription factors recognize and bind to DNA through specific contacts between protein sidechains and a variety of atoms or functional groups located in the major groove of DNA (36, 49). Although nonpolar interactions involving the methyls and olefinic protons of the pyrimidine bases are seen, the recognition interface is usually dominated by hydrogen bonds and electrostatic contacts between polar side chains of the protein and nitrogen and/or oxygen atoms of the DNA. In contrast the concave underside of TBP interacts with the minor groove of the TATA element, and somewhat surprisingly, the protein-DNA interface is dominated by hydrophobic or van der Waals contacts. Illustrative of this hydrophobic predominance, 70% of the 3000 Å^2 of buried surface area resulting from complex formation is hydrophobic. In addition, 12

110   BEWLEY, GRONENBORN & CLORE

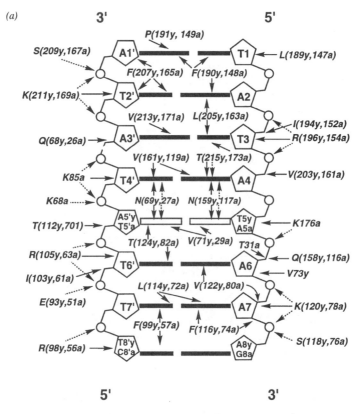

Figure 2 Schematic representations of protein-DNA contacts for each of the five minor groove-binding architectural proteins. The numbering for the DNA bases and the protein residues is the same as in the original papers, and the DNA is viewed looking into the minor groove. Deoxyribose rings are represented as *pentagons*, phosphates as *hollow circles*, and purine (A,G) and pyrimidine (C,T) bases as *long black rectangles* and *short black rectangles*, respectively. Hydrophobic contacts are shown by *solid arrows*, hydrogen bonds and electrostatic contacts by *dashed arrows*, and contacts between protein backbone amides and DNA as *dotted arrows*. (For clarity, no distinction is made between hydrogen bonds and direct or indirect electrostatic interactions.) The identity of each nucleotide is shown in the center of its deoxyribose ring, and the protein residues are shown in italics. Intermolecular contacts are shown for (*a*) yeast TBP and the TATA element from the yeast CYC1(-52) promoter and *Arabidopsis thaliana* TBP and the TATA element of the adenovirus major late promoter; labels end with *y* or *a*, respectively (note that the bases of basepair 5 are represented as *hollow rectangles* because A or T is observed at this site); (*b*) the HMG box domain of SRY and the *MIS* gene consensus sequence; (*c*) the HMG box domain of LEF-1 and the TCRα gene consensus sequence; (*d*) IHF and the H′ site of phage 8 (the asterisk by T29-G30 indicates the site of the nick); (*e*) DBD2 of HMG I(Y) and a dodecamer comprising PRDII of the IFN β enhancer.

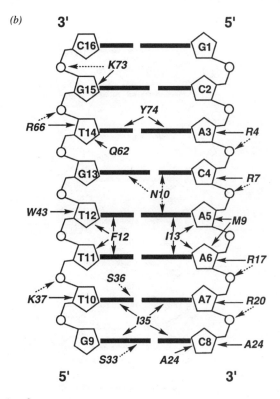

Figure 2   (Continued)

of the 16 hydrogen bond acceptors in the minor groove remain unsatisfied, with most of them being within van der Waals contact of nonpolar atoms. Upon binding, the TATA element is severely distorted, resulting in a widened and shallow minor groove. This distortion occurs largely by the insertion of a pair of phenylalanine residues located in the symmetrically displaced stirrups of TBP that insert into the first and last base steps within the 8 bp TATA box and kink the DNA (Figures 2a, 3a). In addition to the intercalating phenylalanines, the interface comprises eleven more hydrophobic residues that are within van der Waals contact of the minor groove bases (shown in the central portion of Figure 2a). With one exception, all of these interactions are symmetrical with respect to the pseudo-dyad of the complex and contact the central six base pairs of the TATA element; Pro191 contacts A1' just outside of the upstream kink but the symmetrically displaced residue Ala100 makes no such contacts on the downstream side of the DNA.

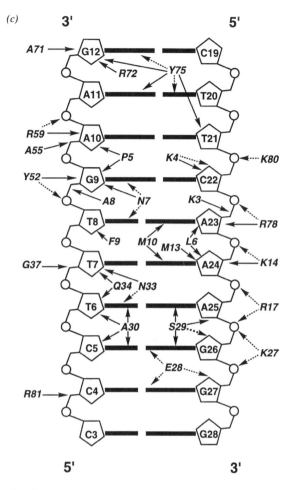

Figure 2   (*Continued*)

Only six hydrogen bonds are observed between the side chains of TBP and the base edges (Figure 2*a*). Asn159 and Asn69 are located in the center of the TATA box and contribute four hydrogen bonds to A4 and T5, and to T4′ and A5′, respectively. One base pair removed on either side, Thr215 and Thr124 hydrogen bond to N3 of A4 and A5′, respectively. Six direct contacts to the phosphate backbone from protein sidechains are seen in both crystal structures. They include contacts from the hydroxyl protons of Ser209 and Ser118 to the phosphate oxygens of A1′ and A8; and from the guanidinium groups of Arg98,

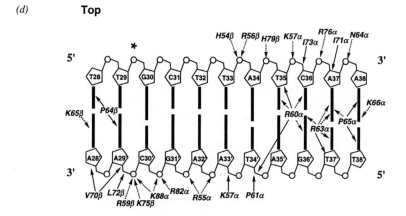

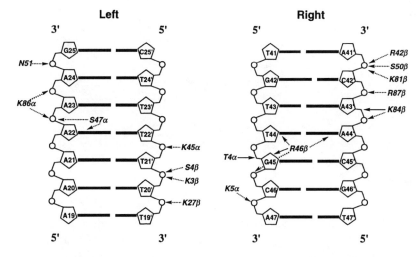

Figure 2   (Continued)

Arg105, and Arg196 to the phosphates near T8′, T6′, and T3, respectively. Located near to the phosphate backbone in both structures are several lysine residues; in the yeast TBP complex these lysine sidechains do not contact the DNA backbone either directly or indirectly, and are reported to be directed away from the backbone and stabilized by water-mediated intramolecular contacts (26). In contrast, in the structure of the *Arabidopsis* complex refined to 1.9 Å (24), lysines 85 and 176 contact the phosphate backbone directly, and lysines

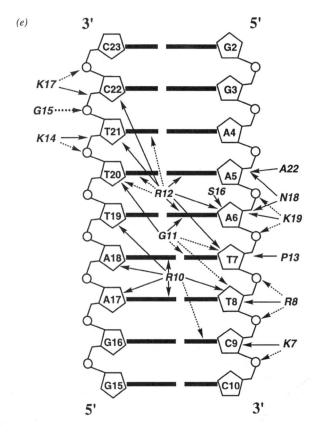

Figure 2   (*Continued*)

68, 78, 159, and 169 make water-mediated hydrogen bonds to the phosphate backbone. Despite the subtle differences in interactions seen in the two structures for the lysine sidechains, mutagenesis studies indicate that most of them are important for binding affinity, DNA recognition, or both (63).

When bound to TBP, the TATA element deviates significantly from canonical B-DNA and actually adopts several features characteristic of A-DNA, the most noteworthy being the extremely wide and shallow minor groove. Indeed, in the center of the TATA box the minor groove width exceeds 9 Å as compared to ~4 Å for B-DNA (42). This prominent distortion results from an effective combination of interactions. The intercalating phenylalanine residues impart ~45° kinks at the outer two basepair steps of the TATA box, and their nearly orthogonal orientations relative to one another cause buckling of the inner two basepairs

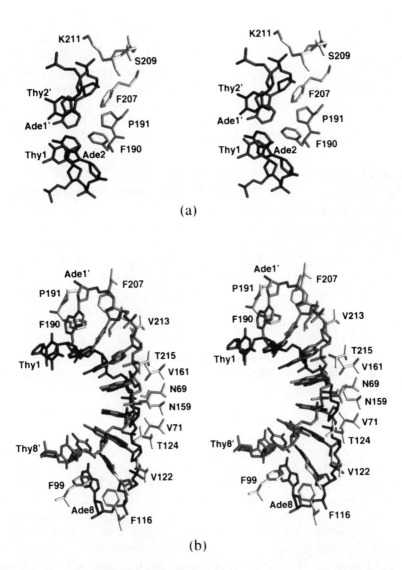

Figure 3 Stereoviews illustrating (*a*) hydrophobic residues in the stirrup of the C-terminal domain of yeast TBP inserted between the first basepair step T1-A1'/A2-T2' of the TATA element; (*b*) the nearly symmetrical array of sidechains protruding from the concave underside of the saddle contacting the 8 bp TATA element.

which become unstacked (Figure 3a; rise = 5.4–5.9 Å). The hydrophobic interface coupled with the electrostatic interactions involving protein sidechains and the phosphate backbone induce a continuous and smooth bend of ~80° toward the major groove, as evidenced by the large average roll angle of +26° compared to ~0° for B-DNA. Although the DNA is underwound by 105° in only seven base steps (average twist angle = 21° for the TATA element as compared to 36° in B-DNA), this distortion is compensated for by one-third of a turn of positive supercoiling; thus, TBP exhibits no net effect on DNA supercoiling. Watson and Crick base-pairing is preserved throughout the DNA.

Architectural Factors That Contain HMG-Box Domains: The Male Sex Determining Factor SRY and Lymphoid Enhancer Binding Factor 1 (Lef-1)

Of the numerous architectural proteins that contain the ~80 residue DNA binding domains known as HMG boxes, the structures have been solved for only two in complex with DNA, namely SRY and LEF-1. The majority of HMG box-containing proteins bind nonspecifically to DNA, recognizing distinct structural features such as prebent or cruciform DNA rather than specific sequences (reviewed in 4, 18). SRY and LEF-1 are members of the high-mobility group proteins HMG-1/2 characterized by a single ~80 residue HMG-box domain (reviewed in 17). Although structurally distinct from TBP, SRY and LEF-1 also serve to bend DNA and do so in a manner analogous to TBP, namely by insertion of a hydrophobic amino acid between base steps from the minor groove side. Specific to preB- and T-cells, LEF-1 plays a requisite structural role in the formation of several multiprotein-DNA complexes, the best characterized of which is the T-cell receptor α (TCRα) gene enhancer (12, 13). Therein, LEF-1 occupies a centrally located site flanked by binding sites for at least three other transcription factors: downstream of LEF-1 the lymphoid specific transcription factors PEBP2 and ETS1 occupy adjacent and phased binding sites, and upstream of LEF-1 is an ATF/CREB binding site. ATF/CREB has been shown to stabilize the ternary nucleoprotein complex containing PEBP2 and ETS1 and to interact with PEBP2 in vitro. Moreover, mutations in the TCRα enhancer that alter the relative spatial relationship of any of these proteins impair enhancer function. These findings are consistent with the formation of a multiprotein-DNA complex mediated by DNA bending by LEF-1. The male sex-determining factor SRY likely plays an analogous role in transcriptional activation of the genes important in sexual development such as the Müllerian inhibiting substance (MIS) gene, whose product accounts for the regression of the female Müllerian ducts in male embryos (14, 60). Mutations in SRY are responsible for 15% of male to female sex reversal (46XY females).

SRY   The structure of a complex of the 78 amino acid HMG box domain of SRY (referred to as SRY below) with a DNA octamer comprising its target site in the *MIS* promoter (Table 1) has been solved by NMR (59). SRY has a twisted L shape that comprises irregular N- and C-terminal strands that lie adjacent to one another and three α helices (Figure 1). The long arm of the L is formed by helix 3 and the N- and C-terminal strands, and the short arm of the L is formed by helices 1 and 2. Orientation of the helices is maintained by three concentrated regions of hydrophobic packing located at the center of the long arm, the tip of the short arm, and the corner of the L. The minor groove binding surface consists of helices 1 and 3, and is bordered at the bottom by a ridge comprising helix 2 and at the top by a ridge comprising the opposing terminal strands. Providing another example of induced fit, the *MIS* sequence is significantly distorted upon SRY binding [NMR studies show the free *MIS* DNA to be essentially B-form (57)] to yield a widened and shallow minor groove whose convex surface is molded perfectly to the concave binding surface of SRY.

Numerous hydrophobic and electrostatic interactions contribute to the severe DNA distortion in the SRY complex, with the most apparent deformations located near the center of the octamer at basepairs 5 and 6, and at the bottom of the octamer at base steps 2 and 3 (Figure 4). At the center, Met9, Phe12, Ile13 and Trp43 form a hydrophobic wedge that is anchored to basepairs 4 and 5 by electrostatic interactions involving Asn10 (Figure 4b). At the center of the wedge Phe12, which is positioned orthogonally to the bases of the minor groove, and the intercalating Ile13 both interact with the bases to induce a large bend toward the major groove, while Met9 and Trp 43 on the outer sides of the wedge contact the ribose rings to pry open the minor groove. The bend at base steps 2 and 3 occurs as Tyr74 packs against A3 and T14, anchoring SRY to the top of the DNA (Figure 4a); and Ile35 contacts base pairs 7 and 8 to anchor SRY to the bottom of the DNA (Figure 4c). The sidechains of an additional seven basic residues make electrostatic contacts with the phosphodeoxyribose backbone to provide an extensive scaffold for DNA recognition (Figure 2b).

Upon binding to SRY, profound structural changes are induced in the *MIS* DNA as it leaves the essentially B-form conformation to take on structural features comparable to those of A-DNA; indeed, the rms difference between the SRY-bound DNA and classical A-DNA is 2.4 Å as compared to an rms difference of 4.2 Å to classical B-DNA. The minor groove is significantly expanded in the complex as revealed by the average width of 9.4 Å; and the DNA is underwound exhibiting an average interbase helical twist of 26° ± 6°, and an average interbase pair rise of 4.1 ± 0.3 Å, which exceeds that seen in both A-DNA (3.4 Å) and B-DNA (3.6 Å). Six of the seven base steps display positive roll angles, ranging from 10.5° between base pairs 7 and 8 to a maximum of 35° between base pairs 2 and 3, to produce an overall bend angle of ~70°–80°,

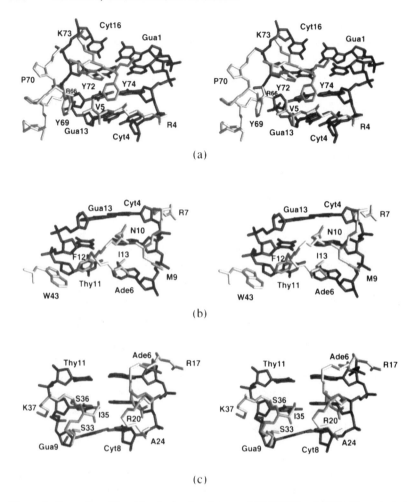

Figure 4 Stereoviews illustrating interactions between hSRY-HMG and DNA. These include (*a*) sidechains at the C-terminal end of helix 3 and the C-terminal and N-terminal strands; (*b*) the clustering of hydrophobic residues at the center of the octamer with partial intercalation of Ile13; (*c*) sidechains from helices 1 and 2 near the 3′ end of the coding strand of DNA.

and all but two of the ribose rings exhibit sugar puckers indicative of A-DNA (O1′-endo to C3′-endo).

LEF-1   The NMR structure of LEF-1 complexed to a 15 bp oligonucleotide from the TCRα enhancer (Table 1) is very similar to that of the SRY complex (30). LEF-1 exhibits the twisted L shape of the minor-groove binding HMG domains, and the wide and shallow DNA is bent by ∼117° toward the major groove. LEF-1 uses a methionine (Met10) residue rather than an isoleucine for intercalation, which is stabilized by hydrophobic contacts from Phe9 and Met12 to nearby bases. An additional difference between the two structures is seen in the length and interactions of the C-terminal strands where the construct used in the LEF-1 structure contains five additional amino acids, four of which are lysines. Thus, the C-terminal tail extends across the compressed major groove to make electrostatic contacts to the phosphate backbone of the DNA from the major groove side. These additional contacts may account for the larger bend angle seen in the LEF-1 complex.

Integration Host Factor

Integration host factor (IHF) is a prokaryotic architectural protein that takes DNA bending to a new extreme: IHF causes the DNA to adopt a U-turn (39). The biological roles in which IHF has been implicated are numerous and varied, but the best characterized is its role in site-specific recombination in bacteriophage λ (16, 31). In this system, several specific IHF binding sites occur near the phage attachment (*att*) sites, which participate either in integrative recombination or excisive recombination. IHF comes into play because its main function is to bend the DNA so as to bring into proximity the distant promoter binding sites of the heterobivalent λ integrase. Indicative of IHF's role as a classical architectural protein, λ recombination can occur when IHF's binding sites are replaced by intrinsically curved DNA or by binding sites of other architectural proteins that also serve to bend DNA (48). Specifically, recombination has been demonstrated where IHF was replaced with the closely related nonspecific DNA-binding protein HU, the otherwise unrelated architectural proteins HMG-1 and HMG-2, and the eukaryotic histone dimer H2A-H2B.

Interestingly, IHF appears to play a dual role in the initiation of replication: Besides its defined structural role, IHF acts as a regulatory protein in concert with FIS [factor for stimulation of inversion (5)], another site-specific DNA-bending protein. In a more traditional sense, IHF can function as a transcriptional activator or a repressor, and repression can occur via two different mechanisms: Namely, IHF can stabilize binding of a given repressor (1) or it can occlude binding of an activator by directly occupying its specific binding site. Thus, IHF's multifaceted role arises from its ability to bind sequences specifically as well as to bend DNA.

IHF is a heterodimeric protein composed of two ∼10 kDa homologous subunits referred to as α and β. The two subunits intertwine to produce a unique protein fold that resembles a body with two long arms reaching out to wrap around the DNA (Figure 1). The bottom of the body is made up of two helices per subunit that are packed orthogonally against their equivalent in the second subunit, and the top of the body is formed by a third short helix and two antiparallel β-sheets from each subunit. Extending away from the top of the body are the two arms, each comprised of two antiparallel β-sheets. Together, the β-sheets of the top of the body and the arms reach out to "embrace" the DNA, continuously following the minor groove so that binding occurs concomitantly on opposite faces of the DNA.

The crystal structure of IHF complexed to a 35 bp oligonucleotide from the H′ site of phage λ (Table 1) shows that the DNA is bent by ~160° (Figure 1). Although the overall structure of the complex appears to be symmetrical, the opposing DNA and protein sequences and their detailed interactions are asymmetrical. Like other IHF consensus binding sites, the H′ site contains three characteristic sequences, namely two conserved elements, 5′-TATCAA-3′ and 5′-TTG-3′, and a 6-bp A-tract. The center of the U-turn is positioned at the 5′ end of the TATCAA consensus site, and the dA/dT-rich sequence and the TTG consensus are located one helical turn 5′ and 3′ to the start of the TATCAA element, respectively. Together, the contacts between the DNA and the arms and body of the protein bury in excess of 4500 Å^2 of surface area accessible to solvent in the uncomplexed molecules.

Analogous to TBP, SRY, and LEF-1, IHF employs two hydrophobic residues, in this case Pro65α and Pro64β, located at the tips of opposing arms, to introduce substantial bends in the DNA. These proline residues, which are absolutely conserved among all members of the IHF and HU families, intercalate between base steps separated by nine basepairs making extensive hydrophobic contact with the DNA bases (Figures 2d, 5a).

In addition, hydrogen bonds between the prolines and N3 of both adenines 5′ to the kinks are observed. The only other hydrophobic interactions occur between hydrophobic sidechains and deoxyribose rings, as opposed to minor groove bases. These involve contacts between the pseudosymmetrically displaced Ile71α/Val70β and Ile73α/Leu72β, and deoxyribose rings nearby the kinks, and contacts from Pro61α to the sugar of T-34. In the crystal structure, the α arm of IHF (Figure 5a) reaches deep into the minor groove of the consensus sequence 5′-TATCAA-3′ as the aliphatic protons of Arg63α and Arg60α pack against basepairs 34–37 and the backbone and sidechains make hydrogen bonds to the same basepairs. On each side of the complex, the N-terminus of helix 1 and the β1β2 loop of one subunit join with the N-terminus of helix 3 of the second subunit to form a "clamp" rich with electrostatic contacts to the DNA backbone. At the tip of the β1β2 loops, Ser47α and Arg46β insert into the minor groove on the left (Figure 5b) and right (Figure 5c) sides of the complex, respectively. The backbone of helices 1 and 3, located below and above the β1β2 loop, contact phosphates located on opposite sides of the minor groove. In addition to the intermolecular interactions centered around the tips of the arms and the sides of the body of the protein, numerous positively charged sidechains contact the phosphate backbone of the DNA, contributing to the overall bend.

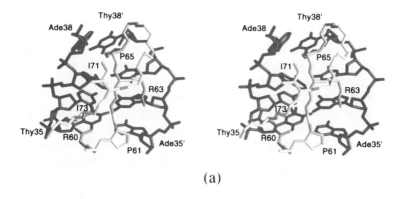

(a)

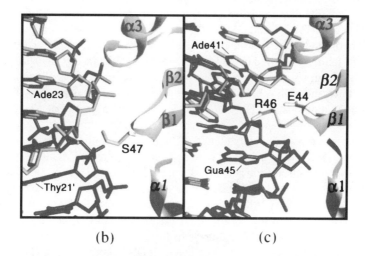

(b)   (c)

Figure 5   (*a*) Stereoview illustrating contacts between the α arm of IHF and the first DNA consensus sequence 5'-TATCAA-3' (T33-A38); (*b*) closeup of the left side of the protein body contacting the A-tract (A19-A24); (*c*) closeup of the right side of the protein body contacting the second DNA consensus sequence T43-T44-G45 [adapted from (39)]. Labels for the α-helices and β-strands of IHFβ are italicized.

The arrangement of protein-DNA interactions seen in the IHF complex, in combination with DNA sequences that are susceptible to deformation, introduce an alternating and phased pattern in the DNA parameters, most notably in the minor groove width (39) (Figure 1). The intercalating prolines introduce short stretches of very wide minor grooves (>10 Å) located approximately one helical turn apart at the top corners of the bent DNA. These are in turn evenly interspersed with three distinct regions of narrowed minor groove, each of which is separated by one helical turn (~10 basepairs), and thus located at the center and sides of the inside of the DNA bend. Thus, the minor groove incorporating the three consensus elements alternates between narrow and wide every half helical turn, and the three sites possessing the narrowest minor grooves are positioned to contact the top and sides of the compact body of the protein. This arrangement accommodates the abundance of direct and water-mediated electrostatic interactions between the body of the protein and the narrow minor grooves. The DNA conformation returns to B-form just outside of the first and last consensus elements. The kink introduced by the prolines is characterized by an unprecedented 57° roll angle, and the widened minor groove surrounding the kinks continues 2 to 3 base steps in either direction. The regions of narrowed minor grooves range from ~2.5–3.5 Å in width.

High Mobility Group Protein I(Y)

The high mobility group I (HMG I) family of proteins, which includes HMG I, its isoform HMG Y, and HMG I-C, are non-histone chromosomal proteins that are entirely distinct from the other HMG box HMG 1/2 family and the HMG 14/17 family (reviewed in 4). Members of the HMG I family are basic proteins ~10 kDa in size that consist of a variable N-terminus, an acidic C-terminus, and three short DNA binding domains (DBDs) that are separated by linkers of 11 to 23 amino acids. HMG I(Y) binds to the minor groove of AT-tracts with nanomolar affinity and appears to use two DBDs for binding, which explains the recurrence of two helically phased AT-tracts in naturally occurring enhancers. Analogous to the architectural proteins described above, HMG I(Y) alone does not activate transcription but plays a critical architectural role in the assembly of enhanceosomes on what appears to be a growing number of cytokine and viral genes (10, 22, 55). Further, HMG I(Y) has been shown to interact directly with transcriptional activators of the Rel, bZIP, ETS, and POU families, stabilizing their binding to DNA. In contrast to the previously described architectural proteins, HMG I does not induce bends in DNA, but instead acts to preserve the B-form character of DNA, and can actually reverse moderate bends in DNA (9). The role of HMG I in facilitating the assembly of a large nucleoprotein structure has been best characterized for the complex, yet compact (~70 bps, all of which are essential for viral induction) interferon β gene enhancer in which HMG I helps to recruit the transcriptional activators NFkB, ATF2/cJun and IRF (55).

The NMR structure of a truncated form of HMG I (residues 50–91) that contains DBDs 2 and 3 complexed to two equivalents of a dodecamer comprising the PRD2 site of the IFN β gene enhancer revealed two distinct DNA binding motifs (21). The high affinity DBD2 (Figure 1) consists of three modular components comprising the extended Arg-Gly-Arg core sequence that inserts deep into the

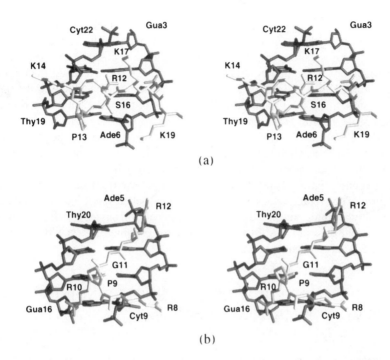

(a)

(b)

Figure 6   Stereoview illustrating contacts between the high-affinity binding domain DBD2 of HMG I(Y) and (*a*) the 5′ end of the AT-tract, and (*b*) the 3′ end of the AT-tract of PRDII in the IFN β enhancer.

minor groove, a pair of lysine and arginine residues that flank the core and make hydrophobic and electrostatic interactions to the sugar-phosphate back-bone, and a polar network of six amino acids C-terminal to the basic core. The four residues directly following the Arg-Gly-Arg core (Pro13, Lys14, Gly15, and Ser16) form a type II β-turn that effectively bridges the minor groove, and the remaining three residues clamp around the lower strand of the DNA using polar and nonpolar contacts (Figure 6*b*). The lower affinity DBDs 1 and 3 (not shown) lack the additional six amino acids, which accounts for their ~100-fold decrease in DNA binding affinity.

The high affinity DNA-binding motif (DBD2) of HMG I is remarkable in that it contains only 13 amino acids that upon DNA binding undergo a conformation change from a random coil (as shown by NMR studies of free HMG I) to a fully structured motif in which every amino acid, with the exception of one proline, contacts the DNA (Figure 2*e*). The Arg-Gly-Arg core lies deep in the minor groove, with the glycine centered between base pairs 6 and 7 and the arginine sidechains extending in either direction along the floor of the minor groove such that every H2 atom of the adenines is encountered by either Arg10 or Arg12 (Figures 2e, 6a, 6b). The guanidinium groups of Arg10 and Arg12 are hydrogen-bonded to the O_2 atoms of C9 and T21, respectively. At the top of the β-turn, Lys14 and Gly15 contact the phosphoribose backbone of the top DNA strand, and Pro13 and Ser16 of the sides of the turn contact the ribose rings of the bottom DNA strand at T7 and A6, respectively (Figure 6a). The backbone of the final three amino acids is oriented orthogonal to the DNA axis and the sidechains extend across the groove again to contact the sugar-phosphate backbone on both sides of the minor groove (Figures 2e, 6a).

The conformation of the PRD2 dodecamer complexed to HMG I is essentially B-form. The average values of 3.6 Å for the local helical rise, 35.6° for the local helical twist angle, and ~1° for the inter-base pair roll angles are all indicative of classical B-form DNA. In addition, the average minor groove width is only ~1–1.5 Å larger than that seen in B-DNA.

FACTORS CONTRIBUTING TO SPECIFIC BINDING AND CONFORMATIONAL CHANGES

Recognition

In contrast to transcriptional activating factors that tend to recognize very specific DNA sequences and features of the major groove, the minor groove architectural proteins are faced with the problem of specific recognition in the barren minor groove (47). Following the determination of the structures of five architectural proteins bound to their DNA targets, it is becoming clear that several strategies are used for recognition and alteration of DNA conformation. These include exploitation of sequence-dependent DNA deformability, recognition of narrower than usual minor grooves, and asymmetric charge neutralization along the sugar-phosphate backbone (50). Of those proteins described above that induce extreme bends, partial insertion or intercalation of hydrophobic residues imparts large positive roll angles (i.e. toward the major groove) that contribute greatly to the overall bending of the DNA (58). Thus far, insertion of these residues occurs at YR or RR/YY steps (where "R" stands for purine and "Y" for pyrimidine) which have been shown in naked duplex DNA to be either inherently bent or subject to deformations (15, 51). In the case of TBP, the phenylalanines of the C-terminal domain insert between the poorly stacked and easily distortable T1-A2 step of the TATA box and impart a greater positive roll angle than is seen at the Y7-Y8 step at the opposite end of the 8 bp TATA element. In SRY, Ile13 is inserted at the RR step A5-A6. Although the RR/YY steps do not appear to be as readily distortable as the YR steps, they still display large deviations in parameters basic to DNA bending, namely roll angle and degree of twist (53). The most obvious differences between YR and RR/YY steps is the degree of base stacking, and for AA/TT sequences the relative positions of the thymine methyl groups. Thus, it follows that in cases where positive roll angles at AA/TT steps are large enough to disrupt base stacking and impose steric clash among the thymine methyls, these energetically costly transformations must be compensated for by the more complete packing or pi-pi interactions that can occur among the sidechains inserted between sequential and similar bases than among alternating (YR or RY) base steps.

Both HMG I(Y) and parts of IHF bind to B-form AT-rich DNA. In the case of HMG I(Y), the crescent formed by the extended Arg-Gly-Arg sequence inserts deeply into, and runs along the floor of, the minor groove, taking advantage of the lack of irregular YR steps. In the case of IHF, the top and both sides of the body of the protein interact with the three regions of unusually narrow minor grooves. Clearly, in two of these interactions, namely at the A-tract and the center of the DNA, the narrow minor grooves are important for recognition considering that binding occurs through water-mediated contacts with the minor groove spine of hydration that persists upon binding. Because IHF induces a nearly 180° turn in its bound DNA, it is only appropriate that this protein should use all three strategies for deformation: The body of IHF is positively charged and lies on the inside of the bent DNA to neutralize the phosphate backbone and contribute to the overall bend.

Specific and Directional Binding

With each new structure of a protein-DNA complex comes the question of how a particular protein recognizes a specific DNA sequence. In the case of TBP, IHF, and HMG I, yet another complexity arises resulting from the fact that each of these proteins uses pseudo-symmetric motifs to interact with DNA. Moreover, they are capable of recognizing more than one sequence while still conserving directional binding. Several thoughtful analyses of TBP-TATA box recognition have appeared recently and provide insight into the role that protein and DNA structure and sequence-specific deformability play in influencing directional binding. In a revealing study by Suzuki et al (52), the coordinates of a cocrystal structure were duplicated and one of the identical structures was rotated 180° about the pseudo-dyad. The resulting oppositely oriented molecules were best fit to β-strands 1 and α-helices 2 located at the center of the dimer. [This exercise was performed for both the Sigler (26) and Burley (25) structures.] These models clearly show that in both structures the β-sheet of the C-terminal domains, which bind to the 5'-TATA-containing side of the DNA, display greater curvature and thus approach more closely to the DNA than the β-sheet of the N-terminal domains which bind to the 3'-A–rich half of the DNA. In turn, the

5'-TATA ends of the DNA display greater curvature and compression of the major groove than the 3'-A–rich sequence. A residue-by-residue comparison of the two protein domains reveals that for the β-sheet residues directed away from the DNA, those in the C-terminal domain are larger than those in the N-terminal domain. [This finding holds true for the uncomplexed TBP structures as well, indicating that the greater curvature is inherent in TBP itself. (6, 33)] Increased curvature of the protein backbone away from the protein interior on the C-terminal side alleviates the greater steric crowding and coincidentally increases curvature toward the DNA. Conveniently, the 5'-TATA side of the DNA can accommodate the increased curvature of the C-terminal domain better than the 3'-A tract because it contains alternating thymines and adenines that do not have to contend with steric clash between the methyls of the thymines in the major groove. Indeed, measurement of the distances between methyls of the A-rich side show that they are at the limit of major groove compression. Also contributing to the greater curvature of the C-terminal side of TBP is the strictly conserved and asymmetrically-positioned proline toward the end of helix two, which causes a slight helical bend directed toward the underlying saddle. In addition to the asymmetric and complimentary curvatures of the protein and DNA, Dickerson and coworkers (23) have noted that a single proline (191y/149a) that packs against the 3' side of A1' may be largely responsible for the preference for T over A as the first site, considering that substitution to AT would introduce unfavorable interactions between atoms of the proline ring and the C2 oxygen of thymine.

It had been proposed that asymmetrical charge distribution might play a role in orienting TBP on the DNA (26). However, Kim and Burley (24) noticed that any considerable asymmetry in charge distribution that would affect DNA binding is limited to the stirrups where Arg55y and Arg56y in the C-terminal domain are replaced by Glu144y and Glu146y in the N-terminal domain. With the exception of Arg56, the sidechains of these residues are directed away from the DNA and probably do not appreciably affect binding polarity. This view was substantiated by the ternary crystal structure of TBP/TFIIB/TATA element that shows Glu144 and Glu146 to be hydrogen bonded to TFIIB residues rather than interacting with the DNA (35). [More recently the ternary crystal structure of a complex comprising an archaeal protein homologous to TBP that recognizes so-called box A motifs, a TFIIB homolog, and a box A DNA target has been solved (27); in this case, charge distributions distinct from those seen in eukaryotic TBPs play a strong role in orientation (8, 27).]

HMG I functions differently from the pseudo-symmetrical DNA-bending proteins TBP and IHF because it stabilizes B-form DNA and can actually reverse moderate bends (9). The core DNA-binding motif of HMG I comprises the palindromic sequence Pro-Arg-Gly-Arg-Pro, which binds to AT-rich sequences, preferably of 5 or 6 base pairs in length. The solution structures of the high- and low-affinity domains of HMG I bound to the sequence 5'-GGGAAATTCCTC-3' showed that both domains are oriented in a single direction (21). Arg10 is in close contact with the H2 atoms of A17 and A18 on the left strand of the DNA, while Arg12 contacts the H2 atoms of A5 and A6 on the opposite strand (Figure 6a). Thus, the extended concave surface of Arg-Gly-Arg inserts deeply into the minor groove and runs parallel with the right handedness of it. If the orientation were reversed, there would be steric clash with the O_2 atoms of the complementary thymine. In regard to specificity, the sequence 5'-AAATT-3' of the PRD II element lacks any disruptive YR steps, and the structure of HMG I complexed to DNA shows that the narrower and more regular the minor groove is, the more extensive are the van der Waals contacts. The contacts will be further augmented by the sequences AAa/tT or AAa/ta/tT, which place the H2 atoms on opposing strands as far apart as possible; that is, they run with the floor of the minor groove. If the DNA sequence were reversed, for example to TTTAA, the H_2 atoms would be positioned more closely atop one another, that is, running more perpendicular to the floor of the groove, which would preclude the extensive van der Waals contacts seen in the structure by virtue of a decreased distance and steric hindrance of the O_2 atoms of the thymines. Further, the sequence would also include an RY (in this case TA) step, which would likely disrupt the straight and narrow groove of the DNA.

HMG I has been reported to be a non-specific binder of AT-rich sequences. It remains possible that it can bind to the less favorable TTAA-containing sequences, given the flexibility of the Arg-Gly-Arg motif and the availability of two more binding motifs that can be used to enhance the overall DNA-binding affinity. We may also find that the orientation is affected in the presence of interactions with other transcriptional activators.

As with TBP and HMG I, the pseudosymmetrical IHF binds in a directional manner. However, compared to TBP and HMG I, IHF is considerably less symmetrical in both protein and DNA sequence at the sites of intermolecular contacts. There are four main areas of protein-DNA interaction in the cocrystal structure of IHF: These include the two sides of the protein body interacting with the narrowed minor grooves on the left and right side of the DNA and the two arms reaching into the upper left and right curves of the U-turn (Figures 5a–c). Further, the top of the protein body and the center of the DNA are connected by a matrix of ordered water molecules that originates as the spine of hydration in the narrowed minor groove of this region. The two conserved consensus sequences are conveniently located on the 3' or right half of the DNA such that together they likely direct the orientation of IHF on the DNA. Given the degree of bending and the extent of complementary surfaces, direct contacts between IHF and the edges of the DNA bases are scant, but a closer look at the interactions about the consensus sequences offers some explanation for specificity and recognition. On the right side of the complex at the second DNA consensus sequence, Arg46β is rigidly positioned, through the support of salt bridges with proximal sidechains, in the center of the groove between basepair steps T-A 44 and G-C 45 (Figure 5c). Arg46β thus contacts the deoxyribose rings on the top and bottom strands of the DNA. Rice et al (38, 39) note that at this site the two sides differ. On the consensus side, helix 1 of the α subunit is recessed toward the body of the protein, and this gap conveniently accommodates the protruding phosphate backbone that results from the over-twisted and slightly kinked YR step T44-G45. On the left side, the A-tract produces a uniform and narrow groove that maintains a spine of hydration through which the protein contacts the DNA indirectly (Figure 5b). This feature could account for the relaxed specificity observed for this site.

The interactions between the arms of IHF and DNA differ in that the α arm, which interacts with the first DNA consensus site, sits more deeply in the minor groove than the β arm. The most obvious differences in the two sides are that Arg60α and Arg63α make direct contacts to conserved bases, while their equivalents in the β arm, Arg59β and Arg62β, do not directly contact the DNA (Figure 2e). This discrepancy may be real or it may be an artifact of the complex as the DNA is nicked between T29 and G30, and non-Watson-Crick base pairing results as the surrounding bases are involved in crystal packing.

CONCLUSIONS

The structures of the five architectural proteins reviewed above have given us an integral view of the variety of ways proteins recognize and remodel DNA conformation purely through intermolecular interactions occurring in the minor groove. All of these proteins play crucial roles in the assembly of very large protein-DNA complexes, such as the intasome (40) or enhanceosome (55), that are necessary for carrying out myriad cellular processes. While the vast majority of "non-architectural" proteins bind to the major groove of DNA, most of the architectural proteins interact with the minor groove, and their precisely spaced binding sites coupled with the degree of bending (or unbending) allows for the controlled assembly of these macromolecular complexes (56).

Just as the initial structures of TBP in complex with TATA elements led the way for larger ternary complexes (11, 35, 54), we can expect the same progression for the other architectural factors as we await ternary (or larger) structures involving IHF, LEF-1, SRY, and HMG I(Y). On the other hand, we still look forward to seeing high-resolution structures of protein-DNA complexes for those architectural proteins that recognize specific DNA structures, such as members of the HMG 1/2 family that bind to prebent or cruciform DNA, and proteins involved in chromatin structure. With the continuing advances in stably modifying DNA structure, whether it be through covalent modifications to force specific degrees of bends (61, 62), or through methods to stabilize particular conformation such as the cruciforms basic to recombination (29, 46), we can anticipate structures for these nonspecific binders as well.

ACKNOWLEDGMENTS

GMC and AMG acknowledge the support of the AIDS Targeted Antiviral Program of the Office of the Director of the National Institutes of Health for experimental work in the authors' laboratory. CAB acknowledges a Cancer Research Institute Postdoctoral Fellowship.

> Visit the *Annual Reviews home page* at
> http://www.AnnualReviews.org.

Literature Cited

1. Betermier M, Rousseau P, Alazard R, Chandler M. 1995. Mutual stabilization of bacteriophage Mu repressor and histone-like proteins in a nucleoprotein structure. *J. Mol. Biol.* 249:332–41
2. Buratowski S, Hahn S, Guarente L, Sharp PA. 1989. Isolation of the gene encoding the yeast TATA binding protein TFIID— a gene identical to the spt15 suppressor of ty element insertions. *Proc. Natl. Acad. Sci. USA* 86:5718–22
3. Burley SK, Roeder RG. 1996. Biochemistry and structural biology of transcription factor IID (TFIID). *Annu. Rev. Biochem.* 65:769–99
4. Bustin M, Reeves R. 1996. High-mobility-group chromosomal proteins: architectural components that facilitate chromatin function. *Prog. Nucleic Acid Res. Mol. Biol.* 54:35–100
5. Cassler MR, Grimwade JE, Leonard AC. 1995. Cell cycle-specific changes in nucleoprotein complexes at a chromosomal replication origin. *EMBO J.* 14:5833–41
6. Chasman DI, Flaherty KM, Sharp PA, Kornberg RD. 1993. Crystal structure of yeast TATA-binding protein and model for interaction with DNA. *Proc. Natl. Acad. Sci. USA* 90:8174–78
7. Cormack BP, Struhl K. 1992. The TATA-binding protein is required for transcription by all three nuclear RNA polymerases in yeast cells. *Cell* 69:685–96
8. DeDecker BS, O'Brien R, Fleming PJ, Geiger JH, Jackson SP, et al. 1996. The crystal structure of a hyperthermophilic ar-

chaeal TATA-box binding protein. *J. Mol. Biol.* 264:1072–84
9. Falvo JV, Thanos D, Maniatis T. 1995. Reversal of intrinsic DNA bends in the IFN beta gene enhancer by transcription factors and the architectural protein HMG I(Y). *Cell* 83:1101–11
10. Farnet CM, Bushman FD. 1997. HIV-1 cDNA integration: requirement of HMG I(Y) protein for function of preintegration complexes in vitro. *Cell* 88:483–92
11. Geiger JH, Hahn S, Lee S, Sigler PB. 1996. Crystal structure of the yeast TFIIA/TBP/DNA complex. *Science* 272: 830–36
12. Giese K, Kingsley C, Kirshner JR, Grosschedl R. 1995. Assembly and function of a TCR alpha enhancer complex is dependent on LEF-1-induced DNA bending and multiple protein-protein interactions. *Genes Dev.* 9:995–1008
13. Giese K, Pagel J, Grosschedl R. 1994. Distinct DNA-binding properties of the high mobility group domain of murine and human SRY sex-determining factors. *Proc. Natl. Acad. Sci. USA* 91:3368–72
14. Goodfellow PN, Lovell-Badge R. 1993. SRY and sex determination in mammals. *Annu. Rev. Genet.* 27:71–92
15. Goodsell DS, Kaczor GM, Dickerson RE. 1994. The crystal structure of C-C-A-T-T-A-A-T-G-G. Implications for bending of B-DNA at T-A steps. *J. Mol. Biol.* 239:79–96
16. Goosen N, van de Putte P. 1996. The regulation of transcription initiation by integra-

tion host factor. *Mol. Microbiol.* 6:2557–63

17. Grosschedl R. 1995. Higher-order nucleoprotein complexes in transcription: analogies with site-specific recombination. *Curr. Opin. Cell Biol.* 7:362–70

18. Grosschedl R, Giese K, Pagel J. 1994. HMG domain proteins: architectural elements in the assembly of nucleoprotein structures. *Trends Genet.* 10:94–100

19. Hernandez N. 1993. TBP, a universal transcription factor? *Genes Dev.* 7:1291–1308

20. Hoffmann A, Sinn E, Yamamoto T, Wang J. 1990. Highly conserved core domain and unique N-terminus with presumptive regulatory motifs in a human TATA factor (TFIID). *Nature* 346:387–90

21. Huth JR, Bewley CA, Nissen MS, Evans JN, Reeves R, et al. 1997. The solution structure of an HMG-I(Y)-DNA complex defines a new architectural minor groove binding motif. *Nat. Struct. Biol.* 4:957–65

22. John S, Reeves RB, Lin JX, Child R, Leiden JM, et al. 1995. Regulation of cell-type-specific interleukin-2 receptor alpha-chain gene expression: potential role of physical interactions between Elf-1, HMG-I(Y), and NF-kappa B family proteins. *Mol. Cell Biol.* 15:1786–96

23. Juo ZS, Chiu TK, Leiberman PM, Baikalov I, Berk AJ, et al. 1996. How proteins recognize the TATA box. *J. Mol. Biol.* 261:239–54

24. Kim JL, Burley SK. 1994. 1.9 Å resolution refined structure of TBP recognizing the minor groove of TATAAAAG. *Nat. Struct. Biol.* 1:638–53

25. Kim JL, Nikolov DB, Burley SK. 1993. Co-crystal structure of TBP recognizing the minor groove of a TATA element. *Nature* 365:520–27

26. Kim Y, Geiger JH, Hahn S, Sigler PB. 1993. Crystal structure of a yeast TBP/TATA-box complex. *Nature* 365:512–20

27. Kosa PF, Ghosh G, DeDecker BS, Sigler PB. 1997. The 2.1-Å crystal structure of an archaeal preinitiation complex: TATA-box-binding protein/transcription factor (II)B core/TATA-box. *Proc. Natl. Acad. Sci. USA* 94:6042–47

28. Lewis M, Chang G, Horton NC, Kercher MA, Pace HC, et al. 1996. Crystal structure of the lactose operon repressor and its complexes with DNA and inducer. *Science* 271:1247–54

29. Lilley DMJ, Clegg RM. 1993. The structure of branched DNA species. *Q. Rev. Biophys.* 26:131–75

30. Love JJ, Li X, Case DA, Giese K, Grosschedl R, et al. 1995. Structural basis for DNA bending by the architectural transcription factor LEF-1. *Nature* 376:791–95

31. Nash H. 1996. The HU and IHF proteins: accessory factors for complex protein-DNA assemblies. In *Regulation of Gene Expression in* Escherichia coli, ed. ECC Lin, AS Lynch, pp. 149–79. Austin, TX: RG Landes

32. Nicholls AJ, Sharp K, Honig B. 1991. Protein folding and associations: insight from interfacial and thermodynamic properties of hydrocarbons. *Proteins: Struct. Func. Genet.* 11:281–96

33. Nikolov DB, Burley SK. 1994. 2.1-Å resolution refined structure of a TATA box-binding protein (TBP). *Nat. Struct. Biol.* 1:621–37

34. Nikolov DB, Chen H, Halay ED, Hoffman A, Roeder RG, et al. 1996. Crystal structure of a human TATA box-binding protein/TATA element complex. *Proc. Natl. Acad. Sci. USA* 93:4862–67

35. Nikolov DB, Chen H, Halay ED, Usheva AA, Hisatake K, et al. 1995. Crystal structure of a TFIIB-TBP-TATA-element ternary complex. *Nature* 377:119–28

36. Pabo CO, Sauer RT. 1992. Transcription factors: structural families and principles of DNA recognition. *Annu. Rev. Biochem.* 61:1053–95

37. Peterson MG, Tanese N, Pugh BF, Tjian R. 1990. Functional domains and upstream activation properties of cloned human TATA-binding protein. *Science* 248:1625–30

38. Rice PA. 1997. Making DNA do a U-turn: IHF and related proteins. *Curr. Opin. Struct. Biol.* 7:86–93

39. Rice PA, Yang S, Mizuuchi K, Nash HA. 1996. Crystal structure of an IHF-DNA complex: a protein-induced DNA U-turn. *Cell* 87:1295–1306

40. Richet E, Abcarian P, Nash HA. 1986. The interaction of recombination proteins with supercoiled DNA: defining the role of supercoiling in lambda integrative recombination. *Cell* 46:1011–21

41. Roeder RG. 1991. The complexities of eukaryotic transcription initiation: regulation of preinitiation complex assembly. *Trends Biochem. Sci.* 16:402–8

42. Saenger W. 1983. *Principles of Nucleic Acid Structure*, ed. CR Cantor. New York: Springer-Verlag. 556 pp.

43. Sawadogo M, Sentenac A. 1990. RNA polymerase B (II) and general transcription factors. *Annu. Rev. Biochem.* 59:711–54

44. Schultz SC, Shields GC, Steitz TA. 1991. Crystal structure of a CAP-DNA complex: the DNA is bent by 90 degrees. *Science* 253:1001–7

45. Schumacher MA, Choi KY, Zalkin H, Brennan RG. 1994. Crystal structure of LacI member, PurR, bound to DNA: minor groove binding by alpha helices. *Science* 266:763–70

46. Seeman NC, Kallenbach NR. 1994. DNA branched junctions. *Annu. Rev. Biophys. Biomol. Struct.* 23:53–86

47. Seeman NC, Rosenberg JM, Rich A. 1976. Sequence-specific recognition of double helical nucleic acids by proteins. *Proc. Natl. Acad. Sci. USA* 73:804–8

48. Segall AM, Goodman SD, Nash HA. 1994. Architectural elements in nucleoprotein complexes: interchangeability of specific and non-specific DNA binding proteins. *EMBO J.* 13:4536–48

49. Steitz TA. 1990. Structural studies of protein-nucleic acid interaction. *Q. Rev. Biophys.* 23:205–80

50. Strauss JK, Maher LJ III. 1994. DNA bending by asymmetric phosphate neutralization. *Science* 266:1829–34

51. Suzuki M, Allen MD, Yagi N, Finch JT. 1996. Analysis of co-crystal structures to identify the stereochemical determinants of the orientation of TBP on the TATA box. *Nucleic Acids Res.* 24:2767–73

52. Suzuki M, Yagi N. 1995. Stereochemical basis of DNA bending by transcription factors. *Nucleic Acids Res.* 23:2083–91

53. Suzuki M, Yagi N, Finch JT. 1996. Role of base-backbone and base-base interactions in alternating DNA conformations. *FEBS Lett.* 379:148–52

54. Tan S, Hunziker Y, Sargent DF, Richmond TJ. 1996. Crystal structure of a yeast TFIIA/TBP/DNA complex. *Nature* 381:127–51

55. Thanos D, Maniatis T. 1995. Virus induction of human IFN beta gene expression requires the assembly of an enhanceosome. *Cell* 83:1091–1100

56. Tjian R, Maniatis T. 1994. Transcriptional activation: a complex puzzle with few easy pieces. *Cell* 77:5–8

57. Werner MH, Bianchi ME, Gronenborn AM, Clore GM. 1995. NMR spectroscopic analysis of the DNA conformation induced by the human testis determining factor SRY. *Biochemistry* 34:11998–12004

58. Werner MH, Gronenborn AM, Clore GM. 1996. Intercalation, DNA kinking, and the control of transcription. *Science* 271:778–84

59. Werner MH, Huth JR, Gronenborn AM, Clore GM. 1995. Molecular basis of human 46X,Y sex reversal revealed from the three-dimensional solution structure of the human SRY-DNA complex. *Cell* 81:705–14

60. Werner MH, Huth JR, Gronenborn AM, Clore GM. 1996. Molecular determinants of mammmalian sex. *Trends Biochem. Sci.* 21:302–8

61. Wolfe SA, Ferentz AE, Grantcharova V, Churchill MEA, Verdine GL. 1995. Modifying the helical structure of DNA by design: recruitment of an architecture-specific protein to an enforced DNA bend. *Chem. Biol.* 2:213–21

62. Wolfe SA, Verdine GL. 1993. Ratcheting torsional stress in duplex DNA. *J. Am. Chem. Soc.* 115:12585–86

63. Yamamoto T, Horikoshi M, Wang J, Hasegawa S, Weil PA, et al. 1992. A bipartite DNA binding domain composed of direct repeats in the TATA box binding factor TFIID. *Proc. Natl. Acad. Sci. USA* 89:2844–48

Annu. Rev. Biophys. Biomol. Struct. 1998. 27:133–64
Copyright © 1998 by Annual Reviews Inc. All rights reserved

THE STRUCTURE AND MECHANISM OF PROTEIN PHOSPHATASES: Insights into Catalysis and Regulation

David Barford, Amit K. Das, and Marie-Pierre Egloff
Laboratory of Molecular Biophysics, University of Oxford, Oxford, OX1 3QU,
United Kingdom; e-mail: davidb@biop.ox.ac.uk

KEY WORDS: protein Ser/Thr phosphatases, protein tyrosine phosphatases, protein
              phosphorylation, signal transduction, metalloenzymes

---

ABSTRACT

Eukaryotic protein phosphatases are structurally and functionally diverse enzymes that are represented by three distinct gene families. Two of these, the PPP and PPM families, dephosphorylate phosphoserine and phosphothreonine residues, whereas the protein tyrosine phosphatases (PTPs) dephosphorylate phosphotyrosine amino acids. A subfamily of the PTPs, the dual-specificity phosphatases, dephosphorylate all three phosphoamino acids. Within each family, the catalytic domains are highly conserved, with functional diversity endowed by regulatory domains and subunits. The protein Ser/Thr phosphatases are metalloenzymes and dephosphorylate their substrates in a single reaction step using a metal-activated nucleophilic water molecule. In contrast, the PTPs catalyze dephosphorylation by use of a cysteinyl-phosphate enzyme intermediate. The crystal structures of a number of protein phosphatases have been determined, enabling us to understand their catalytic mechanisms and the basis for substrate recognition and to begin to provide insights into molecular mechanisms of protein phosphatase regulation.

CONTENTS

133

1056-8700/98/0610-0133$08.00

PERSPECTIVES AND OVERVIEW

The regulation of cellular processes in response to external stimuli is fundamental to all living processes. It is now recognized that the reversible phosphorylation of proteins is an essential element of the numerous and varied mechanisms that have evolved to communicate these stimuli across a cell's surface and subsequently to cause changes in the activities and functions of intracellular proteins. Changes in the state of protein phosphorylation are regulated by two types of enzyme activities: those catalyzed by the protein kinases, which covalently attach a phosphate group to an amino acid side chain, and the reverse activity of protein phosphatases.

The attachment or removal of a phosphate group from a protein may have profound effects on that protein's activities and properties. For example, protein phosphorylation allows the regulation of enzymic activities by mediating allosteric conformational changes, or by directly blocking access to enzyme catalytic sites (64, 65). More recently it has been realized that an essential feature of signaling by protein phosphorylation is to modulate the formation of protein-protein interactions, a process that is coordinated by signaling modules such as src-homology domain 2 and phosphotyrosine binding domains, and by 14-3-3 proteins that recognize phosphotyrosine and phosphoserine residues, respectively, within sequence-specific contexts (89).

Nearly all aspects of cell life are regulated by reversible protein phosphorylation. Some examples include metabolic processes, gene regulation, cell cycle control, transport and secretory processes, the organization of the cytoskeleton, and cell adhesion. Reflecting the diversity and breadth of functions regulated by protein phosphorylation, a large proportion of intracellular proteins (30%) are subject to reversible protein phosphorylation, and it is perhaps not surprising that higher eukaryotes encode approximately 2000 and 1000 protein kinase and phosphatase genes, respectively, corresponding to 3% of their genomes (60).

Protein kinases and phosphatases belong to a small number of gene superfamilies, with each member of the gene superfamily being related by divergent evolution. This is a characteristic of most signal transduction proteins. The protein

Table 1 Nomenclature of protein phosphatases

PPP family

Catalytic subunit	Regulatory subunits
PP1c	G_M, G_L, M_{110} + M_{21}, NIPP-1, RIPP-1, R110, p53BP2, L5, sds22, RB gene product, inhibitor-1, DARPP-32, inhibitor-2, splicing factor, kinesin-like protein, γ134.5 (Herpes simplex), R5
PP2Ac	A subunit (PR65) B subunit (PR55, PR72, PR61), eRF1, PTPA, SET, polyoma middle and small T antigens, SV40 small T antigen
PP2B	B-subunit, calmodulin, AKAP-79

Novel protein phosphatases of the PPP family
PPP1:	PPY, Ppz1, Ppz2, Ppq1
PPP2A:	PP4, PP6, PPV 6A, sit4, Ppc1, Ppg1
PPP5:	PP5, RdgC

PPM family

PP2C
Arabidopsis ABI1
Arabidopsis KAPP-1
Pyruvate dehydrogenase phosphatase
Bacillus subtilis SpoIIE phosphatase

Protein–tyrosine phosphatase family

Tyrosine-specific phosphatases
  Cytosolic, nonreceptor forms
    PTP1B, SHP-1, SHP-2
  Receptor-like, transmembrane forms
    CD45, RPTPμ, RPTPα
Dual-specificity phosphatases
  CDC25
  Kinase-associated phosphatase
  MAP kinase phosphatase-1

phosphatases are defined by three structurally distinct gene families (Table 1). The PPP and PPM families encode protein Ser/Thr phosphatases, whereas the protein tyrosine phosphatase (PTP) family includes both tyrosine-specific and dual-specificity phosphatases. Within each superfamily, considerable structural diversity is generated by the attachment of regulatory and targeting domains and/or subunits to the protein catalytic domain. Regulatory subunits and domains serve to localize the protein to particular subcellular localizations and modulate protein specificity, functions that are regulated by allosteric modification using second messengers and reversible protein phosphorylation.

The state of cellular protein phosphorylation at any time is a dynamic process that depends on the activities of protein kinases and protein phosphatases for their appropriate substrates. To understand these overall processes, we need to understand (*a*) the mechanisms by which protein kinases and protein phosphatases recognize their substrates, (*b*) their catalytic mechanisms, (*c*) how these enzymes are targeted to particular subcellular locations, and finally, (*d*) how these three latter processes are regulated. In this review we will describe recent progress made towards understanding these questions in relation to the protein phosphatases at a molecular level.

PROTEIN SERINE/THREONINE PHOSPHATASES OF THE PPP FAMILY

The protein Ser/Thr phosphatases PP1, PP2A, and PP2B of the PPP family, together with PP2C of the PPM family, account for the majority of the protein serine/threonine phosphatase activity in vivo (Table 1, above). While PP1, PP2A, and PP2B share a common catalytic domain of 280 residues, these enzymes are most divergent within their noncatalytic N- and C-termini and are distinguished by their associated regulatory subunits to form a diverse variety of holoenzymes.

PP1 is involved in controlling multiple cellular functions including glycogen metabolism, muscle contraction, cell cycle progression, neuronal activities, and the splicing of RNA. These different processes are regulated by distinct PP1 holoenzymes in which the same catalytic subunit (PP1c) is complexed to different regulatory and targeting subunits (42, 59). Similar to PP1, the diverse functions of PP2A in vivo result from the (at least) 15 distinct regulatory B-subunits that individually assemble with a core heterodimer consisting of PP2Ac and a 65-kDa A-subunit (106). Specific roles for each of the PP2A holoenzymes are not well delineated, although PP2A regulates processes that include metabolism, cell signaling and the cell cycle, and the control of telomerase activity. Mutations in the PP2A 55-kDa B-subunit lead to defects in cell division in *Drosophila* embryos (80), whereas the association of the small T-antigen of SV40 and polyoma viruses to the core heterodimer inhibits PP2A dephosphorylation of MEK and MAP kinase with resultant activation of the MAP kinase pathway (97). PP2B is characterized by its dependence on Ca^{2+} for activity. The enzyme consists of an A-subunit with an N-terminal catalytic domain and a C-terminal regulatory region containing binding sites for the PP2B B-subunit and calmodulin, and at the extreme C-terminus, an autoinhibitory sequence. Maximal Ca^{2+} stimulation of PP2B requires association of Ca^{2+} to both the B-subunit and to calmodulin. PP2B plays a crucial role in the Ca^{2+} signaling cascade of activated T-cells. Increases in T-cell Ca^{2+} concentrations promoted by antigen presentation to the T-cell receptor stimulates PP2B to dephosphory-late the cytosolic subunit of the transcription factor NFAT1 (61). Dephosphory-lated NFAT1 translocates into the nucleus (probably as a complex with PP2B, 94) where, in concert with other transcription factors, it induces expression of the IL-2 gene, one of the early genes in the T-cell activation pathway. Inhibition of this Ca^{2+} signaling cascade by immunosuppressant drugs suppresses T-cell activation.

PP1 and PP2A are specifically and potently inhibited by a variety of natu-rally occurring toxins such as okadaic acid, a diarrhetic shellfish poison and strong tumor promoter, and microcystin, a liver toxin produced by blue-green algae (77). Whereas PP2B is only poorly inhibited by the toxins that affect PP1 and PP2A, it was recently defined as the immunosuppressive target of FK506 and cyclosporin in association with their major cellular binding proteins, the *cis-trans* peptidyl prolyl isomerases FKBP12 and cyclophilin, respectively (74).

Novel protein phosphatases of the PPP family have been isolated using molec-ular cloning screening techniques (24) (Table 1, above). These proteins are expressed at low abundance, with some having targeting domains attached to the phosphatase catalytic domains in addition to regulatory subunits. One ex-ample, PP5, contains three tetratricopeptide repeat (TPR) domains fused to the N-terminus of the phosphatase domain (20). The TPR repeats are assumed to form protein-protein interactions. Recent data support this notion. For ex-ample, it has been found that the TPR domain of PP5 interacts with the TPR binding site of the protein chaperone hsp90 as a complex with PP5, hsp90, and the glucocorticoid receptor (GR) (95). This association is likely to be important in vivo, because 35% of the hsp90.GR is found in a complex with PP5. The TPR domains of PP5 may directly regulate the phosphatase activity, because proteolytic removal of the TPR domain of PP5 results in a 25-fold enhancement of activity (19). A similar enhancement of activity is observed with unsaturated fatty acids such as arachadonic acid and phosphatidyl inositol, which bind to the TPR domain, allosterically stimulating phosphatase activity (19).

Structure and Catalytic Mechanism

X-ray crystallographic structural data are available for PP1c (39, 40, 49) and PP2B (50, 69), and the crystallization of the PP2A B-subunit has been reported recently. Not surprisingly (given the high level of sequence similarity shared by members of the PPP family), PP1c and PP2B share a common catalytic domain structure and architecture.

The catalytic domain fold of PP1c and PP2B consists of a central β-sandwich of two mixed β-sheets surrounded on one side by seven α-helices and on the other by a subdomain comprising three α-helices and a three-stranded β-sheet

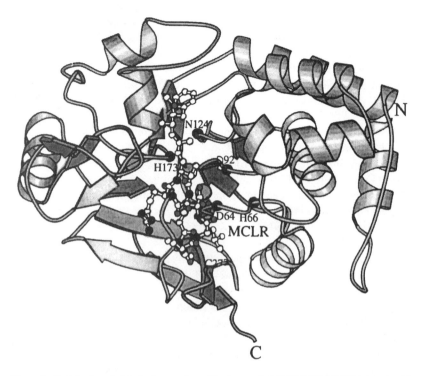

Figure 1 Protein phosphatase 1α in complex with microcystin LR (MCLR). MCLR interacts with the hydrophobic groove (via the Adda side chain), the metal sites (via a carboxylate group and a carbonyl oxygen of the toxin), and to Cys 273 (via the Mdha side chain). This structure, combined with the PP1-tungstate complex structure, reveals that microcystin inhibits the activity of PP1 by directly blocking substrate binding to the catalytic site.

(Figure 1). The interface of the three β-sheets at the top of the β-sandwich creates a shallow catalytic site channel. Amino acid residues present on loops emanating from β-strands of this central β-sandwich are responsible for coordinating a pair of metal ions to form a binuclear metal center.

Crystallographic data on PP1c (39, 49) and PP2B (50, 69) provided the first compelling information for the role of metal ions in the catalytic reaction of the PPP family. The identity of the two metal ions is slightly controversial. Proton-induced x-ray emission spectroscopy performed on PP1c crystals produced from protein expressed in *Eschericia coli* indicated that the metal ions were Fe^{2+} (or Fe^{3+}) and Mn^{2+} (39), whereas atomic absorption spectroscopy of bovine brain PP2B indicated a stoichiometric ratio of Zn^{2+} and iron (68, 111). There have also been conflicting reports concerning the iron oxidation states, with both Fe^{2+} and Fe^{3+} observed (111). Native active PP2B is most likely to contain Fe^{2+}, and the time- and Ca^{2+}/calmodulin-dependent inactivation observed for PP2B results from oxidation of the Fe-Zn center that is prevented by superoxide dismutase in vivo and in vitro (108). Oxidation of the binuclear metal center and phosphatase inactivation may represent a novel mechanism for PP2B regulation by redox potential during oxidative stress (108).

The structures of PP1c with tungstate (39) and PP2B with phosphate (50) indicated that two oxygens of the oxyanion coordinate the metal ions. Two water molecules, one of which is a metal-bridging water molecule, contribute to the octahedral hexacoordination of the metal ions. The metal coordinating residues, aspartates, histidines, and asparagines, are invariant amongst all the PPP family members. These residues, together with Arg and His residues that interact with the phosphate group of the phosphorylated residue, occur within five conserved sequence motifs. These motifs are found in the sequences of other enzymes, including the purple acid phosphatase (99), that catalyze phosphoryl transfer reactions to water, suggestive of divergent evolution of these enzymes from an ancestral metallophosphoesterase (75). Consistent with roles in catalysis, mutation of these residues profoundly reduces catalytic rate (58, 113, 122).

Most data are consistent with the hypothesis that PPPs catalyze dephosphorylation in a single step with a metal-activated water molecule or hydroxide ion. The most compelling evidence for this notion is that the purple acid phosphatase, related to the PPPs at the catalytic site (99), catalyzes dephosphorylation with inversion of configuration of the oxygen geometry of the phosphate ion (85). This indicates that a phosphoryl-enzyme intermediate would not occur, consistent with the inability of PP2B to catalyze transphosphorylation reactions (79), and unlike the PTPs, the lack of detectable phosphoryl-enzyme reaction intermediates. The two metal-bound water molecules are within van der Waals distance of the phosphorus atom of phosphate bound to the catalytic site, one of which is the likely metal-activated nucleophile. Insight into the mechanism of the PPP-catalyzed dephosphorylation reaction has been provided by a recent study employing a phosphate monoester that is coordinated by two octahedral Co(III) centers which are also joined by two hydroxide bridges. This dinuclear Co(III) complex accelerates hydrolysis of the phosphate monoester at a greater rate than any other known chemical system. *Para*-nitrophenol phosphate, for example, is hydrolyzed with a rate constant of 445 M^{-1} s^{-1}. It was proposed that the mechanism of hydrolysis of *para*-nitrophenol phosphate involved a metal-bridging hydroxide that attacked the phosphate and displaced the phenolate. This hypothesis was supported by the finding that ^{18}O is incorporated into the product by labeling the bridging hydroxides with ^{18}OH. The bridging hydroxides do not exchange with solvent owing to the inertness of the binuclear Co(III) complex. In contrast, no label is incorporated into the phosphate when the solvent is labeled with $^{18}OH_2$; hence the incoming nucleophile must be provided by a bridging hydroxide ion.

Further catalytic rate enhancement is provided by other catalytic site residues. For example, it is likely that the catalytic site Arg residues (Arg 96 and Arg 221 of PP1) stabilize the pentacoordinate transition state as loss of these residues dramatically reduces K_{cat} (58). In addition, His 125, which forms an ion pair with an invariant Asp residue, is ideally poised to donate a proton to the leaving group oxygen atom of the P-O scissile bond, a role consistent with the 10^6-fold loss of activity in PP1 (58, 113) and bacteriophage lambda phosphatase mutants of this residue (122). It is worth noting that the oxygen atom of phosphate hydrogen bonded to His 125 is directly opposite and in-line with the metal bridging water molecule.

Phosphatase Regulation

The C-terminal regions of PPP catalytic domains appear to be crucially important for communicating regulatory signals to the catalytic site. For instance, CDK-2 phosphorylation of a C-terminal Thr residue of PP1c inhibits PP1 in a cell-cycle–dependent manner (34, 110), an event that is an important process of cell cycle regulation. CDK2 phosphorylation and inhibition of PP1 prevents the reversal of CDK2-mediated phosphorylation of the retinoblastoma gene product, which must be phosphorylated for cells to enter the S-phase of the cell cycle (7). Methylation of the C-terminal Leu residue of PP2Ac moderately activates catalytic activity (43), and there are reports of tyrosine phosphorylation of the C-terminus of PP2Ac (18). The exact role of PP2A phosphorylation is not understood, but modulation of PP2Ac-regulatory subunit interactions is a possibility. The regulatory B-subunit of PP2B binds to a B-subunit binding helix of the A subunit, immediately C-terminal to the phosphatase catalytic domain (50, 69).

The mechanisms of inhibition of PP1c by microcystin LR (MCLR), and PP2B (both by its natural inhibitor, the autoinhibitory domain, and the FKBP12/FK506 complex) have been defined by the structure of the PP1-MCLR complex (49) and from two PP2B structures (50, 69). Microcystin LR is a complex cyclic heptapeptide that interacts with three distinct regions on the surface of PP1c (Figure 1, above). One of these involves a carboxylate and carbonyl group of the toxin that interacts with two of the metal-bound water molecules, hence blocking substrate binding directly. Other sites consist of a protein hydrophobic groove, and the $\beta 12/\beta 13$ loop where the Sγ atom of Cys 273 of PP1c forms a covalent bond to one of the side chains of the toxin, and the side chain of Tyr 272 packs against a leucine residue of the toxin. Interestingly, the conformation of MCLR does not change from its solution structure when in complex with PP1c (3), whereas the $\beta 12/\beta 13$ loop of PP1 undergoes a conformational change that avoids steric conflict between Tyr 276 of PP1 and the Mdha side chain of MCLR (D Barford and M-P Egloff, unpublished information). The solution structure of another PP1/PP2A toxin, the heptapeptide motuporin, resembles that of MCLR, suggesting a similar model of interaction between PP1 and this inhibitor (3).

The role of the $\beta 12/\beta 13$ loop as a site of interaction with toxins was anticipated earlier from the finding that the substitution of Cys 269 of PP2A to Gly within the $\beta 12/\beta 13$ loop causes resistance to okadaic acid. The equivalent residue in PP1 is a Phe, and replacing this with a Cys enhances okadaic acid binding to PP1 (115). Other studies showed that mutation of Tyr 272 of the $\beta 12/\beta 13$ loop causes a dramatic loss of potency of okadaic acid, caliculyn A, and tautomyocin as well as microcystin and motuporin (114). These findings suggest that toxins of PP1 and PP2A, despite their dissimilar structures, interact with their targets through the $\beta 12/\beta 13$ loop. Significantly, the equivalent loop appears to play a role in interactions of PP2B with immunosuppressant-immunophilin complexes.

In the structure of the full-length PP2B holoenzyme, the autoinhibitory domain lies over the substrate binding channel of the catalytic domain in such a way that a Glu side-chain hydrogen bonds with two of the metal-bound water molecules (69). This interaction sterically hinders substrate binding and is reminiscent of the mechanism of inhibition of PP1 by MCLR (49).

Neither FKBP12 nor FK506 individually are capable of associating with PP2B; their interaction with PP2B requires a composite recognition surface of the binary complex. The quaternary complex of the PP2B holoenzyme with FKBP12 and FK506 indicates that the conformation of FKBP12 is nearly identical to the form in the binary complex of FKPB12 and FK506, with minor flexibilities observed in the His 87 to Ile 90 loop of FKBP12 (50, 69). The major site of interaction on PP2B is the base of the B-subunit binding helix of the A subunit, together with the B-subunit and a minor interaction with the $\beta 12/\beta 13$ loop of the catalytic site. FK506 is situated 25 Å from the catalytic site and cannot participate directly in phosphatase inhibition. FKBP12 sterically blocks access to the catalytic site for large macromolecules, although since its closest approach to the catalytic site is 10 Å, it does not prevent dephosphorylation of small molecule substrates such as *para*-nitrophenol phosphate. The conformation of neither microcystin nor the FKBP12-FK506 complex changes significantly on binding to their cellular targets PP1 (3) and PP2B (103), respectively, perhaps explaining their high affinity binding. It is likely that the mechanism of inhibition of PP2B by FKBP12-FK506 is similar to that for the cyclosporin/cyclophilin complex. Both these complexes compete for binding to PP2B, and mutations of the $\beta 12/\beta 13$ loop of yeast PP2B results in cyclosporin resistance (17). In the brain, PP2B forms a complex with

AKAP-79, an A-kinase anchoring protein, that is a noncompetitive inhibitor of PP2B (23).

Regulatory Subunits of PP1

Multiple proteins are substrates for PP1 and PP2A, the reversible phosphorylation of which are responsible for regulating diverse cellular functions. This seemingly paradoxical situation was resolved by the discovery that distinct forms of PP1 and PP2A holoenzymes occur in vivo, where the same catalytic subunit is complexed to different regulatory or targeting subunits (42, 59). For PP1, it has been shown that the latter class of subunit confer in-vivo substrate specificity by directing particular PP1 holoenzymes to a subcellular location and by enhancing or suppressing activity towards different substrates. For example, the M_{110} subunit, responsible for the association of PP1c with the myofibrils of skeletal muscle and smooth muscle, stimulates the activity of PP1 towards myosin light chain and suppresses activity towards glycogen phosphorylase (63). Similarly, G_L, which targets PP1 to liver glycogen, suppresses PP1 phosphorylase phosphatase activity (63). Besides defining specificity, regulatory subunits allow the activity of PP1c to be modulated by reversible protein phosphorylation and second messengers in response to extracellular stimuli. For example, the G_M subunit of PP1G is phosphorylated by PKA at Ser 67, an event that leads to the dissociation of PP1c from G_M and hence glycogen (27). Rho-mediated regulation of smooth muscle contraction and focal adhesions is exerted in part by Rho-GTP regulated protein kinase (ROK)-mediated phosphorylation of the M_{110} subunit, inactivating the myosin light-chain phosphatase activity of PP1M (67). Currently, ~15 PP1-regulatory subunits are characterized (Table 1, above), but with the recent use of novel techniques such as microcystin-Sepharose affinity chromatography and the yeast–two hybrid system, this number will be greatly exceeded and at least 100 novel PP1-binding proteins have already been identified (16).

The binding of targeting subunits to the catalytic subunit of PP1 (PP1c) is mutually exclusive, suggesting one or more common or overlapping binding site(s), and it is a little surprising that there are no overall sequence similarities amongst most of the PP1-binding subunits. Recent experiments have begun to shed light on the molecular basis for the recognition of regulatory subunits by PP1c. Deletion mutagenesis of PP1 targeting subunits, together with synthetic peptides representing sequences within these subunits, has enabled the PP1c binding region of many PP1 regulatory subunits to be identified. PP1c is targeted to glycogen in liver and to glycogen particles and the sarcoplasmic reticulum in muscle by tissue-specific glycogen-binding subunits (G-subunits) (35, 84, 101). Comparison of G_M and G_L sequences identified three short, highly conserved regions, one being residues 63–86 of G_M (35), the region that encompasses the site of PKA phosphorylation. A peptide corresponding to this sequence ($G_{M[63-75]}$ peptide) disrupts the interaction of PP1c with G_L, and also other PP1-binding subunits such as M_{110} and p53BP2 (40). This result implies that PP1c contains a recognition site for this peptide that overlaps with, or is identical to, its binding sites(s) for other regulatory subunits.

The recently determined crystal structure of PP1c in complex with the $G_{M[63-75]}$ peptide revealed a critical sequence motif important for the interaction of regulatory subunits with PP1c (40). Residues 64–69 of the $G_{M[63-75]}$ peptide are bound in an extended conformation to a hydrophobic channel within the C-terminal region of PP1c that is formed at the interface of the two β-sheets of the β-sandwich opposite to the catalytic site channel. Three residues of the peptide are incorporated into one of the PP1c β-sheets as a sixth β-strand parallel to the edge β-strand ($\beta14$). The predominant interactions between the peptide and PP1c involve Val 66 and Phe 68 of the peptide, which interact with hydrophobic residues of the channel together with Arg 64 and Arg 65 that form electrostatic interactions with acidic residues at the N-terminus of the channel.

The Val 66 and Phe 68 residues of the $G_{M[63-75]}$ peptide are critical in mediating the interactions of G_M and PP1c, because substitution of either of these residues for alanine abolishes (in the case of Phe) or severely reduces (in the case of Val) the ability of $G_{M[63-75]}$ peptides to bind PP1c. Interestingly, it was noted that the sequence RVSF that binds G_M to PP1c is invariant within G_L and related to a sequence (KVKF) within the N-terminal 38 residues of the M_{110} subunit. The $M_{110[1-38]}$ peptide mimics the M_{110} subunit by enhancing the PP1 activity towards myosin light chain (63); however, this activity is abolished if the VKF residues related to VSF of G_M are removed (40). Hence, a motif RVXF found in G_M and M_{110} is responsible for targeting these subunits to the same recognition site on PP1c in a mutually exclusive manner. Other data (reviewed in 40) indicated that relatively short fragments of PP1-binding subunits—for example, NIPP-1 (9, 105), p53BP2 (53), and an RNA splicing factor (55)—that retain the ability to bind to PP1 contain an R/KVXF motif. It is therefore likely that these proteins interact with PP1 in a similar manner to that of G_M. The realization that PP1 contains a binding site for the sequence RVXF provided a basis for understanding earlier published work concerning DARPP-32 and protein inhibitor-1, two proteins that become highly potent, nM, inhibitors of PP1c when phosphorylated on a Thr residue by PKA (Thr 35 of inhibitor-1, Thr 34 of DARPP-32). Previous studies had revealed that the N-terminal 8–38 residues of inhibitor-1 and DARPP-32 mimicked the full-length proteins in their ability to inhibit PP1c. Moreover, the identical sequence KIQF (similar to the R/KVXF motif) at the N-terminus of this sequence is necessary for mediating the inhibition of PP1 by these proteins. Loss of Ile 10 of the KIQF sequence of inhibitor-1

(2), or deletion of the motif, disrupts the inhibitory effects on PP1c by phospho-inhibitor-1 (41). A similar result was found on disrupting the equivalent residue (Ile 9) of DARPP-32 (33, 54). It was also discovered using biosensor studies that inhibitor-1 and DARPP-32 bind to PP1c in both their phosphorylated and nonphosphorylated states. Phosphorylation enhances binding affinity of both inhibitors by only two- to fourfold, whereas it causes a 10^6-fold increase in the inhibitory potency of DARPP-32. Moreover, although dephospho-inhibitor-1 binds to PP1, it is not a PP1c inhibitor (33, 41). These results were interpreted to indicate that inhibitor-1 and DARPP-32 bind to PP1c through two low-affinity sites, one that encompasses the sequence KIQF (similar to the RVXF motif of G_M and M_{110}), and another that includes the phosphorylated Thr residue and which presumably binds at the catalytic site. A peptide fragment of DARPP-32 (residues 8 to 38) completely antagonizes the inhibitory properties of phos-phorylated DARPP-32 at a concentration of 15 μM (70), presumably because of competition between the peptide and protein at the RVxF binding site of PP1c that recognizes the DARPP-32 KIQF sequence.

The identification of a PP1 binding site for the RVxF motif of regulatory subunits (situated opposite to the catalytic site) explains the results that PP1c immobilized to microcystin-Sepharose affinity columns maintains an intact regulatory subunit binding site (83). It also explains how fragments of unphos-phorylated DARPP-32 (residues 8–38) antagonize the inhibitory properties of phospho-DARPP-32 without affecting the inhibitory properties of microcystin, okadaic acid, or caliculyn A (70). An interaction between a relatively short amino acid sequence on PP1 binding subunits with PP1c explains not only the observation that multiple PP1-binding subunits exist, with no overall sequence similarities or shared domains, but also how the binding of targeting subunits to PP1 appears to be mutually exclusive. However, there is evidence that the RVXF motif binding site is not sufficient for high-affinity binding for all sub-units, similarly to the situation for inhibitor-1 and DARPP-32, and a second low-affinity site is present on the G_M and M_{110} subunits (56, 63, 109).

The site of PKA phosphorylation on G_M, Ser 67, interacts with a Met residue and is in close proximity to a region of negative electrostatic potential on the pro-tein surface. Phosphorylation of Ser 67 would introduce a bulky charged residue at this site that is energetically unfavorable, and this probably accounts for the dissociation of PP1c from phosphorylated G_M. A similar mechanism of con-trol may also operate for other PP1-regulatory subunits. For example, NIPP-1, a nuclear RNA-binding protein, inhibits PP1 with an inhibitory constant of 1 pM (9). Phosphorylation of NIPP-1 by PKA and/or casein kinase 2 in vitro abolishes this inhibition (8) and these sites have been recently mapped to a central acidic region near to the RVXF-motif (104).

Model of PP1c-Phospho-Inhibitor 1 Complex

Using the knowledge that the KIQF sequence of inhibitor-1 and DARPP-32 binds to the RVXF binding site on PP1c, a plausible model of a complex of PP1c with phospho-inhibitor-1 has been constructed (Figure 2).

Secondary structure predictions of inhibitor 1 suggested that residues 9 to 14 and 23 to 31 adopt β-strand and α-helical conformations, respectively. The prediction of the sequence KIQF as a β-strand is consistent with our assumption that this region of inhibitor-1 adopts the same conformation as RVSF of the G_M peptide when bound to the VxF recognition site of PP1c. The residues RRPpTP encompassing the pThr 35 site were positioned within the catalytic site channel in an extended conformation, with the phosphate group of the pThr 35 occupying the phosphate binding site of the catalytic site. The four

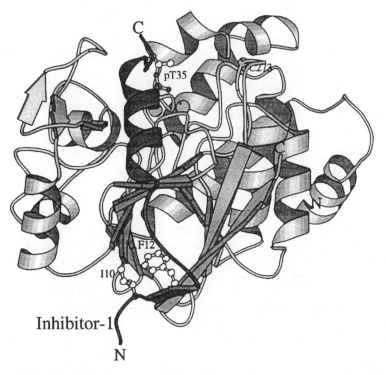

Figure 2   Structure of PP1c in complex with the residues 8 to 38 of phosphorylated inhibitor-1 (*dark shading*). The Ile 10 and Phe 12 residues interact at the (R/K)VXF motif of PP1, whereas the pThr-35 residue binds to the catalytic site.

consecutive Arg residues N-terminus to pThr 35 interact with Asp and Glu residues within an acidic groove of PP1c formed from the $\beta7/\beta8$ loop on one side and the $\beta10/\beta11$ loop and $\beta11$ strand on the other, similar to that proposed by Goldberg et al (49) for their model of DARPP-32 bound to PP1c.

We propose that residues 20 to 30 of inhibitor-1 form an amphipathic helix that folds around the edge of the β-sandwich of PP1c. The N-terminus of this helix is disrupted by prolines at residues 19 and 23. Pro 19 and Pro 15 are probably responsible for introducing turns into the polypeptide chain that allows the β-strand encompassing the KIQF sequence (residues 9 to 14) to connect with the α-helix. The model of the phospho-inhibitor 1-PP1c complex is shown in Figure 2.

A final comment is that the mode of interaction between PP1c and a short peptide is similar to that observed in complexes of phosphotyrosine binding domains (PTB) (121) and PDZ domains (36) with their cognate peptide ligands. In these complexes, short peptides of 4-6 residues engage the protein by forming antiparallel hydrogen bonding interactions with edge β-strands that occur within a β-barrel. Formation of hydrogen-bonds between edge β-strands is observed at protein interfaces within numerous protein-protein complexes. These include (a) the streptococcal protein-G domain interaction with the C_H domain of IgG (31), (b) the Ras-binding domain of Raf kinase with Rap1A (86), and (c) the interaction of p27[Kip1] with Cdk2 within a ternary p27[Kip1]-cyclin A-Cdk2 complex (91).

PROTEIN SERINE/THREONINE PHOSPHATASES OF THE PPM FAMILY

Protein phosphatases of the PPM family are present in both eukaryotes and prokaryotes whose defining member is PP2C. Within the PPM family, the PP2C domain occurs in numerous structural contexts that reflect functional diversity. For example, the PP2C domain of the *Arabidopsis* ABI1 gene is fused with EF hand motifs (73, 81) whereas in KAPP-1, a kinase interaction domain that associates with a phosphorylated receptor precedes the phosphatase domain (98). Other less closely related examples include the Ca^{2+} stimulated mitochondrial pyruvate dehydrogenase phosphatase, which contains a catalytic subunit sharing 22% sequence identity with mammalian PP2C (72), and the SpoIIE phosphatase of *B. subtilis*, which has ten membrane spanning regions preceding the PP2C-like catalytic domain (13, 37). A surprising homologue is a 300-residue region of yeast adenylyl cyclase, present immediately N-terminal to the cyclase catalytic domain, which shares sequence similarity with PP2C (66). This domain may function to mediate Ras-GTP activation of adenylyl cyclase activity and is not known to possess protein phosphatase activity.

In eukaryotes, one of the roles of PP2C is to reverse protein kinase cascades that become activated as a result of stress. For example, in mammalian hepatocytes, PP2C prevents inhibition of cholesterol and fatty acid biosynthesis resulting from elevated AMP/ATP ratios (82). Wip1, a novel PP2C enzyme, is induced in response to ionizing radiation in a p53-dependent manner, and ectopic expression of *wip1* in human cells suppressed colony formation (44). These results suggest that Wip1 might mediate growth inhibitory effects in response to DNA damage. The fission yeast enzyme negatively regulates the PBS2/HOG1-MAP kinase pathway that is activated in response to osmotic and heat shock (78). This may be achieved via dephosphorylation of a protein substrate downstream of the PBS2/HOG1-MAP kinase pathway (48). *Arabidopsis* PP2C is essential for transducing a signal by the hormone abscissic acid, leading to maintenance of seed dormancy, stomatal closure, and growth inhibition (73, 81). The role of PP2C-like protein phosphatases in regulating stress response pathways is also conserved in prokaryotes. The protein phosphatase SpoIIE controls the sporulation of *Bacillus subtilis* by dephosphorylating an antitranscription factor SpoIIAA, reversing the actions of the SpoIIAB protein kinase in a process that is governed by the ADP/ATP ratio (37).

The sequences of protein phosphatases of the PPM family share no similarity with those of the PPP family; however, the structures of these two families are strikingly similar (Figure 3) (26). Mammalian PP2C consists of two domains: an N-terminal catalytic domain with 6 α-helices and 11 β-strands, common to all members of the PP2C family, and a 90-residue C-terminal domain of 3 α-helices, characteristic of mammalian PP2Cs (see again Figure 3). The catalytic domain is dominated by a central, buried β-sandwich formed by the association of two antiparallel β-sheets, both of which are flanked by a pair of antiparallel α-helices inserted between the two central β-strands. The C-terminal domain is formed from three antiparallel α-helices remote from the catalytic site, suggesting a role in defining substrate specificity rather than catalysis.

At the catalytic site of PP2C, two Mn^{2+} ions within a binuclear metal center are coordinated by four invariant aspartate residues and a nonconserved Glu residue. These residues are situated at the top of a central β-sandwich. Six water molecules coordinate the two metal ions. One of these water molecules bridges the two metal ions and four form hydrogen bonds to a phosphate ion at the catalytic site. Dephosphorylation is probably catalyzed by metal-activated water molecules that act as nucleophiles and general acids in a similar mechanism to that proposed for the PPP family. Substitution of Asp residues of the yeast PP2C homologue, TPD1, and the *B. subtilis* SpoIIE phosphatase predicted by sequence alignments to be equivalent to metal coordinating Asps of human PP2C abolishes catalytic activity, supporting a role for metal ions in catalysis and the classification of SpoIIE as a PP2C-like protein phosphatase.

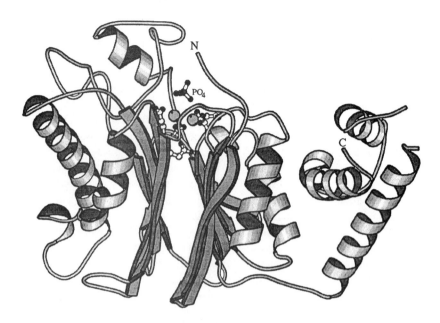

Figure 3   Human protein phosphatase 2C. The catalytic domain consists of a central β-sandwich surrounded by α-helices. The Mn^{2+} ions, *spheres*, are coordinated by Asp and Glu residues from the central β-sandwich structure.

PROTEIN TYROSINE PHOSPHATASES

The evolution of reversible tyrosine phosphorylation is linked to the development of multicellular organisms, being intimately associated with transmembrane signaling events. Numerous extracellular stimuli—for example hormones, growth factors, antigens, and cell-cell and cell-matrix interactions—activate receptor protein tyrosine kinases (PTKs) and/or receptor-associated soluble protein tyrosine kinases, leading to an increase in the levels of cellular tyrosine phosphorylation and the triggering of downstream signaling pathways. These pathways frequently involve the generation of second messengers, regulation of Ser/Thr phosphorylation, and G-protein activation. The importance of tyrosine phosphorylation in mediating intercellular communications is reflected in the increasing number and diversity of protein tyrosine kinases and phosphatases with an increase in eukaryotic complexity. Thus, multicellular organisms may encode approximately 500 PTKs, with perhaps a few hundred PTPs within their genomes. In contrast, yeasts encode no authentic PTKs and only two PTPs.

Similarly to the PTKs, diversity of the PTP family includes receptor-like transmembrane proteins and soluble cytosolic proteins (Table 1). Each PTP contains a highly conserved catalytic domain of ~240 residues that shares high sequence similarity throughout the family. One of the hallmarks of the RPTPs is that most possess (with the exception of RPTPβ) two PTP domains arranged in tandem. The biological significance of this is not understood. For some, such as CD45, the membrane distal domain is inactive, and lacks many of the residues required for catalytic activity (6). Since the structures of PTP catalytic domains are highly conserved, the structural and functional diversity within the family is generated by noncatalytic regulatory and targeting domains attached to the N and C termini of the catalytic domain. Such domains function not only to regulate PTP catalytic activity but also to target the enzyme to particular subcellular locations (87). The net effect of these domains is to confer in vivo substrate specificity upon PTPs, and this is well exemplified by PTP1B and the SH2-domain containing PTPs, SHP-1, and SHP-2. The catalytic domain of PTP1B shares an average of 40% sequence identity with other members of the family and in vitro catalyzes the dephosphorylation of a wide spectrum of tyrosine phosphorylated peptides and proteins, although with some preference for pTyr residues immediately C-terminal to Asp and Glu containing sequences. Ectopic expression of the PTP1B catalytic domain within eukaryotic cells causes uniform reduction in the levels of tyrosine phosphorylation.

Moreover, so-called substrate trapping mutants of PTP1B (D181A) have been generated that inactivate the enzyme but allow formation of stable phosphatase-substrate complexes. When expressed in cells, the catalytic domain of PTP1B D181A associates with numerous tyrosine phosphorylated proteins (45). In contrast, expression of the full-length PTP1B D181A mutant, which contains a C-terminal endoplasmic reticulum targeting domain (46), restricts the association of PTP1B to only three proteins, one of which is the EGF receptor. The related SH2 domain-containing PTPs, SHP-1, and SHP-2, negatively and positively regulate signaling pathways downstream of activated cell-surface receptors, respectively (reviewed in 87). Within these proteins, the N-terminal SH2 domains serve the dual roles of targeting and regulation. Stimulation of receptor-associated PTKs and concomitant phosphorylation of receptor tyrosine residues leads to the engagement of pTyr residues within sequence-specific contexts, by the phosphatase SH2 domains. Hence the enzymes are recruited to their cellular substrates at the cell surface, and this is accompanied by a conformational change within the protein that activates PTP catalytic activity. Other noncatalytic domains of the non-transmembrane PTPs include domains with homology to cytoskeletal and lipid binding domains, SH3 domain-recognition polyproline sequences, and PEST sequences.

Receptor-like PTPs (RPTPs) possess the potential to communicate transmembrane signals via modulation of the activity of their intracellular catalytic domains and resultant change of cellular tyrosine phosphorylation. The regulation of cell adhesion may be an important function of one group of four RPTPs that possess extracellular segments with fibronectin-type III and immunoglobulin-domains, hence sharing structural similarity to cell-adhesion molecules of the N-CAM and V-CAM families. Overexpression of the extracellular segments of RPTPμ and RPTPκ on the surface of insect cells causes homotypic interactions (14, 92). For RPTPμ, RPTPκ, and RPTPλ, an interaction with the cadheren/β-catenin complex has been demonstrated in vitro, consistent with the subcellular localization of these RPTPs to cell adherens junctions in vivo (15, 21, 47). It is likely that these RPTPs regulate the level of tyrosine phosphorylation within adherens junctions and the associated interaction of these junctions with the cytoskeleton.

A subfamily of the tyrosine-specific PTPs is termed the dual-specificity phosphatases (DSPs), so called because in vitro these enzymes catalyze the dephosphorylation of all three phospho-amino acids, although they show strong preferences for particular protein substrates in vitro and in vivo. Examples include the cell cycle regulators CDC25 and kinase associated phosphatase (KAP) and MAP kinase phosphatases. These enzymes are related to the PTPs by their possession of the conserved PTP signature motif, similarities of catalytic mechanism, and (it is now known) similarities in tertiary structure.

Structure

Protein tyrosine phosphatases and the dual-specificity phosphatases are characterized by the PTP signature motif (I/V)HCXAGXGR(S/T) containing the catalytically essential Cys and Arg residues. Within the PTPs and DSPs, the signature motif is situated at the center of the molecule, at the base of the catalytic site. The sequence forms the C-terminus of a β-strand, a loop connecting the β-strand with an α-helix, and the first turn of the α-helix (Figure 4).

The three-dimensional structures of all PTP catalytic domains known share a common architecture of a central, highly twisted β-sheet of nine β-strands with four central parallel β-strands flanked by antiparallel β-strands (5, 100). This sheet is surrounded by α-helices with four on one side and two on the opposite side. Additional secondary structural elements present N- and C-terminal to the conserved PTP domain are accommodated within this domain. For example, in common with the other eukaryotic PTPs, two N-terminal α-helices (α-1' and α-2') pack against α-5 and α-6 of PTP1B. The PTP signature motif, located at the base of the catalytic site cleft, is surrounded by four loops, three of which provide residues necessary for catalysis and substrate specificity. One of these loops, which forms part of the phosphotyrosine recognition region located N-terminus to the β-sheet, is critical in defining the specificity of the PTPs for phosphotyrosine (62).

The catalytic domains of the dual-specificity phosphatases VHR and KAP, despite sharing no sequence-similarity between themselves or with the PTPs,

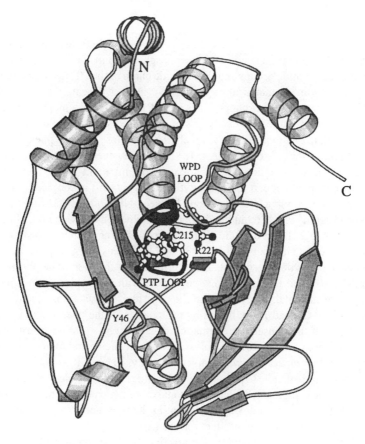

Figure 4 Structure of protein tyrosine phosphatase 1B. The PTP loop (*dark shading*) and WPD loop are indicated, as is Cys 215 and Arg 221 of the PTP loop and the position of the Cα-atom of Tyr 46 of the phosphotyrosine recognition loop.

reveal essentially the same core structural features as the PTPs, namely the central four-stranded parallel β-sheet surrounded on both sides by one and four α-helices (112; N Hanlon, M Groves, and D Barford, unpublished information). However, the DSPs appear to be a truncated version of the PTPs, and have only one of the antiparallel flanking β-strands and lack three of the antiparallel β-strands that flank one side of the β-sheet of the PTPs and which are instead replaced with either one (VHR) or two (KAP) short α-helices. This region of the catalytic domain of PTPs and DSPs has been referred to as the variable insert region. Also lacking within the DSPs is the phosphotyrosine recognition subdomain.

Catalytic Mechanism

Much is now understood concerning the mechanism of PTP catalysis and specificity for pTyr-containing peptides. The phosphate group of pTyr is coordinated by main-chain amide groups and the Arg side chain of the PTP motif so that the phosphorus atom is situated adjacent to the $S\gamma$-atom of the catalytic Cys residue (62). Engagement of phosphopeptides to PTP1B promotes a major conformational change of one of the catalytic site loops (the WPD loop) consisting of residues 179 to 187 that shift by as much as 8 Å to close over the phenyl ring of pTyr and allow the side chain of Asp 181 to act as a general acid in the catalytic reaction. The Arg 221 side chain reorients to optimize salt-bridge interactions with the phosphate bound to the catalytic site. This shift is coupled to motion of the WPD loop via a hydrogen bond between NH2 of Arg 221 and the carbonyl oxygen of Pro 180, and hydrophobic interactions between the aliphatic moiety of Arg 221 and the side chain of Trp 179. These interactions and the hydrophobic packing between Phe 182 and the phenyl ring of pTyr stabilize the closed, catalytically competent conformation of the loop. The phosphotyrosine dephosphorylation reaction commences with nucleophilic attack by the $S\gamma$-atom of the catalytic cysteine on the pTyr phosphorus atom. Cleavage of the scissile P-O bond is facilitated by protonation of the phenolic oxygen by Asp 181 with the consequent formation of a phospho-cysteine intermediate. This transient intermediate is hydrolyzed by an activated water molecule. Phosphoryl transfer reaction to a water molecule catalyzed by PTPs is highly specific because PTPs are unable to phosphorylate a range of primary alcohols and other phosphoryl-acceptors (Z-Y Zhang, personal communication). The structure of a PTP1B-tungstate complex suggests that in the presence of a phosphate, the WPD loop opens, allowing product release (5).

Numerous kinetic data support the reaction mechanism outlined above (see 29 for a review). Cysteinyl-phosphate intermediates have been trapped by rapid denaturation of PTPs and a dual-specificity phosphatase (VHR) during catalytic turnover (22, 52, 90, 120). Moreover, substitution of the catalytic Cys residue for a serine abolishes catalytic activity and the formation of a cysteinyl-phosphate intermediate (52). The nucleophilicity of the Cys residues results from its close proximity to main-chain amide groups and a hydrogen bond with the side chain of Ser 222 of the PTP signature motif, and has an unusually low pK_a of 4.6 (116). The catalytic Asp residue (Asp 181 of PTP1B) contributes to the basic limb of the pH activity profile, and its substitution to Ala causes a 10^5-fold reduction in k_{cat}, suggestive of a role as an acid catalyst (45, 119). This implies that Asp 181 is necessary for the first step of the reaction, namely cleavage of the pTyr P-O bond and intermediate formation, a notion consistent with the finding that Asp 181 mutants of PTP1B allow phosphorylated substrates to form stable complexes with the enzyme in vivo (45). The consequence of the catalytic role played by the catalytic Asp residue (Asp 181 of PTP1B) is that the rate of hydrolysis of a range of aryl-phosphate esters is independent of the pK_a of the leaving-group residue (29).

The structures of PTP complexes with vanadate provided insights into the second step of the reaction, namely the hydrolysis of the cysteinyl-phosphate intermediate (28). Vanadate forms a covalent bond with the $S\gamma$-atom of the nucleophilic Cys residue to produce a pentavalent trigonal bipyramidal configuration that is analogous to the transition state. The apical oxygen atom, which most closely resembles the attacking nucleophilic water molecule, forms a pair of hydrogen bonds to Asp 181 and to Gln 262. This observation led to the hypothesis that the role of Gln 262 is to position a water molecule for nucleophilic attack onto the cysteinyl-phosphate intermediate, and hence substitution of this residue for Ala should decrease the rate of cysteinyl-phosphate hydrolysis without affecting the rate of its formation. In this situation, the rate-limiting step becomes that of phosphocysteine hydrolysis, and hence the intermediate should accumulate. Direct visualization of this intermediate was achieved within PTP1B Q262A molecules by soaking crystals at 4°C in a large molar excess of *para*-nitrophenol phosphate (a pTyr analogue) and freezing the crystals at 100 K to trap, at steady state, the accumulation of the intermediate. The structure of the PTP1B-cysteinyl-phosphate intermediate demonstrates that a water-molecule hydrogen bonded to Asp 181 of the closed WPD loop was situated above the phosphate group of the cysteinyl-phosphate residue. However, the position of the water molecule was not ideal for in-line attack onto the phosphorus atom of the intermediate, being displaced from such a position by 1 Å. It is likely that this accounts for the reduced rate of hydrolysis of the PTP1B mutant, and the shift of this water molecule is probably caused by the loss of hydrogen bonding to the Gln 262 residue. Each step of the reaction pathway catalyzed by the PTPs may now be delineated in detail. A schematic is outlined in Figure 5 (ADB Pannifer and D Barford, unpublished MS).

The reactions catalyzed by PTPs share many features in common with that of GTP hydrolysis by the GTPases. For example, the role of Gln 262 in positioning a water molecule for nucleophilic attack onto the phosphocysteine intermediate of PTP1B is reminiscent of the Gln residue at the catalytic site of most GTPases, including the Ras family and G_α-subunits of the heterotrimeric G-proteins. Mutation of the catalytic site Gln 61 residue in Ras causes cellular transformation (4) and a 10-fold rate-reduction of GTP hydrolysis (12, 30). Similarly, mutations of the equivalent Gln residue within the catalytic sites of $G_{\alpha s}$ and $G_{i\alpha}$ reduces the intrinsic rate of GTP hydrolysis and are associated with thyroid and pituitary tumors (71, 76). Crystal structures of complexes of $G_{\alpha t}$ and $G_{i\alpha}$ with GDP, Mg^{2+} and AlF^{4-} (25, 96) and a recent structure of a Ras-RasGAP, GDP, Mg^{2+}, AlF^3 complex (93) have revealed the active

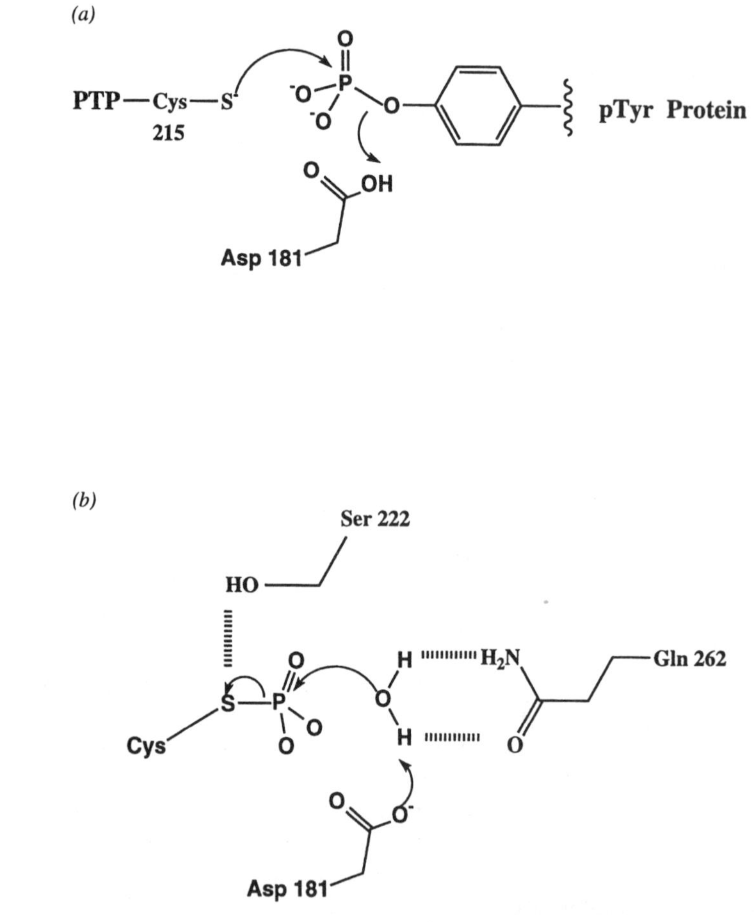

(a)

(b)

Figure 5 Schematic of the reaction mechanism catalyzed by PTP1B. (*a*) Formation of the cysteinyl-phosphate intermediate. (*b*) Hydrolysis of the cysteinyl-phosphate intermediate.

site conformations of these enzymes and the mechanisms of GTP hydrolysis. Gln 61 (and its homologue in the heterotrimeric G-proteins) plays a dual role in catalyzing GTP hydrolysis. First, it coordinates the attacking water molecule and positions it optimally for in-line approach onto the GTP-γ-phosphate. Second, it forms a hydrogen bond with the γ-phosphate oxygen atom as it passes through the transition state, stabilizing the pentavalent phosphorus transition state. In PTP1B, Gln 262 also coordinates the attacking water molecule to position it for in-line attack, although, unlike GTPase, Gln 262 does not hydrogen-bond to the oxygens of the cysteinyl phosphate. In addition to a common Gln residue, both PTPs and GTPases use an essential Arg residue that coordinates and stabilizes the pentavalent phosphorus intermediate (25, 93, 96).

Substrate Specificity

PTPs are absolutely specific for pTyr-containing proteins, being unable to dephosphorylate pSer and pThr proteins (102). Hydrolysis of small-molecule phosphate monoesters such as free pSer and pThr proceeds at a measurable (although extremely low) rate, some 10^5-fold lower than that of pTyr hydrolysis. Amino acids N- and C-terminal to the pTyr residue confer additional binding affinity, and for PTP1B and a number of other PTPs, a preference is displayed for peptides with acidic residues preceding the pTyr residue and C-terminal hydrophobic residues (6, 117, 118). The molecular basis for substrate specificity results from the dimensions of the catalytic site cleft, which measures 9 Å from its base, where the nucleophilic Cys residue is positioned, to its entrance. A key structural component of the catalytic cleft is provided by the phosphotyrosine recognition loop formed from a conserved sequence KNRY (residues 43–46 of PTP1B). The Tyr residue of this motif packs against the phenyl ring of a pTyr substrate and is critical in defining the depth of the catalytic site cleft (62) (Figure 4, above). Other nonpolar residues present within the pTyr recognition loop, the WPD and PTP loops interact with the phenyl ring. An Asp residue present within the pTyr recognition loop forms a bifurcated hydrogen bond to the main-chain amide groups of the pTyr and P+1 residues of the peptide. This forces the pTyr residue to adopt a helical conformation and insert into the catalytic site cleft. Acidic residues present N-terminal to the pTyr residue interact with basic residues on the phosphatase surface, explaining the preference of this enzyme for peptides with acidic residues in these positions. The significance of the depth of the catalytic site cleft as a determinant of substrate specificity was elegantly demonstrated in a study showing that the *Yersinia* PTP was capable of dephosphorylating straight-chain peptide-bound aliphatic phosphates of the general structure: $(Glu)_4-NH-(CH_2)_n-PO_3$. The most efficient substrate is one with seven methylenes, that is, exactly as long as a tyrosine residue (38).

The DSPs differ from the PTPs because of their ability to dephosphorylate pSer and pThr proteins. A comparison of VHR with PTP1B and the *Yersinia* PTP revealed the expected similarities in the structure of the PTP motif at the base of the catalytic site (112). An Asp residue (Asp 92) is equivalent to the catalytic Asps of PTPs within both the three-dimensional structure and approximately 30 residues N-terminal to the PTP motif. The catalytic site of KAP shows more similarities to the PTPs than does VHR (N Hanlon, M Groves, D Barford, unpublished information). For instance, in KAP, as in the PTPs, a Glu residue forms an ion-pair with the catalytic site Arg residue, and an equivalent Gln residue to the nucleophilic water coordinating Gln residue of PTPs (Gln 262 of PTP1B) is present. The most significant difference between the PTPs and DSPs is the absence of the pTyr recognition domain within the DSPs, the consequence of which is to produce a much shallower and open catalytic site with a depth of 6 Å, permitting the hydrolysis of the shorter pSer and pThr residues.

Regulation

PTPs are efficient catalysts, with constitutive activity of these proteins causing the rapid dephosphorylation of intracellular pTyr residues and consequent disruption of signal transduction pathways. Interestingly, this is a mechanism exploited by *Yersinia* bacteria, which inject proteins encoded by the Yop genes, including the YopH PTP, into macrophages, hence preventing immune-directed bacterial phagocytosis and leading to diseases such as the bubonic plague and tuberculosis (51, 11).

The isolated catalytic domains of most PTPs demonstrate activity, hence PTP regulation—at least in part—requires inhibition of this activity. Such a role may be played by the regulatory domains attached to the PTP catalytic domains. For the SH2 domain-containing PTPs, SHP-1 and SHP-2, numerous data support the notion that the N-terminal SH2 domains inhibit catalytic activity, most likely by binding to the PTP domain and blocking substrate access to the catalytic site. Engagement of phosphorylated peptides by the SH2 domains releases this inhibition with concomitant activation of the PTP's activity.

Structural support for such a mechanism of control came unexpectedly with the crystal structure of the membrane proximal domain (domain 1) of RPTPα (10). This structure revealed that the molecule was a homodimer in two independent crystal forms (Figure 6).

The biological significance of this structure lay in the observation that the catalytic site of each subunit was sterically blocked by the insertion of a wedge connecting two helices, $\alpha1'$ and $\alpha2'$, within a helix-turn-helix segment immediately preceding the PTP catalytic domain from the opposite subunit of the dimer. Residues of this wedge directly interact with the equivalent catalytic site residues which were part of the phosphopeptide binding site of PTP1B. Moreover, the WPD loop is stabilized in the open conformation and is sterically prevented from adopting the catalytically closed conformer. The overall tertiary structure of RPTPα is very similar to that of PTP1B; however, two differences in tertiary structure between these two proteins are significant in promoting the dimeric structure that is observed for RPTPα. One is a two-residue insertion within the wedge connecting $\alpha1'$ with $\alpha2'$ of RPTPα. These two residues participate at the dimeric interface of RPTPα and insert into the catalytic site. The second is a small β-sheet formed by βx at the immediate

Figure 6   Domain 1 of receptor protein tyrosine phosphatase α. An example of a receptor-like PTP. In two independent crystal forms, the protein forms a homodimer such that the catalytic site (PTP loop) of each molecule is blocked by a wedge within a helix-turn-helix segment. This inhibits the enzyme by preventing substrate binding. The reason is that Asp 227 of one subunit interacts with the pTyr recognition loop of the opposite subunit and the WPD loop containing the catalytic Asp residue is restrained in the open, inactive conformation.

N-terminus of the $\alpha 1'$ helix and βy, C-terminus to the $\alpha 5$ helix. This sheet, absent from PTP1B, is important in stabilizing the conformation of the helix-turn-helix segment. Similarities in sequence between RPTPα and other RPTPs not shared with the cytosolic PTPs suggest that these two tertiary features will be conserved within the RPTP family. It is therefore possible, as proposed by Bilwes et al (10), that other RPTPs may adopt a similar quaternary structure.

The notion that dimerization of RPTPs may provide a mechanism for the modulation of the catalytic activity of RPTPs provided an attractive explanation of earlier data concerning the signaling properties of an EGF receptor-CD45 chimera. Ablation of expression of CD45, the prototypic RPTP, from T- or B-cells disrupts the normal signaling responses to engagement of antigen receptor. However, signaling can be restored by expression of membrane-targeted

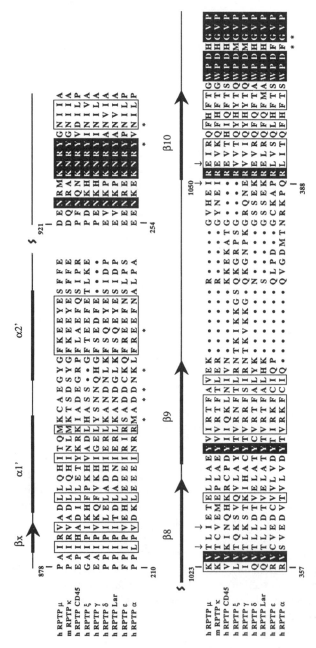

Figure 7 Sequence alignment of representative RPTP D1s in the regions that form the dimer interfaces of RPTPα and RPTPμ. *Top left*, βx-helix-turn-helix segment. *Top right*, residues of the pTyr recognition loop of the catalytic site. *Bottom*, residues from β8 to the WPD loop of the catalytic site. Residues of RPTPμ D1 and RPTPα D1 that form interactions at their respective dimer interfaces are indicated with vertical arrows (*top*) and stars (*bottom*), respectively. The residues that form the dimer interface of RPTPμ D1 are poorly conserved throughout the family, whereas residues of the RPTPα D1 interface are poorly conserved within the helix-turn-helix segment, but well conserved within the catalytic site.

constructs containing the catalytic domain of CD45. For example, a chimeric molecule where the extracellular and transmembrane segments of CD45 were replaced with those of the EGF receptor was able to restore signaling in the absence, but not in the presence, of EGF (32). In other words, EGF, the extracellular ligand of the chimeric molecule, blocked signaling from the phosphatase domain. It was proposed that in the presence of growth factor, dimerization of the extracellular segment of the chimera is induced that causes a trans-membrane signal resulting in dimerization of the PTP catalytic domain with concomitant inhibition of PTP activity. Interestingly, the sequence of the helix-turn-helix segment of CD45 is highly conserved with that of RPTPα, and therefore it is reasonable to suggest that CD45 may dimerize similarly to RPTPα.

For RPTPs with lower sequence similarities to RPTPα, dimerization involving the helix-turn-helix and catalytic sites would appear to be less likely. This assumption is based on the observation that residues of the wedge, which are variable amongst more distantly related RPTPs, interact with invariant catalytic site residues within the RPTPα dimer (Figure 7).

Direct support for this notion is provided by the crystal structure of RPTPμ D1 (57). RPTPμ D1 is a homodimer; however, although the tertiary structures of RPTPα D1 and RPTPμ D1 are very similar, the quaternary structures of these two proteins are different. Neither the catalytic site nor the N-terminal helix-turn-helix segment of RPTPμ D1 participates in protein-protein interactions. The catalytic site of RPTPμ D1 is unhindered and adopts an open conformation similar to that of the cytosolic PTP, PTP1B. The dimer interface of RPTPμ involved residues from $\beta 8$ and $\beta 10$ of the variable insert region.

ACKNOWLEDGMENTS

The work in D Barford's laboratory has been supported by grants from the MRC, Wellcome Trust, and European Union. We thank Andrew Pannifer, Neil Hanlon, Matthew Groves, and Kurt Hoffman for discussions.

Literature Cited

1. Adler E, Donella-Deana A, Arigoni F, Pinna LA, Stragier P. 1996. Structural relationship between a bacterial development protein and eukaryotic PP2C phosphatases. *Mol. Microbiol.* 23:57–62
2. Aitken A, Cohen P. 1982. Isolation and characterisation of active fragments of protein phosphatase inhibitor-1 from rabbit skeletal muscle. *FEBS Lett.* 147:54–58

3. Bagu JR, Sonnichsen FD, Williams D, Anderson RJ, Sykes BD, Holmes CFB. 1995. Comparison of the solution structures of microcystin-LR and motuporin. *Nat. Struct. Biol.* 2:114–16
4. Barbacid M. 1987. Ras genes. *Annu. Rev. Biochem.* 56:779–827
5. Barford D, Flint AJ, Tonks NK. 1994. Crystal structure of human protein

tyrosine phosphatase 1B. *Science* 263: 1397–1404

6. Barford D, Jia Z, Tonks NK. 1995. Protein tyrosine phosphatases take off. *Nat. Struct. Biol.* 2:1043–53

7. Berndt N, Dohadwala M, Liu CWY. 1997. Constitutively active protein phosphatase 1α causes Rb-dependent G1 arrest in human cancer cells. *Curr. Biol.* 7:375–86

8. Beullens M, Van Eynde A, Bollen M, Stalmans W. 1993. Inactivation of nuclear inhibitory polypeptides of protein phosphatase-1 (NIPP-1) by protein kinase A. *J. Biol. Chem.* 268:13172–77

9. Beullens M, Van Eynde A, Stalmans W, Bollen M. 1992. The isolation of novel inhibitory polypeptides of protein phosphatase 1 from bovine thymus nuclei. *J. Biol. Chem.* 267:16538–44

10. Bilwes AM, Den Hertog J, Hunter T, Noel JP. 1996. Structural basis for inhibition of receptor protein-tyrosine phosphatase-alpha by dimerisation. *Nature* 382:555–59

11. Bliska JB. 1995. Crystal structure of the Yersinia protein tyrosine phosphatase. *Trends Microbiol.* 3:125–27

12. Bollag G, McCormick F. 1991. Differential regulation of RasGAP and neurofibromatosis gene products. *Nature* 351:575–78

13. Bork P, Brown NP, Hegyi H, Shultz J. 1996. The protein phosphatase 2C (PP2C) superfamily: detection of bacterial homologues. *Protein Sci.* 5:1421–25

14. Brady-Kalnay SM, Flint AJ, Tonks NK. 1993. Homophilic binding of PTPμ, a receptor-type protein tyrosine phosphatase, can mediate cell-cell aggregation. *J. Cell Biol.* 122:961–72

15. Brady-Kalnay SM, Rimm DL, Tonks NK. 1995. Receptor protein tyrosine phosphatase PTPμ associates with cadherins and catenins in vivo. *J. Cell Biol.* 130:977–86

16. Campos M, Fadden P, Alms G, Qian Z, Haystead TAJ. 1996. Identification of protein phosphatase-1-binding proteins by microcystin-biotin affinity chromatography. *J. Biol. Chem.* 271:28478–84

17. Cardenas ME, Muir RS, Breuder T, Heitman J. 1995. Targets of immunophilin-immunosuppressant complexes are distinct highly conserved regions of calcineurin A. *EMBO J.* 14:2772–83

18. Chen J, Martin BL, Brautigan DL. 1992. Regulation of protein serine-threonine phosphatase type 2A by tyrosine phosphorylation. *Science* 257:1261–64

19. Chen MX, Cohen PTW. 1997. Activation of protein phosphatase 5 by limited proteolysis or the binding of polyunsaturated

fatty acids to the TPR domain. *FEBS Lett.* 400:136–40

20. Chen MX, McPartlin AE, Brown L, Chen YH, Barker HM, Cohen PTW. 1994. A novel human protein serine/threonine phosphatase which possesses four tetratricopeptide repeat motifs and localises to the nucleus. *EMBO J.* 13:4278–90

21. Cheng J, Wu K, Armanini M, O'Rourke N, Dowbenko D, Lasky LA. 1997. A novel protein-tyrosine phosphatase related to the homotypically adhering k and μ receptors. *J. Biol. Chem.* 272:7264–77

22. Cho H, et al. Isolation and structural elucidation of a novel phosphocysteine intermediate in the LAR protein tyrosine phosphatase enzymatic pathway. 1992. *J. Am. Chem. Soc.* 114:7296–98

23. Coghlan VM, Perrino BA, Howard M, Langeberg LK, Hicks JB, et al. 1995. Association of protein kinase A and protein phosphatase 2B with a common anchoring protein. *Science* 267:108–11

24. Cohen PTW. 1997. Novel protein serine/threonine phosphatases: variety is the spice of life. *Trends Biochem. Sci.* 22: 245–51

25. Coleman DE, Berghuis AM, Lee E, Linder ME, Gilman AG, Sprang SR. 1994. Structures of active conformations of $G_{i\alpha}$ and the mechanism of GTP hydrolysis. *Science* 265:1405–12

26. Das AK, Helps NR, Cohen PTW, Barford D. 1996. Crystal structure of the protein serine/threonine phosphatase 2C at 2.0 Å resolution. *EMBO J.* 15:6798–809

27. Dent P, Lavoinne A, Nakielny A, Caudwell FB, Watt P, Cohen P. 1990. The molecular mechanism by which insulin stimulates glycogen synthesis in mammalian skeletal muscle. *Nature* 348:302–8

28. Denu JM, Lohse DL, Vijayalakshmi J, Saper MA, Dixon JE. 1996. Visualization of intermediate and transition-state structures in protein tyrosine phosphatase catalysis. *Proc. Natl. Acad. Sci.* 93:2493–98

29. Denu JM, Stuckey JA, Saper MA, Dixon JE. 1996. Form and function in protein phosphorylation. *Cell* 87:361–64

30. Der CJ, Finkel T, Cooper GM. 1986. Biological and biochemical properties of human RasH genes mutated at codon 61. *Cell* 44:167–76

31. Derrick JP, Wigley DB. 1992. Crystal structure of a streptococcal protein G domain bound to an Fab fragment. *Nature* 359:752–54

32. Desai DM, Sap J, Schessinger J, Weiss

A. 1993. Ligand-mediated negative regulation of a chimeric transmembrane receptor tyrosine phosphatase. *Cell* 73:541–54

33. Desdouits F, Cheetham JJ, Huang H-B, Jwon Y-G, da Cruz e Silva EF, et al. 1995. Mechanism of inhibition of protein phosphatase 1 by DARPP-32: studies with recombinant DARPP-32 and synthetic peptides. *Biochem. Biophys. Res. Comm.* 206:653–58

34. Dohadwala M, da Cruz e Silva EF, Hall FL, Williams RT, Carbonara-Hall DA, et al. 1994. Phosphorylation and inactivation of protein phosphatase 1 by cyclin dependent kinases. *Proc. Natl. Acad. Sci.* 91:6408–12

35. Doherty MJ, Moorhead G, Morrice N, Cohen P, Cohen PTW. 1995. Amino acid sequence and expression of the hepatic glycogen-binding G_L-subunit of PP1. *FEBS Lett.* 375:294–98

36. Doyle DA, Lee A, Lewis J, Kim E, Sheng M, MacKinnon R. 1996. Crystal structures of a complexed and peptide-free membrane protein-binding domain: molecular basis of peptide recognition by PDZ. *Cell* 85:1067–76

37. Duncan L, Alper S, Arigoni F, Losick R, Stragier P. 1995. Activation of cell-specific transcription by a serine phosphatase at the site of asymmetric division. *Science* 270:641–44

38. Dunn D, Chen L, Lawrence DS, Zhang Z-Y. 1996. The active site specificity of the Yersinia protein tyrosine phosphatase. *J. Biol. Chem.* 271:168–73

39. Egloff M-P, Cohen PTW, Reinemer P, Barford D. 1995. Crystal structure of the catalytic subunit of human protein phosphatase 1 and its complex with tungstate. *J. Mol. Biol.* 254:942–59

40. Egloff M-P, Johnson DF, Moorhead G, Cohen PTW, Cohen P, Barford D. 1997. Structural basis for the recognition of regulatory subunits by the catalytic subunit of protein phosphatase 1. *EMBO J.* 16:1876–87

41. Endo S, Zhou X, Connor J, Wang B, Shenolikar S. 1996. Multiple structural elements define the specificity of recombinant human inhibitor-1 as a protein phosphatase-1 inhibitor. *Biochemistry* 35:5220–28

42. Faux MC, Scott JD. 1996. More on target with protein phosphorylation: conferring specificity by location. *Trends Biochem. Sci.* 21:312–15

43. Favre B, Zoinierowicz S, Turowski P, Hemmings BA. 1994. The catalytic subunit of protein phosphatase 2A is carboxyl-methylated in vivo. *J. Biol. Chem.* 269:16311–17

44. Fiscella M, Zhang HL, Fan S, Sakaguchi K, Shen S, et al. 1997. Wip1, a novel human protein phosphatase that is induced in response to ionising radiation in a p53-dependent manner. *Proc. Natl. Acad. Sci.* 94:6048–53

45. Flint AJ, Tiganis T, Barford D, Tonks NK. 1997. Development of "substrate trapping" mutants to identify physiological substrates of protein tyrosine phosphatases. *Proc. Natl. Acad. Sci.* 94:1680–85

46. Frangioni JV, Beahm PH, Shifrin V, Jost CA, Neel BG. 1992. The nontransmembrane protein tyrosine phosphatase PTP1B localises to the endoplasmic reticulum via its 35 amino acid C-terminal sequence. *Cell* 68:545–60

47. Fuchs M, Muller T, Lerch MM, Ullrich A. 1996. Association of human protein-tyrosine phosphatase k with members of the armadillo family. *J. Biol. Chem.* 271:16712–19

48. Gaits F, Shiozaki K, Russell P. 1997. Protein phosphatase 2C acts independently of stress-activated kinase cascade to regulate stress response in fission yeast. *J. Biol. Chem.* 272:17873–79

49. Goldberg J, Huang H, Kwon Y, Greengard P, Nairn AC, Kuriyan J. 1995. Three dimensional structure of the catalytic subunit of protein serine/threonine phosphatase-1. *Nature* 376:745–53

50. Griffith JP, Kim JL, Kim EE, Sintchak MD, Thomson JA, et al. 1995. X-ray structure of calcineurin inhibited by the immunophilin-immunosuppressant FKBP12-FK506 complex. *Cell* 82:507–22

51. Guan KL, Dixon JE. 1990. Protein tyrosine phosphatase activity of an essential virulence determinant in *Yersinia*. *Science* 249:553–56

52. Guan KL, Dixon JE. 1991. Evidence of protein tyrosine phosphatase catalysis proceeding via a cysteine-phosphate intermediate. *J. Biol. Chem.* 266:17026–30

53. Helps N, Barker H, Elledge SJ, Cohen PTW. 1995. Protein phosphatase 1 interacts with p53BP2, a protein which binds to the tumour supressor p53. *FEBS Lett.* 377:295–300

54. Hemmings HC Jr, Nairn AC, Elliot JR, Greengard P. 1990. Synthetic peptide analogs of DARPP-32, an inhibitor of protein phosphatase-1. *J. Biol. Chem.* 265:20369–76

55. Hirano K, Erdodi F, Patton JG, Hartshorne DJ. 1996. Interaction of protein phospha-

tase type 1 with a splicing factor. *FEBS Lett.* 389:191–94

56. Hirano K, Phan BC, Hartshorne DJ. 1997. Interactions of the subunits of smooth muscle myosin phosphatase. *J. Biol. Chem.* 272:3683–88

57. Hoffmann KMV, Tonks NK, Barford D. 1997. The crystal structure of domain 1 of receptor protein tyrosine phosphatase μ. *J. Biol. Chem.* 272:27505–8

58. Huang H-B, Horiuchi A, Goldberg J, Greengard P, Nairn AC. 1997. Site-directed mutagenesis of amino acid residues of protein phosphatase 1 involved in catalysis and inhibitor binding, *Proc. Natl. Acad. Sci.* 94:3530–35

59. Hubbard MJ, Cohen P. 1993. On target with a new mechanism for the regulation of protein phosphorylation. *Trends. Biochem. Sci.* 18:172–77

60. Hunter T. 1995. Protein kinases and phosphatases: the yin and yang of protein phosphorylation and signalling. *Cell* 80: 225–36

61. Jain J, McCaffrey PG, Liner Z, Kerppola TK, Lambert JN, et al. 1993. Calcineurin phosphatase activity in T lymphocytes is inhibited by FK506 and cyclosporin A. *Nature* 365:352–55

62. Jia Z, Barford D, Flint AJ, Tonks NK. 1995. Structural basis for phosphotyrosine peptide recognition by protein tyrosine phosphatase 1B. *Science* 268:1754–58

63. Johnson DF, Moorhead G, Caudwell FB, Cohen P, Chen Y-H, et al. 1996. Identification of protein phosphatase-1-binding domains on the glycogen and myofibrillar targetting subunits. *Eur. J. Biochem.* 239:317–25

64. Johnson LN, Barford D. 1993. The effects of phosphorylation on the structures and function of proteins. *Annu. Rev. Biophys. Biomol. Struct.* 22:199–232

65. Johnson LN, O'Reilly M. 1996. Control by phosphorylation. *Curr. Opin. Struct. Biol.* 6:762–69

66. Kataoka T, Broek D, Wigler M. 1985. DNA sequence and characterization of the *S. cerevisiae* gene encoding adenylate cyclase. *Cell* 43:493–505

67. Kimura K et al. 1996. Regulation of myosin phosphatase by Rho and Rho-associated kinase (Rho-kinase). *Science* 273:245–48

68. King MM, Huang CY. 1984. The calmodulin-dependent activation and deactivation of the phosphoprotein calcineurin and the effect of nucleotides, pyrophosphate, and divalent metal ions. *J. Biol. Chem.* 259:8847–56

69. Kissinger CR, Parge HE, Knighton DR, Lewis CT, Pelletier LA, et al. 1995. Crystal structure of human calcineurin and the human FKBP12-FK506-calcineurin complex. *Nature* 378:641–44

70. Kwon Y-G, Huang H-B, Desdouits F, Girault J-A, Greengard P, Nairn AC. 1997. Characterisation of the interaction between DARPP-32 and protein phosphatase 1 (PP-1): DARPP-32 peptides antagonize the interaction of PP-1 with binding proteins. *Proc. Natl. Acad. Sci.* 94:3536–41

71. Landis CA, Masters SB, Spada A, Pace AM, Bourne HR, Vallar L. 1989. GTPases inhibitory mutations activate the chain of $G_{\alpha s}$ and stimulate adenylyl cyclase in human pituitary tumours. *Nature* 340:692–96

72. Lawson JE, Niu X-D, Browning KS, Trong HL, Yan J, Reed LJ. 1993. Molecular cloning and expression of the catalytic subunit of bovine pyruvate dehydrogenase phosphatase and sequence similarity with protein phosphatase 2C. *Biochemistry* 32:8987–93

73. Leung J, Bouvier-Durand M, Morris P-C, Guerrier D, Chefdor F, Giraudat J. 1994. Arabidopsis ABA response gene ABI1: Features of a calcium-modulated protein phosphatase. *Science* 264:1448–52

74. Liu J, Farmer JD, Lane WS, Friedman J, Weissman I, Schreiber SL. 1991. Calcineurin is a common target of cyclophilin-cyclosporin A and FKBP-FK506 complexes. *Cell* 66:807–15

75. Lohse DL, Denu JM, Dixon JE. 1995. Insights derived from the structures of the Ser/Thr phosphatases calcineurin and protein phosphatase 1. *Structure* 3:987–90

76. Lyons J et al. 1990. Two G protein oncogenes in human endocrine tumors. *Science* 249:655–59

77. MacKintosh C, MacKintosh RW. 1994. Inhibitors of protein kinases and phosphatases. *Trends Biochem. Sci.* 17:444–47

78. Maeda T, Wurgler-Murphy SM, Saito H. 1994. A two-component system that regulates an osmosensing MAP kinase cascade in yeast. *Nature* 369:242–45

79. Martin BL, Graves DJ. 1994. Isotope effects on the mechanism of calcineurin catalysis: kinetic solvent isotope and isotope exchange studies. *Biochim. Biophys. Acta* 1206:136–42

80. Mayer-Jaekel RE, Okhura H, Gomes R, Sunkel CE, Baumgartner S, et al. 1993. The 55 kD regulatory subunit of

Drosophila protein phosphatase 2A is required for anaphase. *Cell* 72:621–33

81. Meyer K, Leube MP, Grill E. 1994. A protein phosphatase 2C involved in ABA signal transduction in *Arabidopsis thaliana*. *Science* 264:1452–55

82. Moore F, Weekes J, Hardie DG. 1991. Evidence that AMP triggers phosphorylation as well as direct allosteric activation of rat liver AMP-activated protein kinase. *Eur. J. Biochem.* 199:691–97

83. Moorhead G, MacKintosh C, Morrice N, Cohen P. 1995. Purification of the hepatic glycogen-associated form of protein phosphatase-1 by microcystin-Sepharose affinity chromatography. *FEBS Lett.* 362:101–5

84. Moorhead G, MacKintosh CW, Morrice N, Gallagher T, MacKintosh C. 1994. Purification of type 1 protein (serine/threonine) phosphatases by microcystin-Sepharose affinity chromatography. *FEBS Lett.* 356:46–50

85. Mueller EG, Crowder MW, Averill BA, Knowles JR. 1993. Purple acid phosphatase: a diiron enzyme that catalyses a direct phospho group transfer to water. *J. Am. Chem. Soc.* 115:2974–75

86. Nassar N, Horn G, Herrman C, Scherer A, McCormick F, Wittinghofer A. 1995. The 2.2 Å crystal structure of the ras-binding domain of the serine/threonine kinase c-Raf1 in complex with Rap1A and a GTP analogue. *Nature* 375:554–60

87. Neel BG, Tonks NK. 1997. Protein tyrosine phosphatases in signal transduction. *Curr. Opin. Cell Biol.* 9:193–204

88. Deleted in proof

89. Pawson T. 1995. Protein modules and signaling networks.1995. *Nature* 373:573–80

90. Pot DA, Woodford TA, Remboutsika E, Huan RS, Dixon JE. 1991. Cloning, bacterial expression, purification, and characterisation of the cytoplasmic domain of rat LAR, a receptor-like protein tyrosine phosphatase. *J. Biol. Chem.* 266:19688–96

91. Russo AA, Jeffry PD, Patten AK, Massague J, Pavletich NP. 1996. Crystal structure of the p27[Kip1] cyclin-dependent-kinase inhibitor bound to the cyclin A-Cdk2 complex. *Nature* 382:325–31

92. Sap JY, Jiang YP, Friedlander D, Grumet M, Schlessinger J. 1994. Receptor tyrosine phosphatase RPTP-k mediates homophilic binding. *Mol. Cell Biol.* 14:1–9

93. Scheffzek K, Ahmadian MR, Kabsch W, Wiesmuller L, Lautwein A, et al. 1997. The Ras-RasGAP complex: structural basis for GTPase activation and its loss in oncogenic Ras mutants. *Science* 277:333–45

94. Shibasaki F, Price ER, Milan D, McKeon F. 1996. Role of kinases and the phosphatase calcineurin in the nuclear shuttling of transcription factor NF-AT4. *Nature* 382:370–73

95. Silverstein AM Galigniana Chen M-S Owens-Grillo JK Chinkers M, Pratt WB. 1997. Protein phosphatase 5 is a major component of glucocorticoid receptor-hsp90 complexes with properties of an FK506-binding immunophilin. *J. Biol. Chem.* 272:16224–30

96. Sondek J, Lambright DG, Noel JP, Hamm HE, Sigler PB. 1994. GTPase mechanism of G proteins from the 1.7-Å crystal structure of transducin GDPAlF$_4$-. *Nature* 372:276–29

97. Sontag E, Fedorov S, Kamibayashi C, Robbins D, Cobb M, Mumby M. 1993. The interaction of SV40 small tumor antigen with protein phosphatase 2A stimulates the MAP kinase pathway and induces cell proliferation. *Cell* 75:887–97

98. Stone JM, Collinge MA, Smith RD, Horn MA, Walker JC. 1994. Interaction of protein phosphatase with an *Arabidopsis* serine-threonine receptor kinase. *Science* 266:793–95

99. Strater N, Klabunde T, Tucker P, Witzel H, Krebs B. 1995. Crystal structure of a purple acid phosphatase containing a dinuclear Fe(III)-Zn(II) active site. *Science* 268:1489–92

100. Stuckey JA, Schubert HL, Fauman EB, Zhang ZY, Dixon JE, Saper MA. 1994. Crystal structure of *Yersinia* protein tyrosine phosphatase at 2.5 Å and the complex with tungstate. *Nature* 370:571–75

101. Tang PM, Bondor JA, Swiderek KM, dePaoli-Roach AA. 1991. Molecular cloning and expression of the regulatory (R$_{Gl}$) subunit of glycogen-associated protein phosphatase. *J. Biol. Chem.* 266:15782–89

102. Tonks NK, Diltz CD, Fischer EH. 1988. Purification of the major protein tyrosine phosphatase of human placenta. *J. Biol. Chem.* 263:6722–30

103. Van Duyne GD, Standaert RF, Karplus PA, Schreiber SL, Clardy J. 1991. Atomic structure of FKB-FK506, an immunophilin-immunosuppressant complex. *Science* 252:839–42

104. Van Eynde A, Beullens M, Stalmans W, Bollen M. 1994. Full activation of a nuclear species of PP1 by phosphorylation

with protein kinase A and casein kinase 2. *Biochem. J.* 297:447–49

105. Van Eynde A, Wera S, Beullens M, Torrekens S, Van Leuven F, et al. 1995. Molecular cloning of NIPP-1, a nuclear inhibitor of protein phosphatase-1, reveals homology with polypeptides involved in RNA processing. *J. Biol. Chem.* 270:28068–74

106. Wera S, Hemmings BA. 1995. Serine/threonine protein phosphatases. *Biochem. J.* 311:17–29

107. Deleted in proof

108. Wang X, Culotta VC, Lee CB. 1996. Superoxide dismutase protects calcineurin from inactivation. *Nature* 383:434–37

109. Wu J, Kleiner U, Brautigan DL. 1996. Protein phosphatase type-1 and glycogen bind to a domain in the skeletal muscle regulatory subunit containing conserved hydrophobic sequence motifs. *Biochemistry* 35:13858–64

110. Yamano H, Ishii K, Yanagida M. 1994. Phosphorylation of dis2 protein phosphatase at the C-terminal cdc2 consensus and its potential role in cell cycle regulation. *EMBO J.* 13:5310–18

111. Yu L, Haddy A, Rusnak F. 1995. Evidence that calcineurin accommodates an active site binuclear metal center. *J. Am. Chem. Soc.* 117:10147–48

112. Yuvaniyama J, Denu JM, Dixon JE, Saper MA. 1996. Crystal structure of the dual specificity protein phosphatase VHR. *Science* 272:1328–31

113. Zhang J, Zhang Z, Brew K, Lee EYC. 1996. Mutational analysis of the catalytic subunit of muscle protein phosphatase 1. *Biochemistry* 35:6276–82

114. Zhang L, Zhang Z, Long F, Lee EYC. 1996. Tyrosine-272 is involved in the inhibition of protein phosphatase-1 by multiple toxins. *Biochemistry* 35:1606–11

115. Zhang Z, Zhao S, Long F, Zhang L, Bai G, et al. 1994. A mutant of protein phosphatase-1 that exhibits altered toxin sensitivity. *J. Biol. Chem.* 269:16997–17000

116. Zhang Z-Y, Dixon JE. 1993. Active site labelling of the *Yersinia* protein tyrosine phosphatase: the determination of the pK_a of the active site cysteine and the function of the conserved histidine 402. *Biochemistry* 32:9340–45

117. Zhang Z-Y et al. 1994. Substrate specificity of the protein tyrosine phosphatases. *Proc. Natl. Acad. Sci. USA* 90:4446–50

118. Zhang Z-Y, Maclean D, McNamara DJ, Sawyer TK, Dixon JE. 1994. Protein tyrosine phosphatase substrate specificity: size and phosphotyrosine positioning requirements in peptide substrates. *Biochemistry* 33:2285–90

119. Zhang Z-Y, Wang Y, Dixon JE. 1994. Dissecting the catalytic mechanism of protein-tyrosine phosphatases. *Proc. Natl. Acad. Sci.* 91:1624–28

120. Zhou G, Denu JM, Wu L, Dixon JE. 1994. The catalytic role of Cys 124 in the dual specificity phosphatase VHR. *J. Biol. Chem.* 269:28084–90

121. Zhou MM, Ravichandran KS, Olejniczak EF, Petros AM, Meadows RP, et al. 1995. Structure and ligand recognition of the phosphotyrosine binding domain of SHC. *Nature* 378:584–92

122. Zhuo S, Clemens JC, Stone RL, Dixon JE. 1994. Mutational analysis of a Ser/Thr phosphatase: identification of residues important in phosphoesterase binding and catalysis. *J. Biol. Chem.* 269:26234–38

Annu. Rev. Biophys. Biomol. Struct. 1998. 27:165–98
Copyright © 1998 by Annual Reviews. All rights reserved

BIOSENSORS IN CHEMICAL SEPARATIONS

Harvey A. Fishman, Daniel R. Greenwald, and Richard N. Zare
Department of Chemistry, Stanford University, Stanford, California 94305;
email: hfishman@stanford.edu; danreif@leland.stanford.edu; zare@stanford.edu

KEY WORDS: capillary electrophoresis, chromatography, molecular recognition, drug-discovery, patch clamp

ABSTRACT

Identification of biomolecules in complex biological mixtures represents a major challenge in biomedical, environmental, and chemical research today. Chemical separations with traditional detection schemes such as absorption, fluorescence, refractive index, conductivity, and electrochemistry have been the standards for definitive identifications of many compounds. In many instances, however, the complexity of the biomixture exceeds the resolution capability of chemical separations. Biosensors based on molecular recognition can dramatically improve the selectivity of and provide biologically relevant information about the components. This review describes how coupling chemical separations with online biosensors solves challenging problems in sample analysis by identifying components that would not normally be detectable by either technique alone. This review also presents examples and principles of combining chemical separations with biosensor detection that uses living systems, whole cells, membrane receptors, enzymes, and immunosensors.

CONTENTS

165

1056-8700/98/0610-0165$08.00

INTRODUCTION

Overview

Identification of biomolecules in complex mixtures represents one of the most difficult challenges of biological and medical research today (54, 55). Powerful methods for detecting biomolecules in these mixtures include the use of chemical separations, biosensors, mass spectrometry, bioassays, and immunoassays. Advances in molecular biology and combinatorial chemical synthesis have allowed researchers to generate new molecular targets, important markers for disease processes, and pharmaceutical products and drugs increasingly rapidly. Such progress demands new detection methodologies with enhanced throughput power, speed, sensitivity, and selectivity. Moreover, ultralow volume reactors for chemical synthesis (e.g. microreaction beads in 96-well plates) and ultrasmall biological samples (e.g. rare stem cells) demand analytical methods that have superior sample handling capabilities and can perform analyses with minimal sample manipulation (52).

Most analytical methods require one or more preliminary steps to eliminate the effects of interference (100). The synergistic combination of selective detectors with a prior separation step offers such opportunities. For example, the combination of separations (e.g. HPLC, LC, GC, CE) with mass spectrometry (20), NMR (115, 116), and other types of molecular spectroscopy and electrochemical methods (118) have made possible the identification of corresponding effluents based on physical properties of the molecule (e.g. mass, charge, and chemical structure). The separation identifies compounds by retention times, and spectroscopic or electrochemical features provide a second dimension to distinguish individual peaks. Many biomolecules can still evade these sensitive detection methods, and consequently, new detectors that can identify biomolecules by other mechanisms are needed.

Coupling chemical separations with biosensor detection provides a new way to analyze analytes based on molecular recognition rather than on physical properties alone (Figure 1). Molecular recognition involves forming a complex between two molecules that is both specific and relatively permanent on the timescale of detection. Biomolecular interactions such as enzyme–substrate, antigen–antibody, and cell–cell interactions are central to biological phenomena in living organisms. The advantage of a separation/biosensor system is that individual components within a complex mixture are first purified and then detected by selective interactions. In many instances in research, however, these

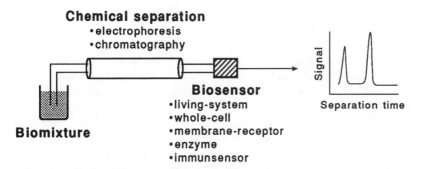

Figure 1   Schematic drawing showing the concept of coupling a separation system to a biosensor detector.

two steps, the chemical separation and the biosensing, are performed individually with some sort of manual transfer step in between.

The success of a separation/biosensor principle is exemplified by Western, Southern, and Northern blots (101). These techniques consist of first performing a gel electrophoresis separation of a protein, DNA, or RNA mixture, then physically pressing a membrane against the gel to transfer the separation pattern onto the membrane. The separated proteins, DNA, or RNA, now on the membrane, can then be detected by the addition of radioactive or fluorescently labeled antibodies or polynucleic acids that interact with specific sites and complements. The separated components are thus identified by antibody–protein interaction, DNA–, or RNA–polynucleic acid hybridization, respectively. The main disadvantages are that the slab gel separation is inefficient, off-line staining and detection are time-consuming, and the system requires a large amount of sample material. Nonetheless, this technique has been a mainstay in modern biomedical research.

An alternative approach is to collect fractions following a separation like chromatography and then test individual collected fractions with an off-line bioassay or biosensor, like the surface plasmon resonance biosensor (Pharmacia's *BIAcore* biosensor) (79, 90). The transfer made necessary by such an approach can result in sample loss and contamination errors, and it is logistically unreasonable to screen complex samples that may contain hundreds of peaks. Sample collection followed by biosensor analysis is a particular problem when analyzing fractionated components that have a short half-life and may not remain in their nascent biological state in a collection vial. For example, some pheromones or drugs with particular stereoisomeric configurations can thermally isomerize before the separation (59). Thus, the combination of an online biosensor with a separation allows both a highly efficient separation process and molecular recognition detection that is fast, sensitive, and eliminates problems of offline sample handling (e.g. loss, dilution, racemization, and alteration).

Coupled chemical separation/biosensor systems have lagged in development because researchers in biosensors have been developing sensors that can discriminate multiple species by molecular recognition alone, and because separation scientists have largely attempted to develop improved separation methods with conventional detectors. The problem is that biosensors are selective but in some cases are not selective enough. Similarly, although chemical separations can be highly efficient, some mixtures are too complicated and overwhelm the separation capacity of the column. The combination of these two methods can enable identification of molecules that are not detectable separately by either method.

One criticism of a biosensor/separation system as opposed to a biosensor system alone has been the long timescale of a separation. With recent advances in microfluidic chip-based separations (39, 46) and microcolumn separations (73), separations are faster and in some cases can be performed even in the subsecond time regime, which better matches the timescale of some biosensor detectors.

This review discusses how chemical separations have been combined with biosensor detection to make a sensing system that can be superior to either of the two technologies alone, one that meets the demands of identifying key molecular species in complex biomolecular mixtures. Although the commercial feasibility of bringing these systems to market is an important issue, this review article focuses instead on examples of separation/biosensor systems in basic research. For this review, we have made a search of *CAS On-Line, Medline, Analytical Abstracts*, and *SCISEARCH* to find examples of separation/biosensor systems where the biosensor is positioned at the end of the separation. Many examples of separation/biosensor systems were found not in systematic searches but in book chapters and cross-referenced with other articles. We present concepts and definitions related to chemical separations and biosensors first, followed by discussions of biosensor/separation systems based on living systems, whole cells, enzymes, membrane receptors, and immunosensors.

Principles

Many different types of biosensors have been coupled to chromatography or electrophoresis to monitor continuously fractionated mixtures (Figure 1). Although biological elements that confer molecular recognition have been combined in a separation format (e.g. affinity chromatography, capillary electrophoresis immunoassay, precolumn derivatization with molecular recognition elements), this review is limited to a discussion of those systems that use a post-separation (e.g. postcolumn) biosensor. A biosensor as defined by *Biosensors and Bioelectronics* is an analytical device "incorporating a biological material (e.g. tissue, microorganisms, organelles, cell receptors, enzymes, antibodies, nucleic acids, etc.), a biologically derived material or biomimetic intimately associated with or integrated within a physiochemical transducer or transducing microsystem, which may be optical, electrochemical, thermoelectric, piezoelectric, or magnetic."

The advantage of a separation approach is that species are physically removed from one another, which simplifies final detection. Conventional physical detectors (e.g. electrochemistry, fluorescence, Raman, refractive index, photothermal) are useful for sensing the presence and quantitating the amount of analyte, but they have difficulty in providing additional information about structure, function, and other properties that would help distinguish one component from others in a mixture. Moreover, it is often difficult to separate components so that the detector has only one to measure. Complex biomolecules such as proteins or chromosomal DNA can overwhelm the separation capacity; biomolecules of interest can elude detection because they lack moieties that can be sensed by physical detectors. Biosensors can overcome many of these separation challenges for a wide range of molecules. When used alone, however, they often cannot distinguish between multiple biologically active components in a mixture, or they miss components when an antagonist/agonist pair is present. They may also fail to differentiate closely related species, like a family of proteins, or new classes of molecules. Furthermore, as Skoog et al (100) point out, few if any analytical signals are so specific as to be free of interference, and biosensors can be plagued by artifactual signals. Thus, the combination of separation and biosensor creates a synergism that makes molecular identification readily available in a complex mixture.

Combining a biosensor with a separation, however, poses several problems. These problems include renewal of the biomaterial over the course of the separation, reproducibility of the biomaterial involving issues of potentiation or desensitization, matching the volume of the effluent with the biosensor surface area, the compatibility (e.g. organic vs aqueous) of the separation medium, and the temperature of the effluent.

METHODS

Separations with Living-System–Based Biosensors

A living-system biosensor is based on the response of a functioning organ or entire organism. Examples of such biosensors are olfactory organs such as the antennules from crustacea (11) and cockroaches (75), tissue slices from kidney (92), intact plant tissue (57), and the human nose (1). Living systems have the inherent advantage of responding to a component in a manner that is physiologically significant and that can reveal a molecule's downstream biological function in a real-world system. For this reason, animals have always been used to test the efficacy of an experimental drug or to determine the side effects of a new drug or a new treatment (50). The use of intact living systems instead of subcellular components like enzymes and receptors has several other advantages. Whole-cell systems provide an optimized enzymatic pathway, a fresh supply of receptors and cofactors to replenish the surface membrane, increased stability, and biologically significant information (113).

A major problem with a living-system biosensor is specificity of response (54). Given the multitude of receptor and enzyme targets for a particular molecule, it is extremely difficult to analyze a mixture of components with such a sensor. When presented with a mixture, the living-system biosensor will respond simultaneously to more than one component; thus that response is difficult or impossible to interpret. Several groups have attempted to overcome this problem by identifying characteristic features of the response, such as kinetics (70), specific enzyme inhibitors (27), or growth and storage conditions (27) that may distinguish the presence of a particular component in a mixture. This approach becomes unsatisfactory if there are multiple similar components. A separation that purifies the components prior to biosensor detection ensures that the response of the biosensor is to one component and not to many. Components are thus identified by both functional recognition and separation retention time.

GAS CHROMATOGRAPHY/OLFACTOMETRY   One of the best and earliest examples of combining a separation with a biosensor was the development of gas chromatography/olfactometry (GCO) (1, 2, 37, 76, 102, 103). GCO is a technique whereby a human sniffs the purified effluents emerging from a GC column, hence the term "GC-sniffers." Shortly after the development of GC in the 1950s, researchers interested in flavors and fragrances used humans as biosensors to identify active components that in many cases were not detectable by any chemical means. Applications of GCO included analysis of odors in river water (51), identification of insect pheromones, fragrances, feed-flavor stability (i.e. aroma decline of stored feed) (23), analysis of odorous compounds from night soil, sewage treatment plants and refuse incinerators (102), waste gases (103), industrial process gas odor, animal rendering, fishmeal drying, brick production, and heat treatment of vegetable material (9).

The GCO system made possible the recognition of some aroma-active compounds with sensitivity levels unequaled by conventional detectors. This high level of sensitivity is not surprising, given recent reports by Firestein and coworkers (71), who demonstrated single-molecule detection sensitivity by single olfactory neurons. Disadvantages of GCO include the cost and training of a human detector, the exposure of humans to chemicals, and psychophysical bias.

Obvious ethical problems exist with the use of humans for testing; biosensors not requiring a human are preferable for many purposes.

GAS CHROMATOGRAPHY/ELECTROANTENNOGRAPHIC DETECTION   In 1969, Moorhouse et al (75) developed an insect-based system that consisted of linking a gas chromatograph (GC) with an insect's antennal sense organ. A similar system, shown in Figure 2a, uses an excised insect antenna to provide retention times of physiologically active compounds in extracts of complex natural products.

The antenna signal, or electroantennographic detection (EAD), is measured by extracellularly placed recording electrodes. The antenna is placed between two chloridized silver wires that are attached to amplifier inputs. A drop of NaCl solution is placed on the antenna to prevent it from drying out. The antenna and wires are then put in a glass tube that is supplied a humidified stream of synthetic air mixed with the effluent from the GC column. Volatile constituents of the pheromonal mixture are separated on the GC column, and the effluent is split between a flame ionization detector (FID) and the antenna. The effluents are mixed with a cool steam of nitrogen so that the gas that reaches the antenna will be below 30°C. By recording simultaneously from the FID and the antenna, Moorhouse et al (75) could correlate retention times with EAD responses.

The GC/EAD system allowed detection of active sex pheromones from female moths and showed distinct differences between female and male antennae in the ability to detect pheromone extracts. Moorhouse et al (75) showed how the GC/EAD could help provide insights into differences in behavior between male and female moths. The sensitivity of the method was such that good EAD responses could be obtained from the equivalent of 10^{-4} female pheromone glands (75). Arn and coworkers (8) obtained dose-response curves with a GC/EAD system that had detection limits of 100 fg (S/N of 3) for Z-7,9-dodecadienyl acetate pheromone from the European grapevine moth, *Lobesia botrana*. Moreover, they found that the signal intensity was approximately linear between 100 fg and 100 ng. Other groups have also used the GC/EAD system successfully to identify insect sex pheromones (10, 16, 78).

One of the benefits of doing a GC separation before using the antenna is the ability to provide chiral discrimination between R/S stereochemical isomers in a pheromone mixture (8, 58, 59). Stereochemical separation can be performed using a chiral GC column. It is often the case in pheromone research that the stereochemistry of pheromones is not analytically determined but inferred from comparative bioassays conducted with all possible synthetic stereoisomers. An antennule biosensor by itself gives no information about the stereochemistry of natural products whose stereoisomers show similar bioreactivity. Using chiral GC columns, Arn et al (8) showed that the GC/EAD could separate positional

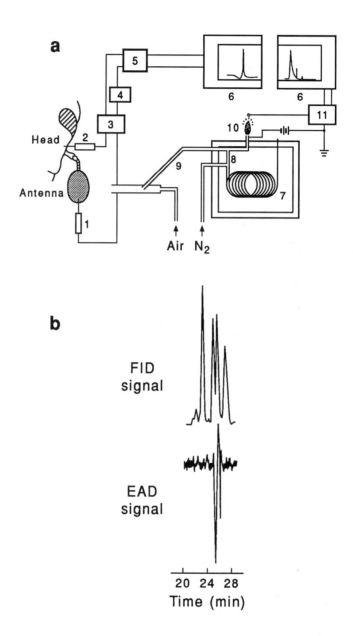

and geometrical isomers, thus giving precise information on the retention times of active compounds and permitting the analysis of insect pheromones with exceedingly small amounts of material. Meinwald and coworkers (58, 59) similarly used chiral GC/EAD to establish that supellapyrone, a female sex pheromone of the brown-banded cockroach, *Supella longipalpa*, has the 2′R,4′R configuration. Meinwald and coworkers show in Figure 2b a separation of four stereoisomers of the brown-banded cockroach pheromone that demonstrates how the EAD only responds to isomers that have biological activity. With the information from the GC/EAD system, an enantiomerically pure sex pheromone can be synthesized for the containment of the population of this cockroach.

Separations with Whole-Cell–Based Biosensors

Whole-cell biosensors operate on the response of individual or multiple disassociated biological cells. Many examples of cells as biosensors, as well as the emergence of commercial devices (e.g. the microphysiometer) using such biosensors, are described in the literature (70). Cell-based biosensors are often referred to as metabolism sensors, because the cell responds to agonist binding by initiating a metabolic pathway, like a G-protein–coupled pathway or other generalized enzymatic pathways (54). Changes in the cell's metabolism can result in changes in the acidification of the extracellular fluid (70) or increases in intracellular calcium (107), two popular methods for transducing the metabolic response. Alternatively, cells can be used as enzyme factories catalyzing a chemical reaction and producing a reaction product that can be measured. Unlike isolated enzymes, cells have complexes in a spatially organized environment that continually replenish supplies of enzyme proteins or cofactors (55). Cells can also be used as detectors in mutagenicity assays, whereby they can screen for potentially carcinogenic materials (6).

Many of the advantages and disadvantages of a living-system biosensor apply as well to a dissociated cell-based system. One of the major advantages of a cell-based biosensor is the possibility of engineering the cell response via specific receptor subtypes expressed on the cell surface. Cultured cell lines can be transfected with DNA coding for a membrane receptor (94), oocytes can be microinjected with RNA coding for a membrane receptor (98), or mast

←——————————————————————————————————

Figure 2 Gas chromatography/electroantennographic detection (GC/EAD). (*a*) Schematic of a GC/EAD system using an insect antenna as the detector. [(16), Figure 1, reprinted with kind permission from Elsevier Science Ltd, The Boulevard, Langford Lane, Kidlington OX5 1GB, UK]; (*b*) Chiral separation of four stereoisomers and detection using GC/FID (*top*) and GC/EAD (*bottom*). The EAD response is from a male *S. longipalpa* antenna. [(58), Figure 3, copyright 1995, National Academy of Sciences, USA, by permission.]

cells can be incubated with antibodies that become cross-linked and signal the cell to degranulate upon the binding of an agonist of choice (89). In contrast to a living-system biosensor, cell cultures derived from tumor-cell lines readily allow replication so that multiple cells can be obtained that are genetically identical or similar and possess many of the same biological functions. Although the ability to design cells improves selectivity, immortalized cell lines used for transfection purposes still may contain endogenous receptors. Moreover, even if a single receptor is expressed, the receptor may often respond to a family of structurally related molecules. Consequently, the coupling of cells to separations overcomes many but not all problems of selectivity.

The coupling of individual cells to separations is particularly difficult because, unlike enzymes or living systems, cells are often more susceptible to damage or death by environmental changes. Cells do not have long-term viability and long-term responsivity. Whereas enzymes can have relatively large physical tolerances and living systems can have several layers of tissue for protection, cells have only a lipid bilayer to maintain an ionic potential difference; consequently, the cell can be adversely affected by subtle changes in pH, temperature, and ionic strength. Accordingly, the effluent from the separation process must also be compatible with the cells. Despite these challenges, cells have been coupled successfully to CE, GC, HPLC, LC, and TLC.

CAPILLARY ELECTROPHORESIS/SINGLE-CELL BIOSENSORS (CE/SCB)   Zare and coworkers have pioneered the coupling of single cells to CE (35, 36, 98). CE is well suited to cells because of its physiologic compatibility, nanoliter to picoliter sample volumes, and analysis times typically in the 5- to 30-minute range. Figure 3 shows schematics of CE/SCB biosensor systems. Rapid electrophoretic separation of analytes is accomplished in a fused silica capillary, and the effluent from the capillary outlet is directed to an individual cell for detection. The CE outlet reservoir is the chamber that contains the cells, and the CE separation buffer is a physiologic cell Ringer's solution and is the same as contained in the outlet chamber bath solution. In Figure 3a, the cellular response is transduced via a cultured cell that has been loaded with a Ca^{2+} indicator dye, fluo-3, that responds to cytosolic Ca^{2+} concentration. Upon agonist binding, cytosolic

$\longrightarrow$

Figure 3   Capillary electrophoresis/single-cell biosensor (CE/SCB) system. (a) A CE/SCB device based on monitoring Ca^{2+} changes within one or more cultured cells with the use of the Ca^{2+}-sensitive dye, fluo-3. (b) A CE/SCB system based on membrane current measurements from a two-electrode voltage clamp of a Xenopus laevis oocyte expressing a cloned membrane receptor. [Reprinted with permission from (98), Figure 1, copyright 1995, American Association for the Advancement of Science.]

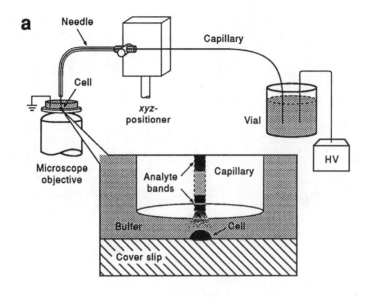

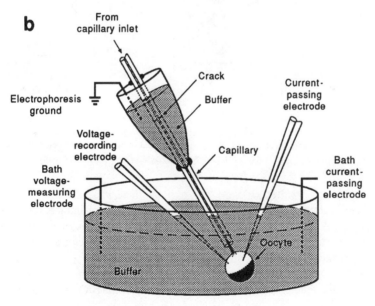

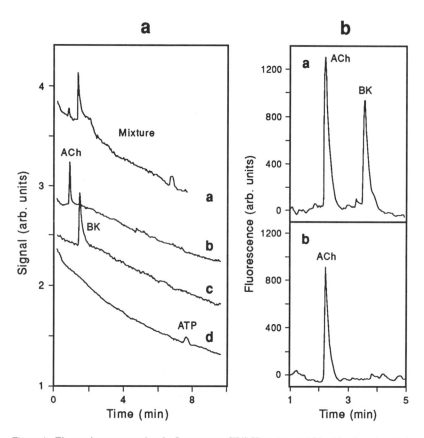

Figure 4 Electropherograms using the fluorescence CE/SCB system. (*a*) Identification of multiple components in a mixture of ACh, BK, and ATP. [Reprinted with permission from (98), Figure 3, copyright 1995, American Association for the Advancement of Science]; (*b*) Identification of BK using the BK antagonist, icatibant. [(36), Figure 1, copyright 1995, National Academy of Sciences, USA, by permission].

Ca^{2+} concentration rises and the fluorescence intensity of intracellular fluo-3 increases. A fluorescence microscope measures the fluorescence. In Figure 3*b*, the SCB is based on the two-electrode voltage response of an oocyte that expresses specific receptors on its outer membrane surface.

Using the cultured-cell, fluorescence-based SCB system, Shear et al (98) demonstrated that a PC12 cell could detect bradykinin (BK), ATP, and acetylcholine (ACh) in a mixture of standards (Figure 4*a*). As a detector for CE, the SCB showed versatility of response by detecting a peptide, nucleotide, and ACh, a traditionally difficult-to-detect transmitter, in a single analysis. In a more challenging test, the SCB/CE system was able to detect ACh in a lysate of nerve-growth-factor–differentiated PC12 cells, and BK in a Hep G2 cell lysate (36). The SCB/CE system was able to detect ACh in the low femtomole range and BK in the low attomole range.

One of the potential uses of the SCB/CE system is to search for unknown agonists to orphan receptors. With the use of specific antagonists included in the medium bathing the cell detector, the SCB/CE system identified ligands by the migration time and by the inhibition of specific receptor subtypes. In particular, comparison of separation runs with and without the antagonist included in the medium provided information about what receptors and receptor subtypes were activated by the electrophoretically separated agonist (Figure 4b). Using the BK antagonist, icatibant, with the CE/SCB system, Fishman et al (36) showed that BK could be detected in a lysate of liver cells (Hep G2 lysate) and that BK was activating the B2 bradykinin receptor in the SCB. Another promising use for the CE/SCB system was shown to be the screening of bioactive products from peptide degradation. Identification of BK degradation products in a plasma sample was accomplished.

A widespread limitation in using cell-based biosensors for repetitive chemical analysis is loss of agonist-induced response caused by receptor desensitization. Loss of receptor response is a general problem regardless of whether the biosensor uses the receptor in the format of an intact cell or reconstituted into an artificial membrane. To overcome this problem, Fishman et al (35) scanned an array of immobilized cells underneath the CE column outlet. In this way, electrophoretically fractionated components that exit the separation capillary are always directed onto cells previously unexposed to receptor agonists. Because the CE column delivers subnanoliter volumes onto the cells that are contained in 500 mL of buffer, the fractionated sample undergoes significant dilution and affects only those cells located directly underneath or immediately adjacent to the capillary outlet.

Shear et al (98) also demonstrated the feasibility of engineering a cell detector with receptors specific to a particular class of agonists. A *Xenopus* oocyte was microinjected with in vitro–transcribed mRNA that encoded for the serotonin 5HT1c receptor, and then it was used as the SCB; thus Shear et al tailored a cellular response to specific components instead of natively occurring receptors on the surface of the cell being used. As shown in Figure 3b, a standard two-electrode voltage clamp setup measured changes in transmembrane current in response to serotonin that eluted from the outlet of the CE column, which was positioned adjacent to the microinjected oocyte. Because the current generated from the CE separation voltage interfered with the two-electrode voltage clamp current signal, the separation and detection currents had to be decoupled. Decoupling involved fracturing the capillary 3 to 5 cm above the outlet and grounding the solution in this fissure, instead of the outlet reservoir. The connection to ground functioned as a voltage divider and thus minimized the CE current that affected the oocyte SCB. With this system, identification of serotonin could be made in a standard solution. Measurements using the fluorescence-based PC12 cell SCB did not require the capillary decoupling current technique because of the robust nature of the PC12 cells.

CAPILLARY ELECTROPHORESIS/PERMEABILIZED SINGLE-CELL BIOSENSORS (CE/ PSCB)   Allbritton and coworkers (63) developed an elegant cell biosensor based on the use of intracellular IP_3 receptors and coupled this IP_3 biosensor detector to CE. Because not all agonist molecules are recognized by membrane receptors located on the surface of a cell, the use of intracellular-receptor-based SCB opens up the possibility of detection to intracellular targets previously not thought possible, including intracellular second messenger molecules like IP_3. The key to using intracellular receptors is the use of permeabilized cells, thus making the effluent from the CE capillary directly accessible to receptors on intracellular organelles such as the endoplasmic reticulum (ER). Using this PSCB, identification of IP_3 was accomplished on the basis of migration time. The concentration of IP_3 in the electrophoresed sample was determined by the amount of Ca^{2+} released from the ER in response to IP_3 binding to ER receptors.

The combination of a separation with the PSCB is particularly important in this example because the ER can release Ca^{2+} in response to other small molecules. Using this system, calibration curves were possible to construct, which allowed the quantitative assay of IP_3 with a mass sensitivity of 1 femtomole and a concentration sensitivity of 100 nM. Detection of endogenous IP_3 in an oocyte stimulated with serum was possible (NL Allbritton, unpublished observations). Allbritton's group is currently using this novel IP_3 detection system along with a subcellular, subsecond microsampling device (64) to understand the role of IP_3 in the generation of Ca^{2+} spikes and waves in *Xenopus* oocytes.

GAS CHROMATOGRAPHY/SINGLE-CELL RECORDING (GC/SCR)   Wadhams and coworkers (15, 109) developed a gas chromatography/single-cell recording system that consisted of coupling the effluent of a GC column to the electrical recording of an individual olfactory cell from an antennal organ. The GC effluent was split between an FID and the antennal preparation. Recordings from individual olfactory cells associated with individual sensilla were made with the use of tungsten microelectrodes. By combining a GC column with a single olfactory cell, Wadhams and coworkers (109) identified stereochemically specific pheromones that could not be detected by the GC/EAD technique. The GC/EAD system responds to pheromones from an ensemble of receptors and from many, but not all, the cells in the antennal organ. For example, the use of single olfactory cells from the antennal organ of bark beetles indicated that specialized groups of olfactory cells interact with different pheromone stereoisomers, whereas other cells presumably do not have receptors that interact with the active pheromone. When a group of cells is recorded as in the GC/EAD system, the signal is diluted by nonresponding cell types (adding background noise from cells without appropriate receptors) and the sensitivity of the system is lowered.

The GC/SCR system, based on the response of a single cell, makes possible a more detailed understanding of the perception of olfactory stimuli because of the increased selectivity and sensitivity. In Wadhams' work on bark beetle pheromones, GC/SCR detection threshold concentrations for certain stereoisomeric pheromones were 10^9–10^{10} molecules/ml of air, two orders magnitude better sensitivity than with the GC/EAD (109). Stimulation of a pair of cells specialized to $(-)$-threo- and $(-)$-erythro-4-methyl-3-heptanol with 200 pg of the mixed isomers resulted in a S/N ratio of 6. Long-term stability of several hours is possible with the GC/SCR system if the stimulus concentrations are low. In summary, the main advantage of the direct coupling of SCR technique to the GC is that it allows the study of the responses of individual olfactory cells to isomers of very high purity. Because small isomeric impurities in synthetic samples are frequently difficult to remove without GC purification, GC/SCR is a useful technique for studying pheromone activity.

CHROMATOGRAPHY/MICROBE- AND TISSUE-BASED BIOSENSORS   Several groups have coupled HPLC and LC to microbial cell– and tissue-based detectors (26, 62). Connor et al (26) coupled rapidly responding tissue- and microbe-based carbon paste electrodes as a detector for LC. Instead of responding via transmembrane current or calcium increases, biosensors based on these "enzyme factories" respond to substrates of the enzyme system by catalyzing a substrate's conversion to an enzyme product. Microbes and tissues are chosen because they contain an enzyme that catalyzes the conversion of a particular substrate of interest. The carbon paste electrode is prepared by doping the carbon paste with the tissue or microbe of interest.

The advantage of the mixed biocatalyst-carbon paste electrode is a substantial reduction of response time owing to the absence of the long diffusion path that occurs when using a support membrane. The fast response time ($\sim$30 s) makes these biosensors suitable for measuring dynamic changes in concentrations that occur in liquid chromatography separations. This system greatly simplifies complex chromatograms because only the substrates to the enzymes present in the cellular material are detected. Thus, a new selectivity dimension, based on bioreactivity, addresses the specificity limitation of some cellular materials used alone as biosensors.

Connor et al (26) coupled a mixed biocompartment carbon paste electrode containing banana, yeast, and mushroom to LC. Using this system, amperometric measurements of biogenic amines, primary alcohols, and monophenols could be performed in complex mixtures. For example, a mixed banana-carbon paste detector was used to measure norepinephrine, epinephrine, and dopamine in a urine sample spiked with these compounds. Only peaks corresponding to reductive monitoring of the quinone products of the biocatalytic reaction were observed despite the complexity of this physiologic mixture. By way of comparison, the use of a conventional unmodified carbon paste detector in a separation of the same urine sample resulted in the detection of five additional peaks, including overlapping peaks of ascorbic acid and uric acid. In addition, Connor et al coupled LC to a dual electrode system, one electrode bare and the other modified with the microbe/tissue. In this dual electrode system, the LC effluent is split between two detectors; thus a ratio of the response to each component is obtained. This ratio allows peaks to be characterized by their "bioactivity ratio." Concentration dependence could be achieved and linear calibration curves over a limited range could be obtained. Detection limits of 10^{-5} M were achieved for dopamine.

THIN-LAYER CHROMATOGRAPHY/MUTAGENICITY BIOASSAY   Mutagenicity assays have also been coupled to separations; a chemical separation is combined with a detector that can provide information about a compound's carcinogenic potential. Ames and coworkers (6) developed the mutagenicity bioassay in 1975. Mutagenicity assays are based on the survival of cells after their exposure to mutagens. The assay consists of bacteria genetically altered to be deficient in histidine synthesis. In the presence of a mutagenic compound that may cause DNA breakage, the bacteria can revert to histidine production in a histidine-deficient medium. The bacteria is unable to survive in a histidine-missing medium unless a revertant mutation event occurs from the chemical in question. The assay typically consists of isolating environmental and occupational chemicals by HPLC and then manually applying the potential mutagens to a *Salmonella typhimurium* bacteria bioassay (7, 93, 95). This procedure of eluting and then collecting the chromatographed compounds from the column or plates and then performing the bioassay is time consuming and inefficient.

Separation methods can be combined with mutagenic bioassays for more efficient identification and study of potentially carcinogenic or mutagenic chemicals. Combined chromatography and mutagenicity tests are simpler, faster, and better suited for screening large numbers of compounds than the bioassay alone (14). Bjorseth et al (14) first detected mutagens in complex samples by directly applying the *Salmonella* assay on thin-layer chromatography (TLC) plates. In these TLC/mutagenicity assays, suspected carcinogens were separated on standard silica, cellulose, and reverse-phase TLC, and then the plates were placed at the bottom of bacterial petri plates. An agar layer was applied above the TLC plates, and the Ames *Salmonella* strain was applied above the agar layer as a top agar suspension and incubated for three days to identify revertant mutants. Areas containing mutagens could then be removed and analyzed for chemical characteristics. This TLC/mutagenicity assay system is similar in concept to that of a Western blot because the biosensor is added after the separation. Nonetheless, this combination greatly reduced the number of bacterial tests needed to screen a sample and has many advantages over the traditional methods of assaying individual collected fractions.

Houk & Claxton (42) simplified the test by eliminating the need to apply a top agar layer on the TLC separation. Instead, suspected toxins were separated in the TLC plates and overlaid with a single bacterial agar layer. This method enhanced direct contact between bacteria and toxin and shortened preparation time. The usefulness of this system was demonstrated by assaying both crude toxic waste samples and 14 known *Salmonella* mutagens. The assay has applications in clinical pharmacology and toxicology as well. For example, a very similar technique was applied in the study of mutagenic metabolites in the urine of patients taking the antiparasitic drug Tinidazole®. Greater mutagenic activity was retained in the TLC plate samples as compared to analysis of fractionated HPLC peaks (34).

Separations with Membrane-Receptor–Based Biosensors

Biosensors based on membrane surface receptors consist of an individual or group of receptors coupled to a transducing device such as an electrode. The receptors are highly labile and require stabilization in some manner (113). Isolated receptors can be placed into a lipid bilayer such as a liposome, synaptosome, or black lipid membrane (BLM). Instead of isolating them, they can be used in their native membrane such as in a whole-cell patch clamp, inside-out patch clamp, or outside-out patch clamp (e.g. sniffer-patch detectors) (4, 43, 53, 74, 119).

All membrane-receptor biosensors have an extracellular binding region that interacts with a diffusable agonist. In metabotropic receptors, the binding event causes the activation of membrane enzymes that produce second-messenger molecules that initiate a biochemical cascade of downstream events to amplify the original signal. Ionotropic receptors are linked to ion channels that open in response to agonist binding to allow the transmembrane flow of ions. Ionotropic receptors have been used almost exclusively in biosensors thus far because the opening of an ion channel can be readily measured with a sensitive electrical sensor. Moreover, ionotropic receptors can be purified and then reconstituted into a lipid bilayer, whereas the metabotropic receptors rely on multiple enzymes and cellular organelles to elicit a response. The ionotropic receptors used include nicotinic acetylcholine receptors (nAChR) (104), and GABA type A (GABA$_A$) receptors (49, 84, 85).

An important advantage of membrane receptors over most antibody binding assays is that they recognize families of chemicals of physiological, pharmacological, and toxocological significance—including amino acids, peptides, therapeutic drugs, narcotics, hallucinogens, neuroleptics, hormones, and toxicants. Because a receptor system is often activated by multiple, structurally related endogenous agonists, class-specific biosensors can be made using membrane receptors. The ability to detect classes of compounds is an important feature, but such biosensors do have difficulty identifying individual members of a family of biomolecules. Receptor-based biosensors using ligand-receptor systems cannot discriminate unless they have absolute specificity for a ligand. Thus, like living-system and cell-based biosensors, receptor-based biosensors suffer from selectivity problems, especially in identifying individual components.

CAPILLARY ELECTROPHORESIS/PATCH CLAMP (CE/PC)   To overcome the problem of absolute specificity with membrane-receptor biosensors, Zare and coworkers (85) pioneered the development of capillary electrophoresis with patch-clamp detection. The CE/PC system is similar to the CE/SCB system in that receptor ligands are separated electrophoretically, delivered onto the surface of a patch-clamped cell, and detected by the cell at a characteristic migration time (Figure 5). Agonist identification is obtained from analysis of electrophoretic migration times, and the cellular response can be measured quantitatively (i.e. the potency of the agonist) or qualitatively (i.e. identification of component). The advantage of the CE/PC system is its ability to derive detailed information about the activated receptors such as kinetics, rates of ion-channel desensitization, distribution of conductance states, open-and-close times, and ion-channel pharmacology.

Orwar et al (49, 84, 85) coupled two variations of patch-clamp detection to CE: whole-cell and outside-out configurations. One of the main problems of coupling the CE separation to the patch-clamp biosensor is decoupling the effects of the electric field generated from the voltage across the CE capillary. Because the potentials from the CE capillary can act on the cellular membrane and interfere with detection of the small ($\sim$pA) current in the patch-clamp electrode, decoupling of the electric field is even more crucial here than in the two-electrode voltage-clamp–based CE/SCB system described above. Although the CE voltage is less problematic in the CE/SCB system, the residual current is still significant. This interference can be avoided if the CE capillary is fractured and connected to ground above the outlet end, a method originally

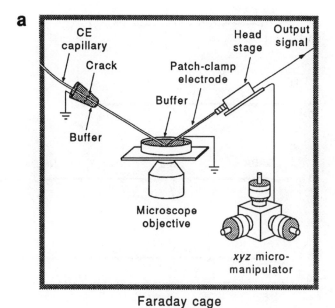

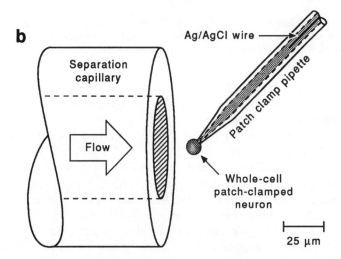

Figure 5 Capillary electrophoresis/patch clamp (CE/PC) system. [Reprinted with permission from (85), Figure 1, copyright 1996, American Association for the Advancement of Science.]

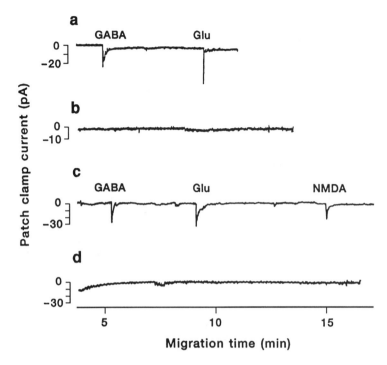

Figure 6 Electropherograms obtained using the CE/PC system based on inward currents from outside-out, patch-clamped olfactory interneurons. [Reprinted with permission from (85), Figure 2, copyright 1996, American Association for the Advancement of Science.]

described by Wallingford & Ewing (110). The residual potential that flows past the fractured capillary is compensated for by applying an offset potential to the patch-clamp amplifier system.

Orwar et al (85) used mammalian neurons freshly dissociated from a rat olfactory bulb as an outside-out PC biosensor. With the use of this CE/PC system, separation and detection of mixed standards of GABA, Glu, and NMDA were accomplished because of the presence of $GABA_A$ receptors and two types of glutamate receptors, AMPA and NMDA, on the olfactory cells (Figure 6). As a demonstration of this system's ability to obtain pharmacological information, the response to GABA was completely blocked by picrotoxin, the response to Glu in a Mg^{2+}-supplemented Gly-free media was completely blocked by the AMPA receptor antagonist 6-cyano-7-nitroquinoxaline-2,3-dione, and the response to NMDA was completely blocked by the addition of Mg^{2+} ions.

Another advantage of using patch-clamp detectors with CE is the ability to identify separated species from the ion permeability of the activated receptor/ion channel complex. That permeability can help isolate the contribution of a single receptor if a cell membrane contains several that can be activated. Current-to-voltage plots of the reversal potential (i.e. measurement of evoked current at different holding potentials) and the use of different intra- and extracellular solutions allow estimation of the ion permeability. The ability to extract the ion permeability from components separated by CE allows identification of electrophoretically separated kainic acid (KA), a molecule that activates non-NMDA glutamate receptors.

Another measurement that can be taken using the whole-cell patch clamp is of mean single-channel conductances and corner frequencies, which are characteristics of the current responses specific to particular agonist/receptor interactions. Whole-cell patch-clamp current is based on an ensemble of channels opening. When a spectral analysis of the whole-cell current traces of separated components is performed, values of conductance through single channels can be obtained as well as a unique power spectrum for each agonist. The power spectrum yields corner frequencies to further characterize receptor interactions for the separated agonist. Combining whole-cell PC/spectral analysis with chemical separations can obtain mean single-channel currents for electrophoretically separated GABA, Glu, and NMDA. Spectral analysis of the PC current is useful only in situations where a single ligand activates a single-receptor ion channel. However, spectral identification of different receptor ion-channel complexes cannot be performed with a mixture of components without either a pharmacological block of receptor systems or a separation step. Because pharmacological blocks are not necessarily complete, the ability to have a separation step is advantageous.

Outside-out detection combined with CE allows the identification of separated ligands based on conductance values of individual ion-channels. Orwar et al (85) used freshly dissociated rat olfactory interneurons as sources of outside-out membranes for the PC biosensor. Separated GABA and NMDA evoked single-channel openings and provided further identification by individual conductances and single-ion-channel currents. Moreover, resolving openings and shuttings at the single-channel level yielded information about channel kinetics, yet another characteristic that can help identify a specific ligand/receptor interaction.

Amplitudes of KA-receptor responses increase in the CE/PC system with higher concentrations of separated KA agonists in the injected sample. A dose-response curve from a single patch preparation, however, cannot be made because of the limited longevity (~20–30 min) of the biosensor. For this reason the dose-response curve was constructed using a new patch preparation for each agonist concentration. Although patch longevity remains a major limitation with longer separation times, faster separations of under 1 min have been achieved with CE (39) and should be able to make quantitation possible with CE/PC.

Finally, Jardemark and coworkers (K Jardemark, C Farre, I Jacobson, RN Zare, O Orwar, manuscript in preparation) showed that the CE/PC system could be used as a drug-screening technique for natural and synthetic receptor antagonists. The assay works by adding an agonist to the CE running buffer so that the receptor is constantly activated. In the presence of an antagonist that has been electrophoretically separated, a negative peak corresponding to the inhibited channel is observed.

Separations with Enzyme-Based Biosensors

A review of the literature reveals that enzyme-based systems are the most prevalent and popular separation/biosensor combination. Enzymes are proteins that catalyze biochemical reactions. The earliest example of an enzyme biosensor was the Clarke enzyme electrode in 1962 in which an enzyme was coupled to an oxygen electrode (25). Two enzymes commonly utilized in separation/biosensor systems are oxidoreductases and oxidases that generate NADH and H_2O_2 as their respective products; in turn these products are transduced by electrochemical, optical, or thermal methods (66). Enzymes can be immobilized directly onto an electrode surface (Figure 7b) or incorporated into an immobilized

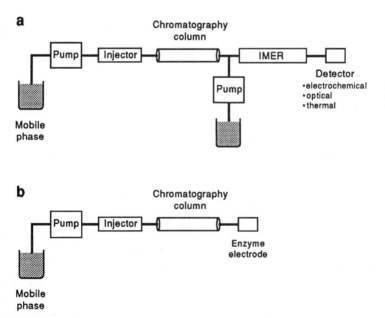

Figure 7   Chromatography/enzyme-based biosensor system. (*a*) Schematic drawing of an IMER-based detector. (*b*) Enzyme-electrode as a postcolumn detector for chromatography.

enzyme reactor (IMER). IMERs are classified as bioreactors rather than biosensors because the biological transducer is separate from the physical transducer (32). This section discusses both biosensors and IMERs because they offer similar benefits in separations detection and because both are generally referred to as biosensors in the literature.

Their selectivity and broad range of interactions make enzymes well suited for analyzing diverse chemical species, and enzyme specificity reduces artifacts much more than separation techniques, which rely on derivitization prior to separation (18). In these systems, separation efficiency and enzyme specificity are parameters that can be manipulated to design the best possible analysis scheme. For example, an efficient separation scheme allows for broader enzyme selectivity to study multiple analytes, and likewise a highly selective enzyme can be used in a separation when one or two compounds are analyzed. Also, because enzymes can turn over multiple substrate molecules, there is inherent amplification, and detection limits have been achieved in the femtomolar range (29). Importantly, immobilized enzyme biosensors can be physically removed from a separation system and exchanged if that is desired, and they are relatively stable and reusable (99). While enzymes can greatly enhance detection, separation systems can help overcome many of the inherent shortcomings of using stand-alone enzyme-based biosensors. For instance, Buttler et al (19) found that an alcohol amperometric biosensor for LC was superior to standard off-line enzyme-based methods for ethanol detection.

Enzymes are gaining in popularity as detectors in biosensor/HPLC separation systems (17, 24, 40, 41, 72, 99, 112) and biosensor/LC separation systems (19, 60, 68, 69, 111, 117). In many of these separation/enzyme biosensor systems, the chosen enzyme is immobilized on a solid support and packed in a reactor in series with the chromatography column and a detector for the enzyme product. Immobilization makes enzyme removal from the reaction easy, enhances its stability in solvents, and protects against shifts in temperature and pH, all of which increase reusability and thus lower operating costs (99). Additionally, enzyme-based reactor systems can improve sensitivity by conversion of the analyte to a more readily detectable product as in the conversion of cholesterol to cholest-4-en-3-one, a molecule that has a more accessible absorption at a longer UV wavelength (82).

Many techniques are employed in the detection of enzyme reaction products, including electrochemical, optical, and thermal methods, and a discussion of them will help to illustrate the versatility of enzyme-based biosensors. Because of the ease with which electrodes can be used to measure enzymatic activity that represents the substrate of interest, electrochemical detection is the most popular method. Electrochemical detectors are highly sensitive, capable of measuring a large range of values, and selective for certain electroactive compounds when modified appropriately (66). The use of NADH- and H_2O_2-generating enzymes is therefore quite common. The measuring electrode is frequently platinum, graphite, glassy carbon, or carbon paste; it acts as the surface on which NADH or H_2O_2 is oxidized or reduced. Often, a chemical mediator is necessary to ensure detection when background current resulting from other oxidized and reduced species is present (66).

CHROMATOGRAPHY/IMMOBILIZED-ENZYME–ELECTRODE BIOSENSORS   Several groups have coupled a chromatographic separation to an immobilized-enzyme–electrode biosensor, which is illustrated in Figure 7*b*. Adeyoju et al (3) coupled to HPLC a glassy carbon electrode modified by co-immobilization of tyrosinase and a conducting poly(1-vinylimidazole)-based osmium polymer. Using this amperometric phenol-based biosensor with HPLC, determination of phenolic compounds including p-aminophenol, phenol, p-cresol, catechol, and p-chlorophenol in cigarettes was performed with a sensitivity 100- to 200-fold greater than UV/VIS spectrophometry. In a similar design, Ortega et al (83) immobilized phenol oxidase tyrosinase on solid graphite electrodes and in carbon paste electrodes. Nordling et al (81) prepared highly specific biosensors by immobilizing flavin-containing oxidases in a redox polymer on an electrode surface. They demonstrated a glucose oxidase and a cellobiose oxidase electrode flow cell sensor for postcolumn quantification of glucose, cellobiose, and higher cellodextrins in an HPLC system. Varying concentrations of glucose and cellobiose were injected onto the column, and the current response was recorded simultaneously from both electrodes. Recorded peak heights were used to form calibration curves.

Marko-Varga et al (68) co-immobilized alcohol oxidase and horseradish peroxidase as the working electrode in an amperometric flow cell connected to LC for the selective detection of methanol and ethanol. The enzymes were covalently immobilized in a carbon paste in the presence of polyethylenimine. To demonstrate its usefulness, this enzyme electrode was utilized in the selective detection of ethanol in industrial paper pulp waste. Buttler et al used a similar LC/enzyme setup to detect carbohydrate-fermented ethanol as well. In particular, dialyzate components were separated by LC, and EtOH was selectively monitored by an amperometric alcohol biosensor (19).

CHROMATOGRAPHY/IMMOBILIZED-ENZYME REACTOR (IMER)   Another format for the use of enzyme-based biosensors is a chromatographic separation coupled to an immobilized-enzyme reactor, which is illustrated in Figure 7*a*. Marko-Varga & Gorton (67) detected carbohydrates using an LC/IMER that consisted of a cobalt phthalocyanine–modified amperometric detector for electrocatalytic oxidation of NADH produced in the enzyme reactor. Hippe & Stadler (40) combined HPLC with a biosensor based on an immobilized hydrogen-peroxide–generating enzyme and a Pt electrode to determine ACh, choline, hypoxanthanine, and xanthine levels in various body fluids. This system melded the resolving capabilities of HPLC, the specificity of the immobilized enzymes, and the sensitivity of electrochemical detection to recognize ACh in the femtomolar range. Similarly, Tsai et al (106) measured femtomole levels of ACh in living rats using both a precolumn and postcolumn reactor coupled to an LC electrochemical detection system. ACh is neither UV-absorbing nor electroactive and requires postcolumn modification by ACh esterase and choline oxidase to produce H_2O_2. The precolumn IMER removed choline by use of choline oxidase and catalase to break down H_2O_2 that was produced precolumn. Thus the precolumn step greatly increased the selectivity of ACh determination. Another system using a hydrogen-peroxide–generating enzyme was developed by Hiramatsu et al (41), in which an HPLC pump, a separation column, an enzyme reactor, and an electrochemical detector were linked in series to quantitate polyamine levels in human urine samples with the goal of speeding diagnosis of certain types of cancer. Moreover, Mogele et al (72) used a postcolumn oxidase IMER and a platinum electrode detector to identify organic acids, amino acids, and sugars separated by HPLC.

Flow calorimetry is another useful method for measuring enzymatic activity in IMERs. In a thermal biosensor system described by Danielsson et al (30), flow calorimetry is used with an enzyme thermistor as the detector. This type of system takes advantage of the fact that most enzymatic reactions are exothermic, and data on released heat are often confirmed online by UV detection. The same instrument can be utilized in an automated, rapid, online thermometric immunoassay for biomolecules other than enzymes (30). Rank et al (91) monitored penicillin V production using a modified enzyme thermistor as a thermal biosensor. An identical offline reference column allowed for correction of any nonspecific heat. Immobilized b-lactamase enabled monitoring of three consecutive penicillin fermentations as broth samples were continuously filtered through a tangential-flow filtration unit in a sterile external loop. The online penicillin V values were 10% higher than those obtained by offline HPLC analysis. The same experiments were performed with immobilized penicillin V acylase and correlated very well with HPLC analysis using traditional detection methods.

Although most LC/enzyme separation systems show greater detection sensitivity and selectivity than conventional absorption detectors, some enzyme-based schemes also rely on those conventional detectors to recognize reaction products. For instance, aromatic enzyme products that differ in migration characteristics from the initial substrate are readily detected with a standard HPLC instrument. Ögren et al (82) employed a postcolumn cholesterol oxidase enzyme reactor to convert cholesterol to cholest-4-en-3-one. Cholesterol absorbs maximally at 202 nm, while the product cholest-4-en-3-one absorbs maximally at a more convenient 241 nm. Detection sensitivity was increased 3.6–4.4 times by adding the enzyme IMER. In a similar setup, Wu (114) used HPLC and $3\beta,17\beta$-hydroxysteroid dehydrogenase IMER with a fluorimeter to detect the resultant change of NAD to NADH to indirectly measure androgen levels.

Separations with Immunosensor-Based Detection

The mammalian immune system is capable of generating enormous diversity and specificity that is needed for the removal of nonself antigens. Antibodies are the proteins secreted by lymphocytes that act as protectors in blood and tissues. Antibodies interact three-dimensionally with amino acid sequences, carbohydrates, and even organic molecules when the antibodies are properly presented on larger carrier molecules to the host immune system (56). Antibodies have even been shown to distinguish between ortho- and para-substituant groups on a benzene ring (47). For years, researchers in biomedical and chemical fields have invoked antibodies as powerful analytical tools in the study and detection of proteins, drugs, hormones, and pathogenic microorganisms. Two of the most common and sensitive stationary tests are the enzyme-linked immunoabsorbant assay (ELISA) and the radioimmunoassay (56), with detection limits in the picogram range. When combined with separation methods (LC, HPLC, and CE), immunoassays can offer added possibilities in the identification of both novel and known determinants. When combined as an analytical tool, the methods of immunolgical assays and separations are more powerful together than alone. While antibodies provide great specificity for known compounds, they often cross-react with compounds that share structural similarities. The addition of a separation step enables discrimination among antigen groups while specificity is retained. Thus, variations that might be missed in a straight immunoassay are detected by a separation/immunoassay system.

A myriad of off-line immunoassays combined with separations has been applied in analytical chemistry, biology, and clinical medicine and is reviewed by de Frutos & Regnier (31). Our review, however, is limited to immunosensors that act as direct postcolumn separation detectors and fit the classic definition of a biosensor as defined above. Numerous antibody-based immunosensors have been developed that take advantage of the binding specificity of antibodies. One type of flow immunosensor relies on displacement of fluorescently labeled molecules bound to antibodies in the reaction column. As the antigen of interest passes through the column, it exchanges place with its labeled counterpart in the column, causing an increase in fluorescence in the effluent. A handful of groups have investigated displacement type assays to detect various compounds in a continuous flow arrangement (120), but only recently has use with LC been investigated.

LIQUID CHROMATOGRAPHY/IMMUNOSENSORS   Irth et al (44) coupled a competitive postcolumn immunoassay to LC for online detection. This technique allowed rapid detection of cross-reactive compounds that were separated by LC, which eliminates fractionation and collection from the LC column. As antigens elute from the LC column, antibodies are injected into the flow to react with them. Fluorescently labeled antigens are then added to absorb unbound antibodies. The fluorescent antigen–antibody complexes pass through a molecular weight filter that removes free-labeled antigen and then are detected by fluorescence.

HIGH PRESSURE LIQUID CHROMATOGRAPHY/SURFACE PLASMON RESONANCE The development of the surface plasmon resonance optical biosensor (Pharmacia's *BIAcore* biosensor) has enabled the real-time measurements of biomolecular reactions, including antibody–antigen interactions (5, 33, 108) of receptor-ligand binding and of interactions in signal transduction pathway molecules (86). *BIAcore* detection relies on optical monitoring of changes in the surface plasmon resonance (SPR). The SPR signal is extremely sensitive to changes in the refractive index at or near the surface of the sensor. A biological component is immobilized on the carboxymethylated gold surface of the sensor. If another biological component interacts with the immobilized component (e.g. an antibody–antigen interaction) at the surface, the SPR signal responds to the changes and thus detects the presence of the absorbed mass or concentration of molecules near the surface (65). Detection limits are in the ng/ml range.

Although the immobilized surface material must be homogeneous, the material to be analyzed can be heterogeneous—for example, crude extracts, tissue culture media, or bacterial broth—making the *BIAcore* biosensor an ideal screening device for antibodies, active drug compounds, and/or binding ligands of interest (79). Nice et al (79) demonstrated this concept by coupling HPLC to an SPR biosensor with immobilized human epidermal growth factor (hEGF) to screen for soluble hEGF receptors from A431 cell extracts.

Surface plasmon resonance (SPR) has also been applied to HPLC in enzyme-based detection. Castillo et al (22) have used HPLC/SPR to monitor enzymatic products in the oxidation of lactate to study lactate enzyme mechanisms. The setup was shown to be a universal, easy-to-use detector in HPLC, and it showed a broad concentration range and consistent reproducibility. Bender et al (12) applied an optical fiber SPR sensor to monitor biochemical and chemical aqueous reactions in HPLC effluent. The SPR/HPLC system showed linear response to concentration and good reproducibility.

LIQUID CHROMATOGRAPHY/SURFACE ACOUSTIC WAVE   Piezoelectric biosensors (acoustic wave sensors) measure the change in resonant frequency of a piezoelectric crystal observed when mass changes occur on its surface—for instance when a test antigen binds to a specific immobilized antibody (96). The frequency of vibration oscillation along the crystal surface generally decreases as analyte binds to it.

Tom-Moy et al (105) have developed an acoustic wave device that uses surface transverse waves (STW) as a liquid chromatography detector. In brief, a STW device is a piezoelectric quartz crystal with microfabricated interdigitated transducers forming a transmitter and receiver. Changes in radio frequency phase are converted to voltage changes by an interferometer. Their system consisted of an HPLC system coupled to the STW device and electronics. The surface transverse wave (STW) device can be linked to the sensing modality of choice, including antibody, antigen, Protein A, Protein G, or any receptor–ligand combination. In a demonstration of its detection capabilities, the apparatus was able to detect the binding of 100 mg/ml of human IgG antibodies to Protein A that was fixed on the STW device. Advantages of this system include continuous real-time measurement without labels or derivitization, peaks consistent with UV/HPLC detection, and quantitative determinations.

PROSPECTS

In preparing this review, it has become clear to the authors that separation/biosensor systems combine two different dimensions for molecular analysis: physical properties of the molecule and molecular recognition. This synergistic combination provides a high confidence level for eliminating chemical interference, identifying known biomolecular species, and discovering new biomolecules in complex biochemical environments. The prospects for future improvements in this combination seem quite promising from advances in capillary-format and chip-format separations to advances in biosensor designs. The latter deserves special mention here.

The newest biosensors that are currently in development have great potential as sensors for chemical separations but have yet to be studied as such. Notable examples of promising biosensor technology that could be coupled to chemical separations include (a) fiber-optic immunosensors (e.g. optrodes or near-field-microscopy–based sensors), in which a biological component is incorporated onto a fiber-optic surface that delivers changes in transmitted or reflected light following a molecular interaction (13, 21, 38, 54); (b) sliding ion-gate biosensors, in which an analyte cross-links antibody fragments on a lipid bilayer, thus opening or closing an ion channel to change the membrane conductance (28); (c) displacement bioassays in which analytes displace fluorescently labeled molecules bound to antibodies in the reaction column and are sensitively detected (61, 77); (*d*) immunoliposome sensors, in which sensing molecules are attached to the surface of the liposome and upon antigen recognition cause lysis and release of its detectable contents (e.g. fluorescent molecules) (45); (*e*) bilayer lipid membranes on solid supports (s-BLMs), wherein membrane receptors are incorporated into highly stable artifical membranes (80); (*f*) field-effect transistors, e.g. enzyme-sensitized field effect transistors (ENFET), in which a biological component is immobilized onto an ion-sensitive field effect transistor (ISFET) (54, 97); (*g*) ultramicroelectrode-based biosensors that have enzymes attached to micron-sized tip diameters (87, 88); and (*h*) commercially existing cell-based biosensor technologies such as the microphysiometer that use a light-addressable potentiometric sensor (LAPS) to transduce pH from cellular metabolism (70). These separation/biosensor combinations offer exciting opportunities in biomedical research, drug discovery, food and environmental monitoring, and medical diagnostics from home healthcare to critical care.

ACKNOWLEDGMENTS

We thank Sheri J Lillard for a critical reading of this manuscript and Nancy L. Allbritton for stimulating discussions. This work was supported by the National Institute of Drug Abuse.

Visit the *Annual Reviews home page* at
http://www.AnnualReviews.org.

Literature Cited

1. Acree TE. 1997. GC/olfactometry. *Anal. Chem.* 69:A170–75
2. Acree TE, Barnard J. 1994. Gas chromatography–olfactometry and charm analysis. *Dev. Food Sci.* 35:211–20
3. Adeyoju O, Iwuoha E, Smyth M, Leech D. 1996. High-performance liquid chromatographic determination of phenols using atyrosinase-based amperometric biosensor detection system. *Analyst* 121:1885–89
4. Allen TGJ. 1997. The sniffer-patch technique for detection of neurotransmitter release. *Trends Neurosci.* 20:192–97
5. Altschuh D, Dubs MC, Wiess E, Zeder-Lutz G, Van Regenmortel MHV. 1992. Determination of kinetic constants for the interaction between a monoclonal antibody and peptides using surface plasmon resonance. *Biochemistry* 31:6298–304
6. Ames BN, McCann J, Yamaski E. 1975. Methods for detecting carcinogens and mutagens with the salmonella/mammalian-microsome mutagenicity test. *Mutat. Res.* 31:347–64
7. Arey J, Harger WP, Helmig D, Atkinson R. 1992. Bioassay-directed fractionation of mutagenic PAH atmospheric photooxidation products and ambient particulate extracts. *Mutat. Res.* 281:67–76
8. Arn H, Staedler E, Rauscher S. 1975. Electroantennographic detector, a selective and sensitive tool in the gas chromatographic analysis of insect pheromones. *Z. Naturforsch. Teil C* 30:722–25
9. Bailey JC, Viney NJ. 1979. Analysis of odors by gas chromatography and allied techniques. *Warren Spring Lab. Rep. LR298.* Stevenage, Herts., UK: Warren Spring Lab.
10. Beevor PS, Hall DR, Lester R, Poppi RG, Read JS, Nesbitt BF. 1975. Sex pheromones of the armyworm moth, *Spodoptera exempta. Experientia* 31:22–23

11. Belli SL, Rechnitz GA. 1986. Prototype potentiometric biosensor using intact chemoreceptor structures. *Anal. Lett.* 19:403–16
12. Bender WJH, Dessy RE. 1994. *US Patent No. 5327225*
13. Betzig E, Chichester RJ. 1993. Single-molecules observed by near-field scanning optical microscopy. *Science* 262:1422–25
14. Bjorseth A, Eidsa G, Gether J, Landmark L, Moller M. 1982. Detection of mutagens in complex samples by the *Salmonella* assay applied directly on thin-layer chromatography plates. *Science* 215:87–89
15. Blight MM, Pickett JA, Wadhams LJ, Woodcock CM. 1995. Antennal preception of oilseed rape, *Brassica napus* (*Brassicaceae*), volatiles by the cabbage seed weevil *Ceutorhynchus assimilis* (*Coleoptera, Curculionidae*). *J. Chem. Ecol.* 21:1649–64
16. Blight MM, Wadhams LJ, Wenham MJ. 1979. The stereoisomeric composition of the 4-methyl-3-heptanol produced by *Scolytus scolytus* and the preparation and biological activity of the four synthetic stereoisomers. *Insect Biochem.* 9:525–33
17. Bowers LD. 1986. Enzyme reaction detectors in HPLC. *Chromatogr. Sci.* 34:195–225
18. Brinkman U. 1987. A review of reaction detection in HPLC. *Chromatographia* 24:190–200
19. Buttler T, Gorton L, Jarskog H, Marko-Varga G, Hahn-Hagerdal B, et al. 1994. Monitoring of ethanol during fermentation of a lignocellulose hydrolysate by on-line microdialysis sampling, column liquid chromatography and an alcohol biosensor. *Biotechnol. Bioeng.* 44:322–28
20. Cai JY, Henion J. 1995. Capillary electrophoresis-mass spectrometry. *J. Chromatogr. A* 703:667–92
21. Carlyon EE, Lowe CR, Reid D, Bennion I. 1992. A single mode fibre-optic evanescent wave biosensor. *Biosens. Bioelectron.* 7:141–46
22. Castillo JR, Cepria G, de Marcos S, Galban J, Mateo J, Garcia Ruiz E. 1993. Surface plasmon resonance sensor as a detector in HPLC and specific lactate determination. *Sens. Actuators A* 37-38:582–86
23. Chang B, Xie F, Li W. 1996. Evaluating feed flavor stability. A new approach to testing flavor stability has been proposed. *Feed Mix* 4:10–12
24. Chen HM, Peterson C. 1994. Quantifying ethanol by high-performance liquid chromatography with precolumn enzymatic conversion and derivatization with fluorimetric detection. *Alcohol* 11:577–82
25. Clark LC, Lyons C. 1962. Electrode systems for continuous monitoring in cardiovascular surgery. *Ann. NY Acad. Sci.* 102:29–45
26. Connor MP, Wang J, Kubiak W. 1990. Tissue-based and microbe-based electrochemical detectors for liquid chromatography. *Anal. Chim. Acta* 229:139–43
27. Corcoran CA, Rechnitz RA. 1985. Cell-based biosensors. *Trends Biotechnol.* 3:92–96
28. Cornell BA, Braach-Maksvytis VLB, King LG, Osman PDJ, Raguse B, et al. 1997. A biosensor that uses ion-channel switches. *Nature* 387:580–83
29. Damsma G, Lammerts van Beuren D, Westerink DHC, Horn AS. 1987. Determination of acetylcholine and choline in the femtomole range by means of HPLC, a post-column enzyme reactor, and electrochemical detection. *Chromotagraphia* 24:827–31
30. Danielsson B, Larson PO. 1990. Specific monitoring chromatography procedures. *Trends Anal. Chem.* 9:223–27
31. de Frutos M, Regnier FE. 1993. Tandem chromatographic immunological analyses. *Anal. Chem.* 65:A17–25
32. Emneus J, Marko-Varga G. 1995. Biospecific detection in liquid chromatography. *J. Chromatogr. A* 703:191–243
33. End P, Panayotou G, Entwistle A, Waterfield MD, Chiquet M. 1992. Tenascin: A modulator of cell growth. *Eur. J. Biochem.* 209:1041–51
34. Espinosa-Aguirre JJ, Delatorre R, Laresasseff I, Rubio J, Dorado V, et al. 1996. Bacterial mutagens in the urine of patients under tinidazole treatment. *Mutat. Res. Sect. Environ. Mutagenesis Relat. Subj.* 359:133–40
35. Fishman HA, Orwar O, Allbritton NL, Modi BP, Shear JB, et al. 1996. Cell-to-cell scanning in capillary electrophoresis. *Anal. Chem.* 68:1181–86
36. Fishman HA, Orwar O, Scheller RH, Zare RN. 1995. Identification of receptor ligands and receptor subtypes using antagonists in a capillary electrophoresis single-cell biosensor separation system. *Proc. Natl. Acad. Sci. USA* 92:7877–81
37. Guth H, Grosch W. 1993. Identification of potent odorants in static headspace samples of green and black tea powders on the basis of aroma extract dilution analysis (AEDA). *Flavour Fragr. J.* 8:173–78
38. Hale ZM, Payne FP, Marks RS, Lowe CR, Levine MM. 1996. The single-mode ta-

pered optical fibre loop immunosensor. *Biosens. Bioelectron.* 11:137–48

39. Harrison DJ, Fluri K, Seiler K, Fan Z, Effenhauser CS, Manz A. 1993. Micromachining a miniaturized capillary electrophoresis-based chemical analysis system on a chip. *Science* 261:895–97

40. Hippe H, Stadler H. 1989. Biosensors on-line in HPLC. *GBF Monogr.* 13:289–92

41. Hiramatsu K, Kamei S, Sugimoto M, Kinoshita K, Iwasaki K, Kawakita M. 1994. An improved method of determining free and acetylated polyamines by HPLC involving an enzyme reactor and an electrochemical detector. *J. Biochem.* 115:584–89

42. Houk VS, Claxton LD. 1986. Screening complex hazardous wastes for mutagenic activity using a modified version of the TLC/*Salmonella* assay. *Mutat. Res.* 169:81–92

43. Hume RI, Role LW, Fischbach GD. 1983. Acetylcholine release from growth cones detected with patches of acetylcholine receptor rich membranes. *Nature* 305:632–34

44. Irth H, Oosterkamp AJ, Tjaden UR, van der Greef J. 1995. Strategies for on-line coupling of immunoassays to high-performance liquid chromatography. *Trend. Anal. Chem.* 14:355–61

45. Ishimori Y, Yasuda T, Tsumita T, Notsuki M, Koyama M, Tadakuma T. 1984. Liposome immune lysis assay (LILA): a simple method to measure anti-protein antibody using protein antigen-bearing liposomes. *J. Immunol. Methods* 75:351–60

46. Jacobson SC, Hergenroder R, Koutny LB, Ramsey JM. 1994. High-speed separations on a microchip. *Anal. Chem.* 66:1114–18

47. Janeway CA, Travers P. 1994. *Immunobiology*, 2:5–6. New York: Garland

48. Deleted in proof

49. Jardemark K, Orwar O, Jacobson I, Moscho A, Zare RN. 1997. Patch clamp detection in capillary electrophoresis. *Anal. Chem.* 69:3427–34

50. Katzung BG. 1995. Basic and clinical evaluation of new drugs. In *Basic and Clinical Pharmacology*, ed. BG Katzung, pp. 60–70. Norwalk: Appleton Lange

51. Kenefick SL, Brownlee BG, Perley TR, Hrudey SE. 1995. A chemical and sensory study of odor compounds in the Athabasca River, Alberta, Canada. *Water Sci. Technol.* 31:15–21

52. Kennedy RT, Oates MD, Cooper BR, Nickerson B, Jorgenson JW. 1989. Microcolumn separations and the analysis of single cells. *Science* 246:57–63

53. Kramer RH. 1990. Patch cramming: monitoring intracellular messengers in intact cells with membrane patches containing detector ion channels. *Neuron* 2:335–41

54. Kress-Rogers E. 1997. Biosensors and electronic noses for practical applications. In *Handbook of Biosensors and Electronic Noses: Medicine, Food, and the Environment*, ed. E Kress-Rogers, pp. 3–39. Boca Raton: CRC

55. Kubo I, Sode K, Karube I. 1991. Whole-organism based biosensors and microbiosensors. In *Advances in Biosensors*, ed. APF Turner, pp. 1–32. London: JAI

56. Kuby J. 1994. Antigen-antibody interactions. In *Immunology*. New York: Freeman. 660 pp.

57. Kuriyama S, Rechnitz GA. 1981. Plant tissue-based bioselective membrane electrode for glutamate. *Anal. Chim. Acta* 131:91–96

58. Leal WS, Shi X, Liang D, Schal C, Meinwald J. 1995. Application of chiral gas-chromatography with electroantennographic detection to the determination of stereochemistry of a cockroach sex-pheromone. *Proc. Natl. Acad. Sci. USA* 92:1033–37

59. Leal WS, Shi X, Nakamuta K, Ono M, Meinwald J. 1995. Structure, stereochemistry and thermal isomerization of the male sex-phermone of the longhorn beetle *Anaglyptus subfasciatis*. *Proc. Natl. Acad. Sci. USA* 92:1038–42

60. Lickl E. 1991. Actual liquid chromatography. *Oesterr. Chem. Z.* 92:136–39

61. Ligler FS, Kusterbeck AW, Ogert RA, Wemhoff GA. 1992. Drug detection using the flow immunosensor. In *Biosensors Design and Application*, ed. PR Mathewson, JW Finley, pp. 73–80. Washington, DC: Am. Chem. Soc.

62. Luo Y, Zhang R, Xie F. 1993. Combination of microbial sensor with high-performance liquid chromatograph. *Fenxi Huaxue* 21:988–91

63. Luzzi V, Fishman HA, Sims CE, Allbritton NL. 1996. A novel strategy for measurement of inositol 1,4,5-trisphosphate concentrations in single *Xenopus oocytes*. *Mol. Biol. Cell* 7 Suppl.:A370

64. Luzzi V, Lee C-L, Allbritton NL. 1997. Localized sampling of cytoplasm from *Xenopus oocytes* for capillary electrophoresis. *Anal. Chem.* 69:4761–67

65. Malmquist M. 1993. Biospecific interaction analysis using biosensor technology. *Nature* 361:186–87

66. Marko-Varga G, Dominguez E. 1991. Enzymes as analytical tools. *Trends Anal. Chem.* 10:290–97

67. Marko-Varga G, Gorton L. 1989. Postcolumn derivitization in liquid chromatography using immobilized enzyme reactor and amperometric detection. *Anal. Chim. Acta* 234:13–29

68. Marko-Varga G, Johansson K, Gorton L. 1994. Enzyme-based biosensor as a selective detection unit in column liquid chromatography. *J. Chromatogr. A* 660:153–67

69. Marko-Varga GA. 1989. Determination of mono- and oligosaccharides in fermentation broths by liquid chromatographic separation and amperometric detection using immobilized enzyme reactors and a chemically modified electrode. *Anal. Chem.* 61:831–38

70. McConnell HM, Owicki JC, Parce JW, Miller DL, Baxter GT, et al. 1992. The cytosensor microphysiometer: biological applications of silicon technology. *Science* 257:1906–12

71. Menini A, Picco C, Firestein S. 1995. Quantal-like current fluctuations induced by odorants in olfactory receptor-cells. *Nature* 373:435–37

72. Mogele R, Pabel B, Galensa R. 1992. Determination of organic acids, amino acids, and saccharides by high-performance liquid chromatography and a postcolumn enzyme reactor with amperometric detection. *J. Chromatogr.* 591:165–73

73. Monnig CA, Jorgenson JW. 1991. On-column sample gating for high-speed capillary zone electrophoresis. *Anal. Chem.* 63:802–7

74. Montal M, Anholt R, Labarca P. 1986. The reconstituted acetylcholine receptor. In *Ion Channel Reconstitution*, ed. C Miller, pp. 157–204. New York: Plenum

75. Moorhouse JE, Yeadon R, Beevor PS, Nesbitt BF. 1969. Method for use in studies of insect chemical communication. *Nature* 223:1174–75

76. Mosandl A. 1992. Capillary gas chromatography in quality assessment of flavors and fragrances. *J. Chromatogr.* 624:267–92

77. Narang U, Gauger PR, Ligler FS. 1997. Capillary-based displacement flow immunosensor. *Anal. Chem.* 69:1961–64

78. Nesbitt BF, Beevor PS, Cole RA, Lester R, Poppi RG. 1973. Sex pheromones of two noctuid moths. *Nat. New Biol.* 244:208–9

79. Nice E, Lackmann M, Smyth F, Fabri L, Burgess AW. 1994. Synergies between micropreparative high-performance liquid chromatography and an instrumental optical biosensor. *J. Chromatogr. A* 660:169–85

80. Nikolelis DP, Krull UJ, Ottova AL, Tien HT. 1996. Bilayer lipid membranes and other lipid-based methods. In *Handbook of Chemical and Biological Sensors*, ed. RF Taylor, JS Schultz, pp. 221–56. Bristol: Inst. Phys.

81. Nordling M, Elmgren M, Staahlberg J, Pettersson G, Lindquist SE. 1993. A combined cellobiose oxidase/glucose oxidase biosensor for HPLC determination on-line of glucose and soluble cellodextrins. *Anal. Biochem.* 214:389–96

82. Ögren L, Csiky I, Risinger L, Nilsson LG, Johansson G. 1980. A post-column enzyme reactor for detection of oxidized cholesterols in HPLC separations. *Anal. Chim. Acta* 117:71–79

83. Ortega F, Dominguez E, Burestedt E, Emneus J, Gorton L, Marko-Vargo G. 1994. Phenol oxidase-based biosensors as selective detection units in column liquid chromatography for the determination of phenolic compounds. *J. Chromatogr.* 675:65–78

84. Orwar O, Jardemark K, Farre C, Jacobson I, Moscho A, et al. 1998. Voltage clamp biosensors for capillary electrophoresis. *Methods Enzymol.* In press

85. Orwar O, Jardemark K, Jacobson I, Moscho A, Fishman HA, et al. 1996. Patch-clamp detection of neurotransmitters in capillary electrophoresis. *Science* 272:1779–82

86. Panayotou G, Bax B, Gout I, Federwisch M, Wroblowski B, et al. 1992. Interaction of the p85 subunit of PI 3-kinase and its N-terminal SH2 domain with a PDGF receptor phosphorylation site: structural features and analysis of conformational changes. *EMBO J.* 11:4261–72

87. Pantano P, Kuhr WG. 1993. Dehydrogenase-modified carbon-fiber microelectrodes for the measurement of neurotransmitter dynamics. 2: Covalent modification utilizing avidin biotin technology. *Anal. Chem.* 65:623–30

88. Pantano P, Morton TH, Kuhr WG. 1991. Enzyme-modified carbon-fiber microelectrodes with millisecond response-times. *J. Am. Chem. Soc.* 113:1832–33

89. Pizziconi VB, Page DL. 1997. A cell-based immunobiosensor with engineered molecular recognition. Part I: Design feasibility. *Biosens. Bioelectron.* 12:287–99

90. Raghavan M, Bjorkman P, Hughs P, Hughs H, Bjorkman PJ. 1995. BIAcore: a microchip-based system for analyzing the

formation of macromolecular complexes. *Structure* 3:331–33

91. Rank M, Danielsson B, Gram J. 1992. Implementation of a thermal biosensor in a process environment: on-line monitoring of penicillin V in production-scale fermentations. *Biosens. Bioelectron.* 7:631–35

92. Rechnitz GA, Arnold MA, Meyerhoff ME. 1979. Bio-selective membrane electrode using tissue slices. *Nature* 278:466–67

93. Rosenkranz HS, McCoy EC, Sanders DR, Butler M, Kiriazides DK, Mermelstein R. 1980. Nitropyrenes: isolation, identificaton, and reduction of mutagenic impurities in carbon black and toners. *Science* 209:1039–43

94. Sambrook J, Fritsch E, Maniatis T. 1989. *Molecular Cloning: A Laboratory Manual.* Cold Spring Harbor, NY: Cold Spring Harbor Lab. Press

95. Schuetzle D, Lee F-C, Prater T, Tejada S. 1981. The identification of polynuclear aromatic hydrocarbon (PAH) derivatives in mutagenic fractions of diesel particulate extracts. *Int. J. Environ. Anal. Chem.* 9:93–144

96. Sethi RS. 1994. Transducer aspects of biosensors. *Biosens. Bioelectron.* 9:243–64

97. Sevilla F, Kullick T, Scheper T. 1994. A bio-FET sensor for lactose based on co-immobilized beta-galactosidase/glucose dehydrogenase. *Biosens. Bioelectron.* 9:275–81

98. Shear JB, Fishman HA, Allbritton NL, Garigan D, Zare RN, Scheller RH. 1995. Single cells as biosensors for chemical separations. *Science* 267:74–77

99. Shimada K, Oe T. 1989. Immobilized enzyme reactors for detection systems in high-performance liquid chromatography. *J. Chromatogr.* 492:345–59

100. Skoog DA, West DM, Holler FJ. 1992. *Fundamentals of Analytical Chemistry,* p. 928. Fort Worth: Saunders

101. Stryer L. 1995. *Biochemistry,* p. 1089. New York: Freeman

102. Takeuchi N, Nagata Y, Okayasu S, Nakayama S, Shigeta Y. 1979. Application of GC-olfactometer for analysis of mixed odor. *Nippon Kankyo Eisei Senta Shoho* 6:97–102

103. Takeuchi T, Nagata Y, Nakayama N, Shigeta Y. 1980. Determination of odor components by gas chromatography-olfactometer. *Akushu no Kenkyu* 9:20–27

104. Taylor RF, Marenchic IG, Cook EJ. 1988. An acetylcholine receptor-based biosensors for the detection of cholinergic agents. *Anal. Chim. Acta* 213:131–38

105. Tom-Moy M, Doherty TP, Baer RL, Spira-Solomon D. 1995. Use of an acoustic wave device as a liquid chromatography detector. In *Biosensor and Chemical Sensor Technology,* ed. KR Rogers, A Mulchandani, W Zhou, pp. 9–18. Washington, DC: Am. Chem. Soc.

106. Tsai TR, Cham TM, Chen KC, Chen CF, Tsai TH. 1996. Determination of acetylcholine by on-line microdialysis coupled with pre-microbore and post-microbore column enzyme reactors with electrochemical detection. *J. Chromatogr. B* 678:151–55

107. Tsien RY. 1989. Fluorescent probes of cell signaling. *Annu. Rev. Neurosci.* 12:227–54

108. VanCott T, Loomis L, Redfield R, Birx D. 1992. Real-time biospecific interaction analysis of antibody reactivity to peptides from the envelope glycoprotein, gp160, of HIV-1. *J. Immun. Methods* 146:163–76

109. Wadhams LJ. 1982. Coupled gas chromatography–single cell recording: a new technique for use in the analysis of insect pheromones. *Z. Naturforsch. Teil C* 37:947–52

110. Wallingford RA, Ewing AG. 1987. Capillary zone electrophoresis w/electrochemical detectors. *Anal. Chem.* 59:1762–66

111. Wang XY, Liao ML, Hung TH, Seib PA. 1988. Liquid chromatographic determination of L-ascorbate 2-polyphosphate in fish feeds by enzymatic release of L-ascorbate. *J. Assoc. Off. Anal. Chem.* 71:1158–61

112. Wessels D, Erdmann H, Galensa R. 1996. Determination of aldehydes in foods by HPLC-biosensor coupling. *Lebensmittelchemie* 50:103–5

113. Wijesuriya DC, Rechnitz GA. 1993. Biosensors based on plant and animal tissues. *Biosens. Bioelectron.* 8:155–60

114. Wu M. 1986. Determination of serum D^5-3b-hydroxysteroid sulphates by combined high-performance liquid chromatography and immobilized 3b, 17b-hydroxysteroid dehydrogenase in column form. *J. Chromatogr.* 377:121–29

115. Wu N, Peck TL, Webb AG, Magin RL, Sweedler JV. 1994. H-1-NMR spectroscopy on the nanoliter scale for static and on-line measurements. *Anal. Chem.* 66:3849–57

116. Wu N, Peck TL, Webb AG, Magin RL, Sweedler JV. 1994. Nanoliter volume

sample cells for 1H NMR: application to on-line detection in capillary electrophoresis. *J. Am. Chem. Soc.* 116:7929–30

117. Yao T, Sato M, Kobayashi Y, Wasa T. 1984. Flow injection analysis for glucose by the combined use of an immobilized glucose oxidase reactor and a peroxidase electrode. *Anal. Chim. Acta* 165:291–96

118. Yeung ES, ed. 1986. *Detectors for Li-quid Chromatography*, p. 366. New York: Wiley

119. Young SH, Poo M-M. 1983. Spontaneous release of transmitter from growth cones of embryonic neurones. *Nature* 305:634–36

120. Yu H, Kusterbeck AW, Hale MJ, Ligler FS, Whelan JP. 1996. Use of the USDT flow immunosensor for quantitation of benzoylecgonine. *Biosens. Bioelectron.* 11:725–34

Annu. Rev. Biophys. Biomol. Struct. 1998. 27:199–224

SIMULATION OF PROKARYOTIC GENETIC CIRCUITS

Harley H. McAdams
724 Esplanada Way, Stanford, California 94305;
e-mail: harleymcadams@worldnet.att.net

Adam Arkin
Department of Developmental Biology, Beckman Center, Stanford University School
of Medicine, Stanford, California 94305; e-mail: arkin@stalk.stanford.edu

KEY WORDS: simulation, genetic circuits, genetic regulation, bacteria, stochastic processes

ABSTRACT
Biochemical and genetic approaches have identified the molecular mechanisms
of many genetic reactions, particularly in bacteria. Now a comparably detailed
understanding is needed of how groupings of genes and related protein reactions
interact to orchestrate cellular functions over the cell cycle, to implement preprogrammed cellular development, or to dynamically change a cell's processes
and structures in response to environmental signals. Simulations using realistic,
molecular-level models of genetic mechanisms and of signal transduction networks are needed to analyze dynamic behavior of multigene systems, to predict
behavior of mutant circuits, and to identify the design principles applicable to
design of genetic regulatory circuits. When the underlying design rules for regulatory circuits are understood, it will be far easier to recognize common circuit
motifs, to identify functions of individual proteins in regulation, and to redesign
circuits for altered functions.

CONTENTS

INTRODUCTION

Biochemical and genetic approaches have identified the molecular mechanisms of many genetic reactions in cells; progress is most advanced for prokaryotic genetics. The Genome Project and advances in experimental techniques will lead to full knowledge of DNA sequences, identification of most genes, and even temporal gene expression patterns for many organisms. A comparably detailed understanding is needed of how groupings of genes and related protein reactions interact to orchestrate cellular functions over the cell cycle, to implement preprogrammed cellular development, or to dynamically change a cell's processes and structures in response to environmental signals. This review addresses the use of simulation models to analyze the dynamical behavior of cellular regulatory networks. Bacterial systems are emphasized since molecular mechanisms of gene expression and regulation are better characterized today in bacteria than in higher organisms. As a result, molecular-level modeling of genetic regulatory networks is also most advanced for bacterial regulation.

Simulations are needed (*a*) to identify design principles for the biochemically based logic, (*b*) to understand the dynamical response of both normal and mutant cells to environmental and internal signals, (*c*) to predict quantitative effects of mutations on regulatory outcomes, and (*d*) to verify consistency and completeness of hypothesized reaction systems. This level of realism requires modeling approximations that have a rationale traceable to physical and chemical mechanisms. Several of the molecular-level simulation models described in a later section treat regulation of systems of coupled intracellular reactions, but either do not involve genetics or have over-simplified models of genetic mechanisms. The challenge now is to develop simulation techniques applicable to cellular processes where genetic regulation is centrally important, such as developmental differentiation, facultative infection processes, and cell cycle control.

Essential features of genetic regulatory systems, as understood today, were recognized 35 years ago. In a prescient report of a 1961 Cold Spring Harbor conference on cellular regulatory mechanisms (68) the importance of regulatory feedback was emphasized, regulatory nets were characterized as "circuits," and regulatory breakdown was postulated as the central initiating event in malignancy, along with numerous other "modern" ideas about cellular regulation.

The operon model of Monod, Jacob, and their coworkers (45–47) stimulated numerous authors to address the integration of genetic regulation into models of enzymatic regulation. In a 1968 review, Rosen (79) summarized the essential methods and approximations that came to be widely used in simulations of genetic regulatory networks: a focus on transcription control, neglect of post-transcriptional control mechanisms, and characterization of protein production as a continuous process modulated by the level of activation or repression of the corresponding operon's operator region.

Genetic regulation is at times characterized using metaphors drawn from the fields of computing and digital electronic circuit design. There is validity to this comparison, but the "hardware" (or "wetware") of cellular logic, chemical reactions in the cytoplasm, is profoundly different from electronic hardware. The next section summarizes organization of genetic regulation in bacterial cells from a regulatory circuit architecture perspective and in comparison with electronic logic.

GENETIC REGULATORY CIRCUITS: ORGANIZATION AND FUNCTION

Bacterial genetic circuits exhibit hierarchical organization: regulons control groups of operons that control gene groupings (32, 69). Global regulons coordinate regulation of operons in multiple metabolic pathways. For example, the σ^{32} heat shock regulator protein (105), a representative sigma factor, is required for RNAP binding at the promoters of a wide spectrum of genes involved in responses to stress. Other global regulators act through control of DNA spatial configuration; integration host factor protein (IHF) is a representative example (23, 31). These global regulators enable the bacterial cell to effect a rapid and coordinated response to threats or opportunities presented by their environment (e.g. heat, cold, presence or absence of essential nutrients, high or low pH) by reconfiguring their biochemical machinery. There are assumptions, explicit or implicit, in every simulation analysis regarding the effects of global regulators. The most common assumption, usually implicit, is that global regulation can be neglected, meaning, in effect, that during the simulation period either the status of global regulators is assumed to be unchanging or the systems changed by global regulators are assumed to be decoupled from the processes under study. Explicit treatment of global regulation will be necessary when we progress to the point of modeling complex cell decision points. For example, regulation of the initiation of sporulation in *Bacillus subtilis* involves two sigma factors, σ_A and σ_H, that compete for binding to core RNA polymerase at promoters of critical genes (42).

The biochemical logic in genetic regulatory circuits provides real-time regulatory control, implements a branching decision logic, and executes stored programs that guide cellular differentiation extending over many cell generations. In higher organisms, the regulatory algorithms may control sequential execution of developmental processes over many years of the organism's life. The mechanisms that implement bacterial genetic logic functions may be entirely within a single cell, may span many cells (43), or may function across cell generations (7, 50). Genetic circuits may cross species boundaries as in symbiotic relations between bacteria and higher organisms (25, 58, 62). More sinister, perhaps, are the bacterial mechanisms that co-opt the internal logic of target cells to facilitate penetration or evade defensive responses (21, 22, 34).

At any moment, cellular functions are both implemented by and controlled by the network of chemical reactions involving the collection of molecular species in the cell. In a growing cell, the molecular composition is continuously changing as the cell cycle progresses and the instantaneous regulatory control function also changes continuously. In these networks of interconnected reactions, one regulatory protein can control genes that produce other regulators, that in turn control still other genes so that complex branching networks of interactions are formed. Multireagent reactions or genetic mechanisms controlled by multiple input signals are key elements for performing sensor or control-logic functions in these networks.

REGULATORY FEEDBACK   Feedback, where the output signal of a network element directly or indirectly influences the value of its input signals, is pervasive in regulatory networks. Autoregulatory feedback loops, where a gene product acts on its gene-expression mechanisms, can lock controlling protein signals on, in turn locking other signals either on or off. In a 1991 inventory of 107 σ^{70} promoters then known in *Escherichia coli* (10), the promoters were organized into 31 regulons, each jointly controlled by one or more regulatory proteins. Twenty-one (68%) of the 31 regulon-controlling proteins are autoregulating, i.e. they repress their own synthesis. Four (13%) of the 31 are autoactivating, that is, they activate their own synthesis.

The complement of distinct molecules in the cell and the state of the DNA (e.g. methylated or not) defines the regulatory logic that establishes how the cell functions at that instant. This logic determines when the cell makes new proteins from DNA-encoded instructions and when existing proteins are destroyed. Specialized enzymes under regulatory control can remove DNA segments, move segments from one site to another, reverse a segment's orientation, or insert foreign segments (14). These DNA changes can lead to temporary or permanent radical changes in the cell morphology, its active metabolic pathways, and importantly, its responses to environmental signals so that future cellular responses to signals differ from current responses. Thus, the cell's stored instructions (the genetic material) can be dynamically changed according to previously stored instructions.

Mechanisms that sense conditions inside and outside the cell are integrated into the regulatory logic so that the cell can adapt to the needs of the moment. Receptors on the cell surface can respond to specific chemical species and affect the regulatory logic by molecular signaling using signal transduction cascades (17). Other signals may affect reactions in the cascade to change the level or character of the signal and thus act as modulating functions (5, 20, 35). In this way, environmental influences originating both within and outside of the organism can evoke complex regulatory responses. The interconnected networks of protein reactions that connect sensors to response mechanisms are, in a sense, the "nervous system" of unicellular organisms (5). Bray has reviewed interconnected biochemical elements that can form information processing circuits and has assessed their similarity to neural networks (5).

CELLULAR REGULATORY APPARATUS   The cellular regulatory apparatus includes both short- and long-term memory mechanisms. The current complement of proteins in the cell and their physical deployment depends on the cell's history, and thus is a memory. Long-term memory mechanisms are implemented by more-or-less permanent changes in the state of the cell (for example, the metabolic enzyme systems that are activated, the global regulators that are active, the complement of surface structures, or major morphological transformations as in sporulation) or in the DNA sequence. In phage lambda and other temperate phage, the integration of the phage DNA into the host chromosome changes the control logic of the phage circuitry. Thus, for example, the state of being either *integrated* or *not integrated* into the host DNA acts as a memory element (61). In higher organisms, successive cellular state changes during organ differentiation are largely irreversible. The self-sustaining, continuous expression of the homeotic genes throughout development and into adulthood is thought to be the long-term memory mechanism recording the differentiated state of each cell as established early in embryonic development (54).

Genetic regulatory networks progress asynchronously through successive reactions, so that biological "time" is based more on the degree of progress along reaction pathways than on clock time. The stochastic pattern of signal protein production (discussed below) may only cause uncertainty in timing of regulatory events, not uncertainty in outcome. (We use the term "stochastic" in this paper in the technical sense of "arising from a random process.") Within broad limits the duration of many cellular functions may be less important to proper cellular function than the proper sequencing of events. For example, cells halt at various checkpoints until conditions (for example, restoration of essential nutrients, completion of precursor cellular events) for further progress

Table 1 Points of similarity between genetic logic and electronic digital logic in computer chips

	Electronic logic	Genetic logic
Signals	Electron concentrations	Protein concentrations
Distribution	Point → point (by wires or by electrically encoded addresses)	Point → point (movement by diffusion or active transport by encoded reaction specificity)
Organization	Hierarchical	Hierarchical
Logic type	Digital, clocked sequential logic	Analog unclocked (can approximate asynchronous sequential logic)
Noise	Inherent noise due to discrete electron events and environmental effects	Inherent noise due to discrete chemical reaction events and environmental effects
Signal/noise ratio	Signal/noise ratio high in most circuits	Signal/noise ratio low in most circuits
Switching speed	Fast ($>10^6$ sec^{-1})	Slow ($<10^{-2}$ sec^{-1})

are satisfied (10, 38, 49, 100). In this case, the indeterminism relates to whether the cell will progress or not along a developmental path at any instant, rather than on the choice of alternate pathways. So, the regulatory decision command sequence is: "HALT until CONDITIONS are met, then PROCEED," where "CONDITIONS" are sensed environmental or cellular signals. The result is dispersion across the cell population in the rate of progression along prescribed pathways rather than dispersion in outcome. However, at developmental switching points (discussed below) stochastic gene expression can lead to random partitioning of the cell population into subpopulations developing on alternative pathways.

Genetic networks have many attributes commonly associated with computing. Table 1 shows points of similarity between genetic logic and the electronic digital logic in chips in today's desktop computers.

Figure 1a shows the simplest of genetic circuits, a regulatory cascade capable of initiating events in sequence as illustrated in Figure 1b. Figure 1c shows a sampling of the control features that are used in cells to create complex control logic structures. The capability to create combinatorial controls with feedback when coupled with memory mechanisms provides every element needed to create a type of asynchronous sequential logic (61). Biological regulatory circuits can have multiparameter combinational control functions at key nodes (for example, promoters controlled by several effectors), reaction cascades that function as "subroutines," the ability to respond conditionally to external

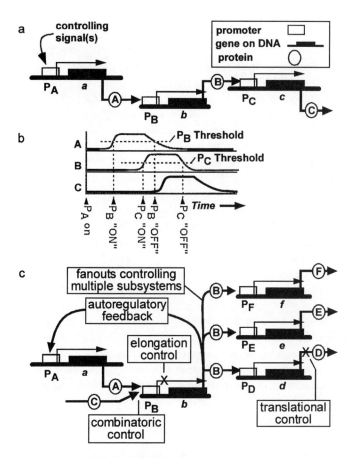

Figure 1 (*a*) A genetic cascade, the simplest genetic circuit. The increasing concentration of signal protein A from transcripts initiated at promoter P_A, turns on the downstream promoter P_B, leading to production of signal B, which similarly activates production of signal C. Signal specificity depends on the addressing created by stereochemically based binding specificity of A, B, and C to the corresponding binding sites in the different promoters. (*b*) The resulting succession of concentration peaks for signals A, B, and C. Decay of the protein signals after the promoters are switched off results from proteolytic degradation of the proteins and also in growing cells from continuous dilution of signal concentration as the cell size increases. (*c*) A small sampling of the numerous additional regulatory mechanisms used in cells to control creation, timing, and decay of protein signals. Posttranscriptional regulatory mechanisms are essential features of regulatory networks and *must* be included in any analysis of the regulatory logic. Small autoregulatory feedback loops are widely used in cells to maintain signals within a concentration range. Switching circuits that control developmental path choices commonly include positive or reinforcing feedback to enhance the commitment to the selected path and negative or repressing feedback to assure that promoters on alternative paths are turned off.

signals, and the ability to read from stored instructions (the DNA). However, the detailed implementation and the manner of processing of information is radically different from the digital information processing paradigm in modern computers. Forcing cellular regulation into the digital information processing paradigm has not been notably productive.

Cellular regulatory circuits implement a complex adaptive control system. A particularly confounding aspect of these cellular control systems is the lack of clear distinction between the mechanisms comprising the *controlling* signals and logic, and the *controlled* process or function. In ordinary engineering control systems, this distinction is usually more apparent. Consider control of traffic lights at an intersection. Buried wires sense cars in turn lanes; a box at the side of the road contains the control logic; and the signal lights over the intersection are the controlled function. In cellular regulation, control reactions and controlled functions are composed of intermingled molecules bumping together, reacting, and forming more-or-less stable assemblages so that identification of roles is more complex.

The genetic regulatory mechanisms of primary concern to this review and the coupled protein reaction-based regulatory networks [reviewed in (5)] together implement the *control system* that enables cells to adapt to their environment. The two systems act with different response speeds: protein reactions govern responses in the range of about 10^{-4} to 10^2 seconds, while genetic mechanisms govern responses in the range of about 10^2 to 10^8 seconds. Additional adaptive capability is provided by (*a*) mutation and selection-driven evolution of the regulatory circuit design and (*b*) acquisition of new functions through horizontal exchange of mobile genetic elements by bacterial conjugation, transformation, and transduction (8, 22).

SIMULATIONS OF CELLULAR REGULATION

Most molecular-level simulations to date have focused on coupled protein reactions with limited treatment of genetic reactions. Where genetics has been included, only control of transcript initiation has usually been considered. Now, however, as details of genetic mechanisms are accumulating rapidly, extension of models to include genetic regulation should be practical. In the following sections we identify several systems where prospects for such extensions are promising.

Metabolic Regulation

Although regulation of the reactions forming the core of intermediary metabolism has been intensively studied, determining how metabolism is regulated has been difficult because there are many complex feedback mechanisms within the pathways. Stress, changes in the environment, or changes in nutrient availability can all instigate mode changes leading to a revised complement of metabolic enzymes in the cell. Modeling of metabolic control is commonly done by characterizing the coupled chemical reactions with systems of ordinary differential equations based on chemical kinetics. Except in the simplest cases, the resulting equations must be solved numerically; representative software packages supporting metabolic analysis are described in (18, 64, 80).

The principal questions that modeling of metabolic regulation has addressed are: (a) How does the cell respond to presence, absence, or changes in nutrient levels? (b) How does the cell change pathways to increase (or decrease) production of selected products?

Metabolic engineering of cells to increase the yield of an industrially important product such as lysine or ethanol could have large economic returns. This prospect has stimulated modeling studies and experiments seeking to maximize yield of desirable molecules. Experiment has shown that simple overexpression of a rate-limiting enzyme rarely increases yield of the final product due to the stabilizing effects of feedback and nonlinear dynamics in metabolic control circuits. These complex control mechanisms apparently evolved to maintain optimal flux distributions in the pathways for balanced cellular growth (88). Metabolic control analysis (MCA) (40, 48) techniques show that the biosynthetic flux is usually insensitive to perturbations in any single enzyme; rather, flux control is distributed among many enzymes (101). Thus, expression of many enzymes must be changed to effect a significant change in flux. MCA studies use linear and polynomial models to predict which enzymes to change (40, 48, 81, 85, 86). Detailed enzymological models have been used to analyze pancreatic glycolysis (1, 2), red blood-cell metabolism (55), and glycolytic/gluconeogenic switching (3). Linear and polynomial models are commonly used for deriving local dynamical models to predict changes in flux within a pathway that reflect changes in experimental conditions. Complex enzymological models are used to analyze endogenous cellular control and regulatory circuits that effect large mode changes, such as switching from glycolysis to gluconeogenesis. In these analyses, the kinetics of reactions involved in gene expression are generally assumed to be "enzyme-like" (52, 102) and regulation of transcript elongation or translation is neglected. However, for many pathways these additional genetic mechanisms cannot be neglected. Extension of metabolic modeling methods to include more realistic genetic regulatory mechanisms is a current challenge to the field.

Integrating Environmental Signals into Regulatory Circuits

In the bacterial chemotactic response, attractant or repellent molecules bind to specialized receptors on the cell surface and initiate a phosphorylation cascade that controls the rotary flagellar "motor." The first comprehensive model of the phospho relay–based chemotaxis signaling network (6), constructed from known reactions and kinetics, reproduced the observed patterns of runs, tumbles, and pauses, matched responses to pulses of chemotactic agents, and matched behavioral changes in chemotactic mutants with altered enzyme activities. With addition of several hypothetical reactions, the model explained both the wild-type strain and over 30 mutants. Later models added adaptation (4, 39, 87). These simulation studies made essential contributions to understanding of the chemotactic response system. The controlled element in chemotaxis is the flagellar motor rather than gene expression, so modeling of genetic mechanisms has not been important in this system. However, other similar sensor-response pathways are widely used in bacteria to control gene expression. Bacteria use the histidyl-aspartyl phosphorelay (the "two-component system") as their predominant mode of signal transduction in regulation of adaptive responses to the environment (17). [In the *E. coli* genome, at least 62 open reading frames have been identified as putative members of the two-component signal transducers (67).] Two-component signal transducers have also been identified in diverse eukaryotic species including plants, fungi, yeast, and slime molds (104).

Cell Cycle Models

The central questions in cell cycle regulation are: (*a*) "What is the cycle of coupled reactions that drives cellular progression through DNA replication and cell division?" and (*b*) "How is genetic regulation coupled to this cycle so that genes active in cell replication, division, creation of cell structures, and other events are expressed at appropriate times?" The large size of the *Xenopus laevis* oocyte and the discovery that cytoplasmic extracts from the oocyte cycle periodically, closely replicating timing of cleavages of intact eggs, facilitated identification of cytoplasmic reactions controlling the early embryonic cell cycle. Modeling studies were undertaken to demonstrate that the known biochemical reactions alone could support oscillations of the correct frequency and with the appropriate chemical concentrations. Hyver & Le Guyader (44) were among the first to propose a rough molecularly based dynamical (differential equation) model for the system that included activation of $p34^{cdc2}$, cyclin/$p34^{cdc2}$ interactions, and cyclin degradation. The only genetic component of this model was the implicit steady production of cyclin through the cell cycle. The model demonstrated the sufficiency of the coupled cytoplasmic reactions for explaining cell cycle oscillations and was used to discriminate between competing hypotheses regarding activation of $p34^{cdc2}$ by cyclin into an active mitosis promoting factor. Later models were more elaborate (29, 70, 73, 97, 98), with the Tyson model (98) providing the most detailed early embryonic cell cycle model. Obeyesekere et al extended the model of M-phase control in embryogenesis to the full cell-cycle in human somatic cells (72). Swanson et al used the Tyson model to analyze calcium control of embryonic cell-division (90). The mechanisms for coordinate control of cell-cycle regulated genetic mechanisms are only partially identified and have not been integrated into the eukaryotic cell-cycle models yet.

Recent discoveries that progression through the bacterial cell cycle and communication between cellular compartments are mediated by two-component signal transduction systems and signaling pathways involving transcription factor activation by proteolytic processing are reviewed in (82). The coupled reactions controlling cell cycle progression in prokaryotes have not been identified. However, the recent discovery that a member of a phospho relay system that regulates several key cell cycle regulatory proteins in *Caulobacter crescentus* is controlled by both phosphorylation and temporally and spatially regulated proteolysis, suggests that paradigms of cell cycle control have been conserved among prokaryotes and eukaryotes (12, 76). Many of the genetic cascades controlling chromosome replication, cell division, and synthesis of cell structures are well characterized (11, 13, 28, 78) so that an integrated simulation model of bacterial cell cycle regulation may be possible soon.

Developmental Switches

Virtually all bacteria contain genes for many alternative physiological states. The specific metabolic and morphological features expressed are determined by the cell's history and its current environment. The mechanisms for initiating switching between states are composed of transducers on the cell's surface that detect external signals, internal status signals, internal signaling pathways, and the regulatory switching circuitry that turns promoters on or off in response to the signals. The genetic and biochemical details of these integrated switch-sensor subsystems are being identified at an accelerating rate. Two bacterial systems where molecular mechanisms are relatively well identified are sporulation in *Bacillus subtilis* and the lysis-lysogeny switch in phage lambda. Also, in many bacterial pathogens, environmental signals control developmental switches essential to progress of infections (89). Examples include: BvgA/BvgS in *Bordetella pertussis*, ToxR/toxS in *Vibrio cholerae*, *Salmonella* survival within macrophages, and outer membrane porin regulation in *Salmonella* and *E. coli* (22). Integrated simulation models of the molecular mechanisms of environmental sensing, signal transduction, and gene expression that govern global regulation in bacteria are needed now to explain dynamics of these switching mechanisms.

The cell-density-dependent gene expression found in some bacteria is another promising area where simulation models of the regulatory system are needed to explain dynamics of population behavior. The regulatory architecture in many of these "quorum-sensing" systems involves secretion of a pheromone that is detectable by a surface-bound receptor [reviewed in (33, 51)]. Typically, the receptor acts through a two-component response regulator that mediates gene expression to produce an altered phenotype at differing pheromone concentrations. High cell densities lead to high pheromone concentrations, so this mechanism provides an indicator of local cell concentration. Examples of such quorum-sensing mechanisms as components of genetic switches include the initiation of genetic competence in *Bacillus subtilis* and *Streptococcus pneumoniae*, initiation of sporulation in *Bacillus subtilis*, the virulence response in *Staphylococcus aureus*, and social motility in *Myxococcus*. The regulatory mechanism controlling aggregation of *Dictyostelium discoideum*, which also involves quorum sensing, has been extensively analyzed and simulated (30, 53, 56, 57).

The regulation of the λ phage development immediately after infection provides a paradigmatic model of a switch controlling developmental commitment. Bacteriophage λ phage genes, regulatory mechanisms, and related protein reactions have been intensively studied for forty years. Within five minutes after infection, an *E. coli* cell becomes committed to one of two fates: lysis, where the phage reproduce rapidly and soon lyse the host to release 60–100 new phage particles, or lysogeny, where the λ DNA is integrated into the host chromosome, the cell is immunized against further infection, and many generations may pass before induction of the phage continues the infection. The molecular basis of the regulatory mechanisms controlling the lysis or lysogeny decision are generally known (15, 16, 24, 41, 61, 75). As a result, λ phage regulation has been an attractive model system for studying integrated behavior of multi-gene regulatory subsystems. The central questions in phage λ dynamics are: (*a*) How does the regulatory logic that selects the lytic or lysogenic pathway work? and (*b*) How does the regulatory logic after commitment implement the genetic program leading to lysis or lysogeny?

Thomas et al (95) defined a qualitative λ lysis-lysogeny decision model in 1976 using a Boolean model of promoter regulation that predicted a subsequently constructed mutant phenotype and exhibited the necessary bistable behavior. In 1985 Shea & Ackers (83) modeled the statistical mechanics of the overlapping operator regions of the P_R and P_{RM} promoters [the λ "switch" (75)] and predicted the dynamics of maintenance of lysogeny and phage induction, as well as expected effects on lysogeny maintenance of changes in repressor cooperativity in binding to the operator region. (See discussion of the Shea–Ackers promoter control model in the next section.)

Building on the work of the Ackers group, both Reinitz & Vaisnys (77) and Chung & Stephanopoulos (9) modeled the lambda lysis-lysogeny circuit to analyze the bistability of the switch. Reinitz & Vaisnys defined a differential equation model of the production of CI and Cro based on the Shea-Ackers P_R/P_{RM} promoter model. Though degradation and dilution of the proteins were included phenomenologically in the model, the actions of CII, CIII and the Hfl proteolytic system as well as the mechanisms of elongation control were ignored due to lack of information about these subsystems and because inclusion of these mechanisms would have made analysis of the circuit too difficult. Reinitz & Vaisnys concluded that the resulting model of the switch, even with the best measured promoter kinetics, was not sufficient to explain the bistability of the reaction mechanism. Rather, they suggested either the promoter kinetics were incomplete or other neglected mechanisms in the pathway caused the bistability. Chung & Stephanopoulos (9) analyzed induction from the lysogenic state, a state in which the only phage protein expressed is the repressor, CI, by defining a simple differential equation model for dynamics of CI concentration. The model includes promoter control, CI monomer and dimer production kinetics, and decay kinetics. In the same paper, Chung & Stephanopoulos show that a similar feedback circuit is found in the lactose operon.

In 1995 McAdams & Shapiro (61) defined the first model of the λ circuit that followed the qualitative dynamics of the phage from infection through the decision to outcome. They concluded that detailed simulation of genetic mechanisms determining the temporal pattern of protein production and of the coupled protein reactions would be necessary to model regulatory circuits quantitatively. While investigating how to simulate molecular level regulatory mechanisms quantitatively, McAdams & Arkin analyzed dynamics of a representative single genetically-coupled link, that is, a one promoter-gene complex whose protein product regulates another promoter (60). In that study, an integrated molecular level model of the effector-operator reactions in the promoter control region, including the closed- to open-complex isomerization reaction and the message-translation control reactions, was developed. Owing to the low intracellular concentrations of the reacting species and the slow reaction rates in these reactions, they concluded that conventional methods of modeling coupled chemical reactions are frequently invalid for modeling the time profile of regulatory protein production. Rather, McAdams & Arkin suggest it is necessary to explicitly include consideration of the randomness in protein production that is inevitable in chemical systems where the reacting species are at low concentrations and reaction rates are slow as is typically the case for genetic regulatory proteins (36, 60). Determining the implications of this observation regarding stochastic regulatory gene expression mechanisms for the dynamics of developmental switches is a current challenge to the field.

MODELING ISSUES

This section discusses several modeling issues central to simulation of genetic regulatory circuits: (*a*) promoter control models, (*b*) stochastic processes in regulatory kinetics, (c) modeling macromolecular complexes, and (d) uncertainty in intracellular environment and reaction rates.

Promoter Control Models

The notion that promoter regulation can be modeled using a Boolean threshold logic paradigm is attractive in that it enables algebraic analysis of regulatory networks and rapid simulation algorithms. In a representative example of this approach, Thomas and coworkers analyzed the behavior of different feedback configurations in hypothetical small genetic networks (92–94, 96). Effector concentration is modeled by a differential equation of the form

$$\dot{x}_i = k_i F_i(x_1, x_2, \ldots, x_n) - k_{di} x_i,$$

where the x_i's are concentrations of the ith protein species, $\dot{x}_i$ is the time derivative of x_i, k_i is the rate of protein production when the gene type i is "on," and k_{di} is the degradation rate constant for protein type i. The F_i are step-functions, similar to the limiting form of a Hill function at high levels of cooperativity, assumed to equal 0 or 1 depending on the concentration of the x_i relative to threshold values determined by the kinetics of the promoter sites. The possible "states" of the system are identified with the distinct value ranges of the x_i. Using this formulation, a form of logical analysis is defined that provides qualitative insights into the dynamics to be expected from small genetic circuits with different combinations of positive and negative feedback loops (96). The approach is also applied to analysis of phage lambda immunity control (92). Tchuraev and co-workers use a similar Boolean threshold approximation to promoter control to simulate behavior of genetically controlled systems in an approach they call a "generalized threshold model" (74, 91).

The Boolean threshold approximation to promoter control is also applied to modeling of large networks in so-called Boolean Network models. Assumptions in the Boolean Network approach are summarized in (84): (a) the state of each gene or other network element can be characterized as either *on* (one) or *off* (zero), (b) the combinational control of gene expression can be reduced to a "wiring diagram" of the network, (c) the computation of the interactions indicated by the wiring diagram can be approximated by Boolean combinational logic rules, and (d) all elements (to first approximation) update their *on* or *off* states synchronously. A Discrete Dynamics Lab (DDL) software package (103) is available that computes the behavior of hypothetical networks. Proponents suggest that the Boolean Network models provide insight into behavior, evolution, and self-organizing capabilities of large-scale genetic networks and that this paradigm offers an approach to reverse engineering data describing temporal patterns of gene expression to extract the logical structure of the underlying physical gene regulatory network.

The Boolean characterization of genetic activation and repression is frequently a poor approximation of promoter control functions. For example, the P_{RM} promoter activation function plotted in Figure 2 is distinctly non-Boolean. Furthermore, there are numerous control mechanisms outside of promoter activation control that are equally or more important in regulatory logic. Examples include actively controlled termination sites, the many types of posttranscriptional regulation, and protein-mediated controls (proteolysis, phosphorylation, methylation).

Shea & Ackers (83) define a physically-based promoter control model for the common operator region of the divergent P_R and P_{RM} promoters that are central elements of phage lambda's so-called "switch." This switch is implemented by the intricate biochemistry of the operator region, which includes three closely situated operator sites where homodimers of two phage-encoded molecules, Cro and CI, bind competitively and in sequence, but in opposite order (59, 65, 66, 75). The respective RNA polymerase (RNAP) footprints of promoters P_R and P_{RM} overlap the operator sites. In this well-studied system,

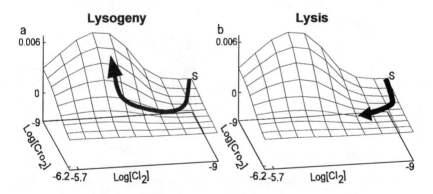

Figure 2   The phage λ P_{RM} promoter is controlled by the concentration of both Cro and CI dimers; the promoter activation level in open complexes per second (OC/s), is plotted in the upward or z-direction versus the log of the molar dimer concentrations plotted in the x–y plane. The temporal pattern of P_{RM} promoter activation immediately after phage infection of an *E. coli* cell depends on the way the concentrations of the controlling effector grows. *Arrows* illustrate the "path" of P_{RM} activation for a lysogenic outcome (*a*) and a lytic outcome (*b*). Each cell starts from the (1 nM Cro_2, 1 nM CI_2) point marked with *S* at the right rear of *a* and *b*. (In an *E. coli* cell, one molecule/cell is roughly equivalent to a 1 nM concentration.) In the lysogenic case, *a*, the system eventually enters a region of positive autoregulation locking repressor production on, while in the lytic case, *b*, repressor production from P_{RM} is never activated.

the 40 possible occupancy configurations (states) of the various binding sites by Cro_2, CI_2, or RNAP are known, as well as transcript-initiation rates for those configurations that are transcriptionally active. Also, the binding free energies for each site and each species binding at the site were measured along with incremental contributions from cooperative binding. Shea & Ackers assumed that the operator binding sites are in near equilibrium with the free concentration of Cro_2, CI_2, and RNAP. Knowing the total binding energy of each state, the fractional occupancy is calculated using the partition function. Then, the transcriptional activity of each promoter is calculated by summing the transcript initiation rates of each transcriptionally active state multiplied by the fraction of time that the system spends in that state. As the concentration of repressor molecules increases, the probability of occupancy of transcriptionally active sites decreases, and that of transcriptionally inactive states increases so that the rate of transcript initiation is repressed. Figure 2 shows the activation surface of the P_{RM} promoter as a function of Cro_2 and CI_2 concentrations calculated using the Shea–Ackers scheme. An advantage of the activation surface representation is that the progression of regulatory decisions implemented by changing concentrations of signal proteins can be visualized as a path on the activation surfaces of the controlling promoters. The differing paths in phage λ-infected cells that commit to lysogeny versus those that become lytic is illustrated schematically in Figure 2.

Cellular regulatory logic is inherently a logic based on continuously variable parameters, that is, it is an "analog" logic. Accordingly, it seems inevitable that the most useful heuristic for simulating promoter control will prove to be the one that best approximates the n-dimensional promoter activation surface rather than one that forces a nonphysical discrete logic approximation. Whenever a Boolean approximation is valid, the analysis and modeling of system behavior can be simplified. However, validity of the Boolean approximation has to be examined critically for each regulatory subelement in a system. Hybrid models with behavior of some elements characterized as Boolean and other elements treated with detailed kinetics may prove to be the most efficient compromise.

Stochastic Processes in Regulatory Kinetics

Numerous studies have analyzed cellular regulation using ordinary differential equations (ODE) to model the macroscopic kinetics of coupled chemical reactions. Analytical or numerical methods are used to solve the equations. Examples include models addressing (a) bacterial chemotaxis control (6, 39); (b) the oocyte cell cycle (71, 90); (c) T7 phage infection (19); (d) conditions for lambda lysogen induction (9); and (e) the phage λ lysis-lysogeny decision

(77). In defining the differential equations for these models, there is an implicit assumption of continuously varying chemical concentration and deterministic dynamics. For a chemical system to be compatible with these assumptions the number of molecules of each type must be large compared to thermal fluctuations in concentration, and for each type of reaction in the system, the number of reactions per unit time must be large in each observation interval. In vivo genetic reactions usually violate the assumptions of determinism and continuity underlying conventional kinetics because they occur at low concentrations, are isolated spatially, and have slow reaction rates.

McQuarrie (63) analyzes the kinetics of chemical systems with small numbers of participating molecules; the behavior of such "small" chemical systems, predicted using a more exact stochastic formulation, is shown to differ from the prediction using conventional deterministic kinetics. Analytical solution to stochastic reaction equations is only practical for simple reactions. However, numerical solutions can be computed for complex systems of coupled stochastic reactions using the Monte Carlo algorithm described by Gillespie (26). The Gillespie algorithm produces a stochastic realization of the temporal behavior of the system by calculating the probabilistic outcome of each discrete chemical event and resulting changes in the number of each molecular species. If the physical model and its assumptions are valid, and parameter estimates are sound, then this stochastic simulation algorithm produces a more realistic and complete description of the time-dependent behavior of stochastic reaction systems than a deterministic kinetic calculation (26, 27).

The Gillespie stochastic simulation algorithm is based on application of the chemical master equation. The master equation is a stochastic differential difference equation describing the time evolution of the probability densities for the concentrations of the chemical species comprising the reaction system (26, 27, 99). States of the system are characterized by a "state vector." Each component of the state vector represents the number of molecules of a particular molecular species in the chemical system at a given time. Every feasible chemical reaction represents a transition between states and the probability of that transition is determined by the probability of the corresponding reaction. The transition probabilities in these master equations are related to the conventional macroscopic rate coefficients of the reactions that comprise the chemical network.[1]

---

[1] The stochastic kinetic parameters in (26) are related to conventional deterministic kinetic parameters: For reactions of the form $X \xrightarrow{k} anything$, $k_{stoch} = k_{det}$; for reactions of the form $X + Y \xrightarrow{k} anything$, $k_{stoch} = k_{det}/(A_g V_{cell})$; for reactions of the form $X + X \xrightarrow{k} anything$, $k_{stoch} = k_{det}/(2 A_g V_{cell})$, where A_g is Avogadro's number and V_{cell} is the cell volume.

In application of the Gillespie algorithm to simulation of bacterial regulation, each simulation run represents a possible evolution of a single cell from a starting condition for that case. Multiple runs are used to develop a statistical characterization of the outcomes expected for a cell population. Statistical sampling theory is used to determine how many simulation runs must be included to achieve a target confidence level in the statistics of outcomes. The Shea–Ackers promoter model can be adapted to the Gillespie simulation algorithm by calculating the instantaneous probability of each distinct transcriptionally active state of a promoter using the partition function, and then using this probability in calculating the reaction probabilities for the transcript initiation reactions.

The predicted temporal pattern of regulatory protein production from a representative activated bacterial promoter is described by McAdams & Arkin (60) and is shown here in Figure 3. They define a detailed model of gene expression mechanisms that includes an integrated molecular-level model of the effector-operator reactions in the promoter control region, the closed- to open-complex isomerization reaction, transcript elongation, and the reactions controlling message translation.

The simulated homodimer concentration growth for three runs is shown in Figure 3a; each run exhibits a substantially different pattern of dimer concentration growth and is illustrative of the wide range of regulatory expression patterns that can be expected in a homogenous cell population. Figure 3b shows the mean and standard deviation of the expected number of dimers in the cell at each time for gene dosage = 1, 2, and 4. The horizontal lines at 25 and 50 nM delineate a representative range over which switching is effected by bacterial regulatory proteins. These simulations of the pattern of regulatory protein production suggest that proteins are produced in short bursts of variable numbers of proteins that occur at random intervals. As a result, the genetic switching time in growing cells can have considerable uncertainty. Stronger promoters, higher gene dosage (or equivalently in many cases, multiple promoters per gene), and lower signal thresholds all act to reduce timing uncertainty (60). These observations suggest that the validity of using conventional kinetic analysis for in vivo regulatory functions must always be examined critically, particularly for processes in cells that are regulated by low concentrations of short-lived effector molecules.

If we accept McAdams & Arkin's prediction that the temporal pattern of regulatory protein production in individual cells can be quite different for each cell in a population, then this "noise" phenomenon should affect the cellular outcomes for competitively regulated switching mechanisms. As a simple example, consider the situation shown schematically in Figure 4, where an activating and a repressing protein expressed from two independent promoters competitively regulate an operon transcribed from promoter P_G.

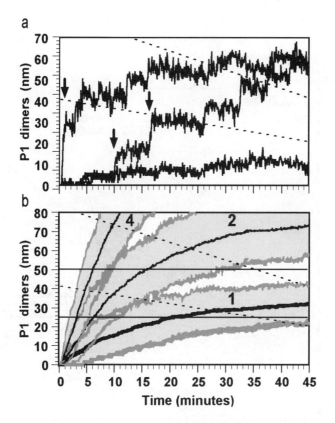

Figure 3   (*a*) Three simulation runs showing a different realization of the pattern of homodimer production from a representative bacterial promoter in a single cell. *Dashed lines*, declining concentrations equivalent to 25 and 50 dimer molecules in the growing cell. Parameters: dimerization equilibrium constant = 20 nM; protein half-life = 30 min. Initial cell volume = 1×10^{-15} l, doubling in 45 min. (*b*) Mean and $\pm 1 \sigma$ results at gene dosages of 1, 2, and 4. At higher gene dosages, protein P1 is being produced from more genes; the concentration rises more rapidly, and the effective concentration range is reached quicker. Also, the dispersion in time to effectiveness (i.e. the switching delay) is lower for faster-growing signals [from Figure 3 in (60)].

Illustrative contours for P_G activation are shown versus the activator and repressor concentrations. The bold line is the 50% activation contour. Hypothetical successive distributions for the activator and repressor concentrations from the two independent operons are shown at times T_1, T_2, and T_3. The situation at T_3 illustrates how activation of P_G can vary widely from cell to cell because of the statistical differences in activator and repressor production. In developmental switches, such competitively regulated promoters are found as

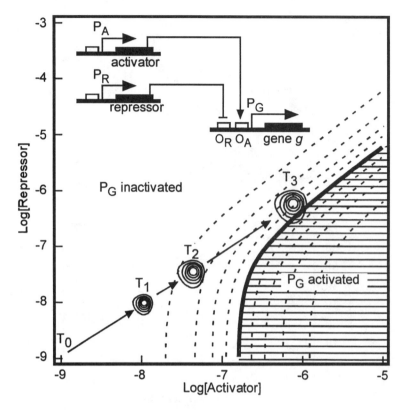

Figure 4   Illustration of differential promoter activation across a cell population resulting from statistical variations in concentrations of competitive effectors. The activator and repressor operons shown are assumed to be independent so that stochastic gene expression mechanisms in each operon produce the respective protein types in a different pattern in each cell. *Small circular contour patterns*, concentration distributions with increasing means at successive times T_1, T_2, and T_3 after activation of P_A and P_R at T_0. Contours of the illustrative activation surface for P_G as a function of activator and repressor concentration are also shown. *Bold line*, 50% activation contour for promoter P_G. This simple example illustrates how normal dispersion of concentrations of controlling proteins can result in differential activation of controlled operons in different cells. Consequences for the cell will depend on the specific kinetic parameters for a particular case and, importantly, on the larger regulatory circuit responding to proteins from the controlled operons.

elements of the regulatory circuitry that determines cell fate. Examples are found in the phage λ and *Bacillus subtilis* cases cited above. In both these organisms, the switching circuits partition the population into subpopulations following different pathways, e.g. fractional commitment to lysogeny or sporulation. Circuits based on bistable genetic regulatory mechanisms are also used in many organisms to produce subpopulations of distinct phenotypes by random inversion of DNA segments (14). Quantitative verification of the role of molecular-level fluctuations in regulation of these population-level outcomes is a current challenge for experimentalists and modelers.

Modeling Macromolecular Complexes

Multiprotein complexes, such as polymerases, topoisomerases, and ribosomes, are the processing machines that perform the DNA processing and manipulation tasks that are central to execution of genetic regulatory logic. Realistic modeling of the functions of these multiprotein genetic machines is a central challenge in modeling behavior of genetic networks. These complexes, although chemically based and acting to produce chemical changes, behave in many ways more like macroscopic machines than conventional chemical reaction mechanisms. For example, they have to be assembled to function; they can create products from raw materials according to stored instructions (ribosomes and polymerases); they can make macroscopic changes in other cellular objects (integrases and invertases); and many are processive. Heuristic models that capture their dynamical behavior within regulatory networks will differ from conventional chemical reaction models.

Uncertainty of Intracellular Reaction Parameters

The intracellular chemical environment is poorly characterized and probably varies widely from cell to cell in populations and from moment to moment in individual cells. The causes of these variations include the stochastic variations in reaction rate parameters cited above and changes in cellular chemistry as the cell cycle progresses. Except in the best-stirred media, individual cells in a colony can experience wide differences in the local nutrient microenvironment that can affect rates of synthetic reactions or even trigger global regulatory changes within some cells. Furthermore, in growing cells there are significant random components in cell division time, in daughter cell size, and in the partitioning of the molecular endowment between daughter cells. In spite of these perturbations, cells function successfully and regulatory mechanisms have consistent outcomes, suggesting that regulatory circuit designs and the molecular details that determine kinetic parameters are under selective pressure for robust operation in the face of large variations in the intracellular environment. Simulation studies of the signal transduction network in the *E. coli* chemotactic regulatory circuit suggest that that circuit's performance is robust to changes in many parameter values (4, 37). If regulatory circuit designs found in wild-type organisms are indeed selected to have this type of robustness, then construction of adequate simulation models of the circuits may only require rough values for their kinetic parameters. When the "engineering" rules for design of robust regulatory networks are defined, it will be possible to test the proposition that robust performance is a significant source of evolutionary selection pressure.

CHALLENGES AND OPPORTUNITIES

Molecular level models are needed to analyze dynamical behavior of multigene systems, to predict behavior of mutant circuits, and to identify the engineering design principles applicable to design of genetic regulatory circuits. In the near term, the greatest opportunity will be in modeling of bacterial systems. Additional and different mechanisms are present in eukaryotic networks. Key distinctions in eukaryotes include: (*a*) more complex regulatory control regions involving molecular mechanisms that are only beginning to be understood; (*b*) posttranscriptional message processing; and (*c*) compartmentalization of functions, such as separation of transcription and translation, by the nuclear membrane.

Extensive details of many genetic mechanisms are now known in bacterial systems and complete genome sequences are becoming available. Development of simulation models of processes, such as quorum sensing, that involve regulation within the signal transduction networks as well as in the genetic networks will clarify the design principles of cellular regulatory circuits.

In such integrated simulations, the multiprotein complexes that implement genetic regulatory functions (for example, the DNA and RNA polymerase complexes and others that edit and reorganize DNA and RNA) will have to be modeled with heuristic mechanical abstractions that capture their essential regulatory functions. Also, the impact of stochastic intracellular chemistry on regulatory circuit behavior will have to be examined closely. When the underlying design rules for regulatory circuits are understood, it will be far easier to recognize common circuit motifs, to identify functions of individual proteins in regulation, and to redesign circuits for altered functions.

ACKNOWLEDGMENT

This work was supported by Office of Naval Research Grant N00014-96-1-0564.

Visit the *Annual Reviews* home page at
http://www.AnnualReviews.org.

Literature Cited

1. Achs MJ, Anderson JH, Garfinkel D. 1971. Gluconeogenesis in rat liver cytosol, I. *Comput. Biomed. Res.* 4:65–105
2. Achs MJ, Garfinkel D. 1977. Computer simulation of energy metabolism in anoxic perfused rat heart. *Am. J. Physiol.* 232:R164–74
3. Arkin AP, Ross J. 1994. Computational functions in biochemical reaction networks. *Biophys. J.* 67:560–78
4. Barkai N, Leibler S. 1997. Robustness in simple biochemical networks. *Nature* 387:913–17
5. Bray D. 1995. Protein molecules as computational elements in living cells. *Nature* 376:307–12

6. Bray D, Bourret RB, Simon MI. 1993. Computer simulation of the phosphorylation cascade controlling bacterial chemotaxis. *Mol. Biol. Cell* 4:469–82

7. Brun YV, Marczynski G, Shapiro L. 1994. The expression of asymmetry during *Caulobacter* cell differentiation. *Annu. Rev. Biochem.* 63:419–50

8. Cheetham BF, Katz ME. 1995. A role for bacteriophages in the evolution and transfer of bacterial virulence determinants. *Mol. Microbiol.* 18:201–8

9. Chung JD, Stephanopoulos G. 1996. On physiological multiplicity and population heterogeneity of biological systems. *Chem. Eng. Sci.* 51:1509–21

10. Collado-Vides J, Magasanik B, Gralla JD. 1991. Control site location and transcriptional regulation in *Escherichia coli*. *Microb. Rev.* 55:371–94

11. Domian IJ, Quon KC, Shapiro L. 1996. The control of temporal and spatial organization during the *Caulobacter* cell cycle. *Curr. Opin. Genet. Dev.* 6:538–44

12. Domian IJ, Quon KC, Shapiro L. 1997. Cell type-specific phosphorylation and proteolysis of a transcriptional regulator controls the G1-to-S transition in a bacterial cell cycle. *Cell* 90:415–24

13. Donachie WD. 1993. The cell cycle of *Escherichia coli*. *Annu. Rev. Microb.* 47:199–230

14. Dorman CJ. 1995. DNA topology and the global control of bacterial gene expression: implications for the regulation of virulence gene expression. *Microbiology (Reading)* 141:1271–80

15. Echols H. 1986. Multiple DNA-protein interactions governing high-precision DNA transactions. *Science* 233:1050–56

16. Echols H, Guarneros G. 1983. Control of integration and excision. In *Lambda II*, ed. R Hendrix, JW Roberts, FW Stahl, RA Weisberg, pp. 75–92. Cold Spring Harbor, NY: Cold Spring Harbor Lab. Press

17. Egger LA, Park H, Inouye M. 1997. Signal transduction via the histidyl-aspartyl phosphorelay. *Genes Cells* 2:167–84

18. Ehlde M, Zacchi G. 1995. Mist: a user-friendly metabolic simulator. *Comp. Applic. Biosci.* 11:201–7

19. Endy D, Kong D, Yin J. 1997. Intracellular kinetics of a growing virus: a genetically structured simulation for bacteriophage T7. *Biotech. Bioeng.* In press

20. Errington J. 1993. *Bacillus subtilis* sporulation: regulation of gene expression and control of morphogenesis. *Microbiol. Rev.* 57:1–33

21. Finlay BB, Cossart P. 1997. Exploitation of mammalian host cell functions by bacterial pathogens. *Science* 276:718–25

22. Finlay BB, Falkow S. 1997. Common themes in microbial pathogenicity revisited. *Microbiol. Mol. Biol. Rev.* 61:136–69

23. Freundlich M, Ramani N, Mathew E, Sirko A, Tsui P. 1992. The role of integration host factor in gene expression in *Escherichia coli*. *Mol. Microbiol.* 6:2557–63

24. Friedman DI. 1992. Interaction between bacteriophage lambda and its *Escherichia coli* host. *Curr. Opin. Genet. Dev.* 2:727–38

25. Galan JE, Bliska JB. 1996. Cross-talk between bacterial pathogens and their host cells. *Annu. Rev. Cell. Dev.* 12:221–55

26. Gillespie DT. 1977. Exact stochastic simulation of coupled chemical reactions. *J. Phys. Chem.* 81(25):2340–61

27. Gillespie DT. 1992. A rigorous derivation of the chemical master equation. *Physica A* 188:404–25

28. Gober JW, Marques MV. 1995. Regulation of cellular differentiation in *Caulobacter crescentus*. *Microb. Rev.* 59:31–47

29. Goldbeter A. 1991. A minimal cascade model for the mitotic oscillator involving cyclin and cdc2 kinase. *Proc. Natl. Acad. Sci. USA* 88:9107–11

30. Goldbeter A. 1996. *Biochemical Oscillations and Cellular Rhythms: The Molecular Bases of Periodic and Chaotic Behavior.* Cambridge: Cambridge Univ. Press

31. Goosen N, van de Putte P. 1995. The regulation of transcription initiation by integration host factor. *Mol. Microbiol.* 16:1–7

32. Gottesman S. 1984. Bacterial regulation: global regulatory networks. *Annu. Rev. Genet.* 18:415–41

33. Gray KM. 1997. Intercellular communication and group behavior in bacteria. *Trends Microbiol.* 5(5):184–88

34. Gross R. 1993. Signal transduction and virulence regulation in human and animal pathogens. *FEMS Microbiol. Rev.* 10:301–26

35. Grossman AD. 1995. Genetic networks controlling the initiation of sporulation and the development of genetic competence in *Bacillus subtilis*. *Annu. Rev. Genet.* 29:477–508

36. Guptasarma P. 1995. Does replication-induced transcription regulate synthesis of the myriad low copy number proteins of *Escherichia coli*? *BioEssays* 17:987–97

37. Hartwell L. 1997. A robust view of biochemical pathways. *Nature* 387:855–56

38. Hartwell LH, Weinert TA. 1989. Checkpoints: controls that ensure the order of cell cycle events. *Science* 246:629–34
39. Hauri DC, Ross J. 1995. A model of excitation and adaptation in bacterial chemotaxis. *Biophys. J.* 68:708–22
40. Heinrich R, Rapoport SM, Rapoport TA. 1977. Metabolic regulation and mathematical models. *Prog. Biophys. Mol. Biol.* 32:1–82
41. Herskowitz I, Hagen D. 1980. The lysis-lysogeny decision of phage lambda: explicit programming and responsiveness. *Annu. Rev. Genet.* 14:399–445
42. Hicks KA, Grossman AD. 1996. Altering the level and regulation of the major sigma subunit of RNA polymerase affects gene expression and development in *Bacillus subtilis*. *Mol. Microbiol.* 20:201–12
43. Horvitz HR, Herskowitz I. 1992. Mechanisms of asymmetric cell division: two b's or not two b's, that is the question. *Cell* 68:237–56
44. Hyver C, Guyader HL. 1990. MPF and cyclin: Modeling of the cell cycle minimum oscillator. *BioSystems* 24:85–90
45. Jacob F, Monod J. 1962. *Elements of regulatory circuits in bacteria.* Presented at Symp. Biol. Organiz. Cell. Supercell Lev., Varenna, Italy, pp. 1–24. New York: Academic
46. Jacob F, Monod J. 1962. *Genetic repression, allosteric inhibition, and cellular differentiation.* Presented at Symp. Cytodifferent. Macromol. Synth., Asilomar, California, pp. 30–64. New York: Academic
47. Jacob F, Monod J. 1962. On the regulation of gene activity. Symp. Cell. Regul. Mech., pp. 193–209. Cold Spring Harbor, NY: Cold Spring Harbor Lab. Press
48. Kacser H, Burns JA. 1973. *The control of flux.* Presented at Symp. Soc. Exper. Biol. Rate Control Biol. Proc., pp. 65–104. Cambridge: Cambridge Univ. Press
49. Kaufmann WK, Paules RS. 1996. DNA damage and cell cycle checkpoints. *FASEB J.* 10:238–47
50. Kim SK, Kaiser D, Kuspa A. 1992. Control of cell density and pattern by intercellular signaling in myxococcus development. *Annu. Rev. Microbiol.* 46:117–39
51. Kleerebezem M, Quadri LE, Kuipers OP, de Vos WM. 1997. Quorum sensing by peptide pheromones and two-component signal-transduction systems in Gram-positive bacteria. *Mol. Microb.* 24:895–904
52. Koster JG, Destree OHJ, Raat NJH, Westerhoff HV. 1990. Histones in *Xenopus laevis*' early development: The race against

time. *Biomed. Biochim. Acta* 49:855–77
53. Lauzeral J, Halloy J, Goldbeter A. 1997. Desynchronization of cells on the developmental path triggers the formation of spiral waves of cAMP during *Dictyostelium* aggregation. *Proc. Natl. Acad. Sci. USA* 94:9153–58
54. Lawrence PA, Morata G. 1994. Homeobox genes: Their function in *Drosophila* segmentation and pattern formation. *Cell* 78:181–89
55. Lee I-D, Palsson BO. 1992. A Macintosh software package for simulation of human red blood cell metabolism. Section II: Systems and programs. *Comput. Meth. Prog. Biomed.* 38:195–226
56. Levine H, Aranson I, Tsimring L, Truong TV. 1996. Positive genetic feedback governs camp spiral wave formation in *Dictyostelium*. *Proc. Natl. Acad. Sci. USA* 93:6382–86
57. Li Y, Goldbeter A. 1992. Pulsatile signaling in intercellular communication: periodic stimuli are more efficient than random or chaotic signals in a model based on receptor desensitization. *Biophys. J.* 61:161–71
58. Long SR, Staskawicz BJ. 1993. Prokaryotic plant parasites. *Cell* 73:921–35
59. Maurer R, Meyer B, Ptashne M. 1980. Gene regulation at the right operator (OR) bacteriophage lambda. I: OR3 and autogenous negative control by repressor. *J. Mol. Biol.* 139:147–61
60. McAdams H, Arkin A. 1997. Stochastic mechanisms in gene expression. *Proc. Natl. Acad. Sci. USA* 94:814–19
61. McAdams HH, Shapiro L. 1995. Circuit simulation of genetic networks. *Science* 269:650–56
62. McFall-Ngai MJ, Ruby EG. 1991. Symbiont recognition and subsequent morphogenesis as early events in an animal-bacterial mutualism. *Science* 254:1491–94
63. McQuarrie DA, Jachimowski CJ, Russell ME. 1964. Kinetics of small systems II. *J. Chem. Phys.* 40:2914–21
64. Mendes P. 1993. GEPASI: a software package for modelling the dynamics, steady states and control of biochemical and other systems. *Comp. Applic. Biosci.* 9:563–71
65. Meyer BJ, Maurer R, Ptashne M. 1980. Gene regulation at the right operator (OR) of bacteriophage lambda. II: OR1, OR2, and OR3: their roles in mediating the effects of repressor and cro. *J. Mol. Biol.* 139:163–94
66. Meyer BJ, Ptashne M. 1980. Gene regulation at the right operator (OR) of bacterio-

phage lambda. III: Lambda repressor directly activates gene transcription. *J. Mol. Biol.* 139:195–205

67. Mizuno T. 1997. Compilation of all genes encoding two-component phosphotransfer signal transducers in the genome of *Escherichia coli. DNA Res.* 4:161–8

68. Monod J, Jacob F. 1962. *General conclusions: teleonomic mechanisms in cellular metabolism, growth, and differentiation.* Presented at Symp. Cell. Regul. Mech., June 4–12, 1961. Cold Spring Harbor, NY: Cold Spring Harbor Lab. Press

69. Neidhardt FC, Savageau MA. 1996. Regulation beyond the operon. In *Escherichia coli and Salmonella typhimurium: Cellular and molecular biology*, pp. 1310–24. Washington, DC: Am. Soc. Microbiol.

70. Norel R, Agur Z. 1991. A model for the adjustment of the mitotic clock by cyclin and MPF levels. *Science* 251:1076–78

71. Novak B, Tyson JJ. 1993. Numerical analysis of a comprehensive model of M-phase control in *Xenopus* oocyte extracts and intact embryos. *J. Cell Sci.* 106:1153–68

72. Obeyesekere MN, Herbert JR, Zimmerman SO. 1995. A model of the G1 phase of the cell cycle incorporating cyclin E/cdk2 complex and retinoblastoma protein. *Oncogene* 11:1199–205

73. Obeyesekere MN, Tucker SL, Zimmerman SO. 1992. Mathematical models for the cellular concentrations of cyclin and mpf. *Biochem. Biophys. Res. Comm.* 184:782–89

74. Prokudina EI, Valeev RY, Tchuraev RN. 1991. A new method for the analysis of the dynamics of the molecular genetic control systems. II: Application of the method of generalized threshold models in the investigation of concrete genetic systems. *J. Theor. Biol.* 151:89–110

75. Ptashne M. 1992. *A Genetic Switch: Phage λ and Higher Organisms.* Cambridge, MA: Cell Press/Blackwell

76. Quon KC, Marczynski GT, Shapiro L. 1996. Cell cycle control by an essential bacterial two-component signal transduction protein. *Cell* 84:83–93

77. Reinitz J, Vaisnys JR. 1990. Theoretical and experimental analysis of the phage lambda genetic switch implies missing levels of cooperativity. *J. Theor. Biol.* 145:295–318

78. Roberts RC, Mohr CD, Shapiro L. 1996. Developmental programs in bacteria. *Curr. Top. Dev. Biol.* 34:207–57

79. Rosen R. 1968. Recent developments in the theory of control and regulation of cellular processes. In *International Review of Cytology*, ed. GH Bourne, JF Danielli, pp. 25–88. New York: Academic

80. Sauro HM. 1993. SCAMP: A general-purpose simulator and metabolic control analysis program. *Comp. Applic. Biosci.* 9:441–50

81. Savageau MA. 1991. Biochemical systems theory: operational differences among variant representations and their significance. *J. Theor. Biol.* 151:509–30

82. Shapiro L, Losick R. 1997. Protein localization and cell fate in bacteria. *Science* 276:712–18

83. Shea MA, Ackers GK. 1985. The OR control system of bacteriophage lambda: A physical-chemical model for gene regulation. *J. Mol. Biol.* 181:211–30

84. Somogyi R, Sniegoski CA. 1996. Modeling the complexity of genetic networks: Understanding multigenic and pleiotropic regulation. *Complexity* 1:45–63

85. Sorribas A, Savageau MA. 1989. A comparison of variant theories of intact biochemical systems. I: Enzyme-enzyme interactions and biochemical systems theory. *Math. Biosci.* 94:161–93

86. Sorribas A, Savageau MA. 1989. A comparison of variant theories of intact biochemical systems. II: Flux-oriented and metabolic control theories. *Math. Biosci.* 94:195–238

87. Spiro PA, Parkinson JS, Othmer HG. 1997. A model of excitation and adaptation in bacterial chemotaxis. *Proc. Natl. Acad. Sci. USA* 94:7263–68

88. Stephanopoulos G, Vallino JJ. 1991. Network rigidity and metabolic engineering in metabolite overproduction. *Science* 252:1675–81

89. Strauss EJ, Falkow S. 1997. Microbial pathogenesis: genomics and beyond. *Science* 276:707–12

90. Swanson CA, Arkin A, Ross J. 1997. An endogenous calcium oscillator may control early embryonic division. *Proc. Natl. Acad. Sci. USA* 94:1194–99

91. Tchuraev RN. 1991. A new method for the analysis of the dynamics of the molecular genetic control systems. I: Description of the method of generalized threshold models. *J. Theor. Biol.* 151:71–88

92. Thieffry D, Thomas R. 1995. Dynamical behaviour of biological regulatory networks. II: Immunity control in bacteriophage lambda. *Bull. Math. Biol.* 57:277–97

93. Thomas R. 1973. Boolean formalization of genetic control circuits. *J. Theor. Biol.* 42:563–85

94. Thomas R. 1991. Regulatory networks

seen as asynchronous automata: a logical description. *J. Theor. Biol.* 153:1–23

95. Thomas R, Gathoye A-M, Lambert L. 1976. A complex control circuit: Regulation of immunity in temperate bacteriophages. *Eur. J. Biochem.* 71:211–27

96. Thomas R, Thieffry D, Kaufman M. 1995. Dynamical behaviour of biological regulatory networks. I: Biological role of feedback loops and practical use of the concept of the loop-characteristic state. *Bull. Math. Biol.* 57:247–76

97. Tyson JJ. 1991. Modeling the cell division cycle: cdc2 and cyclin interactions. *Proc. Natl. Acad. Sci. USA* 88:7328–32

98. Tyson JJ, Novak B, Odell GM, Chen K, Thron CD. 1996. Chemical kinetic theory: Understanding cell-cycle regulation. *Trends Biochem. Sci.* 221:89–96

99. Van Kampen NG. 1992. *Stochastic Processes in Physics and Chemistry*, p. 460. Amsterdam: North-Holland

100. Wells WAE. 1996. The spindle-assembly checkpoint: aiming for a perfect mitosis every time. *Trends Cell Biol.* 6:228–34

101. Westerhoff HV. 1995. Subtlety in control—metabolic pathway engineering. *Trends Biotech.* 13:242–44

102. Westerhoff HV, van Workum M. 1990. Control of DNA structure and gene expression. *Biomed. Biochim. Acta* 49:839–53

103. Wuensche A, Lesser MJ. 1992. The global dynamics of cellular automata. In *SFI Studies in the Sciences of Complexity.* Reading, MA: Addison-Wesley

104. Wurgler-Murphy SM, Saito H. 1997. Two-component signal transducers and MAPK cascades. *Trends Biochem. Sci.* 22:172–76

105. Yura T. 1996. Regulation and conservation of the heat-shock transcription factor sigma32. *Genes Cells* 1:277–84

Annu. Rev. Biophys. Biomol. Struct. 1998. 27:225–48
Copyright © 1998 by Annual Reviews. All rights reserved

DNA NANOTECHNOLOGY:
Novel DNA Constructions

Nadrian C. Seeman
Department of Chemistry, New York University, New York, NY 10003;
e-mail: ned.seeman@nyu.edu

KEY WORDS: nanotechnology, branched DNA, single-stranded DNA topology, molecular
design, DNA catenanes, DNA knots, DNA polyhedra

ABSTRACT

DNA nanotechnology entails the construction of specific geometrical and topological targets from DNA. The goals include the use of DNA molecules to scaffold
the assembly of other molecules, particularly in periodic arrays, with the objects of
both crystal facilitation and memory-device construction. Many of these products
are based on branched DNA motifs. DNA molecules with the connectivities of a
cube and a truncated octahedron have been prepared. A solid-support methodology has been developed to construct DNA targets. DNA trefoil and figure-8 knots
have been made, predicated on the relationship between a topological crossing
and a half-turn of B-DNA or Z-DNA. The same basis has been used to construct
Borromean rings from DNA. An RNA knot has been used to demonstrate an RNA
topoisomerase activity. The desire to construct periodic matter held together by
DNA sticky ends has resulted in a search for stiff components; DNA double
crossover molecules appear to be the best candidates. It appears that novel DNA
motifs may be of use in the new field of DNA-based computing.

CONTENTS

225

PERSPECTIVES AND OVERVIEW

We are all familiar with DNA as the substance that functions as genetic material for living cells. Its double-helical structure has become one of the cultural icons representing contemporary civilization in much the same way that we associate previous societies with the Pyramids of Egypt, the Colosseum of Rome, or the Great Wall of China. It is often useful to look at such a familiar object from the contrary viewpoint expressed by Sherlock Holmes in *Silver Blaze* (8), when he remarked to the inspector on the "curious incident of the dog in the night-time." When the inspector replied, "The dog did nothing in the night-time," Holmes replied, "That was the curious incident." A similarly curious feature of DNA is its lack of branches: Insofar as we know, the helix axis of genomic DNA is topologically linear.

Nevertheless, branched DNA molecules do appear as key intermediates in DNA metabolism, particularly in the processes of replication, recombination, and repair. For example, the Holliday junction (20) is a recombinational intermediate that contains four strands arranged into four double-helical arms. The branch points of naturally occurring Holliday junctions are flanked by sequences with homologous symmetry. Through an isomerization known as branch migration (21), this symmetry permits the branch point to move.

The instability of the branch point locus impeded the physical characterization of junctions. To solve this problem, it was suggested that the branch point could be immobilized by eliminating the symmetry (45). Other features of symmetry are also minimized in the design of these molecules (45, 47, 49). The advent of synthetic immobile DNA junctions (23) has resulted in the accumulation of much physical data on branched DNA molecules (29, 50). An example of an immobile branched junction is illustrated in Figure 1a.

The ligation of sticky-ended linear DNA molecules (6) is arguably the fundamental reaction of biotechnology. From a geometrical perspective, this reaction corresponds to the concatenation of line segments, leading to long lines and circles, or perhaps knots and catenanes. However, DNA molecules containing stable branch points add vertices to DNA construction: This permits the generation of stick figures and networks, in which the edges consist of double-helical

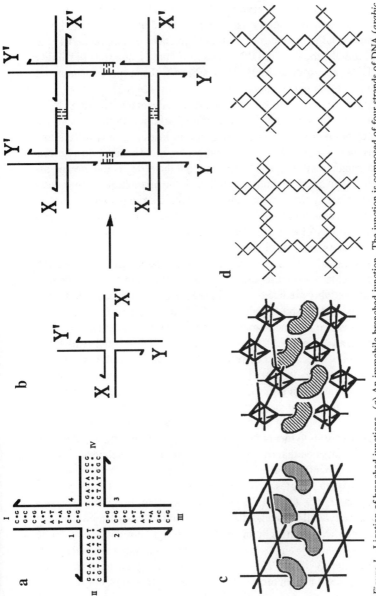

Figure 1 Ligation of branched junctions. (*a*) An immobile branched junction. The junction is composed of four strands of DNA (*arabic numerals*) and double-helical arms (*roman numerals*). The 3' end of each strand is indicated by *half-arrows*. (*b*) Formation of a 2-D Lattice from an immobile junction with sticky ends. *X* and *Y*, sticky ends; *X'* and *Y'*, their complements. DNA ligase can close the gaps where the sticky ends cohere. (*c*) 5- and 6-connected networks acting as hosts for macromolecular guests. *Left*, the 6-connected cubic lattice, the simplest conceptual network. Macromolecular guests, represented as *shaded kidney-shaped objects*, have been added to four edges. *Right*, a 5-connected network composed of octahedra and a truncated cube. (*d*) DNA squares containing even and odd numbers of half-turns per edge. These diagrams represent the same structure as in (*b*), but the plectonemic winding of the DNA is shown. The left structure forms molecular chain mail, but the one on the right forms a meshwork of long strands.

DNA and the vertices are the branch points of junctions. An example of this approach is shown in Figure 1b, where a 4-arm branched junction is ligated to three copies of itself to form a quadrilateral. In addition, the complex in Figure 1b retains a large number of unsatisfied valences that could be used to tile the plane. Ideally, the protocol illustrated in Figure 1b suggests the ability to construct DNA networks and objects of arbitrary shape on the nanometer scale, leading to a DNA nanotechnology.

Why would one want to do this, and what are the advantages to using DNA? A key goal of DNA nanotechnology is a rational solution to the crystallization problem of biological macromolecules for purposes of X-ray diffraction. Figure 1c illustrates a suggestion (45) that molecules could be tethered as guests in an identical manner within a DNA box, and that the boxes could then be assembled into a crystal by sticky-end association: If the orientations of the guests remained the same, they would constitute a crystalline array in their own right, permitting the determination of their structures. The suggestion has also been made that the assembly of molecular electronic components could be directed by periodic DNA network scaffolding (42).

There are several advantages to using DNA for these constructions. First, DNA is the molecule whose intermolecular interactions are the most readily programmed and reliably predicted: Docking experiments reduce to the simple rules that A pairs with T and G pairs with C. Thus, the very properties that make DNA so effective as genetic material also make it an excellent molecule for programmed self-assembly. A second advantage of DNA is the availability of arbitrary sequences because of convenient solid support synthesis (3). The needs of the biotechnology industry have also led to easy chemistry to produce modifications, such as biotin groups, fluorescent labels, and linking functions. Third, DNA can be manipulated and modified by a large battery of enzymes that include DNA ligase, restriction endonucleases, kinases, and exonucleases. In addition, DNA is a stiff polymer (18) in 1–3 turn lengths, it is a stable molecule, and it has an external code that can be read by proteins and nucleic acids (51).

Two further comments about the properties of branched DNA molecules are in order. First, the angles between the arms of branched junctions are variable. In contrast, say, to the tetrahedral carbon atom, branched junctions are not geometrically well-defined. The assembly of the quadrilateral depicted in Figure 1b is predicated on right angles between rigid arms if only a single component is used; variable angles lead to variable products, as seen in ligation-closure experiments (31, 37). Thus, all syntheses discussed here are really topological syntheses, and their proofs are also proofs of topology, not geometry.

Second, it is imperative to recognize that DNA is a helical molecule. For many purposes discussed here, the double-helical half-turn is the quantum of single-stranded DNA topology. Figure 1d illustrates two variants of Figure 1b, one with an even number of half-turns between vertices, and the other with an odd number. With an even number of half-turns, the underlying substructure is a series of catenated single-stranded cycles, much like chain-mail, but an odd number leads to an interweaving of long strands.

This review will discuss the progress that has been made in the assembly of DNA objects and lattices. It will cover the techniques developed to build and characterize DNA objects in a reliable fashion, in solution and on solid supports. A section will be devoted to the construction of DNA and RNA knots, and Borromean rings. Antijunctions and mesojunctions (13, 58) are unusual DNA topological components; they are useful theoretical tools, but their experimental intractability makes them unlikely components of DNA systems. Space requirements preclude treating them or non-Watson-Crick pairing structures. DNA double-crossover molecules (DX) appear to be central to transforming topological control into geometrical control. Much of the activity in this system is directed at building periodic matter. The designs for this goal will be considered, along with the assembly of pseudoperiodic matter, which appears to be a potent direction in the new area of DNA-based computing.

CONSTRUCTION OF DNA GEOMETRICAL OBJECTS

Components of DNA Geometrical Shapes

It is a relatively straightforward matter to design a geometrical object from branched DNA components. The only consideration of significance is the number of arms in the junction. The concept of connectivity is key here (60). An object is N-connected if each of its vertices is connected by an edge to N other vertices; for example, amongst the Platonic solids, the tetrahedron, the cube, and the dodecahedron are 3-connected, the octahedron is 4-connected, and the icosahedron is 5-connected. The number of arms must be at least as large as the number of edges connected to a vertex. DNA branched junctions have been constructed that contain 3 (31), 4 (23), 5, and 6 (59) arms. The 3-arm and 4-arm junctions are well-behaved on nondenaturing gels, when they contain as few as 8 nucleotide pairs per arm (23). However, the stability of 5-arm and 6-arm junctions requires more base pairing in their arms (59); exact lower limits will be a function of sequence, but 16 nucleotide pairs are known to stabilize these junctions. Thus, it would be unwise to design an icosahedron with two-turn edges from 5-arm junctions, because the arms to be ligated (say, octamers plus tetramer sticky ends) would not be stable.

The first attempts to construct target objects from single junctions failed because of the flexibility in the angles between arms (31, 37). However, increasing the specificity of the edges can overcome this problem. For example, the target was obtained when a quadrilateral was constructed from a set of four different

3-arm junctions, whose sticky end pairs can be represented symbolically as Z'-W, W'-X, X'-Y, and Y'-Z (5). This is the approach that has been used for all subsequent constructions of DNA objects. However, it is possible to replace the specificity of sticky ends with stepwise synthesis utilizing a protection scheme (66).

DNA objects can include other variants of branched junctions. Bulged junctions (25, 30) contain a small number of extra nucleotides at the branch point; they have been incorporated into DNA triangles (38). It is sometimes useful to bend a linear piece of DNA by inserting a bulge (e.g. 55); bulges containing dT_4 and dT_6 have been incorporated into DNA molecules designed to be triangular (63). The DX molecule appears to be more rigid than linear DNA (27); it has been incorporated into DNA triangles (63).

Topological Considerations

The plectonemic winding of DNA strands about each other is a dominant aspect of DNA construction. This is particularly important in the design of DNA polyhedra, because it impinges directly on the proof of synthesis. To date, proof has relied on demonstrating that the target molecule can be restricted to yield target catenanes that can be synthesized independently. For example, the left portion of Figure 2a shows a DNA molecule whose helix axes have the connectivity of a cube. Each edge consists of two complete helical turns. Each of the six faces of the cube-like molecule contains a cyclic strand doubly linked to its four neighboring strands. Hence, it is a hexacatenane of single-stranded DNA. Had the cube been designed to contain an odd number of half-turns per edge, the product would have contained four cyclic strands, each corresponding to a projection of the cube down its body diagonals. It might have been possible to construct such an object, but proving it would have been much more difficult.

So far, every polygonal or polyhedral object constructed from DNA has contained an integral number of half-turns per edge. The 3D figures all contain an even number of half-turns, and hence all are single-stranded catenanes, each of whose cycles corresponds to a face. It is possible to design DNA objects that do not contain an exact number of half-turns per edge (46), but both synthesis and characterization appear to be too difficult at present. The exact number of nucleotide pairs per double-helical turn is a critical factor in design. The cube and truncated octahedron both used 10, but 10.5 appears to be a better number for DX components.

Construction of a Cube

The first multiply connected 3-D object to be built from DNA was the cube-like molecule shown on the left of Figure 2a (4). The 3-connected molecule was assembled in solution from two square-like molecules, shown in Figure 2b. It

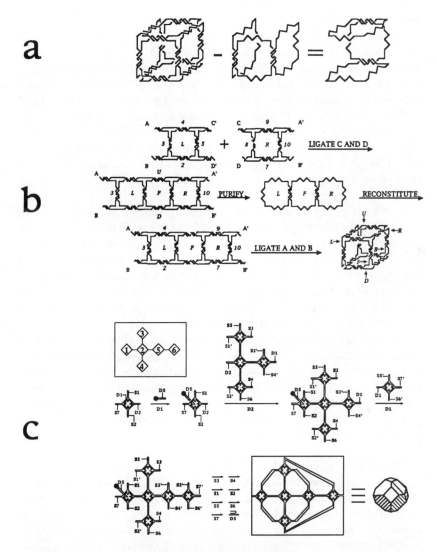

Figure 2   Geometrical constructions from DNA. (*a*) A DNA cube shown as the sum of two linear triple catenanes. *Left*, diagram representing the backbone of a DNA molecule whose helix axes have the connectivity of a cube. *Middle*, left-front-right linear triple catenane that would be removed if the cube were restricted on the left-front and right-front edges. *Right*, the product top-back-bottom linear triple catenane. (*b*) Synthesis of a DNA cube. Two ends of two quadrilaterals were ligated to form a belt-like molecule that needed to be denatured and reconstituted to purify it from side-products. The belt-like molecule was then cyclized to form the cube-like molecule. (*c*) Synthesis of a truncated octahedron. *Upper left*, boxed diagram indicates square numbering. Restriction sites are indicated on each square: *S*, symmetric restriction sites; *D*, restriction sites cut distally. A reaction is indicated by a *line* above a restriction site. The product is shown in two forms.

was designed to contain two double-helical turns per edge; its ultimate folding was predicated on the flexibility of the 3-arm branched junction. Ligation of the two squares resulted in about 10% yield of the target ladder-like intermediate. It was not possible to purify the ladder-like molecule from byproducts in nondenaturing conditions. Consequently, the left-front-right linear triple catenane had to be purified, and the ladder-like arrangement reconstituted. Final cyclization resulted in a 10% yield of the cube-like molecule. The only level of control available in this solution synthesis was the ability to exclude sticky ends from the ligation reaction by not phosphorylating them before hybridization. Thus, only the sticky ends corresponding to C, C′, D, and D′ (Figure 2b) were phosphorylated in the first step. In the final step, all strands contained phosphates.

Each edge of the cube contained a unique restriction site. Connectivity could be demonstrated by restricting each of the edges individually, to generate a tetracatenane. The most robust proof of synthesis is shown in Figure 2a, in which the linear triple catenane starting material for the second ligation step is destroyed by restriction of the purified cube, leaving the top-back-down linear triple catenane. In addition, restriction through the vertical edges leaves the top and bottom circles intact; these can be shown to be the target size for a tetragonal prism, rather than an octagonal prism.

The key lessons learned from this synthesis are (a) that it is possible to construct 3-connected, 3-D molecules from DNA, (b) that greater control over reactants is needed than is available from selective phosphorylation, (c) that it is not convenient to purify target intermediates unless they are stable under denaturing conditions, i.e. unless they are covalently closed and topologically bonded; and (d) that it is feasible to demonstrate the synthesis of these objects by means of restriction analysis.

Solid Support Methodology

A solid-support–based methodology was developed to implement the lessons learned from the construction of the cube (66). This approach allows convenient removal of reagents and catalysts from the growing product. Each ligation cycle creates a robust intermediate object that is covalently closed and topologically bonded together. The method permits one to build a single edge of an object at a time. Thus, it is possible to perform intermolecular ligations under different conditions from intramolecular ligations. Control derives from the restriction of hairpin loops forming each side of the new edge. Intermolecular reactions are done best with asymmetric sticky ends, to generate specificity. Sequences are chosen in such a way that restriction sites are destroyed when the edge forms.

One of the major advantages of using the solid support is that the growing objects are isolated from each other. This permits the use of symmetric sticky ends, without intermolecular ligation occurring. More generally, the solid support methodology permits one to plan a construction as though there were only a single object to consider. Many of the differences between a single molecule and a solution containing 10^{12} molecules disappear when the molecules are isolated on a solid support.

Construction of a Truncated Octahedron

The solid support methodology has been used to synthesize a molecule whose helix axes have the connectivity of a truncated octahedron (67), as shown in Figure 2c. This is a 3-connected object whose faces are ideally six squares and eight hexagons. Each edge contains two turns of DNA, so the structure is a 14-catenane. There is an extra arm at each vertex, because the vertices are the branch points of four-arm junctions. It was hoped that these external arms might be ligated together to form a structure like Zeolite A, but not enough of the polyhedron could be made to use it as a starting material. Figure 2c shows that a square was first attached to the solid-state support, and then a tetrasquare complex was attached to it. This procedure was necessary because some restriction enzymes that worked well in solution were found to be ineffective near the solid support.

The intermolecular assembly was completed by the addition of the last square, to produce the hexasquare complex shown in the lower left. The outer strand of this heptacatenane served as the source of all the hexagons, which were produced by a series of seven intramolecular symmetric-site ligations. Synthesis was confirmed first by using restriction analysis to demonstrate the presence of each of the square strands. The strands corresponding to the hexagons flank each square in a tetracatenane; it was possible to prepare a marker and demonstrate the presence of the tetracatenanes. Note that the characterizations of both the cube and the truncated octahedron have been topological, not structural.

TOPOLOGICAL CONSTRUCTIONS

Catenanes and Knots

The closed polyhedra built from DNA are catenanes of single-stranded DNA. There is a close relationship between catenanes and knots. As illustrated in Figure 3a, it is possible to interconvert knots and catenanes by a simple operation on a node: One can regard a node as consisting of four polar strands connected in pairs, two before the node and two following the node; switching the connected polar pairs destroys the node and alters the topology between catenation and knotting. Hence, molecules that can be used to make catenanes ought to be equally useful in making knots. This is certainly true for DNA.

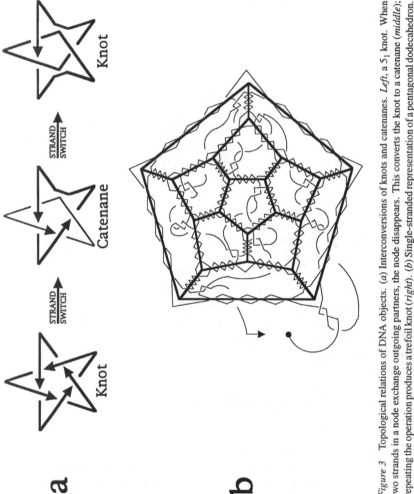

Figure 3 Topological relations of DNA objects. (*a*) Interconversions of knots and catenanes. *Left*, a 5_1 knot. When two strands in a node exchange outgoing partners, the node disappears. This converts the knot to a catenane (*middle*); repeating the operation produces a trefoil knot (*right*). (*b*) Single-stranded representation of a pentagonal dodecahedron. A pentagonal dodecahedron is illustrated with twelve exocyclic arms in a Schlegel diagram (*thickest lines*). Two turns of DNA are wrapped around each edge, and each pentagon contains an exocyclic double arm a single turn long. The DNA representing each face is connected by *curved lines* to a neighboring face via the exocyclic arms, to yield a single long strand. *Arrowhead*, 3' end; *filled circle*, 5' end.

However, one might first ask why it is of interest to make molecular knots at all, and DNA knots in particular. A key motivation in this direction is to achieve biologically based control over the construction of DNA objects. When one thinks of making objects from DNA, the idea of cellular or PCR (e.g. 43) replication comes immediately to mind; unfortunately, DNA polymerases do not reproduce branches. Nevertheless, it is possible to convert a DNA polyhedron to a single stranded motif, as illustrated in Figure 3b. Here, an exocyclic helical arm has been added to the cyclic strand corresponding to each face of a pentagonal dodecahedron. These arms have been connected by the curved lines, so the entire molecule is a long single strand. A single strand of this sort might be produced by PCR, or perhaps within the cell. Once folded, the exocyclic arms could be restricted, and the molecule would be ready to ligate to other copies of itself. Of course, the folding is the hard part. The structure shown is a very complicated knot, and experiments of this sort lie in the future. However, it is useful to establish control on the folding of single-stranded DNA molecules, thereby forming particular knots.

The central features of any closed topological strand-based objects, such as knots or catenanes, are their crossings, or nodes. The placement and signs of crossings about such topological figures distinguish one species from another. A simple relationship exists between DNA and a crossing in a knot or a catenane, as illustrated in the top portion of Figure 4a. A trefoil knot is shown there, and each of its three nodes is surrounded by a dotted square. The strands of the knot act as the diagonals of the squares and divide them into four regions, two between parallel strands and two between antiparallel strands. Six nucleotide pairs corresponding to about a half-turn of DNA are drawn between the strands in the antiparallel regions. Thus, a half-turn of DNA corresponds to a node in a knot or catenane (48). The lower portion of Figure 4a illustrates that nodes of

---

Figure 4 Topological relationships. (*a*) DNA nodes and knot components. *Top*, trefoil knot; *arrowheads* indicate polarity. A *dotted square* is drawn around each node. Six base pairs are drawn between antiparallel strands; a local helix axis and a dyad normal to it are shown. *Bottom*, two mirror-image types of nodes: Right-handed B-DNA generates negative nodes, and left-handed Z-DNA generates positive nodes. (*b*) The synthetic schemes used to produce target knots. *Left side*, a molecule with four pairing regions, X and Y, and their complements X' and Y'. *Middle*, the four solution conditions produce the pairing and helical handedness expected in each case. *Right*, the molecular topology of the products. (*c*) Synthesis and strand passage reaction of cyclic RNA. *Top*, the initial single-stranded RNA molecule, similar to the one in (*b*). The pathway to the left (*long linker*) produces the RNA circle and the one on the right (*short linker*) produces an RNA trefoil knot. *Bottom*, the topoisomerase assay. (*d*) Construction of Borromean rings. *Left*, the two 3-arm branched junctions, one made of B-DNA and the other made of Z-DNA, are ligated to form Borromean rings.

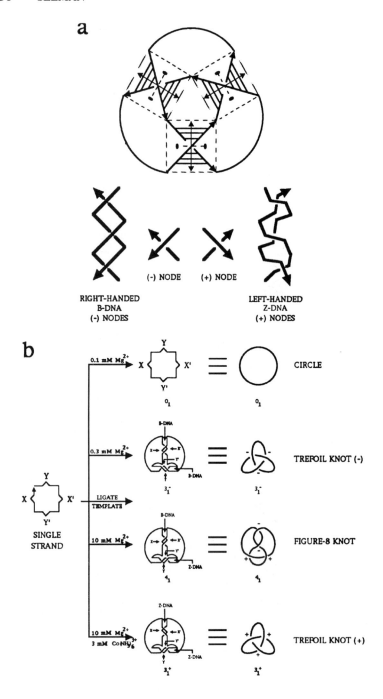

C

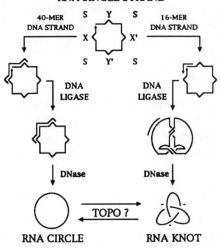

d

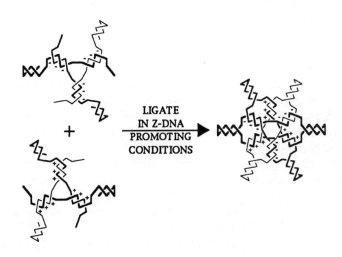

two chiralities can occur. Right-handed B-DNA corresponds to negative nodes, and left-handed Z-DNA (40) corresponds to positive nodes (48).

DNA Knots

The first DNA knot was a trefoil knot synthesized from a 104-mer synthetic single strand of DNA. It contained two double-helical domains, each composed of a single turn of right-handed B-DNA, joined by dT_{15} linkers; the nick present from the synthesis was sealed by T4 DNA ligase (34). A similar 104-mer DNA knot has also been built from a branched junction motif (10). Knots have been characterized by electrophoretic mobility, sedimentation, Ferguson analysis, susceptibility to restriction endonucleases, and gel retention by antibodies (9–11, 34, 56, 57). The B-Z transition is promoted by relatively low concentrations of $Co(NH_3)_6Cl_3$ that do not impair DNA ligase. Consequently, it has been possible to make figure-8 knots (Figure 4b), containing two negative nodes and two positive nodes (9, 11, 57).

A useful property of Z-DNA is that two conditions must be fulfilled in order to obtain this structure: A "proto-Z" sequence with the propensity to form Z-DNA, and Z-promoting conditions. Figure 4b shows that by making both domains of a knot proto-Z sequences, with different Z-forming propensities, it is possible—by varying solution conditions—to produce a circle, trefoil knots of both chiralities, and a figure-8 knot all from a single strand of DNA (11). The ability to change the favored species by changing solution conditions permits one to use this system as a probe for single-stranded topoisomerase activity. E. coli DNA topoisomerases I and III (topo I and topo III) catalyze the interconversion of all the species shown in Figure 4b (12).

Other Backbones: An RNA Knot
and Topoisomerase Activity

The sensitivity of DNA knots to the presence of topoisomerase activity suggested that an RNA knot would provide a good substrate to seek RNA topoisomerase activity (56). Figure 4c illustrates the strategy employed for both the synthesis of an RNA circle and an RNA trefoil knot, as well as in the search for RNA topoisomerase activity. Topo III catalyzes the interconversion shown at the bottom of Figure 4c, but topo I does not. Topo III also catalyzes the catenation of a small amount of the circle. It is not known yet whether RNA topoisomerase activity has a role in vivo, but strand passage must be considered among the possible mechanisms that establish and modify RNA structure.

The assembly of the knot from an RNA molecule highlights by negative example the convenience of working with DNA in the systems described above. RNA synthesis is problematic; RNA ligation is much less convenient than DNA ligation; commercially available exonucleases tend to be contaminated with endonucleases; and the convenient specificity over cleavage available from DNA restriction endonucleases is also unavailable. These disadvantages are not restricted to RNA. The antisense effort (e.g. 7) has generated a large number of alternative nucleic acid backbones, including peptide nucleic acids (35). The problems confronted in RNA construction probably would be exacerbated in constructions involving other backbones.

DNA Borromean Rings

Conventional catenanes are topologically bonded to each other like the links of a chain; we are all aware that a chain is strong as its weakest link, meaning that if one link breaks, we are left with the two pieces of chain that flanked the broken ring. Borromean rings, named for the presence of a 3-ring link on the crest of the Italian Renaissance Borromeo family, are joined differently (28): If one of its rings breaks, all the rings dissociate, so that the product is one broken circle and a number of intact, but unlinked circles. This topology is achieved by placing positive and negative nodes specifically around the link.

It is easier to work with pieces of double helix longer than a single half-turn (10). Thus, the conventional nodes in Borromean rings have been replaced by 1.5 turns of DNA. As shown in Figure 4d, the topology of this link can be provided by joining a 3-arm B-DNA junction with a 3-arm Z-DNA junction. The ligation occurs through hairpins in the plane between them. The hairpins also contain restriction sites that facilitate proof of synthesis: When each ring is cut in turn, the products are a linear molecule and two rings, but no catenanes (32). There is no limit to the number of rings that can be joined to have the Borromean property (28). There may be applications of Borromean rings to DNA-based computing: An intact complex can represent physically the simultaneous truth of a number of propositions, and it is readily separable from the cases where a single proposition is false.

DOUBLE-CROSSOVER MOLECULES

One of the most exciting DNA motifs entails the DNA double-crossover molecule. These structures consist of two 4-arm branched junctions that have been joined at two adjacent arms. There are five distinct isomers of DX molecules (15), shown in Figure 5. The isomers contain parallel (DPE, DPOW, and DPON) and antiparallel (DAE and DAO) helical domains. They are further differentiated by whether they contain an even (DPE, DAE) or an odd (DAO, DPOW, DPON) number of double-helical half-turns between their crossover points. DPOW and DPON molecules differ by having the extra half-turn correspond to a major (wide) or minor (narrow) groove spacing. Parallel DX molecules are not well-behaved on nondenaturing gels, unless their ends have been closed off

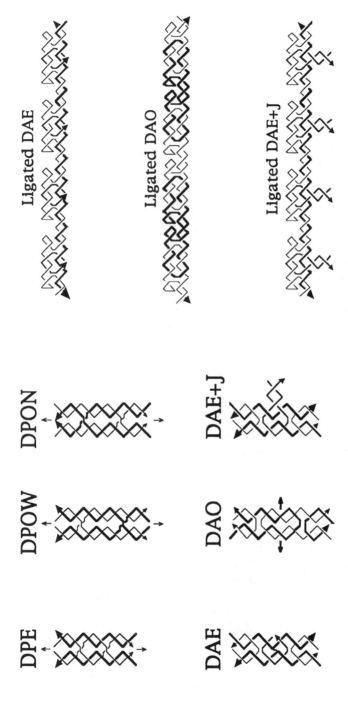

Figure 5   DNA double crossover molecules and their ligation products. *Top left*, the three drawings are the three parallel DX molecules. *Arrowheads* indicate 3′ ends. Symmetry elements are shown, and line thickness is related by symmetry in each of these drawings. *Bottom left*, the DAE and DAO molecules are the antiparallel isomers. Symmetry in DAO is between the thick and thin lines. DAE+J is a molecule in which the cyclic strand of DAE is extended to form a 3-arm bulged junction. *Right*, ligated products of the three antiparallel molecules. Ligated DAE and DAE+J molecules contain a reporter strand, drawn as a *thick line*, but ligated DAO molecules consist of catenated rings.

in hairpin loops (14–16). By contrast, antiparallel DX molecules appear to be stable molecules (15).

The fixed orientations of their helical domains make these molecules convenient for the characterization of Holliday junctions. They have been used to establish the topology of the crossover point (16), to characterize their cleavage by endonuclease VII (14), and to demonstrate the spontaneity of crossover isomerization (26). It is possible to use the DX molecule to make a junction whose branch point is flanked by a symmetric sequence, but which is nevertheless immobile (64). This system has been used to estimate the relative stabilities (54) and crossover isomer populations in molecules where symmetric sequences flank the junction (65).

NETWORKS OF DNA

The Search for Rigidity

A key motivation for constructing objects from DNA is to generate rational means for constructing periodic matter. At least three properties are necessary for the components of systems where this is possible: (*a*) The predictable specificity of intermolecular interactions between components; (*b*) the local structural predictability of intermolecular products; and (*c*) the structural rigidity of the components (30). The sequence-specificity of sticky-ended association appears to be adequate to satisfy the first criterion. The second criterion is also met by sticky-ended association; recently the crystal structure of a DNA decamer containing a sticky end has been determined, and the structure is an infinite helix of B-DNA (39). The key obstacle to the formation of periodic matter from DNA is the third point, the lack of structural integrity.

There are two entwined routes out of the rigidity problem. First, one can build everything out of triangles or deltahedra, polyhedra whose faces are all triangles. For convex polyhedra, it can be shown that deltahedra are rigid (24). Thus, using deltahedral components is desirable for the construction of periodic matter. However, this approach is not sufficient to guarantee rigidity. The 5-connected network in Figure 1*c* could not be guaranteed to form from isolated octahedra, because the angles determining the orientations of the external edges are not fixed. A rigid DNA structural motif is also needed.

Early reports suggested that the arm opposite the bulge in 3-arm bulged junctions was able to stack on the arm 5′ to it (25). This finding was explored in ligation-closure experiments, which showed that the "stacking" strand cyclized less than the other strands (30). Consequently, triangles were constructed containing bulged 3-arm branched junctions, and these were examined to determine whether they maintained their external angles; unfortunately, they did not (38).

By contrast with the failure experienced with bulged junctions, antiparallel double crossover molecules were found to be very stiff (27). Ligation-closure experiments involving complex motifs require a reporter strand to interpret the results. Figure 5 illustrates that DAO molecules do not produce a reporter strand when ligated, whereas DAE molecules do. DAE molecules can also be used in combination with a bulged 3-arm branched junction that is derived from the central strand (DAE+J in Figure 5). The DAE molecule produces virtually no cyclic products, and the DAE+J molecule produces only a very small amount of cyclic material. As illustrated in Figure 6a, it is possible to incorporate these species into the sides of a triangle, and to oligomerize it quite far (27-mers), without apparent cyclization (63). Figure 6b illustrates how DX molecules could be incorporated into the edges of an octahedron in an arrangement that would span 3-space. It is important to emphasize that DX molecules can be used to establish a direction, but it has not been demonstrated that combining them with triangular or deltahedral motifs serves to establish a fixed angle.

Periodic Designs

It is possible to design 2-D arrays from either DAE or DAE+J triangular components. Figure 6c shows an array of triangles whose edges are DAE molecules; Figure 6d shows an array incorporating a DAE+J molecule into one of the three edges of each triangle; the extra duplex formed might be used to orient a guest molecule. Figure 6e illustrates an array formed exclusively from DAE+J components, using the junction associated with the middle strand as part of each triangular edge. The arrays in Figures 6c and 6d, and the one that would be derived form the octahedron in Figure 6b are examples of using the external domain of a DX molecule to connect to its congener in the next geometrical figure. It appears possible to use DX molecules to link polygons and polyhedra by edge-sharing (52). None of these arrays has yet been constructed.

--→

Figure 6 Double-crossover–containing structures. (*a*) DX molecules incorporated in the edges of a triangle. Two edges of a triangle contain DAE molecules. Oligomerization will take place in the edge containing biotins (*encircled B*'s). (*b*) An octahedron containing DX molecules. The top four faces of an octahedron are shown. Three edges that span 3-space contain double crossover molecules. (*c–e*) Two-dimensional arrays of triangles containing DX molecules. Every triangle edge in (*c*) contains a DAE molecule, but in (*d*) one edge contains a DAE+J molecule, producing an extra double-helical domain in each hexagon. The array in (*e*) is constructed from DAE+J molecules. (*f*) Topological structure of 2D antiparallel DX arrays. The four arrays are built from DAO or DAE molecules; crossings are separated by an even (E) or odd (O) number of double-helical half-turns. Strand polarities are shown by the *arrowheads* on their 3′ ends. Strands are drawn with different thicknesses for clarity.

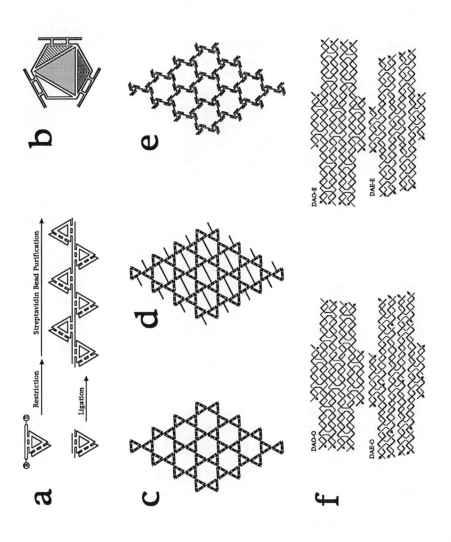

DNA-Based Computing

The worlds of DNA chemistry, molecular biology, and computing were electrified by Adleman's demonstration (1) that it is possible to solve a Hamiltonian Path problem (related to the traveling-salesman problem) by encrypting information in DNA molecules, combining them in arbitrary combinations by ligation, and then establishing criteria to select for the strand representing the right answer. Winfree has offered an intriguing variant on this theme (61). He has suggested using antiparallel DX molecules as cellular automata: Each molecule represents a rule relating the sticky ends on one domain to the sticky ends on the other domain. In essence, he would knit a pseudoperiodic (periodic backbones, aperiodic sequences) 2D molecular fabric of DNA in which the initial edge would represent the program and the final edge would contain the answer. Some experimental work toward validation of this system has occurred (62).

Reif (41) has recently suggested some modifications to the procedure. Recent work by Janoska et al (22) suggests using DX molecules combined in pairs to form quadruple crossovers, a motif originally suggested by Winfree (61). In another computing formalism relevant here, Sakakibara & Ferretti (44) have suggested using Head's splicing theory (19) in branched systems.

It is useful to think about the topological aspects of constructing two-dimensional arrays from antiparallel double crossover molecules alone. Winfree (61) has pointed out that four different topologies exist that can be made with DAO and DAE components, as shown in Figure 6f. DAO molecules can be separated by an even (DAO-E) or odd (DAO-O) number of half-turns; these arrays contain strands that zigzag vertically. The DAE-O array produces four types of continuous strands, those pointed to the left and to the right, and zigzag vertical strands whose polarities are opposite. In addition, there are two cyclic strands, drawn unclosed, to indicate that their polarities are clockwise and counterclockwise. The final array, DAE-E corresponds to molecular chain mail. The individual DX components of these arrays appear small when compared to the geometrical objects discussed above. However, chemically, they are really quite large (ca. 4×12 nm). In addition to their possible utility in working out computational problems, they also present a substrate where one could place many small molecular groups.

CONCLUDING REMARKS

Where is DNA nanotechnology going? The suggestion has been made that the ability to form periodic arrays of DNA could be exploited to use the DNA to organize the structures of other molecules. Prominent among the molecules suggested have been the components of molecular electronics, in order to construct memory devices (42). This target awaits the key goal of forming periodic matter organized by DNA sticky ends (45). The chemistry to attach molecules to DNA in a convenient and useful fashion for this purpose will no doubt be challenging, but until periodic arrays can be achieved, its driving force will not be strong.

In a similar fashion, the suggestion has been made that any knot or catenane could be designed from DNA (48). The simplest members of these classes have been assembled; however, the targets have been limited to those that could be characterized by electrophoretic and restriction analysis. More complex constructions await the ability to characterize topological products by direct physical observation. A crystallographic solution to the characterization problem would be to use topological constructs as the guests of Figure 1c. The efficacy of the cellular automata approach to computing (61) also depends on the ability to generate periodic matter, although the "crystals" will be periodic only in their backbone structures. At present, it seems that the best way in which to make periodic matter from DNA components is to (a) construct the individual components with biotinylated hairpins on a solid support, (b) remove the object from the support, (c) restrict it, (d) purify it with streptavidin beads, and then (e) assemble the crystal (38). It remains to be seen whether some sort of epitaxy is needed in the form of specifically formulated borders that define edges or faces.

One set of goals for DNA nanotechnology does not require periodic matter. This is the aim of using DNA transitions to drive nanomechanical devices. Two transitions have been mentioned prominently, branch migration and the B-Z transition. It is known that applying torque to a cruciform can lead to the extrusion or intrusion of a cruciform (17). A synthetic branched junction with two opposite arms linked can relocate its branch point in response to ethidium (X Yang, A Vologodskii, B Liu, B Kemper, NC Seeman, *Biopolymers* 45:69–83). Likewise, the advent of the DX molecule as a rigid DNA component makes it feasible to use the B-Z transition as the motive force in a simple hinge (C Mao, NC Seeman, manuscript in preparation).

Although many laboratories analyze the properties of DNA and develop systems involving its hybridization and concatenation for bioanalytical purposes, there has been little activity with structural objectives. Fortunately, this situation is beginning to change. Recently, Mirkin et al (33) have attached DNA molecules to colloidal gold, with the goal of assembling nanoparticles into macroscopic materials. Likewise, Alivisatos et al (2) have used DNA to organize nanocrystals of gold. Niemeyer et al (36) earlier used DNA specificity to generate protein arrays. Very recently, Shi and Bergstrom (53) attached DNA single strands to rigid organic linkers; they have shown that they can form cycles of various sizes with these molecules.

The ideas behind DNA nanotechnology have been around for a long time (45). However, as is often the case, their reduction to practice has been slowed by the realities of the experimental situation: The establishment of the conditions, constraints, and protocols that convert ideas into realities. It is to be hoped that many of these are in place now, and that the increasing activity in the field will lead to the achievement of its key goals within the near future.

ACKNOWLEDGMENTS

This research has been supported by grant GM-29554 from NIGMS and by grant N00014-89-J-3078 from ONR. I wish to thank Junghuei Chen, John E Mueller, Tsu-Ju Fu, Yuwen Zhang, Yinli Wang, Shou Ming Du, Hui Wang, Siwei Zhang, Jing Qi, Bing Liu, Hangxia Qiu, Xiaojun Li, Xiaoping Yang, Furong Liu, Chengde Mao, Weiqiong Sun, Ruojie Sha, Zhiyong Shen, and Lisa Wenzler, who have performed experiments that enabled writing this article. Valuable discussions with Erik Winfree and John Reif are also gratefully acknowledged.

Visit the *Annual Reviews home page* at
http://www.AnnualReviews.org.

Literature Cited

1. Adleman L. 1994. Molecular computation of solutions to combinatorial problems. *Science* 266:1021–24
2. Alivisatos AP, Johnsson KP, Peng X, Wilson TE, Loweth CJ, et al. 1996. *Nature* 382:609–11
3. Caruthers MH. 1985. Gene synthesis machines: DNA chemistry and its uses. *Science* 230:281–85
4. Chen J, Seeman NC. 1991. The synthesis from DNA of a molecule with the connectivity of a cube. *Nature* 350:631–33
5. Chen JH, Kallenbach NR, Seeman NC. 1989. A specific quadrilateral synthesized from DNA branched junctions. *J. Am. Chem. Soc.* 111:6402–7
6. Cohen SN, Chang ACY, Boyer HW, Helling RB. 1973. Construction of biologically functional bacterial plasmids in vitro. *Proc. Natl. Acad. Sci. USA* 70:3240–44
7. DeMesmaeker A, Haner R, Martin P, Moser HE. 1995. Antisense oligonucleotides. *Acc. Chem. Res.* 28:366–74
8. Doyle AC. 1936. Silver blaze. In *The Complete Sherlock Holmes*, p. 297. New York: Literary Guild
9. Du SM, Seeman NC. 1992. Synthesis of a DNA knot containing both positive and negative nodes. *J. Am. Chem. Soc.* 114:9652–55
10. Du SM, Seeman NC. 1994. The construction of a trefoil knot from a DNA branched junction motif. *Biopolymers* 34:31–37
11. Du SM, Stollar BD, Seeman NC. 1995. A synthetic DNA molecule in three knotted topologies. *J. Am. Chem. Soc.* 117:1194–1200
12. Du SM, Wang H, Tse-Dinh Y-C, Seeman NC. 1995. Topological transformations of synthetic DNA knots, *Biochemistry* 34:673–82
13. Du SM, Zhang S, Seeman NC. 1992. DNA junctions, antijunctions and mesojunctions. *Biochemistry* 31:10955–63
14. Fu T-J, Kemper B, Seeman NC. 1994. Endonuclease VII cleavage of DNA double crossover molecules. *Biochemistry* 33:3896–3905
15. Fu T-J, Seeman NC. 1993. DNA double crossover molecules. *Biochemistry* 32:3211–20
16. Fu T-J, Tse-Dinh Y-C, Seeman NC. 1994. Holliday junction crossover topology. *J. Mol. Biol.* 236:91–105
17. Gellert M, Mizuuchi K, O'Dea MH, Ohmori H, Tomizawa J. 1978. DNA gyrase and DNA supercoiling. *Cold Spring Harbor Symp. Quant. Biol.* 43:35–40

18. Hagerman PJ. 1988. Flexibility of DNA. *Annu. Rev. Biophys. Biophys. Chem.* 17: 265–86
19. Head T. 1987. Formal language theory and DNA. *Bull. Math. Biol.* 49:737–59
20. Holliday R. 1964. A mechanism for gene conversion in fungi. *Genet. Res.* 5:282–304
21. Hsieh P, Panyutin IG. 1995. DNA branch migration. In *Nucleic Acids and Molecular Biology*, ed. F Eckstein, DMJ Lilley, 9:42–65. Berlin: Springer-Verlag
22. Janoska N, Karl SA, Saito M. 1997. Creating 3-dimensional graph structures with DNA. *Proc. DNA-Based Comput. Conf., 3rd, Philadelphia.* In press
23. Kallenbach NR, Ma RI, Seeman NC. 1983. An immobile nucleic acid junction constructed from oligonucleotides. *Nature* 305:829–31
24. Kappraff J. 1990. *Connections*, p. 273. New York: McGraw-Hill
25. Leontis NB, Hills MT, Piotto M, Malhotra A, et al. 1993. A model for the solution structure of a branched, three-strand DNA complex. *J. Biomol. Struct. Dyn.* 11:215–23
26. Li X, Wang H, Seeman NC. 1997. Direct evidence for Holliday junction crossover isomerization. *Biochemistry* 36:4240–47
27. Li X, Yang X, Qi J, Seeman NC. 1996. Antiparallel DNA double crossover molecules as components for nanoconstruction. *J. Am. Chem. Soc.* 118:6131–40
28. Liang C, Mislow K. 1994. On Borromean links. *J. Math. Chem.* 16:27–35
29. Lilley DMJ, Clegg RM. 1993. The structure of the four-way junction in DNA. *Annu. Rev. Biophys. Biomol. Struct.* 22: 299–328
30. Liu B, Leontis NB, Seeman NC. 1994. Bulged 3-arm DNA branched junctions as components for nanoconstruction. *Nanobiol.* 3:177–88
31. Ma RI, Kallenbach NR, Sheardy RD, Petrillo ML, Seeman NC. 1986. Three-arm nucleic acid junctions are flexible. *Nucleic Acid Res.* 14:9745–53
32. Mao C, Sun W, Seeman NC. 1997. Assembly of Borromean rings from DNA. *Nature* 386:137–38
33. Mirkin CA, Letsinger RL, Mucic RC, Storhoff JJ. 1996. A DNA-based method for rationally assembling nanoparticles into macroscopic materials. *Nature* 382: 607–9
34. Mueller JE, Du SM, Seeman NC. 1991. Design and synthesis of a knot from single-stranded DNA. *J. Am. Chem. Soc.* 113:6306–8
35. Nielsen PE, Egholm M, Berg RH, Buchardt O. 1991. Sequence selective recognition of DNA by strand displacement with a thymine-substituted polyamide. *Science* 254:1497–1500
36. Niemeyer CM, Sano T, Smith CL, Cantor CR. 1994. Oligonucleotide-directed self-assembly of proteins. *Nucleic Acid Res.* 22: 5530–39
37. Petrillo ML, Newton CJ, Cunningham RP, Ma RI, Kallenbach NR, Seeman NC. 1988. Ligation and flexibility of four-arm DNA junctions. *Biopolymers* 27:1337–52
38. Qi J, Li X, Yang X, Seeman NC. 1996. The ligation of triangles built from bulged three-arm DNA branched junctions. *J. Am. Chem. Soc.* 118:6121–30
39. Qiu H, Dewan JC, Seeman NC. 1997. A DNA decamer with a sticky end. *J. Mol. Biol.* 267:881–98
40. Rich A, Nordheim A, Wang AH-J. 1984. The chemistry and biology of left-handed Z-DNA. *Annu. Rev. Biochem.* 53:791–846
41. Rief JH. 1997. Local parallel biomolecular computing. *Proc. DNA-Based Comput. Conf., 3rd, Philadelphia.* In press
42. Robinson BH, Seeman NC. 1987. The design of a biochip. *Prot. Eng.* 1:295–300
43. Saiki R, Bugawan TL, Horn GT, Mullis KB, Ehrlich HA. 1986. The analysis of enzymatically labeled b-globin DQα DNA with allele-specific oligonucleotide probes. *Nature* 324:163–66
44. Sakakibara Y, Ferretti C. 1997. Splicing on tree-like structures. *Proc. DNA-Based Comput. Conf., 3rd, Philadelphia.* In press
45. Seeman NC. 1982. Nucleic acid junctions and lattices. *J. Theor. Biol.* 99:237–47
46. Seeman NC. 1985. Macromolecular design, nucleic acid junctions and crystal formation. *J. Biomol. Struct. Dyn.* 3:11–34
47. Seeman NC. 1990. De Novo design of sequences for nucleic acid structural engineering. *J. Biomol. Struct. Dyn.* 8:573–81
48. Seeman NC. 1992. The design of single-stranded nucleic acid knots. *Mol. Eng.* 2:297–307
49. Seeman NC, Kallenbach NR. 1983. Design of immobile nucleic acid junctions. *Biophys. J.* 44:201–9
50. Seeman NC, Kallenbach NR. 1994. DNA branched junctions. *Annu. Rev. Biophys. Biomol. Struct.* 23:53–86
51. Seeman NC, Rosenberg JM, Rich A. 1976. Sequence-specific recognition of double helical nucleic acids by proteins. *Proc. Natl. Acad. Sci. USA* 73:804–8
52. Seeman NC, Zhang Y, Fu T-J, Zhang S, et al. 1994. *Mater. Res. Soc. Symp. Proc.* 330:45–56
53. Shi J, Bergstrom DE. Assembly of novel

DNA cycles with rigid tetrahedral linkers. *Angew. Chem. Int. Ed. Engl.* 36:111–13

54. Sun W, Mao C, Seeman NC. 1997. The sequence dependence of branch migratory minima. *J. Biomol. Struct. Dyn.* 14:818–19 (Abstr.)

55. Tang RS, Draper DE. 1990. Bulge loops used to measure the helical twist of RNA in solution. *Biochemistry* 29:5232–37

56. Wang H, Di Gate RJ, Seeman NC. 1996. An RNA topoisomerase. *Proc. Natl. Acad. Sci. USA* 93:9477–82

57. Wang H, Du SM, Seeman NC. 1993. Tight DNA knots. *J. Biomol. Struct. Dyn.* 10:853–63

58. Wang H, Seeman NC. 1995. Structural domains of DNA mesojunctions, *Biochemistry* 34:920–29

59. Wang Y, Mueller JE, Kemper B, Seeman NC. 1991. The assembly and characterization of 5-Arm and 6-Arm DNA junctions, *Biochemistry* 30:5667–74

60. Wells AF. 1977. *Three-Dimensional Nets and Polyhedra.* New York: Wiley. 268 pp.

61. Winfree E. 1996. On the computational power of DNA annealing and ligation. In *DNA Based Computing*, ed. EJ Lipton, EB Baum, pp. 199–219. Providence: Am. Math. Soc. 219 pp.

62. Winfree E, Yang X, Seeman NC. 1997. Universal computation via self-assembly of DNA. *Proc. DNA-Based Comput. Conf., 2nd, Princeton, NJ.* In press

63. Yang X, Qi J, Li X, Seeman NC. 1997. The incorporation of DNA double crossovers into DNA triangles. *J. Biomol. Struct. Dyn.* 14:820–21 (Abstr.)

64. Zhang S, Fu TJ, Seeman NC. 1993. Construction of symmetric, immobile DNA branched junctions. *Biochemistry.* 32:8062–67

65. Zhang S, Seeman NC. 1994. Symmetric Holliday junction crossover isomers. *J. Mol. Biol.* 238:658–68

66. Zhang Y, Seeman NC. 1992. A solid-support methodology for the construction of geometrical objects from DNA. *J. Am. Chem. Soc.* 114:2656–63

67. Zhang Y, Seeman NC. 1994. The construction of a DNA truncated octahedron. *J. Am. Chem. Soc.* 116:1661–69

Annu. Rev. Biophys. Biomol. Struct. 1998. 27:249–84

INHIBITORS OF HIV-1 PROTEASE:
A Major Success of Structure-Assisted Drug Design[1]

Alexander Wlodawer and Jiri Vondrasek[2]

Macromolecular Structure Laboratory, ABL-Basic Research Program, National Cancer Institute-Frederick Cancer Research and Development Center, Frederick, Maryland 21702; e-mail: wlodawer@ncifcrf.gov

KEY WORDS: AIDS, protease, drug design, inhibitors

ABSTRACT

Retroviral protease (PR) from the human immunodeficiency virus type 1 (HIV-1) was identified over a decade ago as a potential target for structure-based drug design. This effort was very successful. Four drugs are already approved, and others are undergoing clinical trials. The techniques utilized in this remarkable example of structure-assisted drug design included crystallography, NMR, computational studies, and advanced chemical synthesis. The development of these drugs is discussed in detail. Other approaches to designing HIV-1 PR inhibitors, based on the concepts of symmetry and on the replacement of a water molecule that had been found tetrahedrally coordinated between the enzyme and the inhibitors, are also discussed. The emergence of drug-induced mutations of HIV-1 PR leads to rapid loss of potency of the existing drugs and to the need to continue the development process. The structural basis of drug resistance and the ways of overcoming this phenomenon are mentioned.

CONTENTS

---

[1] The US Government has the right to retain a nonexclusive royalty-free license in and to any copyright covering this paper.

[2] Also at: Institute of Organic Chemistry and Biochemistry, AS CR, Flemingovo nam. 2, 166 10 Prague 6, Czech Republic.

INTRODUCTION

Acquired immunodeficiency syndrome (AIDS) was the first major epidemic caused by a previously unknown pathogen to appear during the 20th century, the period corresponding to the modern development of pharmaceutical sciences. This disease is caused by human immunodeficiency virus type 1 (HIV-1), a member of the family of retroviruses. At the onset of the epidemic in the early 1980s, no existing drug was known to be useful against AIDS and completely new pharmaceutical agents had to be created. Although azidothymidine (AZT), the first drug shown to counteract the effects of HIV-1 infection, was previously known as a potential anticancer agent, the rapid progress in the understanding of the structure and life cycle of the virus led to unprecedented development of other drugs targeted to a variety of viral proteins. The retroviral enzymes—reverse transcriptase (RT), integrase (IN), and protease (PR)—were the obvious targets for drug discovery.

The first drugs to be identified were inhibitors of RT (23), which were discovered and developed long before the structure of RT itself was solved (48, 60). However, newer RT-targeted drugs, nonnucleoside inhibitors, are being developed bearing the enzyme structure in mind. Even now, only fragmentary structural data have been described for IN (7–9, 27) and no drugs are available. Retroviral protease, however, was identified early as a potential target (59), and the discovery and development of its inhibitors are an unqualified success of modern pharmacology and structural biology.

Analysis of the nucleotide sequence of the HIV-1 genome (88) led to the discovery that the virus encodes an aspartic protease (HIV-1 PR). Inactivation of HIV-1 PR by either mutation or chemical inhibition leads to the production of immature, noninfectious viral particles (59, 72, 106), thus the function of this enzyme was shown to be essential for proper virion assembly and maturation. It is not surprising, then, that HIV-1 PR was identified over a decade ago as the prime target for structure-assisted (sometimes called "rational") drug design.

It is much more surprising that by now four drugs have already been approved by the US Food and Drug Administration (FDA), and several others are in advanced clinical trials.

The structure-assisted drug design and discovery process (3) utilizes structural biochemical methods, such as protein crystallography, NMR, and computational biochemistry, to guide the synthesis of potential drugs. This information can, in turn, be used to help explain the basis of their activity and to improve the potency and specificity of new lead compounds. Crystallography plays a particularly important role in this process. The past eight years have seen a virtual explosion of crystallographic studies aimed at the characterization of the structures of HIV PR and of HIV PR/inhibitor complexes on an atomic level (note that HIV PR as used here refers to both HIV-1 and HIV-2 PRs). Indeed, the level of involvement of crystallographers in this area is unprecedented in the history of the field, with over 25 laboratories worldwide reporting crystal structures of this enzyme (Table 1). In addition, several more structures were

Table 1   Availability of crystal structures of HIV/SIV PRs (10/97)

Laboratory	Location	#HIV PR database	#in PDB
NCI-ABL	Frederick, MD	17	12
NCI-SAIC	Frederick, MD	9	9
Abbott	Abbott Park, IL	3	3
Merck	Rahway, NJ	8	6
	West Point, PA		
Roche	Nutley, NJ	2	1
	Hertfordshire, UK		
SmithKline	King of Prussia, PA	8	8
Agouron	San Diego, CA	7	0
Upjohn	Kalamazoo, MI	12	8
Birkbeck College	London, UK	2	2
Pasteur Institute	Paris, France	1	1
Glaxo	Greenford, UK	7	3
Boehringer	Ridgefield, CT	4	3
Du Pont-Merck	Wilmington, DE	22	22
Ciba-Geigy	Basel, Switzerland	2	2
Vertex	Cambridge, MA	5	1
Univ. of Brisbane	Brisbane, Australia	2	2
NIDR	Bethesda, MD	2	2
OMRF	Oklahoma City, OK	3	3
UCSF	San Francisco, CA	3	3
Marion Merrell-Dow	Strasbourg, France	7	0
Uppsala University	Uppsala, Sweden	4	2
Bristol-Myers Squibb	Princeton, NJ	2	0
Totals		132	93

solved by NMR. This review will discuss the current structural knowledge of inhibitor complexes of HIV PR and how the use of this information was crucial to the process of drug design. The review will also discuss new and emerging areas of investigation—in particular, the studies of resistance to protease inhibitors.

STRUCTURAL INVESTIGATIONS OF RETROVIRAL PROTEASES

Comparing the genomic sequence of HIV-1 with that of several other retroviruses, Ratner et al (88) postulated that the HIV-1 genome encodes a protease. Subsequently, based on the observation of a signature sequence (Asp-Thr-Gly) and the overall similarity of primary structure between retroviruses and retrotransposons, Toh et al (113) suggested that their proteases might be related to the family of eukaryotic aspartic proteases, exemplified by pepsin. HIV-1 PR and other retroviral proteases also exhibit other characteristics of aspartic proteases, such as inhibition by pepstatin (92, 106) and inactivation by mutation of the putative active-site aspartates (54, 59, 68, 106). Structural studies on HIV-1 PR were initially hampered by the fact that it constituted a minor component of mature virions (45), which therefore necessitated the use of recombinant and synthetic technologies to produce the milligram quantities needed for structural investigations. HIV-1 PR was cloned in a variety of vectors (13, 18, 20) and it was also prepared by total chemical synthesis (101). In contrast, Rous sarcoma virus (RSV) PR was isolated from viral cultures in amounts sufficient for structural studies.

Crystallographic Studies of Retroviral Proteases

The breakthrough that made structure-assisted design of protease-targeted drugs against AIDS possible was the determination in early 1989 of the structures of retroviral proteases, first from RSV (75) and subsequently from HIV-1. The structure of HIV-1 PR was also modeled using the known structures of eukaryotic aspartic proteases as templates (83, 84). In these models, HIV-1 PR was built as a dimer of two identical aspartic protease-like domains. A more accurate model of HIV-1 PR was constructed using the three-dimensional (3D) structure of RSV PR and homology modeling techniques (127). The experimental crystal structures of native HIV-1 PR were reported for the recombinant and synthetic enzymes in several laboratories (66, 79, 110, 132). These studies confirmed that the molecule is a homodimer and that its active site closely resembles the active sites of pepsin-like proteases. Other retroviral proteases for which crystal structures subsequently became available include the enzymes from HIV-2 (77, 116), simian immunodeficiency virus (SIV) (95, 128, 137), feline immunodeficiency virus (FIV) (131), and equine infectious anemia virus (EIAV) (41). The structures of the latter two enzymes have been reported only for inhibitor complexes; no apoenzyme structures are available at this time. Structures of artificially constructed single-chain enzymes are also available (5).

The crystals of native HIV-1 PR used in all published investigations were isomorphous and belonged to the space group $P4_12_12$. They diffracted to only medium resolution, with the data measured to, at best, only 2.7 Å. The asymmetric unit contained one monomer, and thus the dimer was crystallographically symmetric in the absence of any active-site ligands (other than a water molecule positioned adjacent to the aspartates). In contrast, the RSV PR dimer (50) comprised the asymmetric unit in the space group $P3_121$ crystals, such that the two subunits were in nonequivalent crystal environments. The deviation from exact twofold symmetry for the two subunits was quite small (0.4 Å rms for the Cα atoms, with a rotation angle of 178°) and may have been the result of crystal packing forces. The crystals of RSV PR were more highly ordered than those of native HIV-1 PR and diffracted to 2.0 Å (the structure was refined to an R-factor of 0.144). Nonetheless, all the amino acid side chains could be located in the electron density maps for HIV-1 PR, whereas residues 61–70, belonging to the flaps, were crystallographically disordered in both molecules of RSV PR.

The flaps in native HIV-1 PR were about 7 Å distant from the active site and in a very open conformation. This conformation could be considered a consequence of kinetic trapping resulting from the crystallization process and should not necessarily be taken as an indication of a preferred, highly stable conformation in solution (79, 132). Although structures of apparently uninhibited HIV-1 and HIV-2 PRs with flaps closed have been seen (K Watenpaugh and TN Bhat, personal communication), it is likely that, in each of these cases, peptide fragments were still present in the active sites.

A number of crystal forms of the complexes of HIV and SIV PRs with inhibitors have been reported. Some of these crystals diffracted to very high resolution, with at least two structures refined at a resolution of 1.7 Å with R-factors better than 0.2 (108, 115). Most of the crystal forms contained a dimer of the protease and a single inhibitor molecule in the asymmetric unit, although in some cases only a monomer was present (26, 78), whereas two molecules were present for some other structures (108). The availability of multiple crystal forms with vastly different packing should make it possible to differentiate between the intrinsic structural properties of the enzyme and crystal-induced conformational adjustments. Although the inhibitors were clearly ordered in unique orientations in some structures (e.g. 51, 112), they were often present in two superimposed orientations (26, 33, 78). In a particular investigation, only a single orientation was initially claimed (76), whereas two orientations were detected after careful reanalysis of the data (74). In some cases, especially for the hexagonal crystals of HIV-1 PR, almost completely isomorphous crystals were reported with either a monomer or a dimer in the asymmetric unit. Because some disorder is always present even for completely symmetric inhibitors (26,41), this difference is more quantitative than qualitative.

Description of the HIV-1 PR Molecule

The initial knowledge of the structures of retroviral proteases came from the crystallographic studies described above. The general topology of the HIV-1 PR monomer is similar to that of a single domain in pepsin-like aspartic proteases, with the main difference being that the dimer interface in the former is made up of four short strands, rather than the six long strands present in the pepsins (Figure 1a). In addition, because the molecular weight of dimeric HIV-1 PR is less than two/thirds that of pepsin, the retroviral enzyme is clearly a parsimonious member of the family (87).

The N-terminal β-strand a (residues 1–4) forms the outer part of the interface β-sheet. The β-strand b (residues 9–15) continues through a turn into β-strand c, which terminates at the active-site triplet (Asp25-Thr26-Gly27). Following the active-site loop is β-strand d, containing residues 30–35. In pepsin-like proteases, strand d is followed by helix h, which also has been seen in EIAV PR (41). In HIV-1 PR, this segment is quite distorted and forms a broad loop (residues 36–42). The second half of the molecule is topologically related to the first half by an approximate intramolecular twofold axis. Residues 43–49 form β-strand a', which, as in pepsin-like proteases, belongs to the flap. The other strand in the flap (residues 52–58) forms a part of the long β-chain b' (residues 52–66). The β-chain c' comprises residues 69–78 and, after a loop at residues 79–82, continues as strand d' (residues 83–85), which leads directly to the well-defined helix h' (residues 86–94). The hydrogen-bonding pattern within this helix is intermediate between an α helix and a 3_{10} helix. Helix h' is followed by a straight C-terminal strand (residues 95–99), which can be designated as q and which forms the inner part of the dimer interface. Four of the β-strands in the molecular core are organized into a Ψ-shaped sheet characteristic of all aspartic proteases. One of the "Ψ-sheets" comprises chains c (residues 23–25), d, and d', and the other is made up of strands c' (residues 76–78), d', and d.

The active-site triad (Asp25-Thr26-Gly27) is located in a loop whose structure is stabilized by a network of hydrogen bonds similar to that observed in eukaryotic enzymes (19). The carboxylate groups of Asp25 from both chains are nearly coplanar and show close contacts. The network is quite rigid due to the interaction (called "fireman's grip") in which each Thr26 OG1 accepts a hydrogen bond from the Thr26 main-chain NH of the opposing loop. Thr26 also

(a)

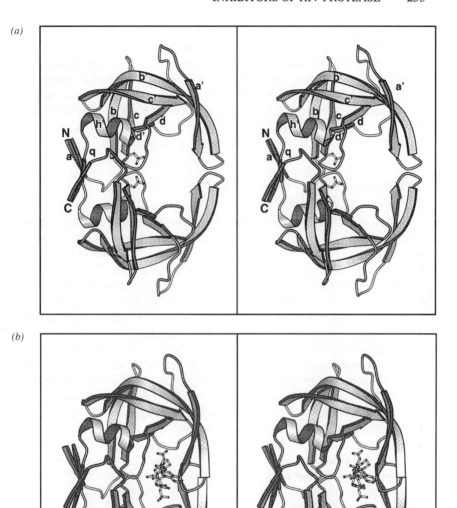

(b)

Figure 1   Stereoviews of the chain tracing of HIV-1 PR, prepared with the program Molscript (61). (*a*) Apoenzyme with the elements of secondary structure marked as discussed in the text; (*b*) Inhibited enzyme in the complex with Saquinavir (17).

donates a hydrogen bond to the carbonyl O atom of residue 24 on the opposite loop. Although the central features of the catalytic site are very similar between retroviral and cellular aspartic proteases, the residue following the triad differs, with Ala invariably present in retroviral proteases, whereas Ser or Thr are most common in the pepsin-like family of proteases. Another difference is the presence of only one flap in the pepsins, whereas a pair of twofold related flaps is present in HIV-1 PR. The flap is a β hairpin that covers the active site and participates in the binding of inhibitors and substrates (Figure 1b).

Common Structural Features of the Inhibitor Complexes of HIV-1 PR

Cocrystals of HIV-1 PR with a variety of inhibitors have been grown in a number of different crystal forms. The structures of these complexes (Figure 1b) have been used to investigate the binding of substrate-based modified oligopeptide inhibitors as well as of the inhibitors of non-peptidic nature. Binding of an inhibitor introduces substantial conformational changes to the enzyme. The overall movement of the subunits can be described as a rotation of up to about 2° around a hinge axis located in the subunit β-sheet interface. This motion, which slightly tightens the cavity of the active site, is also accompanied by a very large motion of the flap region—as much as 7 Å for the tips of the flaps (114). However, the enzyme structure is well conserved among the different complexes, with rms deviations between the Cα atoms seldom exceeding 0.6 Å. Such differences are well within the agreement range for protein structures refined independently or crystallized in different space groups (133).

Most of the inhibitors cocrystallized with HIV PR, including all peptidomimetic inhibitors, are bound in the enzyme active site in an extended conformation so that when they are superimposed upon one another, their functional elements align quite well overall (130). The contacts between the main chain of the peptidomimetic inhibitors and the protease are almost uniform for all the complexes (Figure 2). Following a similar pattern, the hydrogen bonds are made mostly between the main-chain atoms of both the enzyme and the inhibitor. The hydroxyl group at the nonscissile junction, present in inhibitors other than those containing the reduced peptide bond isosteres, is positioned between the Asp25/Asp25' carboxyls of the protease, within hydrogen-bonding distance to at least one carboxylate oxygen of each aspartate. A feature common to almost all complexes of HIV-1 PR is a buried water molecule that bridges the P2 and P1' CO groups of the inhibitor and Ile50 and Ile150 NH groups of the flaps. This water is approximately tetrahedrally coordinated and is completely separated from the bulk solvent (76). The functional substitution of this water has led to the design of urea-based inhibitors (see below).

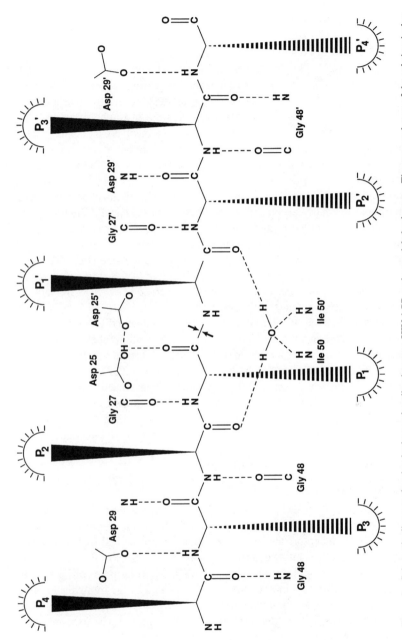

Figure 2 Schematic diagram showing hydrogen bonding between HIV-1 PR and a modeled substrate. The nomenclature of the subsites is that of Schechter & Berger (99). (Reprinted from 130.)

Subsites of the Inhibitor-Binding Pockets

A number of distinct subsites that accommodate side chains of the inhibitors can be identified in HIV PR. Three subsites on each side of the nonscissile bond (S1–S3 and S1′–S3′) are very well defined, whereas more distant subsites are not as clear. The protease side chains comprising the pockets S1 and S1′, with the exception of the active-site aspartates, are mostly hydrophobic. The side chains of the active-site aspartates and the main-chain hydroxyl of those inhibitors that contain such a central group are involved in polar contacts. Almost all of the documented inhibitors have hydrophobic moieties at P1 and P1′ with the exception of the statine- and glycine-containing inhibitors, in which no groups occupy the protease subsite S1′.

Although the S2 and S2′ pockets are hydrophobic, both hydrophilic and hydrophobic residues can occupy these sites. The P2 and P2′ hydrophobic side chains are observed in different orientations for the different inhibitors, forming contacts with different groups in the enzyme-binding pocket. For inhibitors containing asparagine or glutamine, the amide side chains are also stabilized by polar contact with the carbonyl O atom of the previous residues in the inhibitor. Some polar contacts are also observed between P2/P2′ amide groups and polar side chains of the protease.

Distal to S2/S2′, the subsites are not as well defined, and diverse side chains are accommodated in subsites S3 and S3′. Only a small number of inhibitors have standard amino acids located in the subsite S4. This subsite does not form an actual binding pocket, and only the carboxyl-most end of the P4 residue is surrounded by protease atoms. Only two inhibitors have been reported with a moiety at P4′: AG-4, which has one side of the glutamine fork directed into the S4′ subsite, and PS-1, which has a proline at this position. There is really no complementary S5 or S5′ pocket on the protease; P5 or P5′ residues of the inhibitor extend out of the binding groove of the enzyme, making few contacts with the protease.

NMR Studies

NMR spectroscopy is a technique that, in the last decade, has been successfully used for the determination of 3D structures of a large number of macromolecules, including receptors and ligand/receptor complexes. NMR has also become a useful tool for rapidly determining the conformations of receptor-bound ligands (32). Initial applications of this technique to the studies of HIV-1 PR complexed with different inhibitors were complicated by the limited solubility of the protein, but these difficulties were ultimately overcome. Taken together with data from crystallographic experiments, NMR provides an excellent tool for mapping enzyme-inhibitor interactions in a dynamic state.

The solution-state NMR technique was used to study the symmetric versus asymmetric binding of penicillin-based symmetric inhibitors of HIV-1 PR (134). In this study, the spectra of HIV-1 PR complexed with an inhibitor that contained two symmetrically disposed trifluoro groups indicated the symmetric binding mode. The compounds traced a novel S-shaped path through the active site, with almost no contact with the catalytic aspartates but with full occupancy of the S1/S1' and S2/S2' subsites. This work was later continued in a study of penicillin-based asymmetric inhibitors and revealed that such inhibitors occupied binding subsites in a manner equivalent to half of a dimeric C2-symmetric inhibitor (52).

An interesting attempt to design protease inhibitors utilizing NMR in combination with computational methods was reported by Podlogar et al (85). A novel macrocyclic inhibitor in which the P1 and P3 side chains had been joined was found to be an excellent inhibitor of HIV PR. NMR analysis of the precursor showed that the conformation of the cyclic region was very similar to that observed in the enzyme-bound inhibitor complex as determined by computational approaches. These results confirmed that computational models and simulations (see below), together with NMR data, can provide a basis for further modification and design.

Complexes of HIV-1 PR with cyclic urea-based inhibitors have been subject to extensive NMR studies, starting with a complex with the inhibitor DMP-323 (136). The derived assignments of the resonances opened the way to determining 3D solution structures and suggested methods for reducing the time required for this task (135). DMP-323 was also used for mapping the water molecules bound in such complexes (124), as well as for comprehensive conformational analysis studies (65). Its high affinity made it possible to study the relationship between the flexibility of HIV-1 PR and the function of the enzyme (80). Analysis of ^{15}N spin relaxation parameters of all but 13 backbone amides revealed the presence of significant internal motions of the protein backbone. The flaps covering the protease active site underwent large-amplitude motions on the picosecond to nanosecond time scale, whereas the tips of the flaps underwent a conformational exchange on the microsecond time scale. These studies confirmed the importance of changes in the conformation of the flaps during the catalytic process.

Two NMR studies of KNI-272, a tripeptide inhibitor of HIV-1 PR, have recently been published. In the first one (81), solution conformation of KNI-272 was examined, showing that the backbone of the inhibitor had a fairly rigid conformation. The question of the ionization state of the catalytic aspartyl groups was addressed in the second study (125). The ionization state of the catalytic residues was also examined using chemically synthesized HIV-1 PR in which Asp25 in each monomer was specifically labeled with ^{13}C (109). In the presence of pepstatin, the catalytic carboxylates did not titrate in the pH range where the enzyme was active. Throughout the pH range of 2.5–6.5, one Asp25 side chain was protonated and the other was deprotonated. In the absence of an inhibitor, the two aspartate side chains were chemically equivalent and both were deprotonated at pH 6, the optimum for enzymatic activity.

Computational Studies

A number of quantum-chemistry based computational techniques can be potentially useful for the description of ligand-enzyme interactions or for the prediction of ligand affinity. Some of these computational approaches have been utilized to probe the binding of various inhibitors and substrates to HIV PR. These methods have ranged from simple molecular mechanics calculations or molecular docking techniques to free-energy perturbation methods using molecular dynamics. In principle, the aims of all these methods have been similar—namely, to find computational techniques for prediction of inhibitor-binding affinity. Molecular dynamics calculations have also been used for studying enzyme dynamics and the influence of certain mutations on structure and stability. A combination of ab initio, semiempirical, and empirical calculations has been used for the description of the catalytic mechanism of HIV-1 PR.

An attempt to find a correlation between the experimentally obtained data and the computational results for three inhibitor complexes of HIV-1 PR with known crystal structures (MVT-101, JG-365, and U-85548e) involved energy minimization using molecular mechanics (98). Because of the very different nature of these inhibitors, no correlation between the interaction energy and the binding constants could be found. From the structural point of view, only minor changes of the hydrophobic core and of the inhibitor binding site were reported. The largest change was for the surface loop with the highest B-factors. Improved energy calculations on the same set of inhibitors were later performed, with the aim of determining general rules for inhibitor and substrate binding to the HIV-1 PR (42). A comparison with another 15 published X-ray structures of the complexes of HIV-1 PR with inhibitors was made in order to understand the importance of the hydrogen-bonding interactions between the main-chain atoms of the inhibitor and those of the enzyme. Conserved hydrogen bonds were observed in the subsites ranging from P3 to P3'. The calculated contribution of the main-chain interactions to the total interaction energy ranged from 56% to 68%. It was concluded that the protease-inhibitor interactions with the main chain provided a substantial contribution to the total binding energy. The relative contribution to the total interaction energy of main-chain and side-chain atoms from individual residues was largest for subsite P2.

A study successfully utilizing simple energy minimization of HIV-1 PR inhibitors in the active site in order to predict their activity was performed by a group from Merck (47). Using the MM2X force field and the program OPTIMOL, they found a satisfactorily high correlation between the interaction energy and the experimentally determined IC_{50} constants for almost 50 inhibitor-enzyme complexes. Thirty-four of the complexes were used as a training set and the others were examined as a set for prediction. The interaction energy corresponded to the sum of van der Waals and electrostatic interactions between the inhibitor and the enzyme when the inhibitor was minimized in the rigid active site of the enzyme. The proposed correlation was premised on the assumptions that the interaction energy (E_{inter}) might be proportional to the enthalpy of binding (ΔH_{bind}), while the entropy of binding (ΔS) might be small or, more likely, constant. The use of this simple model is limited to inhibitors that were neutral and of approximately the same size, and it obviously neglected some factors which were key to binding. For example, the enzyme active-site flexibility and the difference in energy between the solution and bound conformations of the inhibitor were not taken into account.

Weber & Harrison (126) used molecular mechanics in their calculations of enzyme-substrate interactions and found correlations between the interaction energy and the kinetic characteristics for 21 peptide substrates and their reaction intermediates. They provided a statistical mechanics interpretation of the molecular mechanics energy and discussed its justification. Another study involved molecular dynamics (MD) calculations on HIV-1 PR with a bound peptide substrate (43). A stable minimum energy position for a proton artificially placed between the two aspartates and the carboxyl oxygen of the cleaved peptide bond was determined, and this study served as a basis for the later runs of energy minimization.

Calculations utilizing molecular dynamics coupled with the free energy perturbation method have served as relatively reliable tools for the prediction of the free energy of binding by computational methods. The early utilization of free-energy perturbation theory (FPT) was reviewed by McCarrick & Kollman (71). The computational studies by Ferguson et al (31) and Tropsha & Hermans (117), focusing on the difference in free energy of binding between the S- and R-hydroxy stereoisomers of the inhibitor JG-365, have shown that two independent experiments could lead to similar results. The FPT method was recently used in several cases to explain the differences between the binding constants of similar inhibitors (53, 86), to analyze HIV-1 PR mutants and their affinity to different inhibitors (102), or to serve as a tool for molecular modeling and drug design (123). Activated molecular dynamics calculations were used to model flap opening (14, 15), a crucial step during the binding of a substrate or an inhibitor. These studies compared the wild-type protease with the M46I mutant associated with drug resistance and indicated that this mutation stabilizes the flaps in a closed conformation.

The knowledge of the ionization state of the two catalytic aspartates is extremely important in determining the correct binding mode of the substrate and the free energy, so considerable efforts have been spent on this problem (11, 31, 37, 44), as well as on theoretical modeling of the catalytic mechanism. Different steps of the reaction were modeled using ab initio and MD calculations (108). Another recent approach to that subject utilized a combination of quantum and classical molecular dynamics (67). Both of these studies reported protonation of only one aspartic acid during catalysis. It has been indicated that the nucleophilic water molecule bound at a position different from the positions of the hydroxyl groups observed in various aspartic protease-inhibitor complexes. The carboxyl group of the scissile peptide bond also adopted a different orientation. During the approach to this bond, the reaction center changed gradually to a conformation close to that derived from X-ray structures of HIV-1 PR with various inhibitors.

The interactions of HIV-1 PR with different inhibitors, determined from their crystal structures, have served as a starting point for tests of various docking techniques. The first of such docking studies of HIV-1 PR was performed by the Kuntz laboratory (21), who discovered that haloperidol could be an inhibitor of this enzyme. However, subsequent crystal structure determination revealed a different orientation for haloperidol than the one predicted (97). Docking methods and algorithms were tested using the known structural data and experimental characteristics by Monte Carlo docking (10) or by comparison with de novo constructed inhibitors by a fragment-based method (96), in which the inhibitors were constructed entirely from individual functional groups chosen from a predefined library. A method of continual energy minimization implemented in the program SCULP was a new paradigm for modeling proteins in interactive computer graphic systems (111). This physically realistic attempt made possible the modeling of very large changes and aided the understanding of how different energy terms interact to stabilize a given conformation. Other recent studies examined empirical free energy as a target function in docking and design, showing the advantages of this approach over studies using the calculation of interaction energy (58).

Database of Three-Dimensional Structures of HIV-1 PR

With the rapid progress in determining the structures of HIV PRs, it had been postulated as early as 1993 that a collection of such structures in a single database would be beneficial (130). The HIV PR database was established three years later at the National Cancer Institute (122). It is an Internet-based service that now provides direct access to more than 130 crystal structures. Almost 40 of these structures of HIV-1, HIV-2 or SIV PRs in complexes with various inhibitors are not publicly available elsewhere (Table 1). There are two main reasons why this database was created. First, with a number of inhibitors having reached approval by the FDA as anti-AIDS drugs and with others in advanced clinical trials, there was some danger that many of the structures with no direct clinical relevance would ultimately be lost. Second, the database provides a unique source of information about ligand-enzyme interactions in a well-characterized system, which could be essential for formulation of new drug-design principles and synthetic strategies.

A detailed description of the database was provided elsewhere (122). Its shell contains structural files that had been previously deposited in the Protein Data Bank (PDB) or were directly placed into the HIV PR database. The information about these complexes is placed in the chronological order of deposition in the main table of contents. Branched links provide more detailed information about the inhibitors, their chemical formulas, literature references, and 3D structures visualized by a Web-based browser applet. Special attention was paid to the kinetic parameters for the inhibitors, including the conditions of such measurements. Information contained in this part of the database can be easily accessed using a simple search engine. The core of the database consists of the Analytical Part, designed as a source of various tools for the statistical analysis of the archived complexes. Some results of this analysis are immediately accessible. The more complicated calculations or analytical programs are run in batch mode and the results are returned by e-mail. This part also contains coordinates of the complexes transformed into a common frame of reference, as well as the separate files of the proteases, inhibitors, and solvent. For those who perform molecular modeling and are interested in different modes of superimposing the structures, a fit based on the user's definition is provided using the program ProFit.

Particular attention was paid to volume and surface calculations for the protein and the inhibitors. These characteristics are very important when combined with reasonable template structure and docking algorithms in searching directly for novel inhibitors and in formulating new rules for docking. An initial example of the analysis of structures in the database involved construction of minimal and maximal binding volumes in the active site of HIV PR. The volume calculations were performed for all the stored structures from which the inhibitors and the water molecules were removed. These volumes spanned a surprisingly wide range of magnitudes, although no correlation between the volume of the inhibitor and the volume of the binding cavity could be found.

Difference-distance matrix calculations were used to correlate some structural features of the complexes with crystal packing. The basic assumption was that, for isomorphous structures, any differences would have to be caused by inhibitors rather than by crystal packing forces. On the other hand, comparison of complexes crystallized in different space groups should also show the changes caused by different packing forces. Such calculations have shown that the most rigid main-chain regions of HIV PR consist of residues 1–4, 25–28, 49–52 and 94–99, possibly indicating the importance of these areas to the process of enzyme folding.

DESIGN, STRUCTURE, AND PROPERTIES OF SELECTED INHIBITORS

Saquinavir (Ro 31-8959, Invirase): The First Approved Protease Drug

The discovery and development of the Hoffmann–La Roche drug Saquinavir (Figure 3), the first inhibitor of HIV-1 PR to be approved by the FDA, proved to be a classic example of serendipity coupled with hard work. Initial inhibitors created in that study were peptide derivatives utilizing transition-state mimetic concepts (94). The basic design criterion relied on the observation that HIV-1 PR, unlike other proteases, is able to cleave Tyr-Pro or Phe-Pro sequences in the viral polyprotein. Because the amide bonds of proline residues are not susceptible to cleavage by mammalian endopeptidases, the design of HIV-1 PR inhibitors based on this criterion was expected to bring potential advantages of higher selectivity. Reduced amides and hydroxyethylamine isosteres most readily accommodate the imino acid moiety characteristic of a Phe-Pro or Tyr-Pro retroviral substrate and, therefore, were chosen for further studies. As was shown later, the reduced amide isosteres were relatively poor inhibitors but, in contrast, the compounds incorporating the hydroxyethylamine moiety were very potent and highly selective inhibitors of HIV PR.

A minimum sequence required for potent inhibition, as well as the unexpected preference for R stereochemistry at the hydroxyl-bearing carbon, was determined by enzymatic studies of a series of related compounds. The minimum length inhibitor included three residues on the N-terminal side of the isostere and two residues on the C-terminal side. Varying the side chains of the residues in all subsites did not lead to dramatic improvement of the potency of inhibitors. The most marked improvements in potency were achieved by varying the amino acid at subsite P1', via replacement of proline by (S, S, S)-decahydro-isoquinoline-3-carbonyl (DIQ). The resulting compound (later designated as Ro 31-8959) had a K_i value of 0.12 at pH 5.5 against HIV-1 PR and an even

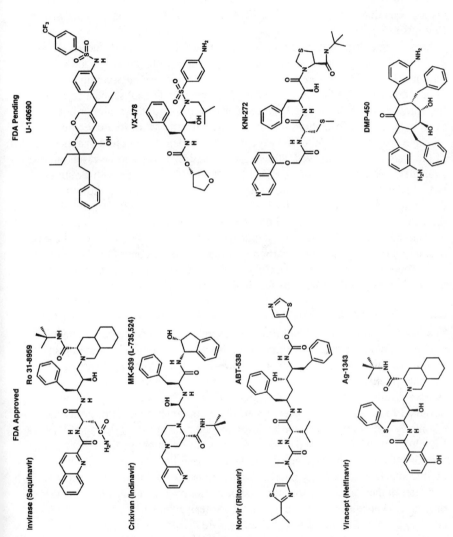

Figure 3 Chemical structures of the HIV PR inhibitors which have either been approved as anti-AIDS drugs by the FDA or are known to be in advanced clinical trials in late 1997.

better inhibition constant against HIV-2 PR ($K_i < 0.1$) (94). It was also shown to be highly selective, causing less than 50% inhibition of the human aspartic proteases. The compound was subsequently used for further clinical trials and was finally approved by the FDA in 1995 under the name Saquinavir (Invirase).

This design effort was accompanied by only limited structural studies. The first crystal structure to be solved was of a complex with another peptidic inhibitor, Ro 31-8588 (Figure 4), which exhibited the expected S-configuration of the carbon bearing the central hydroxyl group (38). The subsequent crystallographic study of Ro 31-8959 showed that, as predicted, this inhibitor bound in an extended conformation, forming a characteristic set of hydrogen bonds with the enzyme (62). With the exception of the flap, the twofold symmetry of the enzyme was preserved, allowing the S and S' subsites to be essentially equivalent. A comparison of the HIV-1 PR/Ro 31-8959 structure with the structure of HIV-1 PR complexed with a longer inhibitor, JG-365 (112), showed that the conformation of the inhibitor in the binding cavity critically depended on the nature of the P1' residue and on the presence or absence of the extension beyond subsite S2'. It was also established that short inhibitors preferred the R-configuration of the central carbon. Moreover, the carbonyl O atom of the DIQ group was able to maintain the hydrogen bond between the water molecule connecting the inhibitor with the flap regions (Wat301).

Ritonavir (ABT-538, Norvir)

The development of the Abbott drug Ritonavir is an interesting case showing how the thinking of the designers shifted from the creation of symmetric inhibitors of this inherently symmetric enzyme to their ultimate conversion to asymmetric compounds. The concept was first tested with the synthesis and characterization of symmetric inhibitors of HIV-1 PR (28, 29, 95), which were designed to match the C2 symmetry of the homodimeric HIV PR. Although symmetry was not thought to be an absolute requirement for the design of HIV PR inhibitors, it was expected to be useful in tightly constraining the rather rigid ligands (40). It was also expected that the less peptidic nature of the inhibitors might enhance their stability in vivo. Such symmetric inhibitors were expected to confer higher specificity for retroviral proteases over the related mammalian proteases, whose substrate binding sites are less symmetric. A hypothetical tetrahedral intermediate of the cleaved peptide divided by the C2 axis of the enzyme was taken as the template for the development of inhibitors. This hypothetical axis was placed on the carbonyl O atom or between the C-N atoms of the cleaved peptide bond respectively, and one half of the template was deleted. The C2 operation was then implemented on the remaining template, generating symmetric inhibitors in either the mono-ol or diol form.

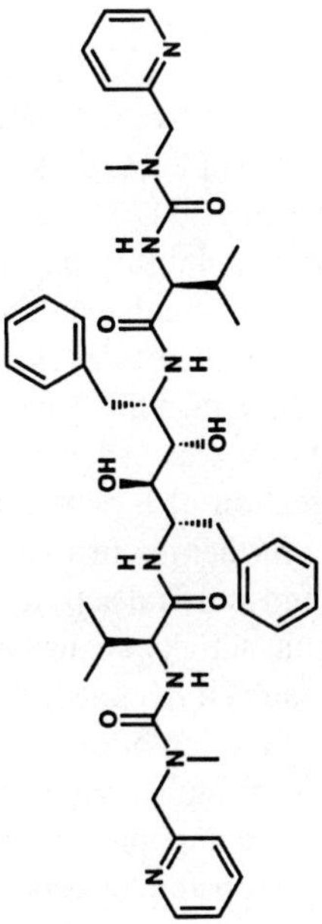

A-77003

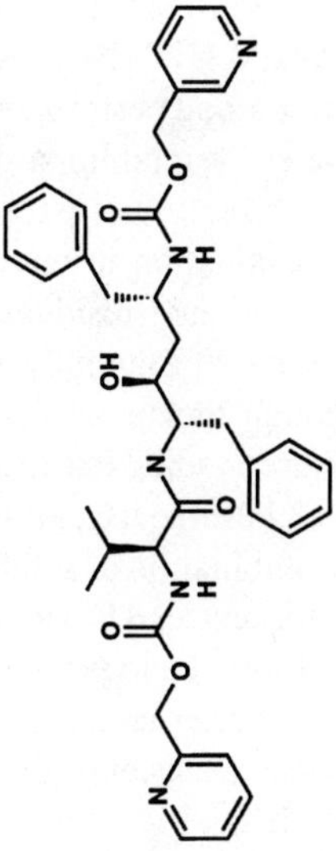

A-80987

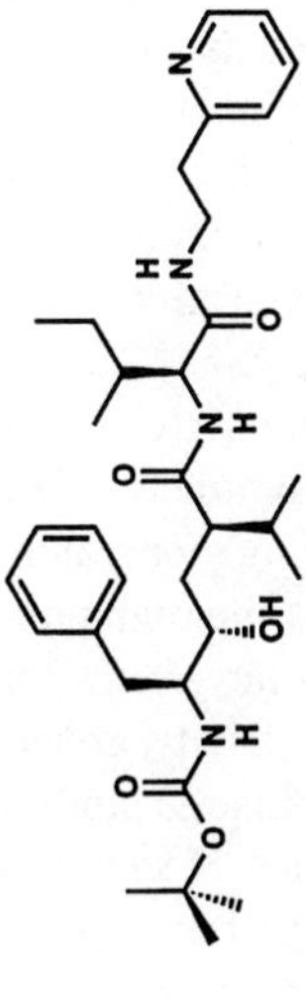

Ro 31-8588

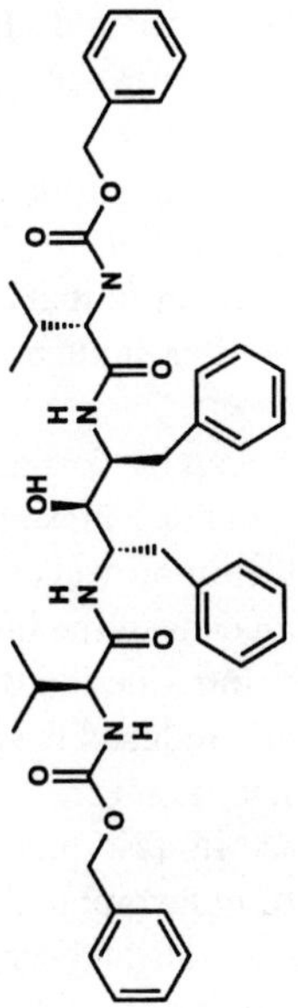

A-74704

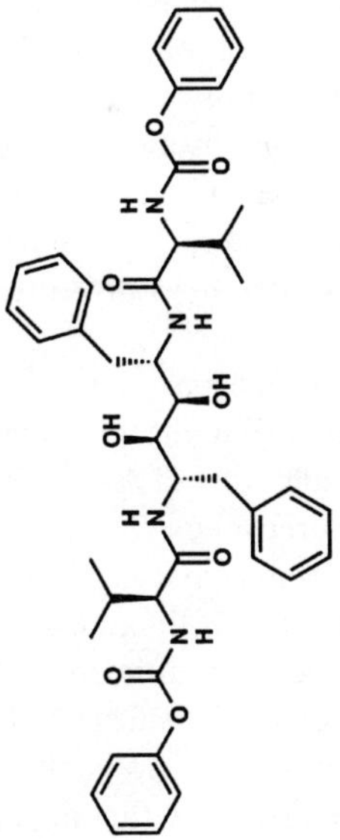

A-75925

Figure 4 Chemical structures of compounds that were intermediates in the design of Saquinavir and Ritonavir.

The first of these symmetric inhibitors showed good kinetic profiles, and the concept of symmetry seemed to work remarkably well in cell cultures. The antiviral activity against HIV-1 in H9 cells determined by IC_{50} varied from 0.4 μM to 20 nM. However, good performance in vitro did not result in acceptable bioavailability. The early inhibitors, designated A-74704 and A-75925 (Figure 4), had high lipophilicity and poor aqueous solubility and therefore presented difficulties for evaluation in vivo. In order to enhance their aqueous solubility, the terminal phenyl residues were modified to pyridyl groups (57). The diol inhibitors were substantially more active than the corresponding mono-ol inhibitors, although their aqueous solubility was at least one order of magnitude lower. These studies led to the creation of a new compound, A-77003 (Figure 4), which became a candidate for further in vitro kinetic evaluations based on a good combination of solubility and antiviral activity. Further examination of the inhibitor revealed broad-spectrum activity against both HIV types in a variety of transformed and primary human cell lines. Moderate oral bioavailability was observed after administration of the inhibitors to rats. The concept of symmetry was also successfully used for pseudosymmetric difluoroketones, highly potent HIV-1 PR inhibitors; these compounds also demonstrated good antiviral activity via inhibition of the cytopathic effects (107).

Dreyer et al (25) obtained the surprising result that even symmetric inhibitors may bind to HIV-1 PR in an asymmetric fashion. It was shown that crystal packing forces were not responsible for the observed asymmetry, but that, more probably, the asymmetric binding mode represented a lower energy complex in solution. In addition, some of the examined mono-ol and diol inhibitors had the unexpected ability to inhibit a prototypical cellular aspartic protease, porcine pepsin. These observations were important in guiding some groups, including the one from Abbott, in changing the direction of the development of new clinical candidates. It was also more difficult to make symmetric compounds with good oral bioavailability, which is often influenced by the termini of the inhibitor.

For these reasons, the process that began by designing symmetric or pseudosymmetric inhibitors resulted in compounds with significant asymmetry. The aqueous solubility of A-77003 was further improved by introducing moderately polar, heterocyclic groups at one or both ends of the inhibitors while maintaining inhibition activity against HIV PR. Introduction of more polar groups for the attenuation of lipophilicity drastically reduced the antiviral activity, apparently owing to insufficient cellular penetration (55). Pharmacokinetic studies in rats indicated a substantial difference in absorption properties of mono-ol and diol inhibitors, probably because of unfavorable desolvation effects of the diol. The discovery that the deshydroxy diols had superior potency led to the development of A-80987 (Figure 4), a shorter, orally bioavailable analog of

A-78791 (Figure 4), and its use in clinical trials. A-80987 was the penultimate compound in the synthesis of ABT-538 (Ritonavir) (56). The latter compound was designed by utilizing data from a study of a series of analogs of A-80987, which yielded valuable insight into the relationship of chemical structure to antiviral activity, aqueous solubility and hepatic metabolism. In this form the inhibitor reached clinical trials and was approved by the FDA in early 1996 under the name Norvir (Figure 3).

Indinavir (MK-639, L-735,524, Crixivan)

The discovery and development of the Merck drug Indinavir (Figure 3) was a long and complicated research project. Similarly to the approach taken at Roche, the original design strategy began with a compound based on the transition-state mimetic concept (91). This approach was successfully implemented in an earlier design of renin inhibitors, although no approved drugs resulted from the project (39). One important structural feature present in most tight-binding aspartic protease inhibitors is a critical hydroxyl group that hydrogen bonds to the carboxyl groups of the catalytically active aspartic acids. Incorporation of a hydroxyethylene isostere as a dipeptide mimic resulted in compounds that were potent and selective inhibitors of HIV PR. The available structure-activity data indicated that an S-hydroxyl was the preferred configuration. The constituent hydroxyethylene isostere was extensively examined in a series of peptidomimetic inhibitors of different length and with particular residues occupying subsites on both sides of the nonscissile isostere. Residues in these positions were systematically changed to establish the relationships between particular modifications and the efficiency of the inhibitors. The important questions of bioavailability were also addressed by these modifications. Some of the useful directions of synthesis were based on the results of molecular modeling and calculations.

Further approach to the successful design of HIV PR inhibitors with nanomolar inhibition constants led to a series of tetrapeptide analogs of a pentapeptide, L-682,679 (Figure 5), in which the C terminus had been shortened and modified (22). The inhibitory properties of these compounds were measured in peptide cleavage assays, with selected inhibitors also tested for their antiviral properties in cell culture. The first studies addressed the influence of the C terminus, with particular emphasis on the variation of the P2′ amino acid and elimination/replacement of the P3′ amino acid. The compounds that were systematically varied in P2′ were almost exclusively aliphatic. Only one amino acid with a hydroxyl group (serine) was examined, without any indication of an improvement in the inhibitory activity. Substitution by (aminomethyl) benzimidazole provided the most potent compounds in this series, as the imidazole portion appeared to be mimicking a carboxamide, whereas the phenyl portion

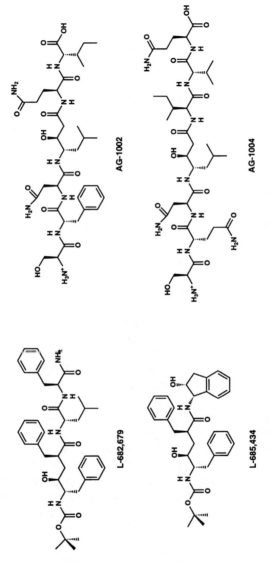

Figure 5 Chemical structures of compounds that were intermediates in the design of Indinavir and Nelfinavir.

was probably contributing additional hydrophobic binding, essentially in the P4' site. Important observations were made by testing the ability to inhibit HIV-1 infection in cell culture. Some of the inhibitors were considerably less potent in cell culture than would have been predicted by their IC_{50} values, potentially reflecting their inability to penetrate the hydrophobic cell membrane. The important conclusion was that as the terminal amide increased in size or polarity, the intrinsic potency improved but the minimum inhibitory concentration did not improve. Inhibitors with benzimidazole were the most potent compounds in this series.

More than 150 compounds were described in several papers as intermediate steps in the design of Indinavir. The drug lead compound was L-685,434 (70, 120), a hydroxyethylene-based inhibitor with a benzocycloalkyl amine at the C terminus (Figure 5). The properties of this compound were improved by variation at the N terminus. Although very potent, the molecule lacked solubility in aqueous media and did not show an acceptable pharmacokinetic profile. Incorporation of a basic amine into the backbone of the L-685,434 series provided antiviral potency combined with highly improved pharmacokinetic profiles in animal models. The design of L-735,524 (Figure 3) was guided by molecular modeling and X-ray crystal structure determination of the inhibited enzyme complex (24, 119). The inhibitor was potent and competitively inhibited both HIV-1 and HIV-2 PRs with K_i values of 0.52 and 3.3 nM, respectively. This inhibitor, highly selective for retroviral proteases, showed no inhibition against a variety of mammalian proteases including human renin and cathepsin D, porcine pepsin, and bovine chymosin. It also was capable of preventing the growth of HIV-1-infected MT4 lymphoid cells at concentrations of 25–50 nM. L-735,524 was orally bioavailable in three animal models and therefore was tested as a promising drug in clinical trials. In early 1996, the compound (under the name Crixivan) was approved by the FDA as a drug against HIV infection.

Nelfinavir (AG-1343, Viracept)

The pathway of the discovery and development of Viracept (Figure 3) by Agouron Pharmaceuticals is the least completely described in the literature of the four FDA-approved protease inhibitor drugs. Little is known about the basis of its synthesis, and no crystal structure of the complex with HIV-1 PR has been released. This inhibitor is the only compound among these four that does not utilize a peptidomimetic concept, although its development pathway may have utilized some peptidomimetics. Two inhibitors developed by Agouron, AG-1002 and AG-1004 (Figure 5), had a statine isostere instead of a normal peptide bond (2). These compounds were peptidomimetic inhibitors with the flanking amino acid sequences naturally recognized by HIV-1 PR and were bound to the active site in an extended conformation. They could form 16 and 18 hydrogen bonds, respectively, due to the presence of hydrophilic side chains. Despite the large number of hydrogen bonds, the inhibitors had relatively low potency, with binding constants of 0.55 μM for AG-1002 and 0.32 μM for AG-1004. A possible explanation for this low potency was the absence of a P1' group, as well as the large free energy required for desolvating of the hydrophilic side chains.

In another study, the structure of HIV-1 PR complexed with MVT-101 was utilized for modeling and synthesis of a lead compound, still based on the peptidomimetic concept (121). The best inhibitor in this series had an inhibition constant of about 30 nM and was characterized by the determination of its crystal structure, as well as by the calculations based on the free-energy perturbations method. The C terminus of the lead compound was replaced by an indole ring occupying the P3' pocket and replacing the phenyl group and was still able to maintain the hydrogen bond with Gly48. Iterative protein cocrystal structure analysis of peptidic inhibitors and the replacement of parts of the inhibitors by other substituents of nonpeptidic character (89) were used in order to achieve the goal of designing orally bioavailable, nonpeptidic inhibitors. A Monte Carlo program that could generate ligands was used for filling in subsite S1 (35), resulting in the placement of a large cyclopentylethyl group in this position. Combining the 5-chloro with the dimethylbenzyl and cyclopentyl amides resulted in the best compound in this series, with a K_i value of about 2 nM (comparable to the efficiency of Saquinavir).

Little information about the design of Agouron's approved drug, AG-1343 (Nelfinavir), can be found, although clearly this compound is the logical endpoint of a well-conceived design effort. One terminus of Nelfinavir contains the same DIQ group as Saquinavir. Studies examining the physicochemical properties of the former utilized the unpublished crystal structure of this inhibitor complexed with HIV-1 PR for testing of conformationally flexible docking by evolutionary programming (36, 69). This work was followed by further developments in the design strategy of nonpeptidic inhibitors (73, 90). Nelfinavir was rapidly approved by the FDA (under the name Viracept) and was the first of the protease inhibitors to be approved for the treatment of pediatric AIDS.

Inhibitors Designed to Replace Wat301

One of the completely unexpected features of the structures of complexes between HIV-1 PR and the inhibitors was the finding of a conserved water molecule mediating the contacts between the P2/P1' carbonyl O atoms of the peptidic inhibitors and the amide groups of Ile50/Ile50' in the enzyme. This tetrahedrally coordinated water, usually denoted Wat301 [but originally listed as Wat511 (76)], has been reported in practically all structures of not only the complexes of HIV-1 PR, but also HIV-2 and SIV PRs. Not surprisingly, in-corporation of its replacement into the ligands has long been postulated as a possible way of making highly specific protease inhibitors (112), and this sug-gestion has been implemented by several groups. Although no approved drugs have emerged as yet, it is likely that this approach will ultimately succeed and thus we will discuss it here.

One of the approaches to finding the starting points for the design of such inhibitors was to search databases of small-molecule compounds for molecules that contain two appropriately spaced O atoms, one capable of replacing Wat301, and the other able to bind to one or both of the active site aspartates. Chenera et al (12) identified core structures containing *trans*-1, 4-cyclohexanediol or hydro-quinone by using the program DOCK (63) and showed that six-membered rings with *para*-related oxygens could make the desired interactions. With phenyl rings placed adjacent to one of these oxygens and the other replaced by a better-fitting sulfoxide group, it was possible to create inhibitors with K_i values as low as 7 μM. The molecules created in this experiment, however, lacked hydrophobic moieties that could occupy the S2 and S2' pockets of the enzyme, and thus it was not possible to enhance their binding further.

A much more extensive and successful effort by the scientists from Du Pont Merck led to the development of a number of very potent inhibitors of HIV-1 PR and to the creation of a candidate drug compound, DMP-450 (Figure 3). The crucial difference in this approach was the utilization of a seven-membered cyclic urea ring as the starting pharmacophore. This design step was accomplished by an analysis of the existing experimental structures of the enzyme-inhibitor complexes as well as by modeling those structures that were not directly available (64). Cyclic ureas derived from L- and D-phenyl-alanine showed inhibition constants of about 4 μM, in good agreement with the data presented above. The ring nitrogens, however, offered the opportunity of further modifications—in particular, by the addition of large hydrophobic groups expected to bind in the S2/S2' pockets. The use of groups such as *para*-hydroxymethylbenzyl led to the development of DMP-323 (Figure 6), an inhibitor having a subnanomolar inhibition constant. This compound showed significant oral bioavailability in dogs and rats, indicating its possible useful-ness in humans. It inhibited SIV PR only weakly, however, suggesting that it would not be a broad-spectrum drug. Although for a while DMP-323 was a clinical candidate (64), it was ultimately abandoned because of its poor oral bioavailability in humans.

Because this poor bioavailability was most likely due to low solubility in aqueous or lipid solvents, the next design step involved the addition of charged groups to the benzyl rings. Although the attempts to introduce highly ba-sic groups did not succeed, it was possible to replace the hydroxymethyl

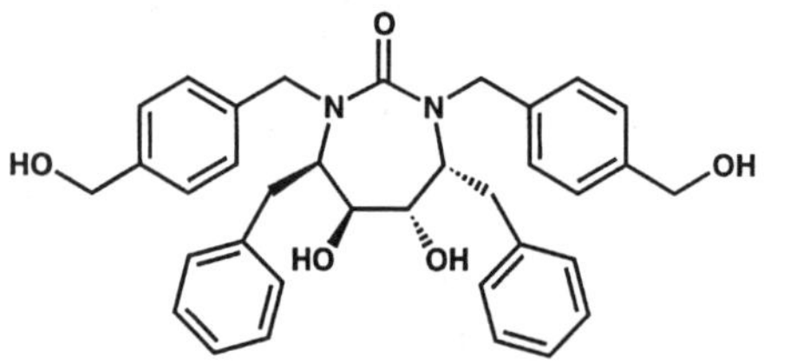

DMP-323

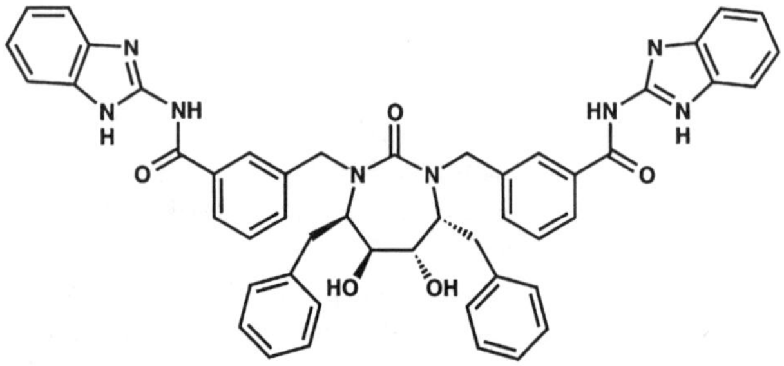

SD-146

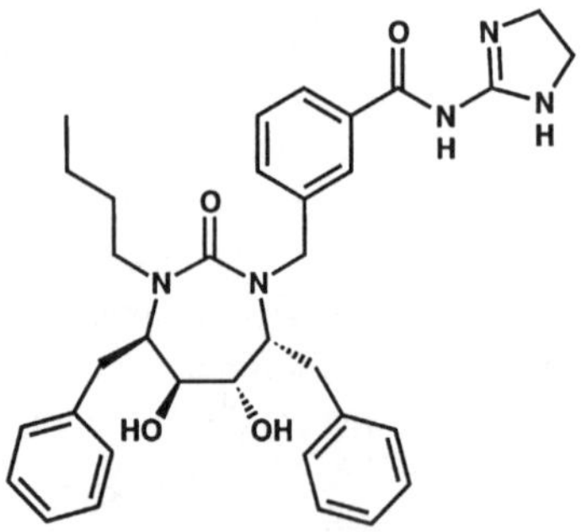

SD-152

Figure 6   Chemical structures of several inhibitors of HIV-1 PR in which an oxygen atom replaces Wat301.

substituents by *meta*-amino groups. The inhibitory properties of the resulting compound, DMP-450, were very similar to those of DMP-323 ($K_i = 0.3$ nM), yet DMP-450 was very potent against the virus in cell culture and was shown to be orally available in humans (46). Like most other clinically useful protease inhibitors, DMP-450 would lose potency against the HIV-1 PR double V82F/I84V mutant by as much as two orders of magnitude (1). Nevertheless, at the time of this writing, this inhibitor is still in active clinical trials, conducted by Avid Therapeutics, Inc.

All of the above-mentioned inhibitors with six- or seven-membered rings in their centers are symmetric or quasisymmetric. This design recalls the initial approaches taken at Abbott (28) (see above). The presence of strict symmetry has not, however, correlated with the usefulness of the Abbott compounds as drugs, and the design rules have ultimately been relaxed. An analogous observation was also relevant to the cyclic urea–based compounds. Further development of these inhibitors, aimed at increasing their effectiveness against drug-resistant mutants of the virus, often utilized asymmetric design, in which the two ring nitrogens were substituted by different groups. Some of them, such as SD-152 (Figure 6), showed good activity profiles against most of the protease mutants, although the best new inhibitors in this series, such as SD-146 (Figure 6), were again symmetric (49). The ring substituents of the latter compounds were much larger than in DMP-450 and were capable of making more hydrogen bonds with the polar groups of the enzyme, especially with the mainchain N and O atoms of Gly48, as well as with the amide N and side-chain carboxyl of Asp30. Although these newer compounds had high antiviral activity and very good resistance profiles, their poor solubility in both water and oils prevented their formulation as drugs. Further developments in this elegantly designed series are still needed.

A parallel effort in designing this class of inhibitors yielded a puzzling result: When the seven-member cyclic urea ring was modified to a cyclic sulfamide and all the side chains contained phenyl groups, the pockets occupied by the S1′ and S2′ side chains were reversed. The unexpected presence of the putative S2′ residue in the P1′ pocket, and vice versa, was attributed to the more rigid and predefined structure of the seven-member ring utilized in this case (4).

DEVELOPMENT OF DRUG RESISTANCE

In common with other retroviral polymerases, HIV RT is unable to edit transcription errors during nucleic acid replication, and thus enhances the mutational rates of the virus (93). As one of the results, divergent viral populations are present during infection and the sequences of the proteases from these different strains differ, sometimes substantially. Many of these differences do not affect the activity of the enzyme, and the structures of fully active proteases that differ in a number of positions in their sequences, from strains such as NY5 or SF2, have been reported. However, high rates of viral turnover in HIV infection and the inability of HIV reverse transcriptase to correct transcriptional errors also mean that populations of resistant virus will eventually emerge during any antiviral therapy as a result of drug selection of viral strains (6). It has previously been shown that the clinical use of RT inhibitors has led to the rapid development of resistance and cross-resistance against different RT inhibitors (100). Similarly, drug-induced mutations in HIV PR alter the susceptibility of the enzyme to inhibition by specific inhibitors.

A recent survey of the mutations associated with drug resistance has shown the modifications of 45 residues in HIV-1 PR, almost half of the total, for enzyme isolated from samples obtained with the help of 21 drugs (100). An obvious and expected mechanism for the development of resistance to HIV PR inhibitors is caused by the changes of specificity-determining residues that can directly interfere with the binding of the inhibitor to the enzyme. The mutations that do not directly change the shape or character of the binding cavity can indirectly influence inhibitor binding via long-range structural perturbations of the active site, or they can change the efficiency of catalysis and the stability of the enzyme. Other possible pathways in the development of resistance to the protease have been discussed in an earlier review (30).

A characterization of resistant variants isolated from patients undergoing therapy with the protease inhibitor MK-639 (Indinavir) was published in 1995 (16). Some of these variants exhibited cross-resistance to all members of a panel of six structurally diverse protease inhibitors. This study provided the first evidence that inhibition of HIV-1 PR can also lead to the emergence of drug-resistant mutants in vivo and that combination therapy with multiple protease inhibitors may not preclude the loss of antiviral activity resulting from resistance selection. A similar study using clinical isolates was also reported by Winslow et al (129). Five noncontiguous regions of HIV-1 PR, as described originally by Fontenot et al (34), were found to be conserved across all examined isolates. These regions include residues 1–9 (N terminus), 21–32 (the sequence surrounding the catalytic aspartate found in the active site), 47–56 (flap region), 78–88 (substrate-binding region), and 94–99 (C terminus and the dimerization region). The mutational analyses have shown that diversity is allowed at some positions, whereas mutations in these conserved regions often result in abnormal *gag* processing in vitro.

CONCLUSIONS AND PERSPECTIVES

The numerous studies leading to the discovery and development of HIV PR inhibitors that are now approved as anti-AIDS drugs are a unique source of information that could, in the future, be used in other attempts of structure-based drug design. Obviously, structural studies are only one part of this complicated process. Detailed analysis of a large ensemble of crystal structures (such as, for example, the HIV PR database) can provide a surprising perspective to the problem of drug-target interactions and lead to the design of more efficient drugs. The coupling of such data with other in vitro and in vivo studies makes it possible to enhance the process of design. It is not always possible to correlate such data directly with inhibition activities toward a particular system, but in some respects they can be used for a qualitative estimation of their influence.

Some other approaches to designing HIV PR inhibitors were not reviewed here, since they have not resulted in the creation of successful drugs. One such approach is the design of dimerization inhibitors, based on the observation that, at higher pH, HIV PR is present in a monomeric form. Dimerization could be prevented by low-molecular-weight ligands with an affinity to the dimer interface regions. Short peptides from the termini of HIV-1 PR were first documented to be weak inhibitors of the protease and even better inhibitors in in vitro studies (103–105). The follow-up efforts met with only partial success. Some of the new inhibitors had better K_i values, but it is still unclear whether they were indeed bound to the dimer interface region. No X-ray structures, and only indirect proofs of the proposed inhibitory mechanism, were published.

Uhlikova et al (118) published a study showing the design of new, modular inhibitors which combined in one molecule the activities towards both the active site and dimerization domain. These inhibitors, longer than the longest inhibitors which bind only in the active site, showed good inhibition activity and relatively stable pH profiles. Obvious disadvantages of such a design is the length and the peptidic character of the inhibitors, because it is not clear how to prevent their degradation by cellular enzymes.

All of the inhibitors reviewed here are reversible, although some of them bind very tightly. Another promising concept is to design irreversible inhibitors of HIV PR, able to bind covalently to the catalytic aspartates of the enzyme. Epoxide-containing, symmetric, irreversible inhibitors with high potency were a result (82). The principle of the design was to enable the attack by the catalytic water molecule on the epoxide ring and to create a covalent bond between the inhibitor and one of the catalytic aspartates. Because it is necessary to maintain the right orientation of the epoxide so that it could make favorable contacts with the two active-site aspartates, such a design is quite challenging.

It is difficult to provide general principles of inhibitor design at this time. Structural properties of the compounds are not the only consideration; ease of chemical synthesis, low molecular weight, bioavailability, and stability are also of crucial importance. The development of protease inhibitors as antiviral drugs has showed that it was necessary to keep in mind the conditions under which the inhibition takes place, both in vitro and in vivo. The phenomenon of drug resistance will require preparation of new generations of drugs. Although the knowledge of structural principles of inhibition has been very important, it is still not completely clear why some of the compounds have been successful, while others have failed. Obviously, this field will continue its development, resulting in new, more powerful drugs.

ACKNOWLEDGMENTS

We wish to thank all the present and former members of the Macromolecular Structure Laboratory at the National Cancer Institute–Frederick Cancer Research and Development Center who contributed to these studies. We are indebted to Dr. Clare Sansom and Ms. Anne Arthur for their editorial comments. Research was sponsored in part by the National Cancer Institute, DHHS, under contract with ABL. The contents of this publication do not necessarily reflect the views or policies of the Department of Health and Human Services, nor does mention of trade names, commercial products, or organizations imply endorsement by the US Government.

Visit the *Annual Reviews home page* at
http://www.AnnualReviews.org.

Literature Cited

1. Ala PJ, Huston EE, Klabe RM, McCabe DD, Duke JL, et al. 1997. Molecular basis of HIV-1 protease drug resistance: structural analysis of mutant proteases complexed with cyclic urea inhibitors. *Biochemistry* 36:1573–80
2. Appelt K. 1993. Crystal structures of HIV-1 protease-inhibitor complexes. *Perspect. Drug Discovery Des.* 1:23–48
3. Appelt K, Bacquet RJ, Bartlett CA, Booth CL, Freer ST, et al. 1991. Design of enzyme inhibitors using iterative protein crystallographic analysis. *J. Med. Chem.* 34:1925–34
4. Backbro K, Lowgren S, Osterlund K, Atepo J, Unge T, et al. 1997. Unexpected binding mode of a cyclic sulfamide HIV-1 protease inhbitor. *J. Med. Chem.* 40:898–902
5. Bhat TN, Baldwin ET, Liu B, Cheng YS, Erickson JW. 1994. Crystal structure of a tethered dimer of HIV-1 proteinase complexed with an inhibitor. *Nat. Struct. Biol.* 1:552–56
6. Boucher C. 1996. Rational approaches to resistance: using saquinavir. *AIDS 10 Suppl.* 1:S15–19
7. Bujacz G, Alexandratos J, Zhou-Liu Q, Clement-Mella C, Wlodawer A. 1996. The catalytic domain of human inmmunodeficiency virus integrase: ordered active site in the F185H mutant. *FEBS Lett.* 398:175–8
8. Bujacz G, Jaskolski M, Alexandratos J, Wlodawer A, Merkel G, et al. 1995. High resolution structure of the catalytic domain of the avian sarcoma virus integrase. *J. Mol. Biol.* 253:333–46
9. Bujacz G, Jaskolski M, Alexandratos J, Wlodawer A, Merkel G, et al. 1996. The catalytic domain of avian sarcoma virus integrase: conformation of the active-site residues in the presence of divalent cations. *Structure* 4:89–96
10. Caflisch A, Niederer P, Anliker M. 1992. Monte Carlo docking of oligopeptides to proteins: proteins. *Struct. Funct. Genet.* 13:223–30
11. Chen X, Tropsha A. 1995. Relative binding free energies of peptide inhibitors of HIV-1 protease: the influence of the active site protonation state. *J. Med. Chem.* 38:42–48
12. Chenera B, DesJarlais RL, Finkelstein JA,

Eggleston DS, Meek TD, et al. 1993. Non-peptide HIV protease inhibitors designed to replace a bound water. *Bioorg. Medic. Chem. Lett.* 3:2717–22
13. Cheng YS, Yin FH, Foundling S, Blomstrom D, Kettner CA. 1990. Stability and activity of human immunodeficiency virus protease: comparison of the natural dimer with a homologous, single-chain tethered dimer. *Proc. Natl. Acad. Sci. USA* 87:9660–64
14. Collins JR, Burt SK, Erickson JW. 1995. Flap opening in HIV-1 protease simulated by "activated" molecular dynamics. *Nat. Struct. Biol.* 2:334–38
15. Collins JR, Burt SK, Erickson JW. 1995. Activated dynamics of flap opening in HIV-1 protease. *Adv. Exp. Med. Biol.* 362: 455–60
16. Condra JH, Schleif WA, Blahy OM, Gabryelski LJ, Graham DJ, et al. 1995. In vivo emergence of HIV-1 variants resistant to multiple protease inhibitors. *Nature* 374:569–71
17. Daopin S, Piez KA, Ogawa Y, Davies DR. 1992. Crystal structure of transforming growth factor-2: an unusual fold for superfamily. *Science* 257:369–73
18. Darke PL, Nutt R, Brady S, Garsky V, Ciccarone T, et al. 1988. HIV-1 protease specificity of peptide cleavage is sufficient for processing of *Gag* and *Pol* polyproteins. *Biochem. Biophys. Res. Commun.* 156:297–303
19. Davies DR. 1990. The structure and function of the aspartic proteinases. *Annu. Rev. Biophys. Biophys. Chem.* 19:189–215
20. Debouck C, Gorniak JG, Strickler JE, Meek TD, Metcalf BW, Rosenberg M. 1987. Human immunodeficiency virus protease expressed in *Escherichia coli* exhibits autoprocessing and specific maturation of the *gag* precursor. *Proc. Natl. Acad. Sci. USA* 84:8903–6
21. DesJarlais RL, Seibel GL, Kuntz ID, Furth PS, Alvarez JC, et al. 1990. Structure-based design of nonpeptide inhibitors specific for the human immunodeficiency virus-1 protease. *Proc. Natl. Acad. Sci. USA* 87:6644–48
22. deSolms SJ, Giuliani EA, Guare JP, Vacca JP, Sanders WM, et al. 1991. Design and synthesis of HIV protease inhibitors. Variations of the carboxy terminus of the HIV protease inhibitor L-682,679. *J. Med. Chem.* 34:2852–57
23. DeVita VT Jr., Broder S, Fauci AS, Kovacs JA, Chabner BA. 1987. Developmental therapeutics and the acquired immunodeficiency syndrome. *Ann. Intern. Med.* 106:568–81
24. Dorsey BD, Levin RB, McDaniel SL, Vacca JP, Guare JP, et al. 1994. L-735,524: the design of a potent and orally bioavailable HIV protease inhibitor. *J. Med. Chem.* 37:3443–51
25. Dreyer GB, Boehm JC, Chenera B, Des-Jarlais RL, Hassell AM, et al. 1993. A symmetric inhibitor binds HIV-1 protease asymmetrically. *Biochemistry* 32:937–47
26. Dreyer GB, Lambert DM, Meek TD, Carr TJ, Tomaszek TA Jr., et al. 1992. Hydroxyethylene isostere inhibitors of human immunodeficiency virus-1 protease: structure-activity analysis using enzyme kinetics, x-ray crystallography, and infected T-cell assays. *Biochemistry* 31:6646–59
27. Dyda F, Hickman AB, Jenkins TM, Engelman A, Craigie R, Davies DR. 1994. Crystal structure of the catalytic domain of HIV-1 integrase: similarity to other polynucleotidyl transferases. *Science* 266:1981–86
28. Erickson J, Neidhart DJ, VanDrie J, Kempf DJ, Wang XC, et al. 1990. Design, activity, and 2.8 Å crystal structure of a C2 symmetric inhibitor complexed to HIV-1 protease. *Science* 249:527–33
29. Erickson JW. 1993. Design and structure of symmetry-based inhibitors of HIV-1 protease. In *Perspectives in Drug Discovery and Design*, ed. PS Anderson, GL Kenyon, GR Marshall, pp. 109–128. Leiden, The Netherlands: ESCOM Science
30. Erickson JW, Burt SK. 1996. Structural mechanisms of HIV drug resistance. *Annu. Rev. Pharmacol. Toxicol.* 36:545–71
31. Ferguson DM, Radmer RJ, Kollman PA. 1991. Determination of the relative binding free energies of peptide inhibitors to the HIV-1 protease. *J. Med. Chem.* 34:2654–59
32. Fesik SW. 1993. NMR structure-based drug design. *J. Biomol. NMR.* 3:261–9
33. Fitzgerald PMD, McKeever BM, Van-Middlesworth JF, Springer JP, Heimbach JC, et al. 1990. Crystallographic analysis of a complex between human immunodeficiency virus type 1 protease and acetyl-pepstatin at 2.0 Å resolution. *J. Biol. Chem.* 265:14209–19
34. Fontenot G, Johnston K, Cohen JC, Gallaher WR, Robinson J, Luftig RB. 1992. PCR amplification of HIV-1 proteinase sequences directly from lab isolates allows determination of five conserved domains. *Virology* 190:1–10
35. Gehlhaar DK, Moerder KE, Zichi D, Sherman CJ, Ogden RC, Freer ST. 1995.

De novo design of enzyme inhibitors by Monte Carlo ligand generation. *J. Med. Chem.* 38:466–72

36. Gehlhaar DK, Verkhivker GM, Rejto PA, Sherman P, Fogel DB, et al. 1995. Molecular recognition of the inhibitor AG-1343 by HIV-1 protease: conformationally flexible docking by evolutionary programming. *Chem. Biol.* 2:317–24

37. Geller M, Miller M, Swanson SM, Maizel J. 1997. Analysis of the structure of HIV-1 protease complexed with a hexapeptide inhibitor, part II: molecular dynamic studies of the active site region. *Proteins* 27:195–203

38. Graves BJ, Hatada MH, Miller JK, Graves MC, Roy S, et al. 1991. The three-dimensional x-ray crystal structure of HIV-1 protease complexed with a hydroxyethylene inhibitor. *Adv. Exp. Med. Biol.* 306:455–60

39. Greenlee WJ. 1990. Renin inhibitors. *Med. Res. Rev.* 10:173–236

40. Greer J, Erickson JW, Baldwin JJ, Varney MD. 1994. Application of the three-dimensional structures of protein target molecules in structure-based drug design. *J. Med. Chem.* 37:1035–54

41. Gustchina A, Kervinen J, Powell DJ, Zdanov A, Kay J, Wlodawer A. 1996. Structure of equine infectious anemia virus proteinase complexed with an inhibitor. *Protein Sci.* 5:1453–65

42. Gustchina A, Sansom C, Prevost M, Richelle J, Wodak SY, et al. 1994. Energy calculations and analysis of HIV-1 protease-inhibitor crystal structure. *Protein Eng.* 7:309–17

43. Harrison RW, Weber IT. 1994. Molecular dynamics simulations of HIV-1 protease with peptide substrate. *Protein Eng.* 7:1353–63

44. Harte WE Jr., Beveridge DL. 1994. Probing structure-function relationships in human immunodeficiency virus type 1 protease via molecular dynamics simulation. *Methods Enzymol.* 241:178–95

45. Henderson LE, Copeland TD, Sowder RC, Schultz AM, Oroszlan S. 1988. *Human Retrovirus, Cancer and AIDS: Approaches to Prevention and Therapy*, ed. D Bolognesi, pp. 135–147. New York: Liss

46. Hodge CN, Aldrich P, Bacheler LT, Chang C-H, Eyermann CJ, et al. 1996. Improved cyclic urea inhibitors of the HIV-1 protease: synthesis, potency, resistance profile, human pharmacokinetics and X-ray crystal structure of DMP 450. *Chem. Biol.* 3:301–14

47. Holloway MK, Wai JM, Halgren TA, Fitzgerald PM, Vacca JP, et al. 1995. A priori prediction of activity for HIV-1 protease inhibitors employing energy minimization in the active site. *J. Med. Chem.* 38:305–17

48. Jacobo-Molina A, Ding J, Nanni RG, Clark AD, Jr., Lu X, et al. 1993. Crystal structure of human immunodeficiency virus type 1 reverse transcriptase complexed with double-stranded DNA at 3.0 Å resolution shows bent DNA. *Proc. Natl. Acad. Sci. USA.* 90:6320–24

49. Jadhav PK, Ala P, Woerner FJ, Chang CH, Garber SS, et al. 1997. Cyclic urea amides: HIV-1 protease inhibitors with low nanomolar potency against both wild type and protease inhibitor resistant mutants of HIV. *J. Med. Chem.* 40:181–91

50. Jaskolski M, Miller M, Rao JKM, Leis J, Wlodawer A. 1990. Structure of the aspartic protease from Rous sarcoma retrovirus refined at 2-Å resolution. *Biochemistry* 29:5889–98

51. Jaskolski M, Tomasselli AG, Sawyer TK, Staples DG, Heinrikson RL, et al. 1991. Structure at 2.5 Å resolution of chemically synthesized human immunodeficiency virus type 1 protease complexed with a hydroxyethylene-based inhibitor. *Biochemistry* 30:1600–9

52. Jhoti H, Singh OM, Weir MP, Cooke R, Murray-Rust P, Wonacott A. 1994. X-ray crystallographic studies of a series of penicillin-derived asymmetric inhibitors of HIV-1 protease. *Biochemistry* 33:8417–27

53. Kato R, Takahashi O, Kiso Y, Moriguchi I, Hirono S. 1994. Solution structure of HIV-1 protease-allophenylnorstatine derivative inhibitor complex obtained from molecular dynamics simulation. *Chem. Pharm. Bull. (Tokyo)* 42:176–78

54. Katoh I, Yoshinaka Y, Rein A, Shibuya M, Odaka T, Oroszlan S. 1985. Murine leukemia virus maturation: protease region required for conversion from immature to mature form and for virus infectivity. *Virology* 145:280–92

55. Kempf DJ, Codacovi L, Wang XC, Kohlbrenner WE, Wideburg NE, et al. 1993. Symmetry-based inhibitors of HIV protease. Structure-activity studies of acylated 2,4-diamino-1,5-diphenyl-3-hydroxypentane and 2,5-diamino-1,6-diphenylhexane-3,4-diol. *J. Med. Chem.* 36:320–30

56. Kempf DJ, Marsh KC, Denissen JF, McDonald E, Vasavanonda S, et al. 1995. ABT-538 is a potent inhibitor of human immunodeficiency virus protease and has

high oral bioavailability in humans. *Proc. Natl. Acad. Sci. USA* 92:2484–88

57. Kempf DJ, Marsh KC, Paul DA, Knigge MF, Norbeck DW, et al. 1991. Antiviral and pharmacokinetic properties of C2 symmetric inhibitors of the human immunodeficiency virus type 1 protease. *Antimicrob. Agents Chemother.* 35:2209–14

58. King BL, Vajda S, DeLisi C. 1996. Empirical free energy as a target function in docking and design: application to HIV-1 protease inhibitors. *FEBS Lett.* 384:87–91

59. Kohl NE, Emini EA, Schleif WA, Davis LJ, Heimbach JC, et al. 1988. Active human immunodeficiency virus protease is required for viral infectivity. *Proc. Natl. Acad. Sci. USA* 85:4686–90

60. Kohlstaedt LA, Wang J, Friedman JM, Rice PA, Steitz TA. 1992. Crystal structure at 3.5 Å resolution of HIV-1 reverse transcriptase complexed with an inhibitor. *Science* 256:1783–90

61. Kraulis PJ. 1991. MOLSCRIPT: a program to produce both detailed and schematic plots of protein structures. *J. Appl. Crystallogr.* 24:946–50

62. Krohn A, Redshaw S, Ritchie JC, Graves BJ, Hatada MH. 1991. Novel binding mode of highly potent HIV-proteinase inhibitors incorporating the (R)-hydroxyethylamine isostere. *J. Med. Chem.* 34:3340–42

63. Kuntz ID, Blaney JM, Oatley SJ, Langridge R, Ferrin TE. 1982. A geometric approach to macromolecule-ligand interactions. *J. Mol. Biol.* 161:269–88

64. Lam PY, Jadhav PK, Eyermann CJ, Hodge CN, Ru Y, et al. 1994. Rational design of potent, bioavailable, nonpeptide cyclic ureas as HIV protease inhibitors. *Science* 263:380–84

65. Lam PY, Ru Y, Jadhav PK, Aldrich PE, DeLucca GV, et al. 1996. Cyclic HIV protease inhibitors: synthesis, conformational analysis, P2/P2' structure-activity relationship, and molecular recognition of cyclic ureas. *J. Med. Chem.* 39:3514–25

66. Lapatto R, Blundell T, Hemmings A, Overington J, Wilderspin AF, et al. 1989. X-ray analysis of HIV-1 proteinase at 2.7Å resolution confirms structural homology among retroviral enzymes. *Nature* 342:299–302

67. Liu H, Muller-Plathe F, van Gunsteren WF. 1996. A combined quantum/classical molecular dynamics study of the catalytic mechanism of HIV protease. *J. Mol. Biol.* 261:454–69

68. Loeb DD, Hutchison CA, 3d, Edgell MH, Farmerie WG, Swanstrom R. 1989. Mu-

tational analysis of human immunodeficiency virus type 1 protease suggests functional homology with aspartic proteinases. *J. Virol.* 63:111–21

69. Longer M, Shetty B, Zamansky I, Tyle P. 1995. Preformulation studies of a novel HIV protease inhibitor, AG1343. *J. Pharm. Sci.* 84:1090–93

70. Lyle TA, Wiscount CM, Guare JP, Thompson WJ, Anderson PS, et al. 1991. Benzocycloalkyl amines as novel C-termini for HIV protease inhibitors. *J. Med. Chem.* 34:1228–30

71. McCarrick MA, Kollman P. 1994. Use of molecular dynamics and free energy perturbation calculations in anti-human immunodeficiency virus drug design. *Methods Enzymol.* 241:370–84

72. McQuade TJ, Tomasselli AG, Liu L, Karacostas B, Moss B, et al. 1990. A synthetic HIV protease inhibitor with antiviral activity arrests HIV-like particle maturation. *Science* 247:454–6

73. Melnick M, Reich SH, Lewis KK, Mitchell LJ Jr, Nguyen D, et al. 1996. Bis tertiary amide inhibitors of the HIV-1 protease generated via protein structure-based iterative design. *J. Med. Chem.* 39:2795–811

74. Miller M, Geller M, Gribskov M, Kent SB. 1997. Analysis of the structure of chemically synthesized HIV-1 protease complexed with a hexapeptide inhibitor, part I: crystallographic refinement of 2 Å data. *Proteins* 27:184–94

75. Miller M, Jaskolski M, Rao JKM, Leis J, Wlodawer A. 1989. Crystal structure of a retroviral protease proves relationship to aspartic protease family. *Nature* 337:576–79

76. Miller M, Schneider J, Sathyanarayana BK, Toth MV, Marshall GR, et al. 1989. Structure of complex of synthetic HIV-1 protease with a substrate-based inhibitor at 2.3 Å resolution. *Science* 246:1149–52

77. Mulichak AM, Hui JO, Tomasselli AG, Heinrikson RL, Curry KA, et al. 1993. The crystallographic structure of the protease from human immunodeficiency virus type 2 with two synthetic peptidic transition state analog inhibitors. *J. Biol. Chem.* 268:13103–9

78. Murthy KH, Winborne EL, Minnich MD, Culp JS, Debouck C. 1992. The crystal structures at 2.2 Å resolution of hydroxyethylene-based inhibitors bound to human immunodeficiency virus type 1 protease show that the inhibitors are present in two distinct orientations. *J. Biol. Chem.* 267:22770–78

79. Navia MA, Fitzgerald PM, McKeever BM, Leu CT, Heimbach JC, et al. 1989. Three-dimensional structure of aspartyl protease from human immunodeficiency virus HIV-1. *Nature* 337:615–20
80. Nicholson LK, Yamazaki T, Torchia DA, Grzesiek S, Bax A, et al. 1995. Flexibility and function in HIV-1 protease. *Nat. Struct. Biol.* 2:274–80
81. Ohno Y, Kiso Y, Kobayashi Y. 1996. Solution conformations of KNI-272, a tripeptide HIV protease inhibitor designed on the basis of substrate transition state: determined by NMR spectroscopy and simulated annealing calculations. *Bioorg. Med. Chem.* 4:1565–72
82. Park C, Koh JS, Choy N, Son Y, Lee CS, et al. 1996. In *Peptides: Chemistry, Structure and Biology*, ed. TP Kaumaya, RS Hodges, pp. 581–82. Kingswinford, UK: Mayflower Scientific
83. Pearl LH, Taylor WR. 1987. A structural model for the retroviral proteases. *Nature* 329:351–54
84. Pechik IV, Gustchina AE, Andreeva NS, Fedorov AA. 1989. Possible role of some groups in the structure and function of HIV-1 protease as revealed by molecular modeling studies. *FEBS Lett.* 247:118–22
85. Podlogar BL, Farr RA, Friedrich D, Tarnus C, Huber EW, et al. 1994. Design, synthesis, and conformational analysis of a novel macrocyclic HIV-protease inhibitor. *J. Med. Chem.* 37:3684–92
86. Rao BG, Murcko MA. 1996. Free energy perturbation studies on binding of A-74704 and its diester analog to HIV-1 protease. *Protein Eng.* 9:767–71
87. Rao JKM, Erickson JW, Wlodawer A. 1991. Structural and evolutionary relationships between retroviral and eucaryotic aspartic proteinases. *Biochemistry* 30:4663–71
88. Ratner L, Haseltine W, Patarca R, Livak KJ, Starcich B, et al. 1985. Complete nucleotide sequence of the AIDS virus, HTLV-III. *Nature* 313:277–84
89. Reich SH, Melnick M, Davies JF, 2nd, Appelt K, Lewis KK, et al. 1995. Protein structure-based design of potent orally bioavailable, nonpeptide inhibitors of human immunodeficiency virus protease. *Proc. Natl. Acad. Sci. USA* 92:3298–302
90. Reich SH, Melnick M, Pino MJ, Fuhry MA, Trippe AJ, et al. 1996. Structure-based design and synthesis of substituted 2-butanols as nonpeptidic inhibitors of HIV protease: secondary amide series. *J. Med. Chem.* 39:2781–94
91. Rich DH, Sun CQ, Vara Prasad JV, Pathiasseril A, Toth MV, et al. 1991. Effect of hydroxyl group configuration in hydroxyethylamine dipeptide isosteres on HIV protease inhibition: evidence for multiple binding modes. *J. Med. Chem.* 34:1222–25
92. Richards AD, Roberts R, Dunn BM, Graves MC, Kay J. 1989. Effective blocking of HIV-1 proteinase activity by characteristic inhibitors of aspartic proteinases. *FEBS Lett.* 247:113–17
93. Roberts JD, Bebenek K, Kunkel TA. 1988. The accuracy of reverse transcriptase from HIV-1. *Science* 242:1171–73
94. Roberts NA, Martin JA, Kinchington D, Broadhurst AV, Craig JC, et al. 1990. Rational design of peptide-based HIV proteinase inhibitors. *Science* 248:358–61
95. Rose RB, Rose JR, Salto R, Craik CS, Stroud RM. 1993. Structure of the protease from simian immunodeficiency virus: complex with an irreversible nonpeptide inhibitor. *Biochemistry* 32:12498–507
96. Rotstein SH, Murcko MA. 1993. GroupBuild: a fragment-based method for de novo drug design. *J. Med. Chem.* 36:1700–10
97. Rutenber E, Fauman EB, Keenan RJ, Fong S, Furth PS, et al. 1993. Structure of a non-peptide inhibitor complexed with HIV-1 protease: developing a cycle of structure-based drug design. *J. Biol. Chem.* 268:15343–46
98. Sansom CE, Wu J, Weber IT. 1992. Molecular mechanics analysis of inhibitor binding to HIV-1 protease. *Protein Eng.* 5:659–67
99. Schechter I, Berger A. 1967. On the size of the active site in proteases, I: papain. *Biochem. Biophys. Res. Commun.* 27:157–62
100. Schinazi RF, Larder BA, Mellors JW. 1997. Mutations in retroviral genes associated with drug resistance. *Antivir. News* 5(8):129–42
101. Schneider J, Kent SB. 1988. Enzymatic activity of a synthetic 99 residue protein corresponding to the putative HIV-1 protease. *Cell* 54:363–68
102. Schock HB, Garsky VM, Kuo LC. 1996. Mutational anatomy of an HIV-1 protease variant conferring cross-resistance to protease inhibitors in clinical trials: compensatory modulations of binding and activity. *J. Biol. Chem.* 271:31957–63
103. Schramm HJ, Billich A, Jaeger E, Rucknagel KP, Arnold G, Schramm W. 1993. The inhibition of HIV-1 protease by interface peptides. *Biochem. Biophys. Res. Commun.* 194:595–600

104. Schramm HJ, Breipohl G, Hansen J, Henke S, Jaeger E, et al. 1992. Inhibition of HIV-1 protease by short peptides derived from the terminal segments of the protease. *Biochem. Biophys. Res. Commun.* 184:980–85
105. Schramm HJ, Nakashima H, Schramm W, Wakayama H, Yamamoto N. 1991. HIV-1 reproduction is inhibited by peptides derived from the N-and C-termini of HIV-1 protease. *Biochem. Biophys. Res. Commun.* 179:847–51
106. Seelmeier S, Schmidt H, Turk V, von der Helm K. 1988. Human immunodeficiency virus has an aspartic-type protease that can be inhibited by pepstatin A. *Proc. Natl. Acad. Sci. USA* 85:6612–16
107. Sham HL, Betebenner DA, Wideburg N, Saldivar AC, Kohlbrenner WE, et al. 1993. Pseudo-symmetrical difluoroketones. Highly potent and specific inhibitors of HIV-1 protease. *FEBS Lett.* 329:144–46
108. Silva AM, Cachau RE, Sham HL, Erickson JW. 1996. Inhibition and catalytic mechanism of HIV-1 aspartic protease. *J. Mol. Biol.* 255:321–46
109. Smith R, Brereton IM, Chai RY, Kent SB. 1996. Ionization states of the catalytic residues in HIV-1 protease. *Nat. Struct. Biol.* 3:946–50
110. Spinelli S, Liu QZ, Alzari PM, Hirel PH, Poljak RJ. 1991. The three-dimensional structure of the aspartyl protease from the HIV-1 isolate BRU. *Biochimie* 73:1391–96
111. Surles MC, Richardson JS, Richardson DC, Brooks FP Jr. 1994. Sculpting proteins interactively: continual energy minimization embedded in a graphical modeling system. *Protein Sci.* 3:198–210
112. Swain AL, Miller MM, Green J, Rich DH, Schneider J, et al. 1990. X-ray crystallographic structure of a complex between a synthetic protease of human immunodeficiency virus 1 and a substrate-based hydroxyethylamine inhibitor. *Proc. Natl. Acad. Sci. USA* 87:8805–9
113. Toh H, Ono M, Saigo K, Miyata T. 1985. Retroviral protease-like sequence in the yeast transposon Ty1. *Nature* 315:691
114. Tomasselli AG, Howe WJ, Sawyer TK, Wlodawer A, Heinrikson RL. 1991. The complexities of AIDS: an assessment of the HIV protease as a therapeutic target. *Chim. Oggi* 9:6–27
115. Tong L, Pav S, Mui S, Lamarre D, Yoakim C, et al. 1995. Crystal structures of HIV-2 protease in complex with inhibitors containing the hydroxyethylamine dipeptide isostere. *Structure.* 3:33–40
116. Tong L, Pav S, Pargellis C, Do F, Lamarre D, Anderson PC. 1993. Crystal structure of human immunodeficiency virus (HIV) type 2 protease in complex with a reduced amide inhibitor and comparison with HIV-1 protease structures. *Proc. Natl. Acad. Sci. USA* 90:8387–91
117. Tropsha A, Hermans J. 1992. Application of free energy simulations to the binding of a transition-state-analogue inhibitor to HIV protease. *Protein Eng.* 5:29–33
118. Uhlikova T, Konvalinka J, Pichova I, Soucek M, Krausslich HG, Vondrasek J. 1996. A modular approach to HIV-1 proteinase inhibitor design. *Biochem. Biophys. Res. Commun.* 222:38–43
119. Vacca JP, Dorsey BD, Schleif WA, Levin RB, McDaniel SL, et al. 1994. L-735,524: an orally bioavailable human immunodeficiency virus type 1 protease inhibitor. *Proc. Natl. Acad. Sci. USA* 91:4096–100
120. Vacca JP, Fitzgerald PM, Holloway MK, Hungate RW, Starbuck KE, et al. 1994. Conformationally constrained HIV-1 protease inhibitors. *Bioorg. Medic. Chem. Lett.* 4:499–504
121. Varney MD, Appelt K, Kalish V, Reddy MR, Tatlock J, et al. 1994. Crystal-structure-based design and synthesis of novel C-terminal inhibitors of HIV protease. *J. Med. Chem.* 37:2274–84
122. Vondrasek J, van Buskirk CP, Wlodawer A. 1997. Database of three-dimensional structures of HIV proteinases. *Nat. Struct. Biol.* 4:8
123. Wallqvist A, Jernigan RL, Covell DG. 1995. A preference-based free-energy parameterization of enzyme-inhibitor binding. Applications to HIV-1-protease inhibitor design. *Protein Sci.* 4:1881–903
124. Wang Y, Freedberg DI, Grzesiek S, Torchia DA, Wingfield PT, et al. 1996. Mapping hydration water molecules in the HIV-1 protease/DMP323 complex solution by NMR spectroscopy. *Biochemistry* 35:12694–704
125. Wang YX, Freedberg DI, Yamazaki T, Wingfield PT, Stahl SJ, et al. 1996. Solution NMR evidence that the HIV-1 protease catalytic aspartyl groups have different ionization states in the complex formed with the asymmetric drug KNI-272. *Biochemistry* 35:9945–50
126. Weber IT, Harrison RW. 1996. Molecular mechanics calculations on HIV-1 protease with peptide substrates correlate with experimental data. *Protein Eng.* 9:679–90
127. Weber IT, Miller M, Jaskolski M, Leis J, Skalka AM, Wlodawer A. 1989. Molecular modeling of the HIV-1 protease and its

substrate binding site. *Science* 243:928–31

128. Wilderspin AF, Sugrue RJ. 1994. Alternative native flap conformation revealed by 2.3 Å resolution structure of SIV proteinase. *J. Mol. Biol.* 239:97–103

129. Winslow DL, Stack S, King R, Scarnati H, Bincsik A, Otto MJ. 1995. Limited sequence diversity of the HIV type 1 protease gene from clinical isolates and in vitro susceptibility to HIV protease inhibitors. *AIDS Res. Hum. Retrovir.* 11:107–13

130. Wlodawer A, Erickson JW. 1993. Structure-based inhibitors of HIV-1 protease. *Annu. Rev. Biochem.* 62:543–85

131. Wlodawer A, Gustchina A, Reshetnikova L, Lubkowski J, Zdanov A, et al. 1995. Structure of an inhibitor complex of the proteinase from feline immunodeficiency virus. *Nat. Struct. Biol.* 2:480–88

132. Wlodawer A, Miller M, Jaskolski M, Sathyanarayana BK, Baldwin E, et al. 1989. Conserved folding in retroviral proteases: crystal structure of a synthetic HIV-1 protease. *Science* 245:616–21

133. Wlodawer A, Nachman J, Gilliland GL, Gallagher W, Woodward C. 1987. Structure of form III crystals of bovine pancre- atic trypsin inhibitor. *J. Mol. Biol.* 198: 469–80

134. Wonacott A, Cooke R, Hayes FR, Hann MM, Jhoti H, et al. 1993. A series of penicillin-derived C2-symmetric inhibitors of HIV-1 proteinase: structural and modeling studies. *J. Med. Chem.* 36: 3113–19

135. Yamazaki T, Hinck AP, Wang Y, Nicholson LK, Torchia DA, et al. 1996. Three-dimensional solution structure of the HIV-1 protease complexed with DMP323, a novel cyclic urea-type inhibitor, determined by nuclear magnetic resonance spectroscopy. *Protein Sci.* 5:495–506

136. Yamazaki T, Nicholson LK, Torchia DA, Stahl SJ, Kaufman JD, et al. 1994. Secondary structure and signal assignments of human-immunodeficiency-virus-1 protease complexed to a novel, structure-based inhibitor. *Eur. J. Biochem.* 219: 707–12

137. Zhao B, Winborne E, Minnich MD, Culp JS, Debouck C, Abdel-Meguid SS. 1993. Three-dimensional structure of a simian immunodeficiency virus protease/inhibitor complex. Implications for the design of human immunodeficiency virus type 1 and 2 protease inhibitors. *Biochemistry* 32:13054–60

Annu. Rev. Biophys. Biomol. Struct. 1998. 27:285–327

STRUCTURE, DYNAMICS, AND FUNCTION OF CHROMATIN IN VITRO

J. Widom

Department of Biochemistry, Molecular Biology, and Cell Biology, and Department of Chemistry, Northwestern University, Evanston, IL 60208; e-mail: j-widom@nwu.edu

KEY WORDS: DNA, histone, nucleosome, gene regulation, transcription, replication, recombination, repair

ABSTRACT

The substrates for the essential biological processes of transcription, replication, recombination, DNA repair, and cell division are not naked DNA; rather, they are protein-DNA complexes known as chromatin, in one or another stage of a hierarchical series of compactions. These are exciting times for students of chromatin. New studies provide incontrovertible evidence linking chromatin structure to function. Exceptional progress has been made in studies of the structure of chromatin subunits. Surprising new dynamic properties have been discovered. And, much progress has been made in dissecting the functional roles of specific chromatin proteins and domains. This review focuses on in vitro studies of chromatin structure, dynamics, and function.

CONTENTS

285

1056-8700/98/0610-0285$08.00

INTRODUCTION, PERSPECTIVES, AND OVERVIEW

The substrates for the essential biological processes of transcription, replication, recombination, DNA repair, and cell division are not naked DNA; rather, they are protein-DNA complexes known as chromatin, in one or another stage of a hierarchical series of compactions. Cells regulate the folding state of their chromatin both temporally and spatially: There are progressive changes in bulk chromatin folding throughout the cell cycle, and, at any moment in time, the chromatin structure is altered at specific positions along each chromosomal DNA molecule. For these reasons, it is important to determine the structures of each level of chromosome folding, to determine the mechanisms by which cells regulate the folded state of their chromatin, and to elucidate the relationships between chromosome structure and chromosome function.

This is a period of tremendous and increasing excitement for students of chromatin structure and function, for two main reasons: First, new studies provide incontrovertible evidence linking chromatin structure to essential aspects of function. Most notably, they establish a clear relationship between chromosome structure and gene regulation. Connections are established to both gene activation and silencing; numerous mutants and suppressor mutations point to a host of regulatory and effector molecules providing bridges between chromosome structure and function; and suddenly, several of these molecules have been identified, isolated, and their genes cloned. Second, there has been great progress in studies of chromosome structure and dynamics. High resolution structures of key chromatin components and subassemblies have been determined. Much progress has been made toward understanding higher levels of chromosome structure, although here the studies are at low resolution and many conclusions are tentative and controversial. Surprising new dynamical properties have been discovered. And, much progress has been made dissecting the functional roles of specific chromatin proteins and domains. Collectively, these data take us well on our way toward an understanding of the molecular basis of chromosome function.

At the same time, this progress raises a wealth of important new questions and highlights some significant puzzles. Many treasures await discovery. The coming years promise to be exceptionally interesting.

This review will focus on in vitro studies of chromatin structure, dynamics, and function, and especially on results obtained since the author's previous review in 1989 (112). Much of what had been learned at that time continues to be important in current thinking, so the interested reader should consult that review for more detailed discussion of certain points. For general background information in this field, three books are particularly helpful (102, 107, 122). Other helpful recent reviews of aspects of chromatin structure and function include (24, 49, 50, 81, 82, 105).

STRUCTURE OF THE NUCLEOSOME AND NUCLEOSOME CORE PARTICLE

DNA in chromatin is closely associated with a number of highly conserved proteins known as histones that fold the DNA in a hierarchical series of stages, ultimately yielding a ≈10,000-fold linear compaction preparatory to cell division. The initial or lowest level of chromatin organization consists of the local wrapping of a short stretch of DNA, 147 bp in length, in ≈1 3/4 turns of a flat superhelix around an octameric histone protein core, which is composed of two molecules each of histones H2A, H2B, H3, and H4. This complex of the histone octamer and 147 bp of DNA is known as the nucleosome core particle. This local packing motif is repeated at intervals, millions of times along the entire DNA length, with short variable-length stretches of "linker" DNA between consecutive core particles.

In most cases in vivo, each nucleosome core particle is associated with one additional molecule of a "linker histone," H1 or H5 (a particular gene variant of H1; hereafter referred to simply as H1). Particles containing the complete core particle plus histone H1 and the linker DNA at each end are called nucleosomes. Nucleosomes are traditionally considered to be the fundamental units of chromatin structure.

Octamer and Core Particle Structure

There have been important new advances in our understanding of the structure of the nucleosome core particle. The structure of the histone octamer in the absence of DNA was solved by X-ray crystallography at 3.1 Å resolution (4); and, more recently, the crystal structure of the complete nucleosome core particle was solved at 2.8 Å resolution [(61); for review, see (116)]. The new structure provides a detailed view of the protein and DNA organization; it provides tantalizing glimpses of the histone tail domains; it suggests a model for the structure of the 30 nm fiber; and it has many surprises. This very important contribution will serve as a focus for much future work.

The structures reveal a tripartite assembly of the octamer, reflecting its two H2A–H2B heterodimer and one $H3_2$–$H4_2$ tetramer subunits (82, 102, 112). Interestingly, the tetramer can be seen as a stable complex of two H3–H4 heterodimers, which have a "handshake" interlocking protein fold very similar in structure to that of the H2A–H2B heterodimers. This protein architectural motif is now referred to as the "histone fold." Each histone dimer has a pseudo-twofold (dyad) symmetry, and the octamer has an overall pseudo-dyad symmetry. There is an evident positively charged superhelical ramp, important for the DNA organization. The histone fold domains organize the central 121 bp of DNA, with the additional 13 bp at each end organized by an N-terminal alpha-helical extension to the histone fold of H3 and preceding residues from the tail domain. Each histone dimer organizes $\approx$27–28 bp, with 4 bp stretches between them.

DNA binding is primarily to the sugar phosphate backbone over the short stretches where the minor groove (and hence the DNA backbone) faces in towards the octamer surface. Each histone dimer contributes three main DNA binding motifs, in two types, referred to as L1L2 and "1"1, with overall pseudo-twofold symmetry for the three sites. Contacts between the histones and DNA include extensive salt bridges and hydrogen bonds to the phosphate groups contributed by both main-chain and side-chain groups; extensive nonpolar contacts with the DNA sugar; electrostatic interactions of the positively charged N-termini of alpha helices with DNA phosphates; and a smaller number of base-specific contacts, including nonpolar contact of the 5-methyl group of thymidine in the major groove.

The overall DNA trajectory approximates 1.65 turns of a superhelix, but the diameter and bending are not uniform. In general, short stretches of DNA centered on each L1L2 or "1"1 binding site appear only slightly bent, while the DNA is bent relatively sharply over a few bp between these sites (which are spaced $\approx$10 bp center-to-center) so as to create the overall superhelical path. The helical twist of the DNA averages 10.2 bp turn^{-1}, but varies in detail along the DNA.

Two additional modes of histone-DNA interaction are particularly striking. First, an arginine sidechain is inserted into the minor groove every time it faces inward to the histone surface. In most cases the arginine is held by additional bonds to protein functional groups so as to prevent it from penetrating deeply into the groove and making base-specific hydrogen bonding contacts.

The second striking additional mode of histone-DNA interaction arises from the histone tails. Each of the core histones has a $\approx$10–40 aa–long highly positively charged N-terminal region; and histones H2A and H3 have shorter but analogous domains at their C-termini, as well. These domains are referred to as "tails" because they are known to be highly extended and mobile. They are relatively highly conserved throughout evolution, and are of great interest because they are the sites of numerous posttranslational modifications known to be essential in chromatin function. They are seen only for a fraction of their length in the crystal structure. Several of the tails act together to bracket turns of DNA, passing over and between the DNA gyres. Other aspects of the structure and function of the tail domains are discussed in more detail in the section on 30 nm fiber structure, below.

Histone H1

H1 STRUCTURE   Progress on the structure and function of histone H1 has led to large new puzzles and surprises. H1 proteins have a conserved central ~80 aa globular domain, and two long, highly positively charged tails. The structure of the globular domain of histone H5 (GH5) has now been determined to high resolution by X-ray crystallography (83); and that of histone H1 (GH1) has been determined by NMR (14). Interestingly, the structures resemble those of several other prokaryotic and eukaryotic transcription factors. The long C-terminal extensions of the proteins have a propensity towards alpha helix formation (16).

LOCATION AND ROLE OF H1 IN THE NUCLEOSOME   Earlier studies (112) established that H1 was located on the surface of the nucleosome and suggested that the globular domain was located on the nucleosomal dyad axis over the region where DNA enters and exits the core particle. Both H1 and GH1 (and H5, GH5) bind cooperatively to two molecules of double stranded DNA at once (21, 97), suggesting that the globular domain must have at least two DNA-binding surfaces, and that these might both be required for function in chromatin.

Analysis of the structure of GH5 identified a potential second DNA binding surface in addition to the one identified by homology to the other structurally similar known DNA binding domains. Mutation of this second site shows it to be required for formation of the cooperative complexes with pairs of DNA molecules and for proper binding to H1-depleted nucleosomes (33). New electron and atomic force microscopy studies confirm and extend earlier findings that H1 influences the entry/exit angle of linker DNA, i.e. the trajectory taken by DNA as it enters and exits the nucleosome (7, 36, 54). When H1 is present, the points at which DNA enters and exits the nucleosome are close, whereas when H1 is removed the points of DNA entry and exit are further apart, appearing to be on approximately opposite sides of the nucleosome from each other. All of these data are consistent with the earlier model in which GH1 is located over the nucleosomal dyad, binding simultaneously to the pair of DNA segments entering and leaving the nucleosome.

It came as a great surprise, therefore, when a pair of papers appeared that used chemical crosslinking methods to map the location of GH5 in the nucleosome, and yielded a very different location (40, 80). These results suggest instead that GH5 packs underneath the DNA where the DNA leaves the core particle, i.e. that it effectively continues the superhelical ramp on one side of the histone octamer. At present, this matter is still open (82).

Adding further to the puzzles surrounding histone H1, a series of new discoveries leaves us knowing even less about its function than before. Many lines of evidence had suggested that H1 played an essential role in the 30 nm fiber, through its effects on the organization of nucleosomal linker DNA. Several new studies reopen this question. The genomic DNA sequence of the yeast *Saccharomyces cerevisiae* has been determined and reveals one and only one protein having significant homology to the conserved globular domain of higher cell H1s; this protein has now been eliminated by gene knockout, and cells remain viable (101), although there are detectable alterations in gene regulation. This is likely not to be a peculiarity unique to yeast. Physical studies of isolated chromatin in vitro show that at least some yeast chromatin is capable of higher order folding (58), as is H1-depleted chromatin from other sources (see section on 30 nm fiber structure, below). Consistent with the view that H1 may in general not be essential, no candidates for an H1-like protein have been identified in the embryogenic stages of *Drosophila* development, and the one identified candidate for an H1-like protein present during *Xenopus* early development can be eliminated, with little evident consequence for nuclear assembly or, indeed, for the development of the organism (10, 18, 72).

Fundamental Repeating Unit

These data force one to reevaluate the view that an H1-containing nucleosome is the fundamental or minimal repeating unit of chromosome structure. At least for *S. cerevisiae*, and quite likely for *Drosophila* and *Xenopus* during early development, this is simply not the case. The fundamental unit of chromosome organization is a nucleosome without H1.

Another surprise concerns the amount of DNA associated with each nucleosome. A long-held view, supported by analyses of the time-course of micrococcal nuclease digestion of chromatin, had been that H1 bound to and stabilized an additional 10 bp at each end of the core particle DNA, so that a minimal nucleosome contained at least 167 bp. Indeed, such particles (called chromatosomes) can be isolated by controlled micrococcal nuclease digestion of chromatin obtained from suitable cell types (112). However, recent measurements of the nucleosome repeat length, which yield the length of DNA per nucleosome averaged over an entire genome or over distinct genomic regions (using hybridization methods), reveal numerous instances of a substantially shorter repeat length, ≈156–157 bp (8, 31, 114). At this point, the fundamental repeating unit of chromosome structure appears to be a nucleosome containing only the core histone octamer and ≈156–157 bp of DNA.

It is appropriate to define as linker DNA the total length of DNA associated with a nucleosome minus the 147 bp of the core particle. An analysis of measurements of nucleosome repeat lengths reveals that bulk average linker DNA lengths are not uniformly distributed; rather, they occur at a preferentially quantized set of lengths, differing by integral multiples of the DNA helical repeat, ≈10 bp (114). The preference for having a length equal to one of the quantized set is pronounced but not absolute.

Nucleosome Positioning

This area is the subject of much misunderstanding. The facts in outline are these: In vivo mapping methods reveal that in some cases nucleosomes are preferentially localized at specific genomic positions, often correlated with the underlying regulatory organization of genes (49). The preferred positions can be influenced by the presence of other proteins (92), but often are the same as those found when histones are reconstituted on the same naked DNA in vitro. And, when nucleosomes are reconstituted in vitro with a unique but arbitrary DNA sequence of length L that is longer than the 147 bp of the core particle (so that the octamer could in principle be located starting at any of the L-146 positions while still being fully occupied by DNA), it is often found that the octamer exhibits a pronounced preference for location at one or a few specific positions (i.e. for initiating nucleosomal wrapping at one or a few specific basepairs within the sequence).

We distinguish translational and rotational positioning. Translational positioning refers to the extent to which a histone octamer selects a particular contiguous stretch of 147 bp of DNA in preference to other stretches of the same length that are translated forwards or backwards along the DNA. Rotational positioning is a degenerate form of translational positioning in which a set of discrete translational positions, differing by integral multiples of the DNA helical repeat, are all occupied in preference to the set of other possible locations. DNA sequences that are intrinsically bent or are anisotropically bendable may lead to rotationally positioned nucleosomes (87, 93). As discussed below, other interactions too may contribute to translational or rotational positioning.

DNA SEQUENCE-DIRECTED POSITIONING   The following discussion focuses on DNA sequence-directed nucleosome positioning, for which the determinants of positioning are contributed solely by the DNA sequence and the histone octamer.

Nucleosomes [lacking histone H1 (75)] are mobile in physiological conditions [(65, 98, 103); see section on nucleosome mobility, below]. Standard
protocols for nucleosome reconstitution end in approximately physiological
conditions or sweep slowly through such conditions prior to freezing-in the
resulting particles at low ionic strength (59). It follows in either case that the
resulting distribution of nucleosome positions is an equilibrium one.

This fact has several important consequences. It implies that nucleosome
positioning is not "precise" as often stated, but rather is a statistical property,
governed by the laws of chemical equilibrium. Thus, observations of apparent precise positioning actually reflect preferential occupancy of one position
together with a general insensitivity of mapping methods to lower levels of
occupancy at the set of all other positions. More careful recent studies of positioning in vitro (84) reveal occupancy of numerous translational positions that
are not related by the DNA helical twist, although even these studies cannot
quantify the nonzero occupancies that must exist at all possible positions.

Because nucleosome positioning is an equilibrium property, there exists a
particular mathematical relationship between the free energy of histone–DNA
interactions measured in competitive nucleosome reconstitution experiments,
and the time- or ensemble-averaged probability of occupancy of the preferred
site (59). Because free energies are finite, positioning in vivo will be statistical
too, not precise, even though additional forces may contribute to establishing
the positional biases. It is important to recognize this statistical property of
positioning because it has substantial ramifications for mechanisms of gene
regulation. When positioning is not precise, essential DNA sequences will
sometimes be buried when they need to be accessible, or may be accessible when
they need to be repressed (buried). Mechanisms proposed for gene regulation
must be robust with respect to statistical fluctuations in nucleosome positioning,
which are inevitable when free energies are finite.

Previous studies have identified particular protein and DNA determinants of
positioning. Histone octamers lacking the trypsin sensitive tails, and the $H3_2H4_2$
tetramer on its own, adopt the same preferential position (41) as intact octamer.
While these data suggest that the histone fold domains of the tetramer may be
the dominant determinants of positioning on this sequence, there is no reason
why this needs to be true in general. Indeed, two of the four sites of greatest
DNA helical deformation in the nucleosome core structure are consequences
of interactions with the H2A/H2B heterodimer. However, it could turn out in
practice that, simply because so much of the DNA is organized and contacted
by the tetramer, the tetramer usually dominates the positioning.

DNA determinants of nucleosome positioning have been discovered through
analyses of DNA sequences present in isolated natural nucleosomes and of DNA
sequences found by happenstance to be organized in preferentially positioned

nucleosomes [see (115) and references therein]. Many dinucleotide and longer sequence motifs have been discovered that recur with a ≈10.2 bp periodicity. This periodicity matches the average DNA helical repeat seen in the core particle structure (61), implying that genomic DNA has evolved to contribute to its own nucleosomal packaging (110). While such signals are readily detectable in genomic DNA (115), competition experiments show that >95% of bulk genomic DNA contribute 0 ± 0.2 kcal mol^{-1} to the free energy of histone-DNA interactions in nucleosomes, relative to chemically synthetic random DNA (59). However, particular genomic sequences that have substantially greater affinities (i.e. substantially greater nucleosome positioning power) do exist and can be isolated using SELEX methods (109). It will be of great interest to correlate the locations of these high affinity sequences with the underlying genetic organization of the chromosome.

The relative phases of periodic signals from A/T- and G/C-rich motifs together with early notions about the structural and mechanical properties of various base-steps suggested that these motifs make the DNA statically or dynamically bent (anisotropically flexible), thereby reducing the free energy cost of bending and thus increasing the affinity. Artificial sequences according to these principles yield higher affinities in nucleosome reconstitution (93), and the resulting nucleosomes exhibit rotational positioning, as might be expected (20, 76, 93). However, recent compendia of the structural preferences of differing base-steps (23) simply do not uphold the assumptions on which these predictions are based.

It is useful to consider the problem more generally. Positioning achieves equilibrium, so the sites of preferential positioning will be those having minimum free energy. The net free energy for any particular position will reflect favorable contributions from the set of all the bonds that are formed (including van der Waals interactions, hydrophobic forces, etc. in addition to conventional bonds, and including all intermolecular, intramolecular, and solvent bonds) minus the free-energy cost of deforming the protein, the DNA, and the solvent away from their starting (uncomplexed) conformations into their core particle conformations. While the structures of the L1L2-DNA and "1"1-DNA interactions are relatively well conserved throughout the core particle (61), they differ in detail, probably from the necessity of accommodating differing local DNA sequences. We already know that the DNA changes structure upon nucleosome formation, and it is most likely that the histone octamer and the solvent do too. Thus the detailed equilibrium structures of the nucleosome as well as the net affinity will vary in detail with the DNA sequence.

The structure of the core particle shows myriad opportunities for particular DNA sequences to influence the number and strength of bonds that are made in the complex, as well as the energetic cost of changing the bondedness of the separated partners. The structure also shows myriad locations where specific DNA bends or twists may be optimal. Thus, the DNA sequence can also contribute significantly to the energetics in at least four additional ways through the mechanical work involved in changing the position-dependent DNA bending and twist, which reflect contributions from (a) static bending, (b) the bendability (bending force constant), (c) static twist, and (d) the twistability (twisting force constant). Each of these quantities varies with the local DNA sequence (23), but at present the rules remain poorly understood.

A typical arbitrary DNA sequence will by chance combine some optimal local sequences and many suboptimal ones, which will most probably yield a near-average overall free energy in nucleosome reconstitution. The ability of protein side-chains and solvent to adapt to suboptimal sequences by adopting alternative conformations may act to constrain the standard deviation of the distribution of interaction free energies. Nevertheless, one can anticipate the existence of many DNA sequences in the tails of this distribution—i.e. having free energies that are much more favorable (or unfavorable) than average, simply because of the vast number of different sequences, $1/2 \times 4^{147} \approx 1.6 \times 10^{88}$, that exist for sequences of length 147 bp.

Based on these ideas, a SELEX experiment carried out on a large pool of chemically synthetic random DNA sequences has yielded a collection of sequences having higher affinity than previously known natural or nonnatural sequences (59a). Examination of these sequences reveals a large new set of sequence motifs (rules) having much greater statistical significance—and thus correspondingly greater positioning power—than the previously known ones. An important challenge for the future is to understand the functioning of these new rules in the context of the new crystal structure.

OTHER INFLUENCES ON NUCLEOSOME POSITIONING   Biases in nucleosome positioning will arise in part from the population of DNA-binding proteins present in the cell at any moment, since protein binding to a target site will almost certainly restrict the translational or rotational positioning of that site in a nucleosome. These may be considered to be direct effects of proteins on nucleosome positioning. Assuming that positioning is fully equilibrated in vivo (65, 98, 103), these processes can only be understood as a large set of coupled chemical equilibria. Nucleosome positioning biases regulatory protein binding, and regulatory protein binding in turn biases nucleosome positioning.

Protein-dependent positioning can also be indirect. Such effects may arise when other DNA-binding proteins attract or exclude nucleosomes and so delineate a region to be filled-in statistically by other nucleosomes (51).

The requirements of chromatin higher order structure create biases for the mutual positioning of arrays of nucleosomes [(114, 126); and see the section on 30 nm fiber structure].

STRUCTURE OF THE NUCLEOSOME FILAMENT

The lowest level of chromosome organization is a repeating chain of nucleosomes, millions of nucleosomes in length, with nucleosomes separated by variable but preferentially quantized lengths of linker DNA. The actual 3-D structure is highly sensitive to the solution conditions. In solutions containing low concentrations of monovalent cations $[(M^+)]$ and no multivalent cations $[(M^{n+})]$ (111), the chromatin fiber adopts an extended structure; individual nucleosomes separated by extended stretches of linker DNA are readily seen by electron microscopy. This state of chromatin is known as the nucleosome filament.

Previous physical studies reviewed in (112) establish that the nucleosome filament has an extended 3-dimensional zig-zag structure in solution. There are strong positional correlations between nucleosomes even when linker DNA is sufficiently long that the average distance between consecutive nucleosomes significantly exceeds the nucleosomal diameter. Removal of histone H1 leads to an increase in distance between nucleosomes and a loss or weakening of the positional correlations. These effects are likely consequences of an increase in the entry/exit angle of DNA from the nucleosome as expected from studies on individual nucleosomes summarized above.

New studies using atomic force microscopy (AFM) (54) and cryoelectron microscopy (7) are consistent with these prior conclusions and afford direct 3-dimensional views of the structures in the presence and absence of H1. However, while providing a direct determination of 3-D structure is an important benefit, these new methods also introduce their own problems, discussed below.

STRUCTURE OF THE 30 nm FIBER

In solution, titration of chromatin with increasing concentrations of monovalent or multivalent cations up toward physiological ionic conditions leads to a progressive folding of the nucleosome filament into a compact $\approx$30 nm wide filament, or 30 nm fiber (112). In vivo, most chromatin is maintained throughout most of the cell cycle in this 30 nm fiber state or in even more highly folded states reached by further compaction of the 30 nm fiber.

At the time of the previous review, there were several competing models for the structure of the 30 nm fiber. A preponderance of the evidence favored a "solenoid" model (25, 96, 119), although isolated results appear contrary to it. In the solenoid model, the chain of nucleosomes is organized in a one-start contact helix having roughly six nucleosomes per turn; nucleosomes are oriented with their dyad axes perpendicular to the solenoid axis, with the linker DNA entry/exit side facing inward toward the center of the solenoid.

Much progress has subsequently been made toward distinguishing between the competing models and toward an elucidation of the folding mechanism. However, a direct structural determination remains lacking and efforts toward that goal face serious obstacles.

Key Problems for Direct Structural Studies

There are two chief underlying obstacles to a direct determination of the structure of the 30 nm fiber. First, alternative models that have been proposed differ from the solenoid model only in subtle, high-resolution features; moreover, chromatin fibers are ordered but lack crystalline regularity, owing to variability in the length of linker DNA from nucleosome to nucleosome along the fiber. Thus, one obstacle is a general problem of obtaining high resolution structural information from objects that are both large and irregular. AFM or cryoelectron microscopy (cryo EM) both have significant problems. AFM studies are carried out in "tapping mode," but this is something of a misnomer since very large amounts of energy can be deposited into the specimen with each "tap." Moreover, samples are adsorbed to surfaces and examined in air at ambient humidity; there may be distortions upon adsorption, and the solution conditions are not well defined. Problems with cryo EM are discussed below.

The second significant obstacle is that the ionic conditions that stabilize the folded 30 nm fiber state of chromatin also cause its aggregation. Aggregation sets in before structure-sensitive solution probes such as the sedimentation coefficient or the sharpness of X-ray diffraction bands reach titration endpoints (111, 112). 30 nm fibers in the aggregates pack very closely together, so that electron density contrast between individual fibers is diminished or lost; such samples are unsuitable for EM tomographic analysis. On the other hand, when lower cation concentrations are used, the 30 nm fiber state is unstable or marginally stable, and thus subject to artifactual distortions.

Constraints from Short Linker Lengths

Crossed-linker models of chromatin (120) can be tested by examining the folding of chromatin from cell types having very short linker DNA lengths (i.e. very short nucleosome repeat lengths). Experiments on diverse sources of chromatin having short linker lengths revealed fibers having ordinary ≈30 nm diameters and a low pitch angle, in contrast to the requirements of crossed-linker models (58, 112). Recently characterized chromatin from sources having very short nucleosome repeat lengths of ≈156–157 bp (8, 31, 114) allow a stronger test of the model. Geometric calculations suggest that crossed-linker models cannot be constructed with such short linker lengths because there is not enough linker DNA to reach from one nucleosome across the fiber to the next, even if the two opposite nucleosomes are allowed to touch and some DNA is allowed to be partially unwrapped off the surface of each nucleosome (31). Nevertheless, such chromatin undergoes cation-dependent higher order folding in vitro comparable to that of bulk chromatin (8).

These very short ($\approx$156–157 bp) repeat lengths also place substantial constraints on the solenoid model. Geometric calculations suggest that solenoid models can be constructed with such short linker lengths only if the solenoid is right-handed (31).

DEPENDENCE OF FIBER DIAMETER ON LINKER LENGTH   The solenoid model makes no specific prediction regarding the effects of large changes in linker DNA lengths (i.e. corresponding to an increase in the nucleosome repeat length, as opposed to a small change in length leading to twist errors discussed below). Varied linker lengths could be accommodated within the center of a solenoid having constant width, or in an additional loop nested between nucleosomes, or by small changes in the angle between consecutive nucleosomes leading to a changed diameter. Conflicting results have been obtained. One study suggests that the diameter is invariant for the chromatin in situ, but that it can change on isolation of the chromatin in vitro (123). Evidently fiber diameter depends on some uncontrolled experimental variable.

Linker DNA Topology

LINKER DNA BENDING   The solenoid model has the striking requirement that linker DNA must bend to allow consecutive nucleosomes to pack together in space. In contrast, crossed-linker and extended chain models allow the linker DNA to remain straight. Can linker DNA bend as required by the solenoid model? And, does it do so in chromatin? These questions have been addressed in several recent studies, which have led to contradictory results.

Dinucleosomes—oligomers of chromatin containing just two nucleosomes separated by one linker—allow a detection of linker DNA bending through measurement of the nucleosome–nucleosome distance (124). Electron microscopy of fixed, unstained samples, together with quasielastic light scattering of dinucleosomes in solution, showed that, as the concentration of mono- or divalent cations is increased from 2 mM M^+ to 18 mM NaCl or 2 mM $MgCl_2$, the average edge-to-edge separation of the two nucleosomes decreases from $\approx$15 nm (corresponding to fully extended linker DNA) to near-contact. These results are confirmed and extended in subsequent studies on the roles of histone H1 and the core histone tail domains, described below (27, 124). Another study detected a smaller increase in D_t (the translational diffusion coefficient) over the range $\approx$3.2–20 mM M^+ in the same buffer system, and came to a different structural conclusion (7). However, it is not clear that these results are really in conflict. First, much of the overall increase in D_t occurs in the 1–3 mM (M^+) range, which was not investigated in (7) or in frequently cited earlier studies such as (11). The relevant variable is the total monovalent cation concentration (111), not just (NaCl). Second, the data analysis method used in (7) is not the most appropriate for sensitive detection of modest changes in D_t in monodisperse systems.

Cryoelectron microscopy has been used to probe (M^+)-dependent changes in the structure of dinucleosomes and trinucleosomes (7), and led to the conclusion that (M^+)-dependent folding consists only of small changes in the entry/exit angle of linker DNA, with no bending of linker DNA—in clear conflict with the observations using conventional EM on fixed, unstained preparations (124). Similarly, a tomographic reconstruction of 30 nm fibers in situ using low temperature embedding methods (44) revealed a structure in which linker DNA is extended, not bent, conferring an extended zig-zag structure on the chromatin fiber.

While the point of the cryoelectron microscopy and low temperature embedding methods is to better preserve native structure, the evidence suggests that, for the case of chromatin fibers, they have not. The extended zig-zag chain structures seen in the tomographic reconstructions have values of mass per unit length (number of nucleosomes per unit translation along the fiber axis) that are significantly lower than those measured by neutron (30) or X-ray (121) low-angle scattering, or scanning transmission EM (30), and fail to explain the observed protection of linker DNA against nuclease attack that accompanies chromatin folding (130). Rather, the tomographic structures are consistent with the nucleosome filament state of unfolded 30 nm fibers studied in low (M^+) in vitro, suggesting that the chromatin has unfolded during preparation.

Independent evidence that there may be a problem with cryoelectron microscopy methods for DNA-containing specimens comes from studies of the topology of plasmid DNA. Cryoelectron microscopy revealed an unexpected cation-dependent change in plasmid topology leading to tight interwinding of DNA segments (6). Subsequent studies, however, using several different solution physical methods (29, 85) or an in-vitro recombination assay (86) conclude that this unexpected topology does not in fact occur.

One plausible explanation for the discrepancy concerns the temperature dependence to the helical twist of DNA (29). Classic studies establish that there is a substantial temperature dependence to the helical twist of DNA, and provide data on the coefficient of this dependence down to $\approx 0°C$. In cryo EM, samples are plunged into liquid ethane near its freezing point $(-172°C)$. It is estimated that the vitrification process in cryo EM occurs in $\approx 10^{-4}-10^{-5}$ s (6). Thus, for a period of $10^{-4}-10^{-5}$ s, the solution will be rapidly cooling from ambient $(\approx 20°C)$ down toward $-172°C$. During this period the helical twist of DNA will be changing significantly, although one can only estimate its low-temperature value by lengthy extrapolation. In response to the changing helical twist, the overall topology changes. The question is, are such changes rapid or slow compared to the cooling time? Experimental data on the viscosity of super-coiled water show that at temperatures as low as $\approx -35°C$, the viscosity is only $\approx 15\times$ greater than at 20°C (3). Thus, rotational and translational dynamics that occur on an ns timescale at 20°C (e.g. translations and rotations of nucleosomes) will be slowed to a 10–1000 ns timescale—which is still 10^2–$10^4\times$ faster than the cooling rate. Thus, while the cooling rate in cryo EM seems fast by human standards, it is still extremely slow on the timescale of molecular motions. The structures seen by cryo EM reflect structures formed after the DNA twist adopts values appropriate to the very low temperatures; and, as described in the following section, regular structures for the 30 nm fiber have strict requirements for particular values of the integrated twist of linker DNA.

Studies of pyrimidine dimer formation have been used as an indirect assay for the bending state of linker DNA in chromatin. These studies assume that quenching from neighboring proteins can be ignored. But the fact that the pattern near the middle of nucleosome core DNA is sensitive to the presence of H1 (74) suggests that proximity of proteins does contribute significantly.

In summary, present results are in conflict. Studies suggesting that linker DNA is straight have substantial caveats. Relatively fewer studies support the view that linker DNA may be bent; in any case those studies pertain only to dinucleosomes, not to long chromatin oligomers. New approaches to this central question are badly needed.

TWIST CONSTRAINTS IN LINKER DNA   The solenoid model (indeed, any regular structure) has an interesting constraint regarding the twist of linker DNA. Definite protein–protein or protein–DNA contacts between neighboring nucleosomes require particular values for the integrated (total) twist of each linker DNA segment. This requirement may be satisfied not just by a single particular linker length, but by any of a quantized set of lengths that differ one from another by integral multiples of the DNA helical repeat. Of course, any arbitrary DNA length can in principle be under- or overwound to give a needed particular total twist; however, when the twist error approaches 0.5 turns, the free energy penalties become very large and might easily exceed the free energy of any nucleosome-nucleosome contact that could be made. Thus, one might expect that linker DNA lengths would be preferentially quantized. An analysis of nucleosome repeat lengths reveals that linker DNA lengths do indeed occur in such preferentially quantized lengths (114). The quantization is not perfect, and need not be, since there is only a small free energy penalty for small twist errors. Moreover, the DNA twist itself varies with local sequence and on interaction with proteins.

That linker DNA lengths come in preferentially quantized lengths is an experimental truth; however, this particular explanation for that observation is not unique. Evidence in support of this structural explanation is provided by a study of the free energy coupling between (M^+)-dependent folding of dinucleosomes and intercalation of ethidium bromide into linker DNA (126). Consistent with a constraint on the twist of linker DNA, ethidium intercalation causes decondensation of dinucleosomes, and chromatin folding competes with ethidium binding. Results from other laboratories suggest that these effects of ethidium are due to ethidium-induced changes in the twist of linker DNA, and not to a variety of other effects.

Location and Roles of Histone H1 and the Core Histone Tails

LOCATION AND ROLE OF HISTONE H1   The location of histone H1 (more precisely, GH1) within the 30 nm fiber is a subject of considerable interest for two reasons. This information can shed light on the function of H1 itself; and, since the location of H1 within the nucleosome is known at least approximately, knowing the location of H1 within the 30 nm fiber places constraints on possible orientations for the nucleosomes within the 30 nm fiber. Previous studies of 30 nm fiber structure define aspects of the orientation consistent with the solenoid model (112, 118, 119), but do not suffice to specify the orientation with respect to rotations about the axis of the nucleosomal disk (112).

The location of H1 within the 30 nm fiber has been directly determined using neutron scattering (34). H1 is found to be internally located, at roughly the same radius as the innermost surface of nucleosomes in the solenoid model. This implies that nucleosomes have a constant rotational setting about their disk-axis, allowing consecutive nucleosomes to make equivalent nucleosome–nucleosome interactions. An alternative solenoid-like model that allows a variable rotational setting about the nucleosome disk-axis and lacks equivalent interactions between consecutive nucleosomes (112) is inconsistent with this result.

Early data suggested an essential role for H1 in 30 nm fiber structure (112); but H1-depleted chromatin exhibits a (M^+)-dependent compaction too [see (125) and references therein]. More recent studies on defined nucleosome oligomers (91, 125) show that H1-depleted oligonucleosomes can fold to approximately the same compactness as those containing H1. Moreover, this compaction involves a bending of the linker DNA (27), as found for dinucleosomes (124, 125). For folding induced by monovalent cations, the folding transitions are shifted to slightly higher (M^+) (124, 125). This means that H1 contributes to the free energy of stabilization of the folded state, but that it is not solely responsible, hence folding can proceed in its absence.

Electron microscopic and X-ray scattering studies of long H1-depleted chromatin show that the compact states that can be achieved lack the order characteristic of folded native chromatin (125), and led to the conclusion that H1 may be essential for selecting a single ordered conformation from a set of disordered compact conformations that are produced in its absence. However, new data suggesting that H1 may not be essential for viability force one to reexamine these questions.

While H1 may not be an essential protein, its presence in most cell types as a stoichiometric component of chromatin, its evolutionary conservation, and the fact that it does contribute to chromatin folding all point to an important role for H1 in 30 nm fiber structure and function. Variants of H1 are segregated in blocks in chromatin (48, 66). This segregation is inherently a cooperative phenomenon, and indeed H1 does bind cooperatively to DNA (see above); a tendency to self-association has been detected for GH5 but not for GH1 (62). Variants of H1 (e.g. H5) have varied affinities for DNA (17), and exhibit preferences for particular DNA base compositions or methylated states (64). These properties allow H1, in principle, to contribute to the free energy of chromatin folding to a variable and location-specific extent.

ROLES OF THE CORE HISTONE TAILS   The newly completed high resolution structure of the core particle will completely change the nature of future studies of the roles of the core histone tails. Prior to this structure determination, the majority of studies of tail-domain function in vitro focused primarily (although not exclusively) on the collective roles of sets of the trypsin-sensitive tail domains. An underappreciated point concerning many of these studies is that while the texts often refer to the roles of the trypsin-sensitive N-terminal domains, it is well-established that trypsin attacks sites in the N- and C-terminal regions of the histones H2A and H3 as well (102). Thus, effects reportedly due to the N-terminal tails may in some cases prove due to the C-terminal domains instead.

With that caveat, several important conclusions emerge. Oligonucleosomes reconstituted without H1 and lacking the trypsin-sensitive tail domains of all four core histones fail to exhibit the cation-dependent folding and linker DNA bending seen when the core histones are intact (12, 26, 27). Evidently, one or more of the tails has an essential role in chromatin folding. Oligonucleosomes reconstituted using hyperacetylated core histones behave similarly to those produced with trypsinized octamer (28). Moreover, hyperacetylation leads to a decrease in the (time-averaged) amount of DNA wrapped on the nucleosome (5, 68). These results mean that cells can regulate the stability of chromatin folding through changes in the pattern of core histone acetylation, and further suggests that other posttranslational modifications of the tail domains, as well as the use of other histone gene variants, may act in vivo to regulate the stability of chromatin folding.

Subsequent studies examined separately the roles of the tail domains from H2A/H2B heterodimers or $H3_2H4_2$ tetramers by reconstitution with histones in which one or the other subunits, but not both, have been trypsinized. Reconstituted oligonucleosomes lacking the tails of the $H3_2H4_2$ tetramers show little ability to undergo cation-dependent folding or self-aggregation, similar to oligonucleosomes lacking the tails of all four core histones (28, 90). This implies a major role for one or more of these domains in chromatin folding in vitro. In contrast, the tails of H2A/H2B contribute detectably but only slightly to chromatin folding (28).

Many other studies establish roles for these tail domains in protein-protein interactions with nonhistone chromosomal or chromosome-regulatory proteins. For example, the N-terminal tails of both H3 and H4 are recognized and bound by the yeast gene-silencing proteins Sir3 and Sir4, and are essential for the association of Sir3 with telomeric chromatin and for the perinuclear positioning of telomeres (42). The N-terminal tails of H3 and H4 are similarly implicated in direct interactions with the yeast global repressor protein Tup1, and moreover this interaction is negatively regulated by acetylation of the N-terminal domains (22).

There is a degree of functional overlap between the N-terminal domains of H3 and H4 and also between those of H2A and H2B, as assayed by the crude but important measure of viability (56, 89). Importantly, such functional overlap does not imply mechanistic overlap (106). Since their mechanisms of action may differ, it need not seem surprising that these pairs of N-terminal tails could show partial functional overlap despite their different locations in the core particle structure.

NEW INSIGHTS FROM THE CORE PARTICLE CRYSTAL STRUCTURE   The high resolution structure of the nucleosome core particle (61) provides several important new insights into the structure of the 30 nm fiber. Model building studies (61) reportedly show that this structure for the nucleosome core particle is compatible with the solenoid model for the structure of the 30 nm fiber (25, 96, 119).

An especially intriguing observation in the core particle structure is that an N-terminal tail of histone H4 on one nucleosome reaches over and makes an extensive contact with an H2A/H2B heterodimer on an adjacent nucleosome. The contact involves numerous hydrogen bonds and salt links between four basic residues on the H4 tail and a cluster of seven acidic residues on H2A and H2B. This interaction seems likely to have a strongly attractive energy, and is found experimentally to be essential for crystallization in the conditions used for the structure determination (61). The packing of nucleosomes within the crystal differs from that proposed for the packing in the solenoid model, and consequently the H4–H2A/H2B contact in the crystal has a direction opposite to the orientation that it would have in the solenoid model. However, because of the likely flexibility of the N-terminal tail of H4 and the nature of the binding interface, one presumes that similar contacts could be made with the orientation of the neighboring nucleosome reversed to resemble that in the solenoid. Evidence consistent with the possibility that this interaction contributes to chromatin folding in vitro comes from the observation that cation-dependent folding of reconstituted oligonucleosomes (lacking H1) requires that H2A/H2B heterodimers and the tail domains of the $H3_2H4_2$ tetramer both be present (37, 67, 90), while the tail domains of H2A/H2B contribute only slightly (67).

Because the N-terminal domain of H4 is not essential for viability, attention is drawn to other core histone domains, too, for their possible involvement in chromatin folding. The N-terminal tails of histone H3 (which include many conserved acetylation sites) pass between two gyres of DNA, anchoring the 13 bp at each end of the core particle DNA, and extend outward from the particle. Similarly the most C-terminal visible residue of the histone H2A tail is poised for interaction with linker DNA and moreover is the site of ubiquitin attachment (113). Either of these domains could also have direct roles in nucleosome-nucleosome interactions as well as influencing chromatin folding through effects on linker DNA.

Very importantly, studies carried out in vitro show that the N-terminal tail of H3 and the C-terminal tail of H2A do in fact interact with linker DNA. Earlier studies established that the histone octamer on its own provides measurable protection of 167 bp of DNA against attack by micrococcal nuclease [e.g. (55)]—notwithstanding the fact that the relative absence of such protection is often used as an assay for the reconstitution of histone H1. One or more core histone domain(s) must be responsible for this protection. More recently, a study of accessibility of residues to chemical modification provides direct evidence of an interaction of the N-terminal tail of H3 with linker DNA in chromatin (43). Another study analyzed the digestion by micrococcal nuclease of long chromatin reconstituted with chicken erythrocyte H2B, H3, and H4, and wheat H2A, which has an additional 19-amino acid C-terminal extension relative to chicken. The additional length of the H2A C-terminal tail led to the protection of an additional 16 bp of linker DNA against attack by the nuclease (55). This observation implicates the extended C-terminal tail of the wheat protein in an interaction with linker DNA, and it suggests that the shorter C-terminal tail of chicken erythrocyte H2A likely contributes to the protection of the 167 bp fragment and therefore interacts with linker DNA.

The structure suggests that several other tail domains could also be involved in nucleosome-nucleosome interactions, either laterally or vertically within a solenoid. The N-terminal tail of H4 could be involved in contacts distinct from the particular interaction seen in the crystal packing.

HIGHER LEVELS OF STRUCTURE

Low-angle X-ray scattering studies of isolated metaphase chromosomes (52) show a series of diffraction features characteristic of 30 nm chromatin fibers (111,119), suggesting that metaphase chromosomes are produced by further folding of the basic 30 nm fiber. Scanning electron micrographs show stubby 50–70 nm diameter projections emanating from the body of metaphase chromosomes (2), and thin sectioning studies (2) suggest that these projections are composed of a loop of 30 nm fiber that folds back and twists around itself. Similar structures are formed spontaneously by long 30 nm fibers in vitro (111,118,119). Moreover, there is a good correlation between the phase diagram for 30 nm formation in vitro (111) and the appearance of metaphase chromosomes (2). If the concentration of Mg^{2+} or other higher valence cations is too high, the 50–70 nm diameter projections appear to merge together and can no longer be resolved. Taken together, these data provide strong evidence that the 30 nm fiber serves as a basic architectural unit that is further folded into mitotic and probably meiotic chromosomes.

Two studies of higher order chromatin structure have yielded particularly important results: One study uses the natural processes of mitotic chromosome decondensation during the progression from M phase to S phase, and of recondensation during the transition from G2 to M phase, to examine chromosomes when they are less densely packed so that elements of their internal organization may be exposed. This approach in combination with serial thin sectioning electron microscopy and image reconstruction provides evidence for two levels of folding above the 30 nm fiber: fibers with diameters of $\approx$60–80 nm and $\approx$100–130 nm (9). The data suggest that the 30 nm fibers are organized into 60–80 nm fibers by local folding rather than helical coiling; the 60–80 nm fibers may be helically coiled into the 100–130 nm fibers; and these in turn may be locally folded into chromatids. However, an alternative view suggesting that mitotic chromosomes may be organized with a final helical coiling cannot be excluded at present. An important corollary of these results is that a majority of chromatin in the interphase nucleus is organized in levels of folding above that of the 30 nm fiber.

A second important discovery concerns long-range correlations in spatial positions between defined genetic elements along a single chromosome (128) in the interphase nucleus. Experiments using fluorescence in situ hybridization (FISH) methods on fixed nuclei reveal evidence for random walk behavior of interphase chromatin on two lengthscales. On one lengthscale, chromatin appears to be organized in large loops, several Mbp in size, with the chromatin randomly folded within each loop. On an even longer lengthscale, the chromosome behaves as a long chain of such loops, again showing random walk behavior. Individual chromosomes occupy distinct domains in the interphase nucleus.

NUCLEOSOME DYNAMICS AND FUNCTION

Nucleosomes and chromatin fibers are dynamic, not inert. Their dynamic behavior is essential for chromatin function.

Regulatory Protein Binding

DNA sequences that are organized in nucleosomes are largely inaccessible to other proteins because of steric hindrance from the octamer surface and other nearby segments of DNA—both within a nucleosome and from other nucleosomes neighboring in space in the chromatin fiber. Yet most DNA in vivo is packaged in nucleosomes, and many DNA sequences are critical for biological regulation and so must be accessible to regulatory proteins at appropriate times. What, then, are the principles that guarantee that regulatory proteins will have access to their DNA target sequences when necessary? The answer to this important question is not known. For references and for discussion of current ideas and their limitations, see (59, 77, 78, 117).

To investigate these questions, many research groups set up experiments in vitro that assess the ability of eukaryotic transcription factors to bind to their DNA target sites when those are incorporated into nucleosomes [see (77, 78, 117)].

The results were varied and confusing. In some cases, factors were able to bind to nucleosomal target sites, producing complexes that contained the factor, the DNA, and at least one molecule each of all four core histones. The affinities of the factors for their target sites were generally suppressed by one or more orders of magnitude. These studies left open the questions of why the factors had those measured affinities, and, strikingly, how the factors were able to bind to their target sites in the first place, when those sites were sterically occluded on the nucleosome! Even more puzzling, other factors were found not to be able to bind to nucleosomal target sites, including cases in which opposite outcomes were obtained with two closely related factors—one apparently "able" to bind, the other "not able."

Site Exposure Model for Dynamics and Function of Nucleosomal DNA

A new "site exposure model" (77, 78) allows these and other results to be understood and, indeed, quantitatively predicted with no adjustable parameters. This model is illustrated in Figure 1a.

We make the simplifying assumption that sufficient nucleosomal DNA is exposed such that the rates and equilibria for binding to an exposed nucleosomal target sequence or to a naked DNA target sequence are identical. Thus,

$$N \underset{k_{21}}{\overset{k_{12}}{\rightleftarrows}} S + R \underset{k_{32}}{\overset{k_{23}}{\rightleftarrows}} RS \quad \text{and} \quad S + R \underset{k_{32}}{\overset{k_{23}}{\rightleftarrows}} RS \qquad (1)$$

(a)

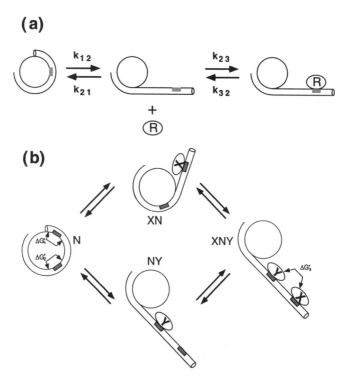

(b)

Figure 1 (*a*) The site exposure model illustrated for a single nucleosome. The histone octamer is shown from above as a disk with the DNA coiling around it. A particular DNA target sequence (*stippled*) is inaccessible to the regulatory protein (*R*) that acts on it. k_{12} and k_{21} are position-dependent apparent-rate constants for site exposure and recapture, respectively. Exposure of sites nearer the middle of the nucleosomal DNA may occur by several successive steps of exposure of shorter segments from an end as illustrated; each smaller step would have its own microscopic rate constant. k_{23} and k_{32} are microscopic-rate constants for binding and dissociation of *R* from its target site, and pertain to naked DNA as well as to the exposed state of nucleosomes. Real nucleosomes exist in long chains, but this need not prevent uncoiling such as illustrated. With just modest deformation of the linker DNA, a combined uncoiling coupled to a motion of the uncoiled DNA in a direction parallel to the axis of the nucleosomal disk allows uncoiling beyond the dyad (which is as far as necessary to allow binding anywhere) with no required crossings and with little motion of other nucleosomes. Higher levels of chromosome structure may need to be disassembled prior to the site-exposure process illustrated here, but are also believed to possess only marginal stability. (*b*) Cooperativity in the binding of multiple proteins to target sites in a single nucleosome. A nucleosome is shown containing binding sites (*stippled*) for two proteins (*X*) and (*Y*). X and Y may be two unrelated proteins, or two molecules of the same protein. *X* is defined as the protein binding to the outer site, and *Y* as binding to the inner site. ΔG_1 is the free energy cost for uncoiling enough DNA so as to expose the site for X. ΔG_2 is the additional free energy cost for uncoiling sufficient additional DNA so as to expose the site for Y. In some cases,

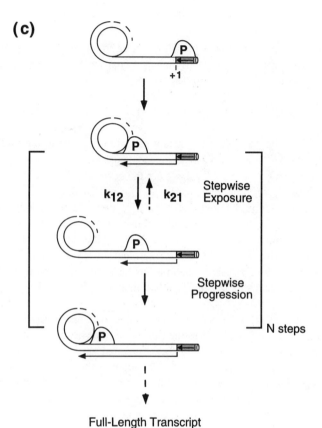

Full-Length Transcript

Figure 1   (Continued)   X and Y may have "conventional" cooperative interactions, also detectable in their binding to naked DNA (e.g. from favorable protein-protein contacts between X and Y); these are collectively represented as ΔG_3. (*c*) Site-exposure model for the mechanism of polymerase elongation through a nucleosomal template. Successive repetition of two steps—partial uncoiling, followed by elongation up to the next point of steric hindrance—allows full-length elongation. (The octamer could be transferred backward during this process, as has been suggested; see text). The number of such steps required for elongation through a complete nucleosome in this model depends on the length of DNA released in each step. Site exposure occurs nondissociatively, so the entire DNA chain is not released in just one step; thus, the number of site-exposure steps required for full-length nucleosome transcription is two or greater. The structure of the nucleosome suggests that contact points of the DNA and histones (likely sites of histone-DNA "bonds") occur once each DNA helical turn, in which case DNA may be exposed in successive ≈10 bp-long steps. Similar suggestions for the mechanism of polymerase progression have been made previously (50).

for nucleosomes and naked DNA, respectively (N is the starting nucleosome, R a DNA-binding protein, and S the site-exposed state of the nucleosome, or naked DNA).

With this assumption, binding of a regulatory protein to a nucleosomal target sequence will occur with a net free energy change ΔG_{net}^0 , and an apparent dissociation constant $K_d^{apparent}$, given by:

$$\Delta G_{net}^0 = \Delta G_{conf}^0 + \Delta G_{naked\,DNA}^0 \quad \text{and} \quad K_d^{apparent} = K_d^{naked\,DNA}/K_{eq}^{conf}, \quad (2)$$

where K_{eq}^{conf} is the equilibrium constant for site exposure in the nucleosome (k_{12}/k_{21}), $K_d^{naked\,DNA}$ is the dissociation constant for binding to naked DNA (k_{32}/k_{23}), and ΔG_{conf}^0 and $\Delta G_{naked\,DNA}^0$ are the corresponding free energies.

In this model, K_{eq}^{conf} depends primarily on the translational position of the target sequence within the nucleosome (ΔG_{conf} depends on the length of DNA being uncoiled—i.e. on the length of protein-DNA interface that is disrupted). However, the effective K_{eq}^{conf} will also depend on other factors such as the size and shape of the regulatory protein, the rotational setting of the target site around the periphery of the DNA helix, and on DNA bending induced by the protein, because these affect the amount of DNA that must be uncoiled to allow the protein to bind.

Studies of the accessibility of nucleosomal sites to restriction enzymes provide a test of this model and allow measurement of position-dependent equilibrium constants for site exposure (77, 78). The most important finding is that site exposure does in fact occur, even over the nucleosomal dyad (the middle and presumably least-accessible region of the nucleosomal DNA), with substantial values for K_{eq}^{conf}. This dynamic property intrinsic to nucleosomes provides a general mechanism guaranteeing that regulatory proteins may have access to their DNA target sequences.

The measured equilibrium constants for site exposure decrease more-or-less progressively as one moves inward from an end into the middle of the nucleosome, from ≈ 1–4×10^{-2} just inside the core particle, to $\approx 10^{-4}$–10^{-5} over the dyad axis. Such behavior is consistent with the simple uncoiling picture as illustrated. The structure shows the DNA to be wrapped on the histone surface as making contacts ("bonds") in a small patch, every ~ 10 bp, each time the phosphodiester backbone (minor groove) faces inward toward the octamer (61). Thus, uncoiling would naturally proceed stepwise, with an incremental increase in energetic cost ΔG_{conf} (i.e. decreased equilibrium constant K_{eq}^{conf}) associated with each additional 10 bp-long segment uncoiled. Theoretical studies of a related model reveal additional stable states (63).

These results explain and clarify the confusing results of the direct binding studies. For those cases where proteins could bind, the site exposure model provides a physically plausible mechanism for how they gain access to their target sites. Moreover, it allows us to predict the outcomes of the equilibrium binding studies: given the (readily measured) affinity of a protein for its target site on naked DNA, and the location of that target site in a nucleosome (for which our results provide the corresponding K_{eq}^{conf}), the predicted affinity for the nucleosomal target site is given by Equations 1 and 2.

The site exposure model also explains why in seemingly arbitrary cases it was found that certain proteins could not bind to their target sites within nucleosomes. In many (possibly all) such cases, the observed failure to bind can be attributed to a simple consequence of ending the titrations too soon, prior to reaching the $K_d^{apparent}$ that we predict for that system.

Studies of the kinetics of restriction enzyme digestion of nucleosomal DNA, and of equilibrium affinities for transcription factor binding to nucleosomal DNA, are unrelated except through the site-exposure model. Nevertheless, they yield equivalent results: That is, using the equations of this model, the results of either experiment allow the prediction of the other. Evidently this model and Equations 1 and 2 provide a framework for analysis and interpretation of the binding studies.

COOPERATIVITY   The site exposure model has within it the potential for important novel cooperative (synergistic) interactions between multiple proteins binding simultaneously to sites within a single nucleosome (78). This cooperativity is distinct from any "conventional" (e.g. direct or other) cooperative interactions that may also exist between the proteins. The origin of this potential cooperativity (synergy) is illustrated in Figure 1b. It arises from the possibility that, once protein Y has bound, the binding of protein X may take place without having to pay the energetic penalty for site exposure (here defined as ΔG_{conf}^0), which otherwise would be required. Similarly, the ability of X to bind facilitates the subsequent binding of Y, since at least some of the final free energy penalty for the required conformational change is already paid. No special properties are required of X or Y: They need only bind DNA for this cooperativity to be manifested. X and Y may be two different proteins, or they may be two molecules of the same protein. The amount of cooperativity between X and Y (the coupling free energy $^*G_{XY}$—the free energy by which the prior binding of X facilitates the binding of Y, or vice versa), equals $-\Delta G_1^0$—i.e. minus one times the energetic cost for exposing the outer site.

This model accounts quantitatively for a diverse set of experimental results on cooperative binding of various proteins to nucleosomal target sites obtained by another laboratory (1). Moreover, there is good agreement between the predictions of this model and the experimental data even using ΔG_{conf} obtained from the restriction enzyme digestion kinetic measurements instead of the $^*G_{XY}$ obtained directly from the primary cooperative binding data. These experiments are completely unrelated except through the site exposure model, so the agreement between the two provides strong evidence for the applicability of the site exposure model to the behavior of real nucleosomes.

These results have three important ramifications. (*a*) Real nucleosomes in vitro do behave in the manner described by Figure 1*b*, with the potential cooperativity of that model fully realized. Such behavior requires mechanical linkage between events at the two binding sites (78), consistent with uncoiling from an end as illustrated. (*b*) This cooperativity, which is intrinsic to nucleosomes, means that cells can control the occupancy at, for example, X's binding site, either by varying the concentration of X itself, or by varying the concentration of Y, with no requirement for conventional direct cooperative interactions between X and Y. This idea provides a natural mechanism for the construction of cooperative (synergistic) multi-protein control modules from the combinatorial action of independent and arbitrarily chosen parts. (*c*) The free energy of this cooperativity ($^*G_{XY}$), obtained as ΔG_{conf} in our earlier studies, ranges from (minus) 2.5–6 kcal mol^{-1}. These large coupling free energies greatly increase the occupancies achieved by binding proteins that are present at realistic concentrations, compared to their occupancies if they act independently.

In real systems, X and Y may have direct "conventional" cooperative interactions, represented by ΔG_3^0 in Figure 1*b*, in addition to the cooperativity that arises from competing against a common competitor. In that case, the net cooperativity will be given by the sum of $^*G_{XY} + \Delta G_3^0$. As one measure of the significance of the inherent cooperativity one can compare $^*G_{XY}$ with typical values for ΔG_3^0 measured in real systems. A survey of several well-known conventional cooperative interactions having clearly established significance in gene regulation reveals typical values for ΔG_3^0 of $\approx$1–2 kcal mol^{-1} (78). The novel cooperativity free energies from the site exposure model are substantially greater than these free energies of previously recognized "conventional" cooperative interactions.

KINETICS   In order for the site exposure model to be relevant in gene regulation in vivo, it is important that the rate of site exposure (measured by k_{12} in Figure 1 and Equation 1) be fast compared to the timescales of biological regulatory decisions (perhaps minutes or faster) or polymerase elongation (6–10 s per nucleosome for RNA pol II). Direct measurement of the rate constants for site exposure and recapture have not yet been made. Simple theoretical estimates, assuming either an activated or a diffusive process for recapture, lead to the expectation that site exposure will occur on the millisecond to microsecond timescale (J Widom, unpublished information). Studies using coupled enzymatic reactions to detect site-exposure events show that site exposure occurs on a timescale of seconds or faster (79a).

NUCLEOSOME STABILITY   Spontaneous site exposure processes are nondissociative: Exposed DNA segments are rapidly recaptured, and the time-averaged most prevalent state is that of an ordinary (fully wrapped) nucleosome. The possibility that simple dissociation of DNA from the histone octamer could explain the observed site exposure is explicitly ruled out by several independent experiments (77).

Site exposure occurring simultaneously on each side of the nucleosome could lead to dissociation of the DNA, but evidently does not do so. How can it be that nucleosomes are stable? The answer is not known. One plausible explanation is that site exposure events at the two ends may not be independent; release at one end may suppress release at the other. Mutual repulsion between nucleosomal DNA segments, which must serve to destabilize the wrapping of DNA, provides one such mechanism; additionally, conformational changes could be transmitted through the histone octamer, allowing binding events on one side to influence affinities and dynamics at the other.

Remarkably, nucleosomes may actually be less stable against DNA dissociation than has previously been imagined. One study reports that simple dilution of nucleosomes—in the presence of a poly dGdC competitor—leads to displacement of labeled DNA tracer from the histone octamer, as monitored both by solution footprinting and by native gel electrophoresis. This instability was apparently not a consequence of the use of a particular pathological DNA sequence (32).

Nucleosome-Disrupting Machines?

One idea that is popular in "active invasion" models of gene regulation [see (77,78)] suggests that certain proteins might act as power-driven levers, harnessing the energy of ATP hydrolysis to pry DNA off a nucleosome. (Such an action is to be distinguished from a simple trapping of spontaneous nucleosome structural fluctuations such as the uncoiling fluctuations of site exposure.) Many protein candidates for such a role have been identified [for references, see (50,77,78)]. These proteins have ATPase activities; they are implicated in facilitating transcription factor access to nucleosomal DNA in vitro; and they are known to interact with nucleosomes and to be involved in transcriptional regulation in vivo.

Whatever the real activity of these proteins proves to be, they are unlikely to act by prying DNA off nucleosomes. Such an activity is not in accord with real properties of molecular motors. Even if molecular motor proteins can act as power-driven levers, a simple calculation shows that RNA polymerase from *E. coli*—currently the strongest molecular motor known (127)—lacks the force by a factor of ten to break even individual, unnaturally weak, models of salt-bridges [bonds that help hold DNA on the nucleosome; see (61)], and can contribute, at most, negligibly or only a few-fold (in the weak-bonding and strong-bonding limits, respectively) to the rate at which DNA would be released in thermally driven (i.e. spontaneous) site-exposure processes (79a).

More plausible mechanisms through which such proteins might act to facilitate the binding of regulatory proteins include the following. (*a*) Simply by binding specifically or nonspecifically to DNA, such proteins would facilitate the ability of other site-specific proteins to bind, in accord with the cooperativity mechanism of Figure 1*b*. (*b*) As will be described in more detail below for the case of RNA polymerase, processive DNA-binding proteins can trap spontaneous uncoiling fluctuations of site exposure processes just after they occur, allowing other proteins to bind to the displaced naked DNA that accumulates behind them. In this case the role of ATP hydrolysis is simply to allow a processive protein to translocate forward when other obstacles do not prevent this. (*c*) The proteins might act by modifying the histones themselves, e.g. by phosphorylating one or more of them, thereby changing rates or equilibria for site exposure; these mechanisms are discussed below.

A particularly telling result is that, when the "swi/snf" class of such ATP-dependent proteins do play a role in expression of a particular gene in vivo, mutations in these proteins can in some cases be suppressed by second site mutations that map to the histones themselves [called "sin" mutants (38)]. The new structure of the nucleosome shows that many of the sin mutations could be expected to destabilize the wrapping of the nucleosomal DNA. Destabilizing the wrapping of DNA would increase the frequency and/or the lifetime of spontaneous site exposure processes, shifting the equilibrium constant for site exposure toward the "exposed," or regulateable, state. In vivo, Sin^- mutants show increased susceptibility to attack from a variety of DNA nucleases and modifying enzymes (108).

The Nucleosome as a Binary Regulatory Switch

A property intrinsic to histone octamers potentially allows them to confer a binary "on/off" character to the binding of regulatory proteins to nucleosomal target sites, as illustrated in Figure 2.

Either simple equilibrium binding of multiple proteins to nucleosomal target sites, or the action of a processive DNA-binding protein (one model for active invasion), can lead to displacement of the histone octamer from its DNA. It is plausible that throughout most of the cell cycle (except, perhaps, S-phase?), the

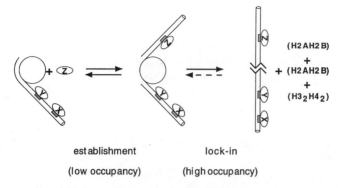

est ablishment   lock-in

(low occupancy)   (high occupancy)

Figure 2 Locking in gene activation. Simple equilibrium binding of sufficient numbers of proteins to nucleosomal target sites, or the action of a processive DNA-binding protein (one model for active invasion) may lead to displacement of the histone octamer from its DNA. Histone octamers that lack their DNA are unstable in physiological conditions: they rapidly dissociate into the H3/H4 tetramer and 2 H2A/H2B heterodimers. Displacement of the histone octamer would then serve as a binary switch. In the initial "establishment" state, a nucleosome is present, and occupancy by bound regulatory proteins is low because of competition from site recapture (the process with rate constant k_{21} in Figure 1); nevertheless, site exposure does allow occupancy greater than zero. Displacement and dissociation of the histone octamer then "locks in" a new state, in which affinities and the corresponding occupancies are much greater, simply because the octamer is no longer an effective competitor.

Alternatively, simple equilibrium binding of proteins to nucleosomal target sites could lead to recruitment of a factor that posttranslationally modifies H1 or the core histones. Preliminary low-occupancy binding, followed by a posttranslational modification that increases site exposure, would provide another way in which a nucleosome could act as a binary regulatory switch.

concentration of free histone subunits may be sufficiently low that nucleosome reassembly—which may be a quaternary process—effectively does not occur. Displacement and dissociation of the histone octamer could switch a gene from an initial "establishment" state, having relatively low occupancy of target sites by regulatory proteins, to a new state, which, because the octamer is no longer an effective competitor, allows the same concentrations of regulatory proteins to achieve and "lock-in" much greater occupancy levels in this new quasi-equilibrium.

Alternatively, simple equilibrium binding of proteins to nucleosomal target sites could lead to recruitment of a factor that posttranslationally modifies H1 or the core histones. As will be discussed in a following section, site exposure processes can be greatly repressed or facilitated by such modifications. Preliminary low-occupancy binding, followed by a posttranslational modification that increases site exposure, would provide another way in which a nucleosome could act as a binary regulatory switch.

Nucleosome Mobility

Another dynamic behavior of nucleosomes that has been discovered is their ability to move along DNA in a process also referred to as nucleosome sliding (65, 76). Nucleosome mobility is readily detected by a 2-dimensional native gel assay, which takes advantage of the dependence of the electrophoretic mobility on the position of the octamer between the ends and the middle of a DNA fragment. The rate of nucleosome mobility is enhanced at elevated temperatures and ionic strengths, but mobility can also be detected in lower temperatures and approximately physiological ionic strengths. Mobility is strongly suppressed by histone H1 (75).

Can nucleosome mobility be the underlying mechanism of site exposure? If mobility were the underlying mechanism of site exposure, the analysis summarized above would still hold true. The measured equilibrium constants would describe the fraction of time that mobile nucleosomes spend in various locations so as to leave particular sites extending off their surface and accessible to other proteins.

The actual mechanism of site exposure has not yet been determined. However, the relative rates argue against a role for mobility in site exposure. Indeed, the evidence suggests that the converse is more likely to be the case: Site exposure may be the initial step in nucleosome mobility. Site exposure sufficient to expose all of the DNA occurs on a seconds timescale, whereas in comparable conditions nucleosome mobility occurs on the hours timescale.

While mobility is often described as a "sliding" process, the nature of the histone:DNA interface would not allow a literal sliding motion; rather, a coupled rotation/translation of the DNA would be required in order to maintain the critical minor groove backbone contacts at multiple points on the histone surface. Such a process would be improbable (although not impossible). However, the site exposure mechanism provides a much simpler alternative, in which a segment of DNA released from the histone surface can loop back and be recaptured at a new position (most likely displaced by a multiple of the DNA helical repeat), creating a nucleosome with a "bulged" loop of DNA. Analogous structures have been postulated as intermediates during nucleosome transcription (50, 95). The bulge could propagate around the nucleosome in a relatively low-energy process; when it runs off the other end, the nucleosome would be found to have moved. Further studies are required to address the molecular mechanisms of both site exposure and nucleosome mobility.

Effects of Histone H1 and Histone Modifications

The presence of histone H1 on nucleosomes strongly suppresses the ability of other proteins to bind to nucleosomal DNA target sites (47), the ability of RNA polymerases to elongate through the nucleosomal DNA (71, 100), and the mobility of nucleosomes on DNA (75). Studies of the direct effects of histone H1 on equilibrium constants for site exposure are not yet available.

From a formal perspective, H1 could act in either of at least two ways: In one mechanism, release of H1 must precede site exposure. Thus,

$$NH1 \underset{k_r}{\overset{k_f}{\rightleftharpoons}} H1 + N \underset{k_{21}}{\overset{k_{12}}{\rightleftharpoons}} H1 + S + R \underset{k_{32}}{\overset{k_{23}}{\rightleftharpoons}} H1 + SR, \tag{3a}$$

where NH1 is an H1-containing nucleosome. In this model, H1 acts effectively as a competitive inhibitor for site exposure. Cells may repress the genetic activity of regions of chromosomes either by increasing the concentration of H1, or by producing H1 variants or posttranslationally modified states of H1 that bind more tightly. Alternatively, histone H1 may always remain bound, but its presence may alter the equilibrium constants for site exposure, K_{eq}^{conf}, through effects on k_{12}, k_{21}, or both.

$$NH1 \underset{k_{21}}{\overset{k_{12}}{\rightleftharpoons}} SH1 + R \underset{k_{32}}{\overset{k_{23}}{\rightleftharpoons}} RSH1, \tag{3b}$$

where SH1 is an H1-containing nucleosome in a conformational state able to bind R, and RSH1 is the ternary complex of nucleosome, R, and H1. In this model, cells may repress genetic activity by producing H1 variants or posttranslationally modified states of H1 that decrease K_{eq}^{conf}. These two models are readily tested and distinguished by experiments in vitro.

Acetylation of the core histones or complete removal of the trypsin-sensitive tail domains facilitates the ability of proteins to bind to nucleosomal target sites (53, 99, 104). Strikingly, several groups have recently identified transcriptional coactivators as having histone acetylase activity [for review, see (105)]. It remains to be seen whether the primary effects of core histone acetylation are direct, through chromatin structure and dynamics, or indirect, through interactions with other proteins as described above.

The site exposure model (Equation 1) provides one simple way in which the effects of histone acetylation may be understood. It is plausible that one effect of histone acetylation is to increase K_{eq}^{conf}, shifting the equilibrium toward the accessible (regulateable) state. Such a change in equilibrium constant is consistent with measured changes in the topology of nucleosomal DNA that accompany histone acetylation (5, 68). While these studies are normally interpreted in terms of a reduced amount of DNA wrapped around the acetylated histone core, this statement may be equivalent (averaged over time) to an increased equilibrium constant for site exposure.

New Roles for DNA Sequences in Gene Regulation

Genomic DNA sequences can contribute in two novel ways to gene regulation through their effects on nucleosome structure and dynamics.

NUCLEOSOME POSITIONING   Nucleosomes having strongly biased positions definitely do exist in vivo, and may play important roles in both positive (60, 88) and negative (49, 50) gene regulation. These roles cannot depend on "precise" positioning, since, as discussed above, this does not exist. Instead, statistical biases in nucleosome positioning can contribute to gene regulation by biasing the time-averaged "accessibility" of regulatory sites. In the context of the site exposure model, one would say that biases in nucleosome positioning produce a particular weighted-average of equilibrium constants for site exposure. Depending on the distribution of occupancies, time-averaged biases in positioning can yield a very wide range of applicable K_{eq}^{conf}. If the predominant time-averaged placement of a regulatory site is in linker DNA regions, this will yield a relatively large K_{eq}^{conf}, possibly even one or greater. Conversely, if the predominant time-averaged placement of a regulatory site is near the nucleosomal dyad, this yields a small K_{eq}^{conf}, approaching 10^{-4}–10^{-5} for an isolated nucleosome.

Importantly, as discussed above, DNA sequence preferences intrinsic to the histone octamer contribute strongly to nucleosome positioning. Many natural sequences that bias positioning at individual sites by factors of $100\times$ or greater are known. This means that the choice of particular genomic DNA sequences can bias, by factors of 100 or greater, whether the time-averaged K_{eq}^{conf} is a number closer to 1 or to 10^{-4}–10^{-5}. Thus, genomic DNA sequence can play a dominant role in governing the occupancy of regulatory sites in chromatin, much greater than the effects attributable to many individual gene regulatory proteins.

POLY (DA:DT) ELEMENTS   A second way that genomic DNA sequence can contribute to gene regulation is through effects on the structure and dynamics of nucleosomes that are (statistically) positioned by other forces. An especially interesting case is that of polypurine [chiefly poly(dA:dT)] tracts of length 15–30 bp that are found in many promoters. The general situation is illustrated in Figure 3.

A nucleosome is positioned (on average) through some combination of forces so as to cover the binding site for an essential gene activating protein and to position that site near the middle of the nucleosome. The presence of this nucleosome suppresses the accessibility of the binding site to the gene activating protein (and to other DNA binding proteins and enzymes that probe accessibility at that site). Nearby, between this binding site and the nearest end of the nucleosomal DNA, is a polypurine tract. Studies in vivo establish that these polypurine tracts are essential elements of the promoters, contributing roughly as much to gene activation as do the gene-activating proteins themselves (45). The function of these elements in vivo evidently depends on their intrinsic

A$_{16}$ MRE or   TATA   +1
          GCN4

Figure 3 Polypurine elements in eukaryotic promoters. The figure illustrates cases studied in two yeasts (45, 129). A nucleosome (indicated by the *ellipse*, roughly to scale) is (on average) positioned so as to cover a binding site (indicated by *MRE* or *GCN4*) for a gene-activating protein. The positions of the TATA box and the start-site of transcription (+1) are indicated. Nearby the MRE or GCN4 sites, also present in that nucleosome, is a poly(dA:dT) element. The presence of this element is essential for the proper functioning of the promoter, contributing roughly as much to gene activation as does the gene-activating protein itself. These elements are thought to function by altering the structure or stability of the nucleosome in which they are packaged. The site-exposure model provides one way in which such effects may be understood.

structure or properties and not on their interaction with sequence-specific DNA binding proteins (45, 129). These elements increase the accessibility of the adjacent DNA regulatory sequences to the gene activating protein and to other proteins. These results suggest that the poly(dA:dT) elements lead to nucleosomes having altered structure or stability, thereby facilitating access by regulatory proteins at those genomic locations.

The site exposure model predicts such behavior and may account for the action of these promoter elements. Stretches of poly (dA:dT) of length 16 bp in a similar location decrease by ≈ 1.2 kcal mol^{-1} the favorable free energy of histone-DNA interactions in nucleosome reconstitution (39). This decreases, by that same amount, the free energy penalty that must be paid in order to uncoil the nucleosomal DNA beyond the poly (dA:dT) stretch so that a protein can have access to a site further inside the nucleosome. Decreasing the free-energy penalty for exposing the site makes the overall process of protein binding more favorable. More generally, for any sequence element that decreases the favorable free energy of histone–DNA interactions by an amount $\Delta\Delta G_{seq}$, the site exposure model predicts that K_{eq}^{conf} and the affinity for binding at a site further inside that same nucleosome will be increased by the factor $\exp(\Delta\Delta G_{seq}/RT)$.

Nucleosome Transcription and Replication

The nucleosomal organization of DNA presents obstacles for the elongation of RNA and DNA polymerase. Early studies from many groups on transcription of isolated nucleosomal templates led to the conclusion that RNA polymerase could not initiate if its promoter was inside a nucleosome; however, if the promoter is located off the nucleosome, the polymerase is able to elongate through the nucleosome to produce full-length transcripts [for reviews, see (24, 50)]. These studies were limited by the presence of multiple nucleosome positioning isomers and the fact that the reactions were run asynchronously over numerous rounds of transcription, until the reactants were exhausted. In many cases, the possibility could not be excluded that most of the products arose from naked DNA, and not from nucleosomes at all.

Subsequent studies eliminated these uncertainties. Problems from multiple nucleosome positioning isomers are reduced or eliminated by purification of single isomers (using native gel electrophoresis) (69, 95), or through the use of nucleosome-positioning sequences that, together with a short overall fragment length, give predominant positioning at a single predominant location (79). Appropriately designed template sequences and experimental protocols allow study of synchronous transcription complexes, in real time, as they progress along the templates in a single passage (79, 95). Using bacteriophage T7 RNA polymerase (79), the timescale can be varied from faster to much slower than the natural rate of RNA pol II elongation, which is ≈6–10 s per nucleosome.

Key conclusions include the following: Transcriptional elongation through a nucleosomal template can occur with high efficiency, approaching 100%. When the elongation rate is slow compared to the natural timescale, the velocities of polymerase progression (elongation) on the nucleosomal templates are slightly but reproducibly slower than on naked DNA. Evidently, polymerases can traverse through a nucleosome with little difficulty. The slight difference in rates is due to a slight increase in pausing on the nucleosomal templates. However, this increased pausing reflects properties of the DNA sequence itself, and not of its nucleosomal organization: The sites of this increased pausing are identical on nucleosomes and naked DNA. Studies on nucleosomes produced with crosslinked or disulfide-linked histone octamers show that complete disassembly or "lexosome" structural transitions of the histone octamer are not essential for polymerase elongation (70, 79).

When the elongation rate is close to or faster than the natural rate, the enhanced pausing is reduced on the second half of the nucleosomal template (79a, 95). This observation, together with a finding that nucleosome transcription is accompanied by backwards translocation of nucleosome on the DNA, led to a model in which the DNA ahead of the octamer uncoils from the histone surface while, at the same time, the DNA behind the polymerase coils back around it (94, 95a, 119a). Another study suggests that, in the presence of competitor DNA, nucleosome transcription leads to complete displacement of the template DNA from the histone octamer and its replacement by the competitor (69, 119a).

Polymerase elongation can lead to accumulation of positive superhelical tension ahead of the polymerase, and negative superhelical tension behind it (57). Positive supercoiling destabilizes nucleosomes while negative supercoiling stabilizes them (15). Thus, transfer of a nucleosome from ahead of to behind the polymerase is an energetically favorable process. Studies on the separate histone subunits suggest that positive superhelical stress leads to displacement of H2A/H2B heterodimers, whereas $H3_2H4_2$ tetramers were found to have a preference for the positively supercoiled DNA (46), possibly accompanied by a major structural rearrangement (35).

How can the polymerase progress through a nucleosomal template? The polymerase cannot pass ghostlike through the atoms of the histone octamer and the non-template DNA strand. Rather, release of the DNA from the surface of the histone octamer must precede or accompany forward motion of the polymerase. (Histone subunits may, but need not be, released from the complex.) We argue above that a motor-like action of the polymerase cannot itself pry DNA off the histone surface. Rather, the polymerase must trap spontaneous uncoiling events originating from an end. Others have also reached this conclusion (50). We now know that spontaneous uncoiling events do in fact occur, and the available data are consistent with their extending inward from an end (see above). One example of this mechanism is illustrated in Figure 1c.

DYNAMICS AND FUNCTION OF HIGHER ORDER STRUCTURE

The lack of concrete information on the structure of the 30 nm chromatin fiber and on higher levels of structure precludes much discussion of their dynamics and function. Nevertheless, the following two points warrant consideration.

Dynamic Equilibrium

Is the 30 nm chromatin fiber an "inert," static structure, so that internal regions of the fiber are inaccessible to proteins and other ligands, or is it "dynamic," such that internal regions are frequently accessible? The question is an important one since most of the chromatin in a cell is maintained in a 30 nm fiber state (or an even higher level of structure), yet the chromatin must be able to unfold to some extent to allow binding by gene-regulatory proteins, elongation by RNA and DNA polymerases, and other essential processes having chromatin as the substrate.

Early studies show that the nucleosome filament folds gradually into the 30 nm fiber with increasing (M^{n+}) (112). For example, studies of the sedimentation coefficient of chromatin fragments show that S increases gradually with increasing (Na^+) (11) or (Mg^{2+}) (111). In general the chromatin precipitates before a clear titration endpoint is reached. Nevertheless, electron microscopic analysis reveals 30 nm fibers at appropriately high (M^{n+}) (111), and measurements of mass per length using STEM and neutron scattering show these to reach plateau values (30). Evidently, in physiological conditions, the 30 nm fiber is only marginally stable.

The simplest interpretation of these data is that the 30 nm fiber is in rapid dynamic equilibrium with the nucleosome filament state; titration with increasing (M^{n+}) gradually shifts the equilibrium constant from a value favoring the nucleosome filament to one favoring the 30 nm fiber. Consistent with this view, histone H1 is found to readily exchange between chromatin fragments in conditions in which the chromatin is folded (on average) into 30 nm fibers (13). Since we now know H1 to have an internal location in 30 nm fibers (34), free exchange of H1 requires dynamic local unfolding of the 30 nm fiber. In this view, posttranslational modifications of the histones, or differing histone variants, could modulate the chromatin folding equilibrium, favoring one side or the other.

Other studies using electron microscopy to investigate the (M^{n+})-dependent folding of chromatin fibers on an individual molecule basis led to the conclusion that the folding of each fiber was a gradual process; at intermediate (M^{n+}), chromatin fibers had intermediate widths (96) and intermediate values of mass per length (30). Continuous folding of the chromatin filament could account for gradual changes in physical properties without a requirement for a dynamic folding equilibrium. This view of the folding process is less able to account for the exchange of free H1 between chromatin fibers.

Both of these views may be true at once if a dynamic folding equilibrium takes place over short lengthscales—e.g. the bending of individual linker segments between consecutive nucleosomes, or the wrapping of an individual turn of $\approx$6–7 nucleosomes in a solenoid. This would satisfy the data behind the dynamic equilibrium view, but could also account for the appearance of the images and the mass per length data since even these single-molecule studies represent averages over stretches of the chromatin fiber.

Site Exposure and Higher Order Structure

Can spontaneous site exposure processes occur in chains of nucleosomes, where the DNA ends are not free, and there may be folding into higher levels of structure? Recent studies suggest that site exposure does occur readily in chains of nucleosomes in ionic conditions where these chains are folded at least to some degree into higher order structures. These studies investigate the ability of GAL4 protein to bind to target sites in a central "test" nucleosome flanked on either side by five nucleosome-long tandem repeats of a nucleosome positioning sequence (73). The affinity of GAL4 protein for sites in the central test nucleosome is similar to that for sites in an isolated nucleosome measured earlier (77). In the context of the site-exposure model, measurements of affinity are equivalent to the restriction enzyme measurements of equilibrium constants for site exposure. Thus, these results imply that burying the test nucleosome in the middle of an 11-nucleosome-long chain has only little effect on the equilibrium constant for site exposure.

How can such binding events be understood structurally? In the nucleosome filament level of folding, a combined uncoiling of DNA on the test nucleosome coupled to a motion of the uncoiled DNA in a direction parallel to the axis of the nucleosomal disk, allows uncoiling beyond the dyad (which is as far as necessary to allow binding anywhere) with no required crossings, only minor deformation of linker DNA, and with little motion of other nucleosomes. Because the 30 nm filament is a marginally stable structure, evidently in dynamic equilibrium with the nucleosome filament state, binding should also be able to occur starting at this level of structure. The binding and chromatin folding equilibria are coupled. Posttranslational modifications of histones or differing histone variants that can influence the stability of the 30 nm fiber will also affect the binding equilibria.

CONCLUSIONS AND PROSPECTS

The tremendous progress in structural analysis of the lowest level of chromatin organization is not yet mirrored by progress in our understanding of higher levels of organization. There are formidable problems. New approaches are plainly required, yet it is not clear at this time what avenues may prove most productive.

Great progress has recently been made in identifying a set of structural proteins and enzymes that are somehow involved in modulating chromatin structure and activity. These represent only a small fraction of the full picture. A host of new proteins and enzymes remain to be discovered; and for all of these, both those discovered already and those yet to be discovered, there remains the problem of elucidating the structures and mechanisms through which they contribute to chromatin function.

It may be appropriate at this time to set ourselves the goal of achieving a quantitative, predictive understanding of gene regulation in vivo. In this case, two problems loom immediately. First, we need to learn how gene-regulatory proteins gain access to their target sites in chromatin, what happens to the chromatin when they do so, and how these processes are coupled energetically. Second, we need to learn what fraction of the total nuclear DNA is accessible to proteins at any moment and thus able to compete for regulatory protein binding.

ACKNOWLEDGMENTS

Research in the author's laboratory is supported by grants from the NIH. I thank J Anderson, PT Lowary, K Polach, and R Protacio for helpful discussions, and Dr. V Ramakrishnan for helpful discussions and for sending a manuscript prior to publication.

Literature Cited

1. Adams CC, Workman JL. 1995. Binding of disparate transcriptional activators to nucleosomal DNA is inherently cooperative. *Mol. Cell. Biol.* 15:1405–21

2. Adolph KW, Kreisman LR, Kuehn RL. 1986. Assembly of chromatin fibers into metaphase chromosomes analyzed by transmission electron microscopy and scanning electron microscopy. *Biophys. J.* 49:221–31

3. Angell CA. 1983. Supercooled water. *Annu. Rev. Phys. Chem.* 34:593–630

4. Arents G, Burlingame RW, Wang B-C, Love WE, Moudrianakis EN. 1991. The nucleosomal core histone octamer at 3.1 Å resolution: a tripartite protein assembly and a left-handed superhelix. *Proc. Natl. Acad. Sci. USA* 88:10148–52

5. Bauer WR, Hayes JJ, White JH, Wolffe AP. 1994. Nucleosome structural changes due to acetylation. *J. Mol. Biol.* 236:685–90

6. Bednar J, Furrer P, Stasiak A, Dubochet J, Engelman EH, et al. 1994. The twist, writhe and overall shape of supercoiled DNA change during counterion-induced transition from a loosely to a tightly interwound superhelix. *J. Mol. Biol.* 235:825–47

7. Bednar J, Horowitz RA, Dubochet J, Woodcock CL. 1995. Chromatin conformation and salt-induced compaction: three-dimensional structural information from cryoelectron microscopy. *J. Cell Biol.* 131:1365–76

8. Bedoyan JK, Lejnine S, Makarov VL, Langmore JP. 1996. Condensation of rat telomere-specific nucleosomal arrays containing unusually short DNA repeats and histone H1. *J. Biol. Chem.* 271:18485–93

9. Belmont AS, Bruce K. 1994. Visualization of G1 chromosomes: a folded, twisted, supercoiled chromonema model of interphase chromatid structure. *J. Cell Biol.* 127:287–302

10. Bouvet P, Dimitrov S, Wolffe AP. 1994. Specific regulation of *Xenopus* chromosomal 5S rRNA gene transcription in vivo by histone H1. *Genes Dev.* 8:1147–59

11. Butler PJG, Thomas JO. 1980. Changes in chromatin folding in solution. *J. Mol. Biol.* 140:505–29

12. Buttinelli M, Leoni L, Sampaolese B, Savino M. 1991. Influence of DNA topology and histone tails in nucleosome organization on pBR322 DNA. *Nucleic Acid. Res.* 19:4543–4549

13. Caron F, Thomas JO. 1981. Exchange of histone H1 between segments of chromatin. *J. Mol. Biol.* 146:513–37

14. Cerf C, Lippens G, Ramakrishnan V, Muyldermans S, Segers A, et al. 1994. Homo- and heteronuclear two-dimensional NMR studies of the globular domain of histone H1: full assignment, tertiary structure, and comparison with the globular domain of histone H5. *Biochemistry.* 33:11079–86

15. Clark DJ, Felsenfeld G. 1991. Formation of nucleosomes on positively supercoiled DNA. *EMBO J.* 10:387–95

16. Clark DJ, Hill CS, Martin SR, Thomas JO. 1988. "-Helix in the carboxy-terminal domains of histones H1 and H5. *EMBO J.* 7:69–75

17. Clark DJ, Thomas JO. 1988. Differences in the binding of H1 variants to DNA. Cooperativity and linker-length related distribution. *Eur. J. Biochem.* 178:225–33

18. Dasso M, Dimitrov S, Wolffe AP. 1994. Nuclear assembly is independent of linker histones. *Proc. Natl. Acad. Sci. USA* 91:12477–81

19. Deleted in proof

20. Dong F, Hansen JC, van Holde KE. 1990. DNA and protein determinants of nucleosome positioning on sea urchin 5S rRNA gene sequences in vitro. *Proc. Natl. Acad. Sci. USA* 87:5724–28

21. Draves PH, Lowary PT, Widom J. 1992. Cooperative binding of the globular domain of histone H5 to DNA. *J. Mol. Biol.* 255:1105–21

22. Edmondson DG, Smith MM, Roth SY. 1996. Repression domain of the yeast global repressor Tup1 interacts directly with histones H3 and H4. *Genes Dev.* 10:1247–59

23. El Hassen MA, Calladine CR. 1997. Conformational characteristics of DNA: empirical classifications and a hypothesis for the conformational behaviour of

dinucleotide steps. *Philos. Trans. R. Soc. London* 355:43–100

24. Felsenfeld G. 1996. Chromatin unfolds. *Cell* 86:13–19

25. Finch JT, Klug A. 1976. Solenoidal model for superstructure in chromatin. *Proc. Natl. Acad. Sci. USA* 73:1897–1901

26. Fletcher TM, Hansen JC. 1995. Core histone tail domains mediate oligonucleosome folding and nucleosomal DNA organization through distinct molecular mechanisms. *J. Biol. Chem.* 270:25359–62

27. Garcia-Ramirez M, Dong F, Ausio J. 1992. Role of the histone "tails" in the folding of oligonucleosomes depleted of histone H1. *J. Biol. Chem.* 267:19587–95

28. Garcia-Ramirez M, Rocchini C, Ausio J. 1995. Modulation of chromatin folding by histone acetylation. *J. Biol. Chem.* 270:17923–28

29. Gebe JA, Delrow JJ, Fujimoto BS, Heath PJ, Stewart DW, et al. 1996. Effects of Na$^+$ and Mg^{2+} ions on the structures of supercoiled DNAs: comparison of simulations with experiments. *J. Mol. Biol.* 262:105–28

30. Gerchman SE, Ramakrishnan V. 1987. Chromatin higher-order structure studied by neutron scattering and scanning transmission electron microscopy. *Proc. Natl. Acad. Sci. USA* 84:7802–6

31. Godde JS, Widom J. 1992. Chromatin structure of *Schizosaccharomyces pombe*: a nucleosome repeat length that is shorter than the chromatosomal DNA length. *J. Mol. Biol.* 226:1009–25

32. Godde JS, Wolffe AP. 1995. Disruption of reconstituted nucleosomes: the effect of particle concentration, MgCl2 and KCl concentration, the histone tails and temperature. *J. Biol. Chem.* 270:27399–402

33. Goytisolo FA, Gerchman S, Yu X, Rees C, Graziano V, et al. 1996. Identification of two DNA-binding sites on the globular domain of histone H5. *EMBO J.* 15:3421–29

34. Graziano V, Gerchman SE, Schneider DK, Ramakrishnan V. 1994. Histone H1 is located in the interior of the chromatin 30-nm filament. *Nature* 368:351–54

35. Hamiche A, Carot V, Alilat M, De Lucia F, O'Donohue M, et al. 1996. Interaction of the histone (H3-H4)2 tetramer of the nucleosome with positively supercoiled DNA minicircles: potential flipping of the protein from a left- to a right-handed superhelical form. *Proc. Natl. Acad. Sci. USA* 93:7588–93

36. Hamiche A, Schultz P, Ramakrishnan V, Oudet P, Prunell A. 1996. Linker histone-dependent DNA structure in linear mononucleosomes. *J. Mol. Biol.* 257:30–42

37. Hansen JC, Wolffe AP. 1994. A role for histones H2A/H2B in chromatin folding and transcriptional repression. *Proc. Natl. Acad. Sci. USA* 91:2339–43

38. Hartzog GA, Winston F. 1997. Nucleosomes and transcription: recent lessons from genetics. *Curr. Opin. Genet. Dev.* 7:192–98

39. Hayes J, Bashkin J, Tullius TD, Wolffe AP. 1991. The histone core exerts a dominant constraint on the structure of DNA in a nucleosome. *Biochemistry* 30:8434–40

40. Hayes JJ. 1996. Site-directed cleavage of DNA by a linker histone-Fe(II) EDTA conjugate: localization of a globular domain binding site within a nucleosome. *Biochemistry* 35:11930–37

41. Hayes JJ, Clark DJ, Wolffe AP. 1991. Histone contributions to the structure of DNA in the nucleosome. *Proc. Natl. Acad. Sci. USA* 88:6829–33

42. Hecht A, Laroche T, Strahl-Bolsinger S, Gasser SM, Grunstein M. 1995. Histone H3 and H4 N-termini interact with SIR3 and SIR4 proteins: a molecular model for the formation of heterochromatin in yeast. *Cell* 80:583–92

43. Hill CS, Thomas JO. 1990. Core histone-DNA interactions in sea urchin sperm chromatin: the N-terminal tail of H2B interacts with linker DNA. *Eur. J. Biochem.* 187:145–53

44. Horowitz RA, Agard DA, Sedat JW, Woodcock CL. 1994. The three-dimensional architecture of chromatin in situ: electron tomography reveals fibers composed of a continuously variable zig-zag nucleosomal ribbon. *J. Cell Biol.* 125:1–10

45. Iyer V, Struhl K. 1995. Poly(dA:dT), a ubiquitous promoter element that stimulates transcription via its intrinsic DNA structure. *EMBO J.* 14:2570–79

46. Jackson V. 1995. Preferential binding of histones H3 and H4 to highly positively coiled DNA. *Biochemistry* 34:10607–19

47. Juan L, Utley RT, Vignali M, Bohm L, Workman JL. 1997. H1-mediated repression of transcription factor binding to a stably positioned nucleosome. *J. Biol. Chem.* 272:3635–40

48. Kamakaka RT, Thomas JO. 1990. Chro-

matin stucture of transcriptionally competent and repressed genes. *EMBO J.* 9:3997–4006

49. Kornberg RD, Lorch Y. 1993. Nucleosome positioning. *Nucleic Acids Mol. Biol.* 7:217–25

50. Kornberg RD, Lorch Y. 1995. Interplay between chromatin structure and transcription. *Curr. Opin. Cell Biol.* 7:371–75

51. Kornberg RD, Stryer L. 1988. Statistical distributions of nucleosomes: nonrandom locations by a stochastic mechanism. *Nucleic Acids Res.* 16:6677–90

52. Langmore JP, Paulson JR. 1983. Low angle x-ray diffraction studies of chromatin structure in vivo and in isolated nuclei and metaphase chromosomes. *J. Cell Biol.* 96:1120–31

53. Lee DY, Hayes JJ, Pruss D, Wolffe AP. 1993. A positive role for histone acetylation in transcription factor access to nucleosomal DNA. *Cell* 72:73–84

54. Leuba SH, Yang G, Robert C, van Holde K, Zlatanova J, et al. 1994. Three-dimensional structure of extended chromatin fibers as revealed by tapping-mode scanning force microscopy. *Proc. Natl. Acad. Sci. USA* 91:11621–25

55. Lindsey GG, Orgeig S, Thompson P, Davies N, Maeder DL. 1991. Extended C-terminal tail of wheat histone H2A interacts with DNA of the "linker" region. *J. Mol. Biol.* 218:805–13

56. Ling X, Harkness TAA, Schultz MC, Fisher-Adams G, Grunstein M. 1996. Yeast histone H3 and H4 amino termini are important for nucleosome assembly in vivo and in vitro: redundant and postition-independent functions in assembly but not in gene regulation. *Genes Dev.* 10:686–99

57. Liu LF, Wang JC. 1987. Supercoiling of the DNA template during transcription. *Proc. Natl. Acad. Sci. USA* 84:7024–27

58. Lowary PT, Widom J. 1989. Higher order structure of *Saccharomyces cerevisiae* chromatin. *Proc. Natl. Acad. Sci. USA* 86:8266–70

59. Lowary PT, Widom J. 1997. Nucleosome packaging and nucleosome positioning of genomic DNA. *Proc. Natl. Acad. Sci. USA* 94:1183–88

59a. Lowary PT, Widom J. 1998. New DNA sequence rules for high affinity binding to histone octamer and sequence-directed nucleosome positioning. *J. Mol. Biol.* 276:19–42

60. Lu Q, Wallrath LL, Elgin SC. 1995. The role of a positioned nucleosome at

the *Drosophila melanogaster* hsp26 promoter. *EMBO J.* 14:4738–46

61. Luger K, Mader AW, Richmond RK, Sargent DF, Richmond TJ. 1997. Structure of the nucleosome core particle at 2.8 Å resolution. *Nature* 389:251–60

62. Maman JD, Yager TD, Allan J. 1994. Self-association of the globular domain of histone H5. *Biochemistry* 33:1300–10

63. Marky NL, Manning GS. 1995. A theory for DNA dissociation from the nucleosome. *J. Mol. Biol.* 254:50–61

64. McArthur M, Thomas JO. 1996. A preference of histone H1 for methylated DNA. *EMBO J.* 15:1705–14

65. Meersseman G, Pennings S, Bradbury EM. 1992. Mobile nucleosomes—a general behavior. *EMBO J.* 11:2951–59

66. Mohr E, Trieschmann L, Grossbach U. 1989. Histone H1 in two subspecies of *Chironomus thummi* with different genome sizes: homologous chromosome sites differ largely in their content of a specific H1 variant. *Proc. Natl. Acad. Sci. USA* 86:9308–12

67. Moore SC, Ausio J. 1997. Major role of the histones H3-H4 in the folding of the chromatin fiber. *Biochem. Biophys. Res. Commun.* 230:136–39

68. Norton VG, Marvin KW, Yau P, Bradbury EM. 1990. Nucleosome linking number change controlled by acetylation of histones H3 and H4. *J. Biol. Chem.* 265:19848–52

69. O'Donohue M, Duband-Goulet I, Hamiche A, Prunell A. 1994. Octamer displacement and redistribution in transcription of single nucleosomes. *Nucleic Acids Res.* 22:937–45

70. O'Neill T, Smith JG, Bradbury EM. 1993. Histone octamer dissociation is not required for transcript elongation through arrays of nucleosome cores by phage T7 RNA polymerase in vitro. *Proc. Natl. Acad. Sci. USA* 90:6203–7

71. O'Neill TE, Meersseman G, Pennings S, Bradbury EM. 1995. Deposition of Histone H1 onto reconstituted nucleosome arrays inhibits both initiation and elongation of transcripts by T7 RNA polymerase. *Nucleic Acids Res.* 23:1075–82

72. Ohsumi K, Katagiri C, Kishimoto T. 1993. Chromosome condensation in *Xenopus* mitotic extracts without histone H1. *Science* 262:2033–35

73. Owen-Hughes T, Utley RT, Cote J, Peterson CL, Workman JL. 1996. Persistent site-specific remodeling of a nucleosome array by transient action of the SWI/SNF complex. *Science* 273:513–16

74. Pehrson JR. 1989. Thymine dimer formation as a probe of the path of DNA in an between nucleosomes in intact chromatin. *Proc. Natl. Acad. Sci. USA* 86:9149–53

75. Pennings S, Meersseman G, Bradbury EM. 1994. Linker histones H1 and H5 prevent the mobility of positioned nucleosomes. *Proc. Natl. Acad. Sci. USA* 91:10275–79

76. Pennings S, Meersseman G, Bradbury ME. 1991. Mobility of positioned nucleosomes on 5S rDNA. *J. Mol. Biol.* 220:101–10

77. Polach KJ, Widom J. 1995. Mechanism of protein access to specific DNA sequences in chromatin: a dynamic equilibrium model for gene regulation. *J. Mol. Biol.* 254:130–49

78. Polach KJ, Widom J. 1996. A model for the cooperative binding of eukaryotic regulatory proteins to nucleosomal target sites. *J. Mol. Biol.* 258:800–12

79. Protacio RU, Widom J. 1996. Nucleosome transcription studied in a real-time synchronous system: test of the lexosome model and direct determination of effects due to histone octamer. *J. Mol. Biol.* 256:458–72

79a. Protacio RU, Polach KJ, Widom J. 1997. Coupled-enzymatic assays for the rate and mechanism of DNA site exposure in a nucleosome. *J. Mol. Biol.* 274:708–21

80. Pruss D, Bartholomew B, Persinger J, Hayes J, Arents G, et al. 1996. An asymmetric model for the nucleosome: a binding site for linker histones inside the DNA gyres. *Science* 274:614–17

81. Ramakrishnan V. 1997. Histone H1 and chromatin higher order structure. *Crit. Rev. Eukaryot. Gene Expr.* 7:215–30

82. Ramakrishnan V. 1997. Histone structure and the organization of the nucleosome. *Annu. Rev. Biophys. Biomol. Struct.* 26:83–112

83. Ramakrishnan V, Finch JT, Graziano V, Lee PL, Seewt RM. 1993. Crystal structure of the globular domain of histone H5 and its implications for nucleosome binding. *Nature* 362:219–23

84. Roberts MS, Fragoso G, Hager GL. 1995. Nucleosomes reconstituted in vitro on mouse mammary tumor virus b region DNA occupy multiple translational and rotational frames. *Biochemistry* 34:12470–80

85. Rybenkov VV, Vologodskii AV, Cozzarelli NR. 1997. The effect of ionic conditions on the conformations of supercoiled DNA. I: Sedimentation analysis. *J. Mol. Biol.* 267:299–311

86. Rybenkov VV, Vologodskii AV, Cozzarelli NR. 1997. The effect of ionic conditions on the conformations of supercoiled DNA. II: Equilibrium catenation. *J. Mol. Biol.* 267:312–23

87. Satchwell SC, Drew HR, Travers AA. 1986. Sequence periodicities in chicken nucleosome core DNA. *J. Mol. Biol.* 191:59–75

88. Schild C, Claret F-X, Wahli W, Wolffe AP. 1993. A nucleosome-dependent static loop potentiates estrogen-regulated transcription from the *Xenopus* vitellogenin B1 promoter in vitro. *EMBO J.* 12:423–33

89. Schuster T, Han M, Grunstein M. 1986. Yeast histone H2A and H2B amino termini have interchangeable functions. *Cell* 45:445–51

90. Schwarz PM, Felthauser A, Fletcher TM, Hansen JC. 1996. Reversible oligonucleosome self-association: dependence on divalent cations and core histone tail domains. *Biochemistry* 35:4009–15

91. Schwarz PM, Hansen JC. 1994. Formation and stability of higher order chromatin sructures. *J. Biol. Chem.* 269:16284–89

92. Shimizu M, Roth SY, Szent-Gyorgyi C, Simpson RT. 1991. Nucleosomes are positioned with base pair precision adjacent to the a2 operator in *Saccharomyces cerevisiae*. *EMBO J.* 10:3033–41

93. Shrader TE, Crothers DM. 1990. Effects of DNA sequence and histone-histone interactions on nucleosome placement. *J. Mol. Biol.* 216:69–84

94. Studitsky VM, Clark DJ, Felsenfeld G. 1994. A histone octamer can step around a transcribing polymerase without leaving the template. *Cell* 76:371–82

95. Studitsky VM, Clark DJ, Felsenfeld G. 1995. Overcoming a nucleosomal barrier to transcription. *Cell* 83:19–27

95a. Studitsky VM, Kassavetis GA, Geiduscheck EP, Felsenfeld G. 1997. Mechanism of transcription through the nucleosome by eukaryotic RNA polymerase. *Science* 278:1960–63

96. Thoma F, Koller T, Klug A. 1979. Involvement of histone H1 in the organization of the nucleosome and of the salt-dependent superstructures of chromatin. *J. Cell Biol.* 83:403–27

97. Thomas JO, Rees C, Finch JT. 1992. Cooperative binding of the globular domains of histones H1 and H5 to DNA. *Nucleic Acids Res.* 20:187–94

98. Ura K, Hayes JJ, Wolffe AP. 1995. A

positive role for nucleosome mobility in the transcriptional activity of chromatin templates: restriction by linker histones. *EMBO J.* 14:3752–65

99. Ura K, Kurumizaka H, Dimitrov S, Almouzni G, Wolffe AP. 1997. Histone acetylation: influence on transcription, nucleosome mobility and positioning, and linker histone-dependent transcriptional repression. *EMBO J.* 16:2096–2107

100. Ura K, Nightingale K, Wolffe AP. 1996. Differential association of HMG1 and linker histones B4 and H1 with dinucleosomal DNA: structural transitions and transcriptional repression. *EMBO J.* 15:4959–69

101. Ushinsky SC, Bussey H, Ahmed AA, Wang Y, Friesen J, et al. 1997. Histone H1 in *Saccharomyces cerevisiae.* Yeast 13:151–61

102. van Holde KE. 1989. *Chromatin.* New York: Springer-Verlag

103. Varga-Weisz PD, Blank TA, Becker PB. 1995. Energy-dependent chromatin assembly and nucleosome mobility in a cell-free system. *EMBO J.* 14:2209–16

104. Vettese-Dadey M, Grant PA, Hebbes TR, Crane-Robinson C, Allis CD, et al. 1996. Acetylation of histone H4 plays a primary role in enhancing transcription factor binding to nucleosomal DNA in vitro. *EMBO J.* 15:2508–18

105. Wade PA, Wolffe AP. 1997. Chromatin: histone acetyltransferases in control. *Curr. Biol.* 7:R82-84

106. Wan JS, Mann RK, Grunstein M. 1995. Yeast histone H3 and H4 N-termini function through different GAL1 regulatory elements to repress and activate transcription. *Proc. Natl. Acad. Sci. USA* 92:5664–68

107. Wassarman PM, Kornberg RD, eds. 1989. *Methods in Enzymology. Vol. 170: Nucleosomes.* San Diego: Academic. 683 pp.

108. Wechser MA, Kladde MP, Alfieri JA, Peterson CL. 1997. Effects of Sin- versions of histone H4 on yeast chromatin structure and function. *EMBO J.* 16:2086–95

109. Widlund HR, Cao H, Simonsson S, Magnusson E, Simonsson T, et al. 1997. Identification and characterization of genomic nucleosome-positioning sequences. *J. Mol. Biol.* 267:807–17

110. Widom J. 1985. Bent DNA for gene regulation and DNA packaging. *Bioessays* 2:11–14

111. Widom J. 1986. Physicochemical stud-
ies of the folding of the 100 Å nucleosome filament into the 300 Å filament. *J. Mol. Biol.* 190:411–24

112. Widom J. 1989. Toward a unified model of chromatin folding. *Annu. Rev. Biophys. Biophys. Chem.* 18:365–95

113. Widom J. 1991. Nucleosomes and chromatin. *Curr. Opin. Struct. Biol.* 1:245–50

114. Widom J. 1992. A relationship between the helical twist of DNA and the ordered positioning of nucleosomes in all eukaryotic cells. *Proc. Natl. Acad. Sci. USA* 89:1095–99

115. Widom J. 1996. Short-range order in two eukaryotic genomes: relation to chromosome structure. *J. Mol. Biol.* 259:579–88

116. Widom J. 1997. Chromatin: the nucleosome unwrapped. *Curr. Biol.* 7:653–55

117. Widom J. 1997. Chromosome structure and gene regulation. *Phys. A.* 244:497–509

118. Widom J, Finch JT, Thomas JO. 1985. Higher-order folding of long repeat chromatin. *EMBO J.* 4:3189–94

119. Widom J, Klug A. 1985. Structure of the 300 Å chromatin filament: x-ray diffraction from oriented samples. *Cell* 43:207–13

119a. Widom J. 1997. Getting around the nucleosomes. *Science* 278:1899–1901

120. Williams SP, Athey BD, Muglia LJ, Schappe RS, Gough AH, et al. 1986. Chromatin fibers are left-handed double helices with diameter and mass per unit length that depend on linker length. *Biophys. J.* 49:233–48

121. Williams SP, Langmore JP. 1991. Small angle x-ray scattering of chromatin: radius and mass per unit length depend on linker length. *Biophys. J.* 59:606–18

122. Wolffe A. 1992. *Chromatin Structure and Function.* London: Academic

123. Woodcock CL. 1994. Chromatin fibers observed in situ in frozen hydrated sections: native fiber diameter is not correlated with nucleosome repeat length. *J. Cell Biol.* 125:11–19

124. Yao J, Lowary PT, Widom J. 1990. Direct detection of linker DNA bending in defined length oligomers of chromatin. *Proc. Natl. Acad. Sci. USA* 87:7603–7

125. Yao J, Lowary PT, Widom J. 1991. Linker DNA bending induced by the core histones of chromatin. *Biochemistry.* 30:8408–14

126. Yao J, Lowary PT, Widom J. 1993. Twist constraints on linker DNA in the 30 nm chromatin fiber: implications for nucleosome phasing. *Proc. Natl. Acad. Sci. USA* 90:9364–68

2

127. Yin H, Wang MD, Svoboda K, Landick R, Block SM, et al. 1995. Transcription against an applied force. *Science* 270:1653–57
128. Yokota H, van den Engh G, Hearst JE, Sachs RK, Trask BJ. 1995. Evidence for the organization of chromatin in megabase pair-sized loops arranged along a random walk path in the human G0/G1 interphase nucleus. *J. Cell Biol.* 130:1239–49
129. Zhu Z, Thiele DJ. 1996. A specialized nucleosome modulates transcription factor access to a *C. glabrata* metal responsive promoter. *Cell* 87:459–70
130. Zlatanova J, Leuba SH, Yang G, Bustamante C, van Holde K. 1994. Linker DNA accessibility in chromatin fibers of different conformations: a reevaluation. *Proc. Natl. Acad. Sci. USA* 91:5277–80

Annu. Rev. Biophys. Biomol. Struct. 1998. 27:329–56

CYTOCHROME *C* OXIDASE:
Structure and Spectroscopy

H. Michel, J. Behr, A. Harrenga, and A. Kannt
Max-Planck-Institut für Biophysik, Frankfurt/Main, Germany;
e-mail: michel@mbibp-frankfurt.mpg.de

KEY WORDS: membrane protein crystallization, oxygen reduction, Raman spectroscopy, respiratory chain, X-ray crystallography

---

ABSTRACT

Cytochrome *c* oxidase, the terminal enzyme of the respiratory chains of mitochondria and aerobic bacteria, catalyzes electron transfer from cytochrome *c* to molecular oxygen, reducing the latter to water. Electron transfer is coupled to proton translocation across the membrane, resulting in a proton and charge gradient that is then employed by the F_0F_1-ATPase to synthesize ATP.

Over the last years, substantial progress has been made in our understanding of the structure and function of this enzyme. Spectroscopic techniques such as EPR, absorbance and resonance Raman spectroscopy, in combination with site-directed mutagenesis work, have been successfully applied to elucidate the nature of the cofactors and their ligands, to identify key residues involved in proton transfer, and to gain insight into the catalytic cycle and the structures of its intermediates. Recently, the crystal structures of a bacterial and a mitochondrial cytochrome *c* oxidase have been determined. In this review, we provide an overview of the crystal structures, summarize recent spectroscopic work, and combine structural and spectroscopic data in discussing mechanistic aspects of the enzyme. For the latter, we focus on the structure of the oxygen intermediates, proton-transfer pathways, and the much-debated issue of how electron transfer in the enzyme might be coupled to proton translocation.

CONTENTS

329

1056-8700/98/0610-0329$08.00

INTRODUCTION

Cytochrome c oxidases (E.C. 1.9.3.1) are the terminal enzymes in the respiratory chains from mitochondria and many bacteria. They use the electrons of cytochrome c to reduce molecular oxygen (dioxygen). The product of the reaction is water. It is essential that the complexes of the respiratory chains are integrated into the (inner) membranes of mitochondria or bacteria, because they create an electrochemical gradient of protons, consisting of a pH-gradient and an electric field, across the membrane. The electrochemical proton gradient drives protons back through the membrane via the ATP-synthases, which use this backflow of protons to synthesize adenosine-5'-triphosphate from adenosine-5'-diphosphate and inorganic phosphate. Adenosine-5'-triphosphate is the immediate energy source for numerous processes, including biosynthesis of many compounds, uptake of nutrients, and motility.

The protons needed for the formation of water originate from the inner side of bacteria or mitochondria, whereas cytochrome c resides on the opposite side of the membrane. This separation of the substrates leads already to the generation of an electrochemical proton gradient during the reaction cycle. In addition, cytochrome c oxidases have developed a mechanism to translocate ("pump") up to four protons across the membrane per reaction cycle, thereby doubling the yield of energy conversion.

Cytochrome c oxidases are members of the superfamily of heme/copper-containing terminal oxidases (6, 16, 23, 57, 84), which also comprises many ubiquinol oxidases, e.g. the well-studied cytochrome bo_3 from *Escherichia coli*, but not the cytochrome bd complex from the same bacterium (26). Membership of the heme/copper-containing terminal oxidase superfamily is indicated by the presence of histidine ligands to two heme groups and to a copper atom (Cu_B) in subunit I, which is the best-conserved subunit. In bacteria, the heme groups can be hemes A, B, or O (16), whereas only heme A is found in mitochondrial cytochrome c oxidases. A low-spin heme, heme a in the cytochrome c oxidases from mitochondria or the proteobacteria *Paracoccus denitrificans* and *Rhodobacter sphaeroides*, accepts electrons from ubiquinol or from a copper A (Cu_A) center bound to subunit II, and transfers them to a binuclear center. The latter consists of a high-spin heme (heme a_3 in the cytochrome *c* oxidases from mitochondria and the proteobacteria), and a copper atom (Cu_B). Within the binuclear center, dioxygen is bound to the high-spin heme iron, reduced, and water is formed.

Subunit II is also well conserved. It is absent (or replaced) in some archaeal heme/copper-containing terminal oxidases, and, surprisingly, in an alternative oxidase complex of the nitrogen-fixing endosymbiont *Bradyrhizobium japonicum* (74). Subunit II contains the binuclear Cu_A center that receives the electrons from cytochrome *c* in cytochrome *c* oxidases. Consequently, the Cu_A center is absent in ubiquinol oxidases. Subunit III is also present in all mitochondrial and most bacterial heme-copper–containing terminal oxidases. In some bacterial and archaeal enzymes it (or a part of it) is fused to subunit I (17). As a result of their occurrence in most terminal heme-copper–containing terminal oxidases, subunits I-III are often called the core subunits. However, a complex consisting of subunits I and II of the cytochrome *c* oxidase from *P. denitrificans* is already fully active with respect to both dioxygen reduction to water and proton pumping (36).

As a consequence of their central position in metabolism, the cytochrome *c* oxidases have been intensively studied using biochemical, genetic, spectroscopic, and crystallographic tools. Nearly all conserved residues of subunit I have been mutated and the mutant enzymes have been characterized (43). The resulting structural predictions were found to be generally in good agreement with the structures obtained by X-ray crystallography. Time-resolved optical and resonance Raman spectroscopy (23, 49) has led to considerable insights into the catalytic cycle of this important enzyme. Successful crystallization was first reported in 1961 (117), but only recently crystals of a quality that allowed to determine the structure at high resolution have been obtained for the cytochrome *c* oxidases from *P. denitrificans* (45, 71, 72) and beef heart mitochondria (89, 90).

In this review, we summarize the results of the structure determinations as well as those of the various spectroscopic investigations. Special emphasis will lie on the coupling of oxygen reduction and proton movement in the light of the possible proton-transfer-pathways identified by mutagenesis work and X-ray crystallography.

HIGH-RESOLUTION STRUCTURES OF CYTOCHROME *C* OXIDASES

Overall Structure, Protein Subunits, and Prosthetic Groups

A landmark in the field of cytochrome *c* oxidase research was the determination of the three-dimensional structures of the bacterial cytochrome *c* oxidase from the soil bacterium *P. denitrificans* (45, 72) and its mammalian counterpart from bovine heart mitochondria (89, 90). These structures now provide the scaffold for the interpretation of the results of spectroscopic studies and mutagenesis experiments, and for the functional discussion.

The key step in the structure determination of membrane proteins is to obtain suitable crystals for X-ray crystallography. This feat was achieved in the case of the bovine heart enzyme by extensive detergent screening and in the case of the bacterial enzyme by an approach of enlarging the polar surface with an F_v fragment of a monoclonal antibody combined with detergent screening (71, 72).

The cytochrome *c* oxidase from *P. denitrificans* consists of the three core subunits I, II, and III and a small non-conserved subunit IV of unknown function (109). The first crystals of the bacterial enzyme were obtained using the four-subunit cytochrome *c* oxidase (71). Later, an improved crystal form of the functionally active two-subunit cytochrome *c* oxidase complexed with the same antibody fragment as the four-subunit cytochrome *c* oxidase was observed, and the structure was determined at 2.7 Å resolution (72). The cytochrome *c* oxidase from beef heart mitochondria possesses ten small subunits in addition to the core subunits. It was crystallized in a dimeric form.

The structures of the bacterial and the mitochondrial enzymes are surprisingly similar. The core parts (subunits I, II, and III) of the two crystal structures look nearly identical at the atomic level. Figure 1 (*top*) presents the overall structure of the bacterial cytochrome *c* oxidase in a view perpendicular to the membrane normal. In this view, the cytochrome *c* oxidase looks like a trapezoid, with an extension at the smaller side. The trapezoid is integrated into the membrane. The extension represents the water soluble globular domain of subunit II. Figure 1 (*bottom*) shows a truncated form of the bacterial cytochrome *c* oxidase in a view from the periplasmic side along the membrane normal. In this projection, cytochrome *c* oxidase has an oval shape.

SUBUNIT III   Although this subunit is present in nearly all cytochrome *c* oxidases, its function remains enigmatic. It does not contribute to the binding of

---→

Figure 1   Top: Ribbon representation of the cytochrome *c* oxidase from the soil bacterium *Paracoccus denitrificans* in a view parallel to the membrane. *Light gray*, subunit I; *medium gray*, subunit II; *dark gray*, subunit III; *black*, subunit IV. The two copper atoms of the Cu_A-center can be seen at the top as *two black spheres*, heme *a* as atomic model in *black*, heme a_3 in *dark gray*. The Cu_B-atom is represented by a *black sphere* near heme a_3.

Bottom: View of the membrane part of the cytochrome *c* oxidase from *P. denitrificans* from the periplasmic side. Only the transmembrane helices, the heme groups (*dark gray*) and Cu_B (*black sphere* near heme *a*) are shown. The transmembrane helices are numbered and the location of pores A, B, and C is indicated. Prepared using MOLSCRIPT (51) and RASTER 3D (58).

(A)

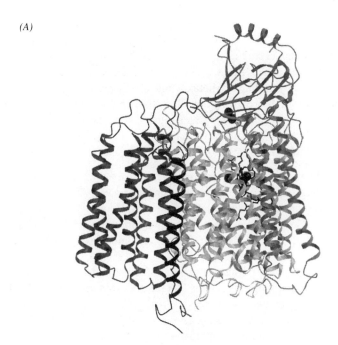

(B)

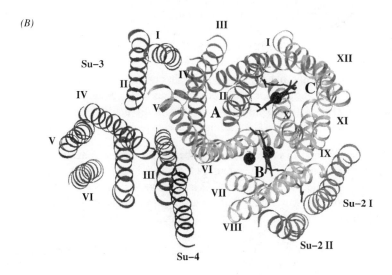

the cofactors nor is it necessary for proton pumping (36). Subunit III may be involved in the assembly of the cytochrome c oxidase (30) or form the entrance to a proposed oxygen channel leading to the active site (82; see below). It possesses seven transmembrane helices that are divided by a large V-shaped cleft into two bundles, one formed by the first two helices, and the other by helices III to VII. In this cleft, lipid molecules are firmly bound to conserved residues. A (putative) phosphatidylcholine has been incorporated into the atomic model of subunit III in the bacterial, and two phosphatidylethanolamine molecules and one phosphatidylglycerol molecule into that of the mitochondrial cytochrome c oxidase.

Subunit II   Subunit II consists of two transmembrane helices interacting with subunit I and a large C-terminal extramembranous domain containing the Cu_A-center, which is located above subunit I in the periplasmic or intermembrane space (Figure 1). The structure of the extramembranous domain was also determined using a soluble quinol oxidase fragment containing an engineered copper center (107).

The fold of the globular domain containing a ten-stranded β-barrel is very similar to that of class I copper proteins like plastocyanin and azurin (2). The main difference is the presence of a mixed-valence [Cu(1.5)-Cu(1.5)] binuclear copper complex, which agrees with previous suggestions based on EPR data (10, 48), and the presence of only eight strands in the β-barrel of type I copper proteins.

The binding site for the two copper atoms, which can be seen in Figure 2, is formed by residues from strand 6 and the loop connecting strands 9 and 10. The ligands for each Cu atom form a distorted tetrahedron. Both copper atoms are ligated by two Cys residues and one His residue (Cu_A1: Su II-Cys 216,[1] Su II-Cys 220, Su II-His 181; Cu_A2: Su II-Cys 216, Su II-Cys 220, Su II-His 224).

Each Cu atom has an additional ligand: in one case a methionine (Cu_A1: Su II-Met 227) and in the other the carbonyl oxygen of a glutamate residue (Cu_A2: Su II-Glu 218). The two Cu atoms are bridged by the two cysteine thiolates, and the copper atoms and Cys sulfurs lie in one plane.

SUBUNIT I   Subunit I is the largest and best conserved subunit of cytochrome c oxidase. It contains 12 transmembrane helices in an approximate threefold rotational symmetric arrangement. When viewed from the periplasmic side, the 12 transmembrane helices that are arranged in an anticlockwise sequential manner appear to form three symmetry-related semicircular arcs consisting of

---

[1]The sequence numbers refer to those of the subunits from the *Paracoccus denitrificans* cytochrome c oxidase. Table 1 contains the numbers of the homologous residues in the beef heart enzyme.

Table 1 Sequence number conversion table for important amino acid residues in subunits I and II of the cytochrome *c* oxidase from *P. denitrificans* and beef heart mitochondria

				Residue number	
				P. denitrificans	Bovine heart
Cu$_A$ ligands	Cu$_A$1	Su II	Cys	220	200
		Su II	Cys	216	196
		Su II	His	181	161
		Su II	Met	227	207
	Cu$_A$2	Su II	Cys	220	200
		Su II	Cys	216	196
		Su II	His	224	204
		Su II	Glu	218	198
Heme ligands	*a*	Su I	His	94	61
		Su I	His	413	378
	a$_3$	Su I	His	411	376
Cu$_B$ ligands		Su I	His	276	240
		Su I	His	325	290
		Su I	His	326	291
Mg ligands		Su II	Glu	218	198
		Su I	His	403	368
		Su I	Asp	404	369
Proton pathways	K-pathway	Su I	Lys	354	319
		Su I	Thr	351	316
		Su I	Tyr	280	244
	D-pathway	Su I	Asp	124	91
		Su I	Asn	199	163
		Su I	Asn	113	80
		Su I	Asn	131	98
		Su I	Tyr	35	19
		Su I	Ser	134	101
		Su I	Ser	193	157
		Su I	Glu	278	242
Electron transfer	Cu$_A$ → heme a	Su II	His	224	204
		Su I	Arg	473	438
		Su I	Arg	474	439
	heme → heme *a*$_3$	Su I	Phe	412	377

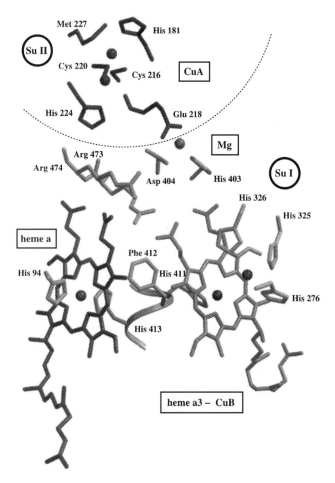

Figure 2 Atomic model for the prosthetic groups and neighboring amino acid residues in the cytochrome *c* oxidase from *P. denitrificans. Dark gray*, residues belonging to subunit II; *medium gray*, residues belonging to subunit I. *Spheres*, metals; *black*, heme *a*; *gray*, heme *a₃*. Prepared using MOLSCRIPT (51) and RASTER 3D (58).

four helices each (see Figure 1*B*, *bottom*). This arrangement generates three pores (A, B, C). Pore A is blocked by mostly conserved aromatic residues.

Subunit I contains the two heme groups, heme *a* being localized in pore C and heme a_3 in pore B. Heme a_3, together with a copper atom (Cu_B), forms the binuclear center that is the catalytic site for O_2 reduction. Both hemes are buried in the enzyme about 15 Å from the periplasmic surface. The heme planes are perpendicular to the membrane surface and the two propionate groups of each point toward the periplasmic side. The heme groups approach each other to a distance of 4.5 Å and form an interplanar angle of 104° in the *P. denitrificans* structure.

Heme a is a low-spin heme with two conserved histidine imidazoles of helices II and X as axial Fe-ligands (Su I-His 94, Su I-His 413). In contrast to heme a_3, its hydroxyethylfarnesyl side chain points downward and remains in pore C. Together with the surrounding hydrophobic residues, it blocks access to heme a from the cytoplasm.

Heme a_3 is a high-spin heme. In the electron density, the iron appears to be fivefold coordinated. A conserved histidine imidazole of helix X is the axial Fe-ligand (Su I-His 411), which is two residues downstream from the heme a histidine ligand. The hydroxyethylfarnesyl group of heme a_3 leaves pore B and penetrates into the lipid bilayer, so that access of protons to the binuclear center is principally possible from the cytoplasmic side of the membrane. The Cu_B ion is 4.5 Å away from the heme a_3 iron. It has three histidine imidazole ligands (Su I-His 276, Su I-His 325, and Su I-His 326). On the basis of strong antiferromagnetic coupling between Cu_B and heme a_3, a bridging ligand was proposed (73), but such a ligand is not clearly visible in the $[2F_o\text{-}F_c]$ electron density maps of the X-ray structures, and bridging by an amino acid side chain can be excluded. However, an $[F_o\text{-}F_c]$ difference map shows positive electron density between both metals. A combination of EXAFS and ENDOR spectroscopy suggests a fourth Cu_B ligand, most likely a water or a hydroxide ion, in the oxidized enzyme (22). A possible bridging structure is a hydroxide ion bound to Cu_B and hydrogen-bonded to a water ligand of the heme a_3 iron.

The cytochrome c oxidases—at least from mitochondria, *Rhodobacter sphaeroides*, and *P. denitrificans*—contain a non-redox–active Mn/Mg-binding site. In mitochondrial enzymes this site is occupied by Mg. Bacteria incorporate a substantial amount of manganese into this site when grown under Mg-limited conditions. This Mn/Mg-binding site is located at the interface between subunits I and II (see Figure 2). The Mg-ion is ligated by Su I-His 403, Su I-Asp 404, Su II-Glu 218, and at least one water (72, 90). An interesting feature is the arrangement of the carbonyl oxygen from Su II-Glu 218 also being a Cu_A ligand and of Su I-His 403 being hydrogen bonded to one of the heme a_3 propionates. Therefore, the Mg site lies directly between Cu_A and heme a_3. The function of the bound metal is not known.

ADDITIONAL SUBUNITS   The bacterial cytochrome c oxidases have none or only one additional subunit (SU IV). The X-ray structure analysis of the *Paracoccus* enzyme revealed that the fourth subunit consists mainly of one transmembrane helix interacting with subunits I and III (45). Its function is unknown.

Even deletion of its gene has no obvious effect on the enzymatic properties, expression, and bacterial growth (109).

The mammalian cytochrome c oxidase from bovine heart has ten additional subunits. Again their function is unknown. The subunits Va and Vb are small globular proteins bound to the matrix side of the core, and the globular subunit VIb faces the intermembrane space. Subunit VIb binds a zinc ion of unknown function in a tetrahedral coordination. The subunits IV, VIa, VIc, VIIa, VIIb, VIIc, and VIII each possess one transmembrane helix. Subunit VIa seems to be responsible for the dimerization of the mitochondrial cytochrome c oxidase (90). It has been suggested that the small subunits act as regulators and bind effectors of enzyme activity like nucleotides (46) or are required for assembly. Tsukihara et al (90) propose two cholate binding sites as potential nucleotide binding sites. The presence of tissue-specific isoforms of several additional subunits supports the proposal of a regulatory function (52, 116).

Electron-Transfer Pathways

The crystal structures provide the distances between the metal centers and their relative orientations, the ligands, and the residues between them. Therefore, it is possible to obtain a deeper insight into the electron-transfer pathways.

Cu_A is generally accepted as being the primary electron acceptor from cytochrome c (37). The electron transfer rate between cytochrome c and Cu_A is very fast, about 70,000 s^{-1} (38). It has been proposed that the formation of the complex between cytochrome c and the cytochrome c oxidase is the rate-limiting step in the reaction between reduced cytochrome c and the oxidase (4). The nature of the binding is still unclear. The strong dependence on ionic strength is indicative for electrostatic interactions stabilizing the complex (4, 81). The corner formed by the globular domain of subunit II and the flat periplasmic surface of subunit I is most likely the cytochrome c binding site (45). This area contains ten exposed acidic residues that could interact with lysine residues at the heme edge of cytochrome c. Indeed, mutagenesis data have indicated a crucial role of these residues (110), although earlier work (53) using a soluble Cu_A domain of subunit II misidentified two residues as important that are actually deeply buried in the interface between subunits I and II.

From Cu_A the electron is transferred to heme a at a high speed (about 20,000 s^{-1}), considering the long metal-to-metal distance (19.5 Å) and small driving force (50 mV; 108). Iwata et al pointed out (45) that there is a conserved possible electron transfer pathway between Cu_A and heme a consisting of 14 covalent bonds and 2 hydrogen bonds. The Cu_A ligand Su II-His 224 forms a hydrogen bond to the carbonyl oxygen of Su I-Arg 473 located in the loop between the transmembrane helices IX and X. There are many contacts between residues in this loop and the heme a propionates. It seems that the combination of a small reorganization energy for the Cu_A-heme a electron transfer caused by the binuclear structure of Cu_A (54) and the presence of an efficient electron transfer pathway is responsible for the rapid electron flow between the metal centers (79). Perturbation of the symmetrical nature of the binuclear Cu_A site indeed results in a strong inhibition of the enzyme (118). Direct electron transfer from Cu_A to heme a_3 is neglectably slow (1–100 s^{-1}), although it was suggested (37), and a regulatory function affecting the H^+/e^- stoichiometry was postulated (14). The crystal structure shows that the distances from Cu_A to the iron atoms of heme a and a_3 are 19.5 Å and 22.1 Å, respectively. This difference in distance, in combination with a much higher reorganization energy for Cu_A–heme a_3 electron transfer, could account for the large difference in transfer rates (13).

From heme a the electron is transferred to heme a_3. As mentioned, these hemes are nearly perpendicular to each other. While the iron-to-iron distance is 13.5 Å, the edges of the hemes approach each other up to 4.5 Å. An edge-to-edge electron transfer is therefore possible as well as a pathway using the iron ligands Su I-His 413 and Su I-His 411 and the polypeptide backbone. Another possibility mentioned (45, 90) is a pathway involving the side chain of the conserved Su I-Phe 412 that is placed approximately equidistant between the hemes (see also Figure 2).

Proton-Transfer Pathways

Based on the crystal structure of the *Paracoccus* enzyme and in agreement with the results of site-directed mutagenesis studies (24, 43, 88), two possible proton transfer pathways have been suggested (45), represented in Figure 3. The shorter one, also referred to as the K-pathway, leads to the binuclear center via the highly conserved residues Su I-Lys 354, Su I-Thr 351, and Su I-Tyr 280 located in the transmembrane helices VI and VIII, and the hydroxyl group of the heme a_3 hydroxyethylfarnesyl chain. The second, longer pathway (D-pathway) involves Su I-Asp 124 and a number of conserved polar residues (Su I-Asn 199, Su I-Asn 113, Su I-Asn 131, Su I-Tyr 35, Su I-Ser 134, and Su I-Ser 193) located around pore C (see Figure 1, *bottom*). Along the pathway, the proton would leave pore C toward Su I-Glu 278, most likely via a solvent-filled cavity. From there, the pathway is less clear but may involve Su I-Pro 277, from where it could reach the binuclear site. Alternatively, pumped protons could be transferred from Su I-Glu 278 to the heme a_3 propionates if these residues possess different conformations during the catalytic cycle.

Inspection of the bovine structure (90) revealed the same K-pathway, but the proposed D-pathway in the bovine structure does not lead to the binuclear site. It uses the same entrance, but after Su I-Ser 193 (*P. denitrificans* numbering; see Table 1 for conversion) it directly reaches the intermembrane space via polar

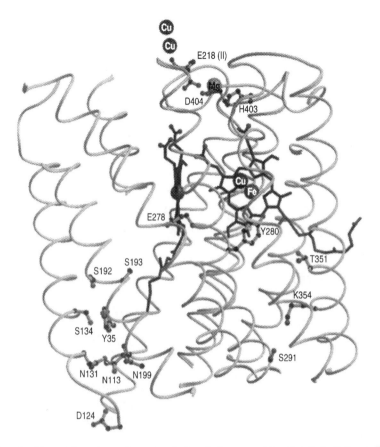

Figure 3   The transfer pathways for protons in the cytochrome *c* oxidase from *P. denitrificans*. The K-pathway including Su I-Lys-354 leads straight to the binuclear site. The D-pathway starting Su I-Asp-124 leads straight up to Su I-Ser-193 and then through a solvent-filled cavity to Su I-Glu-278. The further proton transfer pathway is unclear. It may lead to the binuclear heme a_3/Cu$_B$ site, or to the propionate side chains of heme a_3. *Top*, Mg-binding site and Cu$_A$-center. Prepared using MOLSCRIPT (51) and RASTER 3D (58).

residues not conserved in the *P. denitrificans* enzyme. The latter residues are either alanines or glycines in the bacterial enzyme, thus leaving enough space for bound water allowing proton transfer (90). A third pathway passing heme *a*, which is located mainly between helices XI and XII of subunit I, was described (90). This pathway is also present in the *P. denitrificans* structure, with the exception of one residue. Mutagenesis data supporting these latter pathways do not exist.

Oxygen and Water Channels

For the beef heart cytochrome *c* oxidase, three hydrophobic channels were described and suggested as potential pathways for oxygen to reach the binuclear site (90). Some dynamic sidechain movements would still be needed to allow oxygen diffusion. The channels start at the protein-membrane interface near the center of the lipid bilayer, where oxygen solubility is much higher than in the aqueous phase. One of these channels has also been identified in the bacterial oxidase (82). It starts in the V-shaped cleft of subunit III directly above a tightly bound lipid molecule and leads through subunit I into the binuclear site. Whether oxygen channels are needed is not clear, because oxygen concentrations are high under physiological conditions.

A hydrophilic cleft between subunit I and II proceeds from the binuclear center to the outside of the membrane. This channel involves a number of charged residues and the Mg binding site. Tsukihara et al (90) suggested that this structure serves as an exit pathway for the water produced. Iwata et al (45), who favor a direct coupling of proton pumping, described this cleft as the exit pathway of the pumped protons from the binuclear center to the outside. Further experiments are needed to identify the correct interpretation.

OXYGEN REDUCTION AND ITS COUPLING TO PROTON MOVEMENT

Extensive biochemical and spectroscopic work has been performed to investigate the different oxygen species emerging during the reaction of cytochrome *c* oxidase with dioxygen and to determine the rates of the associated reaction steps.

The reaction of reduced or partially reduced cytochrome *c* oxidase with dioxygen is too fast to utilize conventional stopped-flow techniques. Therefore, a widely used method to initiate the reaction of the reduced enzyme with dioxygen is the flow-flash technique initially developed by Gibson & Greenwood (25, 27), where CO-bound reduced cytochrome *c* oxidase is photodissociated by a short laser flash after mixing with dioxygen-saturated buffer. A similar approach can be used to trap the incomplete forward reaction at intermediate points using the two-electron (18) or the three-electron reduced enzyme (111, 112). An important underlying assumption for the relevance of this technique is that the photodissociated CO does not interfere with the dioxygen reduction mechanism. The great advantage of this method is the high quantum yield in comparison to flash experiments with other ligands such as, for example, cyanide (41), so that a short laser flash results in a complete conversion of the CO complex to the oxy complex (6). However, the observation of the different oxygen intermediates is very difficult, because the reaction with the fully reduced enzyme is extremely fast and the large optical absorbance changes caused by the redox events on the metal centers during the dioxygen reduction complicate the observation of the much smaller changes associated with the oxygen chemistry. Nevertheless, time-resolved optical absorption spectroscopy was used to investigate the kinetics of electron transfer (38, 40, 68, 70, 94) and to determine the spectral characteristics of intermediates (61). EPR studies (12, 35, 47, 111, 112) as well as low-temperature optical absorption measurements (18, 19) have also provided information about some transient intermediates during the reaction with dioxygen. A wealth of information about the structural features of some intermediates has been derived by Raman spectroscopy (32–34, 64–67, 75–77, 91–93).

Adopting a different approach, Wikström (103) originally showed the existence of the different oxygen intermediates in an experiment on intact mitochondria, where he managed to partially reverse the oxygen reaction by energizing mitochondria with ATP, resulting in a backward electron flow.

Two oxygen species have also been generated artificially by addition of different amounts of hydrogen peroxide to the oxidized enzyme (115). Detailed information about these reactions can be obtained from an article by Fabian & Palmer (21).

The Ferrous-Oxy Species

Figure 4 summarizes the catalytic cycle of cytochrome c oxidase with respect to the oxygen chemistry. Starting at the fully oxidized enzyme (O), the first intermediate formed is the one-electron reduced or E-state, where the electron equilibrates between heme a and the binuclear center (62). It has been suggested (95) that the rate of electron transfer from heme a to the binuclear center is proton-controlled in that protonation of a site close to the binuclear center is required to raise the redox potential of heme a_3, thus stabilizing its reduced form. Uptake of the second electron yields the two-electron reduced or R-state, where dioxygen can bind to the reduced heme a_3. The rate of this initial binding reaction, however, is not proportional to [O_2] but saturates at high concentrations of oxygen (27, 56), thus suggesting transient ligation to another site prior to binding to the heme.

Additional evidence has been provided that the initial O_2 adduct does not involve heme a_3 (11). Thus, initiated and supported by the observation of transient but quantitative binding of CO to Cu_B after photolysis from heme a_3 (3, 20), the copper has been proposed as the first binding site for the incoming oxygen (114). Oliveberg & Malmström (69) have attributed absorbance changes at 830 nm to the formation of this Cu_B-O_2 adduct, and the second-order forward rate constant for the Cu_B-O_2 association has been determined

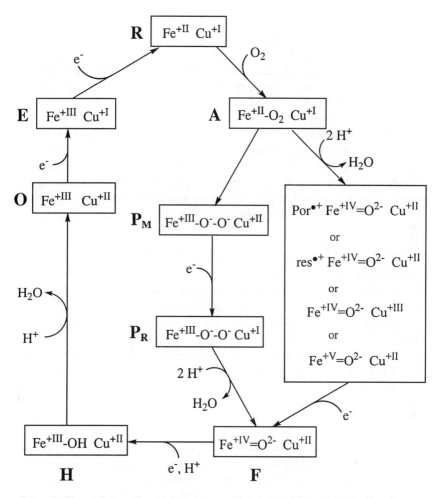

Figure 4 The catalytic cycle of cytochrome *c* oxidase as derived from optical and resonance Raman spectroscopy (23, 49). Starting from the oxidized form (*O*), the one-electron reduced form (*E*) and then the doubly reduced form (*R*) are generated. Upon oxygen binding compound A is observed. Next the peroxy-intermediates P_M, P_R are formed (see also text). Alternative structures are presented on the *right*, based on the proposal that the O-O bond is already split in these states. However, one electron is missing, which could be provided by a porphyin-ring system (por), an amino acid residue (res), Cu_B (leading to a Cu^{3+}-state), or the heme a_3-Fe. There is general agreement about the structure of the oxoferryl-state (*F*) and a hydroxy-state (*H*) formed after protonation of the iron-bound oxygen atom. After water formation and release, the O-state is regenerated.

as 3.5×10^8 M^{-1} s^{-1} (11). Because the binding is transient, the interaction between O_2 and Cu_B is only weak ($K_D = 8$ mM; 8, 94).

The ferrous-oxy species was first observed at low temperatures by Chance and co-workers (18) and termed compound A. At room temperature, it is characterized by an increase in absorbance (relative to the unliganded reduced enzyme) at 595 nm and 430 nm (39, 96) and the ν(Fe-O_2) stretching mode at 572 cm^{-1} (32, 64, 91) in the resonance Raman spectrum that shifts to 546 cm^{-1} when $^{18}O_2$ is used (91). This frequency is well reproduced by an imidazole-heme A-O_2 model compound (63) showing that, similar to oxyhemoglobin, O_2 forms a relaxed, low-energy complex with the ferrous heme and that there are only small distal pocket effects and little interaction of the oxygen with Cu_B (5). Oliveberg & Malmström (69) have determined the pseudo-first–order rate of O_2 binding to be 1×10^5 s^{-1}, in good agreement with values found by Verkhovsky et al (94) and Bailey et al (8). Again, the O_2 association is weak, with a K_D of $\sim$0.3 mM (18, 40, 94).

Electron Transfer and Oxygen Intermediates in the Mixed-Valence Enzyme

The further decay of the oxygen species depends upon the redox state of the enzyme. In the case of the mixed-valence enzyme where no further electrons are available, compound A, through electronic reorganization within the binuclear center, is converted to the so-called compound C (18) at a rate of 5×10^3 s^{-1} (40, 68, 93). At room temperature, this species is characterized by a strong absorbance band at 607 nm ($\epsilon\{607$–630 nm$\} = 11$ mM^{-1}cm^{-1}; 106), and a red-shift of the Soret band to 428 nm. A similar species is observed in the reaction of the oxidized enzyme with low concentrations of hydrogen peroxide at alkaline pH (9, 21, 50, 102) and in reversed-electron flow experiments as the result of a two-electron reversal (103). However, the structure of this species, which is at a redox level two electrons above the oxidized enzyme, has remained a matter of debate. Previous proposals include a ferric-cupric peroxy species P_M (M stands for mixed valence) (Figure 4) (6, 61), a ferryl-cupric (Fe(IV)=O Cu(II)) species with an additional protein radical (101, 102), and a Fe(IV)=O Cu(III) form (21). The latter two are supported by Raman studies of the oxidized enzyme/peroxide reaction, where 607-nm excitation yielded a 803 cm^{-1} mode that was shifted to 769 cm^{-1} when the reaction was initiated with $H_2^{18}O_2$ (75) and thus assigned to a ferryl species. However, this Raman mode has not been observed in cytochrome bo_3 (42), though the oxygen intermediates are the same in the bo_3- and aa_3-type terminal oxidases (60). Additionally, the absorbance spectrum of the 607-nm species observed in the reaction of the fully-reduced enzyme (P_R) is nearly identical to that of P_M, although P_R is at a redox level one electron above P_M, thus favoring a peroxy-type structure for P_M (61; see below).

Oxygen Reduction in the Fully-Reduced Enzyme

The reaction of the fully-reduced enzyme with dioxygen differs from that of the mixed-valence form in that two more electrons are available that can be transferred to the binuclear center after oxygen binding. Again, compound A is formed first (Figure 3). However, compared to the mixed-valence/oxygen reaction, the subsequent electronic step is much faster, namely 3×10^4 s^{-1} (32, 37, 68, 93, 94) and has been attributed to electron transfer from the reduced heme a to the binuclear center (34, 37). Thus, the redox state of the binuclear center in the newly formed species is formally three reducing equivalents above that of the oxidized enzyme, and, assuming a peroxy-like structure, the species was termed P1 (94) or P_R (reduced; 61). It has been shown very elegantly by Verkhovsky et al (97) that it is the heme-heme electron transfer and thus the formation of P_R that traps the oxygen within the binuclear center. As already mentioned above, the spectral properties of P_R are nearly indistinguishable from those of P_M, suggesting that the redox state of heme a_3 and the configuration of the heme-oxygen moiety are the same in the two species (61, 86). As for P_M, the structure of P_R is yet unknown and has been debated extensively over the last years. Two Raman modes at 804 and 356 cm^{-1} have been associated with the two intermediates but interpreted differently by different research groups. Varotsis et al (93) assigned the latter mode to a $\nu(Fe^{3+}-O^-)$ stretching vibration, thus suggesting a ferric-cuprous peroxy species for P_R (Figure 4), while a ferrous-cupric peroxy form has been proposed by Blair et al (12), because they observed an EPR-active intermediate at low temperature, and by Babcock et al (7). However, Kitagawa and co-workers (49, 67, 75, 76) assign the 356 cm^{-1} mode to a $Fe^V=O$ bending motion, thus assuming that the O-O bond is already broken at this stage of the catalytic cycle (Figure 4) (23, 49). It has been pointed out by Morgan et al (61) that, in the light of identical absorbance spectra for P_M and P_R, the ferryl-type structures (21, 101, 102) proposed for P_M seem unlikely. If P_M had the $Fe^{IV}=O$ Cu^{III} structure proposed by Fabian & Palmer (21) then P_R, which is one electron more reduced, would most likely be $Fe^{IV}=O$ Cu^{II}. The latter structure, however, has been unequivocally assigned to intermediate F (see below). Because P_R and F have been shown to be distinct intermediates in the catalytic cycle (61), the P_M structure suggested by Fabian & Palmer seems unlikely. The same is true for the oxoferryl structure with the protein radical, because such a radical species cannot account for the spectral differences between P_M and F as outlined by Morgan et al (61; see also below).

The Ferryl and Hydroxy Species

Proceeding from the P_R state, a ferryl-cupric species F is produced on a time scale of t = 200 μs without further electron input into the binuclear center. This intermediate exhibits a characteristic absorption maximum in the optical difference spectrum (ferryl minus resting) at $\sim$580 nm and it is well established that the 785 cm^{-1} mode observed in resonance Raman spectra and assigned as a $\nu(Fe^{IV}=O)$ stretching mode in $^{16}O_2/^{18}O_2$ mixed-isotope experiments is due to this ferryl species (34, 64, 92). Unexpectedly, this 785 cm^{-1} species was determined to shift to 795–800 cm^{-1} in D_2O experiments (33, 65, 93), which can hardly be explained if a simple $Fe^{IV}=O$ mode is assumed. Han et al (33) have concluded that the ferryl-oxo complex is hydrogen-bonded in H_2O but nonhydrogen-bonded in D_2O, which implicates large structural changes upon deuteration. Ogura et al (67) and Proshlyakov et al (76) assigned the 800 cm^{-1} mode in D_2O to an earlier intermediate in the cycle, which appears at a different time scale because of a significant slowing down of the reaction by the H_2O/D_2O exchange.

The ferryl intermediate can also be generated by a one-electron oxidation of the binuclear center in reversed O_2-reduction experiments (103, 106) or by carefully adding three electrons to the enzyme and further mixing with dioxygen (111, 112). The same state could be obtained by the flow-flash technique using quinol oxidases that contain three electrons in their fully reduced state because of the lack of the Cu_A center (55).

The conversion of the P_R to the F state is accompanied by electron transfer from Cu_A to heme a, resulting in an 50/50 equilibration between the two redox centers, so that the electron hole at heme a produced in the previous phase of the reaction is partially filled up (61, 86). This event was suggested to be initiated by the oxidation of Cu_B because of the anticooperative interaction between Cu_B and heme a (69). This implies that the oxidation of Cu_B is linked to a conversion of the low-potential heme a to a high-potential heme a, resulting in the electron transfer from the Cu_A to heme a. This process occurs on a similar or faster time scale as the formation of the ferryl intermediate ($\tau = 100$–140 μs; 37, 38, 40, 68) and could be detected as a restoration of absorbance at 440 nm in the optical spectrum (21, 94). The partial oxidation of Cu_A was also shown directly by an increase in absorption at 830 nm at room temperature ($\tau = 170$ μs; k = 6 × 10^3 s^{-1}; 40). Recently, Morgan et al (61) have provided evidence that the peroxy species decays into the 580-nm species F at the same time as the low-spin heme becomes partially re-reduced by Cu_A at −25°C.

The rate of the P $\rightarrow$ F transition is pH-dependent, decreasing at increasing pH with a pK_a of 7.9, and as mentioned above, the reaction rate is lowered by H_2O/D_2O exchange. The value obtained for k_H/k_D was 1.4 for this phase (29). These observations led to the suggestion that the rate is limited by proton uptake, which is also supported by the fact that the rate of proton uptake monitored using pH indicators is similar to the rate of the redox reaction (29). Moreover, the pH dependence of the proton uptake parallels that of the redox reaction and the observed deuterium isotopic effect of the proton uptake was also determined to be 1.4 (29). Oliveberg & Malmström (69) therefore proposed that the formation of the F species is controlled by protonation at the binuclear center.

The conversion of the P_M state discussed above to the ferryl state can be obtained by input of a single electron using a photoinducible reductant, which confirms that P_M differs fom F by one electron equivalent (98).

Finally, the F species is reduced by the fourth electron accompanied with the uptake of a proton (29), which leads to the formation of a new species detectable by Raman spectroscopy. The resulting ferric-hydroxy species (H) is characterized by a resonance Raman line at 450 cm^{-1} (31, 33, 65–67, 93) appearing with a rate constant of 800–1000 s^{-1} (29, 38, 68). This fourth phase has also been shown to be pH-dependent and to have a D_2O isotope effect. Like the third phase, this step is suggested to be rate-limited by proton uptake from the medium (29). The following uptake of another proton leads to the ferric/cupric O-state after the release of the second water molecule, so that the dioxygen reduction cycle is completed.

The Coupling of Electron Transfer and Proton Motion

As described above, oxygen reduction in terminal heme-copper oxidases is coupled to proton translocation from the cytoplasm or the mitochondrial matrix ("the i-side") into the periplasm or mitochondrial intermembrane space, thus generating a proton and charge gradient across the membrane. However, the mechanism by which the two processes are coupled to each other at the molecular level remains unclear. In principle, two different schemes are feasible: an indirect mechanism in which the redox chemistry is associated with major conformational changes in the protein, or a direct mechanism where the coupling is achieved by subtle changes occurring very close to the redox centers, e.g. through the involvement of metal ligands. The former has been suggested by Tsukihara et al (90) on the grounds of their proposed proton pathways separated from the oxygen chemistry in the crystal structure of the bovine-heart enzyme. However, many other groups have focussed on a direct coupling since the energy required for proton translocation must be supplied by the oxygen chemistry, and the binuclear centers of the heme-copper–containing terminal oxidase superfamily share a common structure (80).

"Scalar" protons required for water formation are generally distinguished from "vectoral" or "pumped" protons that are translocated across the membrane, although the former term is a misnomer in view of the fact that these protons are proposed to originate from the bacterial cytoplasm or the mitochondrial matrix. Through analysis of the effect of membrane potential on the P/F and F/O equilibria (104) and time-resolved charge-translocation measurements on reconstituted enzyme (99), it has been proposed that only the P $\rightarrow$ F and F $\rightarrow$ O transitions are associated with proton translocation, each to an extent of $2H^+/e^-$. In agreement with this proposal and with the results of proton uptake measurements where two protons were determined to be bound by the enzyme upon two-electron reduction of the binuclear center (15, 59), Rich (80) suggested a model in which electron accumulation at the binuclear center drives the uptake of protons (to maintain local electroneutrality) from the i-side. These protons are stored in a proton trap close to the binuclear site but physically separated from the oxygen chemistry—in agreement with the earlier proposed histidine-cycle model by Wikström and co-workers (105; see below). Upon formation of the reactive oxygen species (i.e. the P- and F-species), protons required for water formation are taken up from the i-side and, through electrostatic repulsion, the trapped protons are expelled into the periplasm. Critical to such a scheme is the nature of the gating process that inhibits the access of the trapped protons to the i-side (i.e. prevents the trapped protons from being expelled back into the cytoplasm) and, at the same time, allows the substrate protons to enter from the i-side. Previous proposals of such a gating mechanism involve protonation and ligand exchanges on heme a_3 (83), between heme a_3 and Cu_B (113), and on Cu_B (the "histidine cycle"; 105). The latter, involving a histidine residue cycling through different conformations and protonation states, was also adapted by Iwata et al (45) on the grounds of possible multiple orientations for the Cu_B ligand His-325, because there was no electron density for the sidechain of this residue in the oxidized, azide-treated enzyme. Consistent with the Rich model, the model by Iwata et al includes two different proton access routes and accounts for strict electroneutrality.

However, recent X-ray crystallographic experiments have shown that His-325 is a Cu_B ligand in both the azide-free oxidized and the fully reduced enzymes (Harrenga et al, unpublished). The latter fact is difficult to interprete within the framework of the histidine shuttle mechanism by Iwata et al (45).

Proton-Binding Groups and Possible Proton Pumping Pathways

Upon reduction of cytochrome c oxidase, 2.4 H^+ have been determined to be taken up at pH 7.5 (15, 59), 0.4 of which appear to be associated with Cu_A/heme a, and the remaining two with the binuclear center (59). Capitanio et al (15) identified four protolytic groups undergoing reversible pK changes upon reduction of the enzyme, two of which were assigned to reduction of heme a_3 ($pK_{ox} \approx 7$, $pK_{red} > 12$, respectively), while the other two were associated with Cu_B ($pK_{ox} \approx 6$, $pK_{red} \approx 7$) and heme a ($pK_{ox} \approx 6$, $pK_{red} \approx 9$), respectively. In the study by Mitchell & Rich (59) individual pKs were not accessible, indicating values <7.2 and >8.5 for the oxidized and the reduced enzyme, respectively. Somewhat differently, Ädelroth et al (1) and Hallen et al (28), studying the heme a_3–heme a backward electron transfer (after flashing off CO from the mixed-valence enzyme) by following conductance and/or absorbance changes, identified a protonatable group close to the binuclear site to which they assigned pKs of 9.7 and 8.5 for reduced and oxidized heme a_3, respectively. Hallen et al (28) have speculated that a hydroxide ion bound to the binuclear center could be the proton-binding group. Such a hydroxide ion has been suggested as a ligand to Cu_B on the grounds of EXAFS and ENDOR measurements on an oxidized aa_3 type quinol oxidase enzyme at high pH (22). Additionally, it could provide the group close to the binuclear center suggested by Verkhovsky et al (95), the protonation of which is required to stabilize the reduced form of heme a_3.

Two possible proton pathways were identified in the *Paracoccus denitrificans* enzyme (45), here referred to as the D- and K-pathways, respectively (see above). The former involves, besides a number of polar residues, the highly conserved Asp-124 and Glu-278, while the latter leads toward the binuclear center via Lys-354. Mutation of Asp-124 to asparagine produces an enzyme that, though still able to reduce oxygen (albeit with a lower activity), is incapable of proton pumping (88), an effect that can be reversed by second-site mutations in the close vicinity of the aspartate (24). Thus, Iwata et al (45) assigned the D-pathway to the translocated protons and the K-pathway to the substrate protons. Such an assignment is also compatible with the observation that terminal oxidases that are expected not to pump protons, e.g. those from archaea, do not possess acidic residues homologous to Asp-124 and Glu-278, while Lys-354 is conserved in these enzymes.

From additional site-directed mutagenesis experiments (43, 44, 50a, 85, 87, 100), it has now become clear that Asp-124, Glu-278, and Lys-354 are indeed key residues for proton transfer to the binuclear site. However, the fact that heme a_3 reduction is inhibited by mutation of Lys-354 to Met (44) and the results of charge-translocation studies (50a, 85) suggest that the lysine is required for the O → R transition but it does not seem to be crucial for the P → O part of the catalytic cycle. Additionally, mutation of Glu-278 was found to completely inhibit proton translocation associated with the P → O reactions (50a, 85), therefore suggesting the two channels to be important for different parts of the catalytic cycle rather than for consumed and pumped protons. One could speculate that oxygen binding to the binuclear center blocks proton access via the K-pathway, e.g. through interaction of the oxygen with Tyr-280 or through structural changes coupled to the reduction of the binuclear site that could block the K-path and/or open the D-path. Such changes could be triggered by Cu_B and heme a_3 moving apart upon reduction as the proposed hydroxide group bound between the two redox sites becomes protonated.

CONCLUSIONS

Substantial progress toward understanding the mechanism of cytochrome c oxidase action has been made in recent years. First, mainly by time-resolved optical and resonance Raman spectroscopy, the catalytic cycle has been investigated and the intermediates have been identified and characterized, although there is some debate about the structure of one major intermediate. Second, site-directed mutagenesis work has provided a good structural picture of the enzyme, e.g. it has led to the identification, in combination with spectroscopy, of the ligands to the metals. Site-directed mutagenesis work has also identified some residues that are involved in proton transfer. Third, two independent structure determinations, one of a bacterial and the other of a mitochondrial cytochrome c oxidase, have yielded a detailed view into the molecular architecture of cytochrome c oxidase. The arrangement of the prosthetic groups and the structures of the protein subunits are now precisely known. Putative proton transfer pathways have been identified, supported by the results of site-directed mutagenesis experiments. The characterization of such mutants has led to a better understanding of the roles of the proton transfer pathways.

However, neither the structural nor the spectroscopic work has led to a convincing proposal how the redox chemistry of oxygen reduction and water formation is coupled to proton pumping. Two basic mechanisms are discussed: direct coupling versus indirect coupling. Indirect coupling would be caused by a structural change distant from the active site that leads to proton release to the outside, whereas in a direct coupling mechanism a change of a ligand to a metal of the binuclear site would be critically involved in proton pumping. Very attractive is the hypothesis (80, 105) that the protons, which are taken up upon reduction of the enzyme, are those being pumped. They would, through electrostatic interactions, be "expelled" by protons, which are taken up later and are "consumed" in the catalytic cycle.

It can be hoped that it will be possible to trap intermediates of the catalytic cycle in the crystals and to determine their structures. These structures should form the cornerstone for a further elucidation of the mechanism, but further spectroscopic experiments will be needed. It will be of critical importance to identify those residues or groups that are protonated upon reduction. Fourier transform infrared spectroscopy using wild-type and mutant enzymes both under steady state conditions (35a, 55a) and kinetic experiments should be very helpful. Thus, there are good reasons to believe that we will understand the mechanism of the coupling of redox chemistry and proton pumping in cytochrome *c* oxidase within a few years.

Visit the *Annual Reviews home page* at
http://www.AnnualReviews.org.

Literature Cited

1. Ädelroth P, Sigurdson H, Hallen S, Brzezinski P. 1996. Kinetic coupling between electron and proton transfer in cytochrome *c* oxidase: simultaneous measurements of conductance and absorbance changes. *Proc. Natl. Acad. Sci. USA* 93:12292–97
2. Adman ET. 1991. Copper protein structures. *Adv. Protein Chem.* 42:145–97
3. Alben JO, Moh PP, Fiamingo FG, Altschuld RA. 1981. Cytochrome oxidase (a_3) heme and copper observed by low temperature Fourier-transform infrared spectroscopy of the CO complex. *Proc. Natl. Acad. Sci. USA* 78:234–37
4. Antalis TM, Palmer G. 1982. Kinetic characterization of interaction between cytochrome oxidase and cytochrome *c*. *J. Biol. Chem.* 257:6194–206
5. Babcock GT, Varotsis C. 1993. Discrete steps in dioxygen activation—the cytochrome oxidase/O_2 reaction. *J. Bioenerg. Biomembr.* 25:71–80
6. Babcock GT, Wikström M. 1992. Oxygen activation and the conservation of energy in cell respiration. *Nature* 356:301–9
7. Babcock GT, Floris R, Nilsson T, Pressler M, Varotsis C, Vollenbroek E. 1996. Dioxygen activation in enzymatic systems and in inorganic models. *Inorg. Chim. Acta* 243:345–53
8. Bailey JA, James CA, Woodruff WH. 1996. Flow-flash kinetics of O_2 binding to cytochrome *c* oxidase at elevated [O_2]: observations using high-pressure stopped-flow for gaseous reactants. *Biochem. Biophys. Res. Commun.* 220:1055–60
9. Bickar D, Bonaventura J, Bonaventura C. 1982. Cytochrome *c* oxidase binding of hydrogen peroxide. *Biochemistry* 21:2661–66
10. Blackburn NJ, Barr ME, Woodruff WH, van der Oost J, DeVries S. 1994. Metal-metal bonding in biology—EXAFS evidence for a 2.5 Å copper-copper bond in the Cu_A center of cytochrome *c* oxidase. *Biochemistry* 33:10401–7
11. Blackmore RS, Greenwood C, Gibson QH. 1991. Studies of the primary oxygen intermediate in the reaction of fully reduced cytochrome oxidase. *J. Biol. Chem.* 266:19245–49
12. Blair DF, Witt SN, Chan SI. 1985. Mechanism of cytochrome *c* oxidase-catalyzed dioxygen reduction at low temperatures: evidence for two intermediates at the three-electron level and entropic promotion of the bond-breaking step. *J. Am. Chem. Soc.* 107:7389–99
13. Brzezinski P. 1996. Internal electron-transfer reactions in cytochrome *c* oxidase. *Biochemistry* 35:5611–15
14. Capitanio N, Capitanio G, Demarinis DA, De Nitto E, Massari S, Papa S. 1996. Factors affecting the H^+/e^- stoichiometry in mitochondrial cytochrome *c* oxidase: influence of the rate of electron flow and transmembrane pH. *Biochemistry* 35:10800–6
15. Capitanio N, Vygodina TV, Capitanio C, Konstantinov AA, Nicholls P, Papa S. 1997. Redox-linked protolytic reactions in soluble cytochrome *c* oxidase from beef-heart mitochondria: redox Bohr effects. *Biochim. Biophys. Acta* 1318:255–65
16. Calhoun MW, Thomas JW, Gennis RG. 1994. The cytochrome oxidase superfamily of redox-driven proton pumps. *Trends Biochem. Sci.* 19:325–30
17. Castresana J, Lübben M, Saraste M, Higgins DG. 1994. Evolution of cytochrome oxidase, an enzyme older than atmospheric oxygen. *EMBO J.* 13:2516–25
18. Chance B, Saronio C, Leigh JS Jr. 1975. Functional intermediates in the reaction of membrane-bound cytochrome oxidase with oxygen. *J. Biol. Chem.* 250:9226–37
19. Clore GM, Andréasson L-E, Karlsson BG, Aasa R, Malmström B. 1980. Characterization of the low-temperature intermediates of the reaction of fully reduced soluble cytochrome oxidase with oxygen by electron paramagnetic resonance and optical spectroscopy. *Biochem. J.* 185:139–54
20. Dyer RB, Einarsdottir O, Killough PM,

Lopez-Garcia JJ, Woodruff WH. 1989. Transient binding of photodissociated CO to Cu_B^+ of eucaryotic cytochrome oxidase at ambient temperature. *J. Am. Chem. Soc.* 111:7657–59

21. Fabian M, Palmer G. 1995. The interaction of cytochrome oxidase with hydrogen peroxide: the relationship of compounds P and F. *Biochemistry* 34:13802–10

22. Fann YC, Ahmed I, Blackburn NJ, Boswell JS, Verkhovskaya ML, et al. 1995. Structure of Cu_B in the binuclear heme-copper center of the cytochrome aa_3-type quinol oxidase from *Bacillus subtilis. Biochemistry* 35:10245–55

23. Ferguson-Miller S, Babcock GT. 1996. Heme/copper terminal oxidases. *Chem. Rev.* 96:2889–907

24. Garcia-Horsman JA, Puustinen A, Gennis RB, Wikström M. 1995. Proton transfer in cytochrome bo_3 ubiquinol oxidase of *Escherichia coli:* second-site mutations in subunit I that restore proton pumping in the mutant Asp–135 Asn. *Biochemistry* 34:4428–33

25. Gibson QH, Greenwood C. 1963. Reactions of cytochrome oxidase with oxygen and carbon monoxide. *Biochem. J.* 86:541–54

26. Green GN, Fang H, Lin RJ, Hewton G, Mather M, et al. 1988. The nucleotide sequence of the cyd locus encoding the two subunits of the cytochrome *d* terminal oxidase complex of *Escherichia coli. J. Biol. Chem.* 263:13138–43

27. Greenwood C, Gibson QH. 1967. The reaction of reduced cytochrome *c* oxidase with oxygen. *J. Biol. Chem.* 242:1782–87

28. Hallen S, Brzezinski P, Malmström BG. 1994. Internal electron transfer in cytochrome *c* oxidase is coupled to the protonation of a group close to the bimetallic site. *Biochemistry* 33:1467–72

29. Hallen S, Nilsson T. 1992. Proton transfer during the reaction of fully reduced cytochrome *c* oxidase and dioxygen: pH and deuterium isotope effects. *Biochemistry* 31:11853–59

30. Haltia T, Finel M, Harms N, Nakari T, Raitio M, et al. 1989. Deletion of the gene for subunit III leads to defective assembly of bacterial cytochrome oxidase. *EMBO J.* 8:3571–79

31. Han S, Ching Y, Rousseau DL. 1989. Evidence for a hydroxide intermediate in cytochrome *c* oxidase. *J. Biol. Chem.* 264:6604–7

32. Han S, Ching Y, Rousseau DL. 1990. Primary intermediate in the reaction of oxygen with fully reduced cytochrome *c* oxidase. *Proc. Natl. Acad. Sci. USA* 87:2491–95

33. Han S, Ching Y, Rousseau DL. 1990. Ferryl and hydroxy intermediates in the reaction of oxygen with reduced cytochrome *c* oxidase. *Nature* 348:89–90

34. Han S, Ching Y, Rousseau DL. 1990. Cytochrome *c* oxidase: decay of the primary oxygen intermediate involves direct electron transfer from cytochrome *a. Proc. Natl. Acad. Sci. USA* 87:8408–12

35. Hansson O, Karlsson B, Aasa R, Vänngård T, Malmström BG. 1982. The structure of the paramagnetic oxygen intermediate in the cytochrome *c* oxidase reaction. *EMBO J.* 1:1295–97

35a. Hellwig P, Rost P, Kaiser U, Ostermeier C, Michel H, Mäntele W. 1996. Carboxyl group protonation upon reduction of the *Paracoccus denitrificans* cytochrome *c* oxidase: direct evidence by FTIR spectroscopy. *FEBS Lett.* 385:53–57

36. Hendler RW, Pardhasaradhi K, Reynafarje B, Ludwig B. 1991. Comparison of energy-transducing capabilities of the two- and three-subunit cytochromes aa_3 from *Paracoccus denitrificans* and the 13-subunit beef heart enzyme. *Biophys. J.* 60:415–23

37. Hill BC. 1991. The reaction of the electrostatic cytochrome *c*–cytochrome oxidase complex with oxygen. *J. Biol. Chem.* 266:2219–26

38. Hill BC. 1994. Modelling the sequence of electron transfer reactions in the single turnover of reduced, mammalian cytochrome *c* oxidase with oxygen. *J. Biol. Chem.* 269:2419–25

39. Hill BC, Greenwood C. 1983. Spectroscopic evidence for the participation of compound A (Fe_{a3}^{2+}-O_2) in the reaction of mixed-valence cytochrome *c* oxidase with oxygen at room temperature. *Biochem. J.* 215:659–67

40. Hill BC, Greenwood C. 1984. The reaction of fully reduced cytochrome *c* oxidase with oxygen studied by flow-flash spectrophotometry at room temperature. *Biochem. J.* 218:913–21

41. Hill BC, Marmor S. 1991. Photochemical and ligand-exchange properties of the cyanide complex of fully reduced cytochrome *c* oxidase. *Biochem. J.* 279:355–60

42. Hirota S, Mogi T, Ogura T, Hirano T, Anraku Y, et al. 1994. Observation of the Fe-O_2 and Fe^{IV}=O stretching Raman bands for dioxygen reduction intermediates of cytochrome *bo* isolated from *Escherichia coli. FEBS Lett.* 352:67–70

43. Hosler JP, Ferguson-Miller S, Calhoun

MW, Thomas JW, Hill J, et al. 1993. Insight into the active-site structure and function of cytochrome oxidase by analysis of site-directed mutants of bacterial cytochrome aa_3 and cytochrome *bo*. *J. Bioenerg. Biomembr.* 25:121–36

44. Hosler JP, Shapleigh JP, Mitchell DM, Kim Y, Pressler MA, et al. 1996. Polar residues in helix VIII of subunit I of cytochrome *c* oxidase influence the activity and the structure of the active site. *Biochemistry* 35:10776–83

45. Iwata S, Ostermeier C, Ludwig B, Michel H. 1995. Structure at 2.8 Å resolution of cytochrome *c* oxidase from *Paracoccus denitrificans*. *Nature* 376:660–69

46. Kadenbach B. 1986. Regulation of respiration and ATP synthesis in higher organisms: hypothesis. *J. Bioenerg. Biomembr.* 18:39–54

47. Karlsson B, Aasa R, Vänngård T, Malmström BG. 1981. An EPR-detectable intermediate in the cytochrome oxidase-dioxygen reaction. *FEBS Lett.* 131:186–88

48. Kelly M, Lappalainen P, Talbo G, Haltia T, van der Oost J, Saraste M. 1993. Two cysteines, two histidines, and one methionine are ligands of a binuclear purple copper center. *J. Biol. Chem.* 268:16781–87

49. Kitagawa T, Ogura T. 1997. Oxygen activation mechanism at the binuclear site of heme-copper oxidase superfamily as revealed by time-resolved resonance Raman spectroscopy. *Progr. Inorg. Chem.* 45:431–479

50. Konstantinov AA, Capitanio N, Vygodina TV, Papa S. 1992. pH changes associated with cytochrome *c* oxidase reaction with H_2O_2: protonation state of the peroxy and oxoferryl intermediates. *FEBS Lett.* 312:71–74

50a. Konstantinov AA, Siletsky S, Mitchell D, Kaulen A, Gennis RB. 1997. The roles of the two proton input channels in cytochrome *c* oxidase from *Rhodobacter sphaeroides* probed by the effects of site-directed mutations on time-resolved electrogenic intraprotein proton transfer. *Proc. Natl. Acad. Sci. USA* 94:9085–90

51. Kraulis PJ. 1991. MOLSCRIPT: a program to produce both detailed and schematic plots of protein structure. *J. Appl. Crystallogr.* 24:946–50

52. Kuhn-Neutwig L, Kadenbach B. 1985. Isolation and properties of cytochrome *c* oxidase from rat liver and quantification of immunological differences between isoforms from various rat tissues with subunit-specific antisera. *Eur. J. Biochem.* 149:147–58

53. Lappalainen P, Watmough NJ, Greenwood C, Saraste M. 1995. Electron transfer between cytochrome *c* and the isolated Cu_A domain: identification of substrate-binding residues in cytochrome *c* oxidase. *Biochemistry* 34:5824–30

54. Larsson S, Källebring B, Wittung P, Malmström BG. 1995. The Cu_A center of cytochrome-c oxidase: electronic structure and spectra of models compared to the properties of Cu_A domains. *Proc. Natl. Acad. Sci. USA* 92:7167–71

55. Lauraeus M, Morgan JE, Wikström M. 1993. Peroxy and ferryl intermediates of the quinol-oxidizing cytochrome aa_3 from *Bacillus subtilis*. *Biochemistry* 32:2664–70

55a. Lübben M, Gerwert K. 1996. Redox FTIR difference spectroscopy using caged electrons reveals contributions of carboxyl groups to the catalytic mechanism of haem-copper oxidases. *FEBS Lett.* 397:303–7

56. Ludwig B, Gibson QH. 1981. Reaction of oxygen with cytochrome *c* oxidase from *Paracoccus denitrificans*. *J. Biol. Chem.* 256:10092–98

57. Malatesta F, Antonini G, Sarti P, Brunori M. 1995. Structure and function of a molecular machine–cytochrome *c* oxidase. *Biophys. Chem.* 54:1–33

58. Merrit EA, Murphy MEP. 1994. Raster 3D version 2.0: a program for photorealistic molecular graphics. *Acta Crystallogr.* 50:869–73

59. Mitchell R, Rich PR. 1994. Proton uptake by cytochrome *c* oxidase on reduction and on ligand binding. *Biochim. Biophys. Acta* 1186:19–26

60. Morgan JE, Verkhovsky MI, Puustinen A, Wikström M. 1995. Identification of a "peroxy" intermediate in cytochrome bo_3 of *Escherichia coli*. *Biochemistry* 34:15633–37

61. Morgan JE, Verkhovsky MI, Wikström M. 1996. Observation and assignment of peroxy and ferryl intermediates in the reduction of dioxygen to water by cytochrome *c* oxidase. *Biochemistry* 35:12235–40

62. Moody AJ, Brandt U, Rich PR. 1991. Single electron reduction of "slow" and "fast" cytochrome *c* oxidase. *FEBS Lett.* 293:101–5

63. Oertling WA, Kean RT, Wever R, Babcock GT. 1990. Factors affecting the iron-oxygen vibrations of ferrous oxy and ferryl oxo heme proteins and model compounds. *Inorg. Chem.* 29:2633–45

64. Ogura T, Takahashi S, Shinzawa-Itoh K, Yoshikawa S, Kitagawa T. 1990. Observation of the $Fe^{4+}=O$ stretching Raman band for cytochrome oxidase compound B at ambient temperature. *J. Biol. Chem.* 265:14721–23
65. Ogura T, Takahashi S, Shinzawa-Itoh K, Yoshikawa S, Kitagawa T. 1991. Time-resolved resonance Raman investigation of cytochrome oxidase catalysis: observation of a new oxygen-isotope sensitive Raman band. *Bull. Chem. Soc. Jpn.* 64:2901–7
66. Ogura T, Takahashi S, Hirota S, Shinzawa-Itoh K, Yoshikawa S, et al. 1993. Time-resolved resonance Raman elucidation of the pathway for dioxygen reduction by cytochrome *c* oxidase. *J. Am. Chem. Soc.* 115:8527–36
67. Ogura T, Hirota S, Proshlyakov DA, Shinzawa-Itoh K, Yoshikawa S, Kitagawa T. 1996. Time-resolved resonance Raman evidence for tight coupling between electron transfer and proton pumping of cytochrome *c* oxidase upon the change from the Fe(V) oxidation level to the Fe(IV) oxidation level. *J. Am. Chem. Soc.* 118:5443–49
68. Oliveberg M, Brzezinski P, Malmström BG. 1989. The effect of pH and temperature on the reaction of fully reduced and mixed-valence cytochrome *c* oxidase with dioxygen. *Biochim. Biophys. Acta* 977:322–28
69. Oliveberg M, Malmström BG. 1992. Reaction of dioxygen with cytochrome *c* oxidase reduced to different degrees: indications of a transient dioxygen complex with copper-B. *Biochemistry* 31:3560–63
70. Orii Y. 1988. Intermediates in the reaction of reduced cytochrome oxidase with dioxygen. *Ann. NY Acad. Sci.* 550:105–17
71. Ostermeier C, Iwata I, Ludwig B, Michel H. 1995. F_v fragment–mediated crystallization of the membrane protein bacterial cytochrome *c* oxidase. *Nat. Struct. Biol.* 2:842–46
72. Ostermeier C, Harrenga A, Ermler U, Michel H. 1997. Structure at 2.7 Å resolution of the *Paracoccus denitrificans* two-subunit cytochrome *c* oxidase complexed with an antibody F_v-fragment. *Proc. Natl. Acad. Sci. USA* 94:10547–53
73. Palmer G, Babcock GT, Vickery LE. 1976. A model for cytochrome oxidase. *Proc. Natl. Acad. Sci. USA* 73:2206–10
74. Preisig O, Anthamatten D, Hennecke H. 1993. Genes for a microaerobically induced oxidase complex in *Bradyrhizobium japonicum* are essential for a nitrogen-fixing endosymbiosis. *Proc. Natl. Acad. Sci. USA* 90:3309–13
75. Proshlyakov DA, Ogura T, Shinzawa-Itoh K, Yoshikawa S, Appelman EH, et al. 1994. Selective resonance Raman observation of the "607 nm" form generated in the reaction of oxidized cytochrome *c* oxidase with hydrogen peroxide. *J. Biol. Chem.* 269:29385–88
76. Proshlyakov DA, Ogura T, Shinzawa-Itoh K, Yoshikawa S, Kitagawa T. 1996. Resonance Raman/absorption characterization of the oxo intermediates of cytochrome *c* oxidase generated in its reaction with hydrogen peroxide: pH and H_2O_2 concentration dependence. *Biochemistry* 35:8580–86
77. Proshlyakov DA, Ogura T, Shinzawa-Itoh K, Yoshikawa S, Kitagawa T. 1996. Microcirculating system for simultaneous determination of Raman and absorption spectra of enzymatic reaction intermediates and its application to the reaction of cytochrome *c* oxidase with hydrogen peroxide. *Biochemistry* 35:76–82
78. Puustinen A, Verkhovsky MI, Morgan JE, Belevich NP, Wikström M. 1996. Reaction of the *Escherichia coli* quinol oxidase cytochrome *bo₃* with dioxygen: the role of a bound ubiquinone molecule. *Proc. Natl. Acad. Sci. USA* 93:1545–48
79. Ramirez BE, Malmström BG, Winkler JR, Gray HB. 1995. The currents of life: the terminal electron-transfer complex of respiration. *Proc. Natl. Acad. Sci. USA* 92:11949–51
80. Rich PR. 1995. Towards an understanding of the chemistry of oxygen reduction and proton translocation in the iron-copper respiratory oxidases. *Aust. J. Plant Physiol.* 22:479–86
81. Rieder R, Bosshard HR. 1980. Comparison of the binding sites on cytochrome *c* for cytochrome *c* oxidase, cytochrome bc_1, and cytochrome c_1. Differential acetylation of lysyl residues in free and complexed cytochrome *c*. *J. Biol. Chem.* 255:4732–39
82. Riistama S, Puustinen A, Garcia-Horsman A, Iwata S, Michel H, et al. 1996. Channeling of dioxygen into the respiratory enzyme. *Biochim. Biophys. Acta* 1275:1–4
83. Rousseau DL, Ching YC, Wang J. 1993. Proton translocation in cytochrome *c* oxidase: redox linkage through proximal ligand exchange on cytochrome a_3. *J. Bioenerg. Biomembr.* 25:165–77
84. Saraste M. 1990. Structural features of

cytochrome oxidase. *Q. Rev. Biophys.* 23: 331–66
85. Siletzky, SA, Kaulen AD, Mitchell D, Gennis RB, Konstantinov AA. 1996. Resolution of two proton conduction pathways in cytochrome *c* oxidase. *Biochim. Biophys. Acta, EBEC Rep.* 9:B27
86. Sucheta A, Georgiadis KE, Einarsdottir O. 1997. Mechanism of cytochrome *c* oxidase–catalyzed reduction of dioxygen to water: evidence for peroxy and ferryl intermediates at room temperature. *Biochemistry* 36:554–65
87. Svensson-Ek M, Thomas JW, Gennis RB, Nilsson T, Brzezinski P. 1996. Kinetics of electron and proton transfer during the reaction of wild-type and helix VI mutants of cytochrome *bo₃* with oxygen. *Biochemistry* 35:13673–80
88. Thomas JW, Puustinen A, Alben JO, Gennis RB, Wikström M. 1993. Substitution of asparagine for aspartate-135 in subunit I of the cytochrome *bo* ubiquinol oxidase of *Escherichia coli* eliminates proton-pumping activity. *Biochemistry:* 10923–28
89. Tsukihara T, Aoyama H, Yamashita E, Tomizaki T, Yamaguchi H, et al. 1995. Structures of metal sites of oxidized bovine heart cytochrome *c* oxidase at 2.8 Å. *Science* 269:1069–74
90. Tsukihara T, Aoyama H, Yamashita E, Tomizaki T, Yamaguchi H, et al. 1996. The whole structure of the 13-subunit oxidized cytochrome *c* oxidase at 2.8 Å. *Science* 272:1136–44
91. Varotsis C, Woodruff WH, Babcock GT. 1989. Time-resolved Raman detection of ν(Fe-O) in an early intermediate in the reduction of oxygen by cytochrome oxidase. *J. Am. Chem. Soc.* 111:6439–40
92. Varotsis C, Babcock GT. 1990. Appearance of the ν(Fe^{IV}=O) vibration from a ferryl-oxo intermediate in the cytochrome oxidase/dioxygen reaction. *Biochemistry* 29:7357–62
93. Varotsis C, Zhang Y, Appelman EH, Babcock GT. 1993. Resolution of the reaction sequence during the reduction of O₂ by cytochrome oxidase. *Proc. Natl. Acad. Sci. USA* 90:237–41
94. Verkhovsky MI, Morgan JE, Wikström M. 1994. Oxygen binding and activation: early steps in the reaction of oxygen with cytochrome *c* oxidase. *Biochemistry* 33:3079–86
95. Verkhovsky MI, Morgan JE, Wikström M. 1995. Control of electron delivery to the oxygen reduction site of cytochrome *c* oxidase: a role for protons. *Biochemistry* 34:7483–91
96. Verkhovsky MI, Morgan JE, Puustinen A, Wikström M. 1996a. The ferrous-oxy intermediate in the reaction of dioxygen with fully reduced cytochromes *aa₃* and *bo₃*. *Biochemistry* 35:16241–46
97. Verkhovsky MI, Morgan JE, Puustinen A, Wikström M. 1996b. Kinetic trapping of oxygen in cell respiration. *Nature* 380:268–70
98. Verkhovsky MI, Morgan JE, Verkhouskaya ML, Wikström M. 1997. Translocation of electrical charge during a single turnover of cytochrome *c* oxidase. *Biochim. Biophys. Acta* 1318:6–10
99. Verkhovsky MI, Morgan JE, Wikström M. 1996. Redox transitions between oxygen intermediates in cytochrome *c* oxidase. *Proc. Natl. Acad. Sci. USA* 93: 12235–39
100. Vygodina TY, Mitchell D, Pecoraro C, Gennis RB, Konstantinov AA. 1996. Effect of amino acid replacements in the two proton channels of *Rh. sphaeroides* cytochrome *c* oxidase on the reaction of the enzyme with H₂O₂. *Biochim. Biophys. Acta, EBEC Rep.* 9:B32
101. Watmough NJ, Cheesman MR, Greenwood C, Thomson AJ. 1994. Cytochrome *bo* from *Escherichia coli*: reaction of the oxidized enzyme with hydrogen peroxide. *Biochem. J.* 300:469–75
102. Weng L, Baker GM. 1991. Reaction of hydrogen peroxide with the rapid form of resting cytochrome oxidase. *Biochemistry* 30:5727–30
103. Wikström M. 1981. Energy-dependent reversal of the cytochrome oxidase reaction. *Proc. Natl. Acad. Sci. USA* 78:4051–54
104. Wikström M. 1989. Identification of the electron transfers in cytochrome oxidase that are coupled to proton-pumping. *Nature* 338:776–78
105. Wikström M, Bogachev A, Finel M, Morgan JE, Puustinen A, et al. 1994. Mechanism of proton translocation by the respiratory oxidases: the histidine cycle. *Biochim. Biophys. Acta* 1187:106–11
106. Wikström M, Morgan JE. 1992. The dioxygen cycle: spectral, kinetic, and thermodynamic characteristics of ferryl and peroxy intermediates observed by reversal of the cytochrome oxidase reaction. *J. Biol. Chem.* 267:10266–73
107. Wilmanns M, Lappalainen P, Kelly M, Sauer-Eriksson E, Saraste M. 1995. Crystal structure of the membrane-exposed domain from a respiratory quinol oxidase with an engineered dinuclear copper center. *Proc. Natl. Acad. Sci. USA* 92:11954–59
108. Winkler JR, Malmström BG, Gray HB.

1995. Rapid electron injection into multiside metalloproteins: intramolecular electron transfer in cytochrome oxidase. *Biophys. Chem.* 54:199–209

109. Witt H, Ludwig B. 1997. Isolation, analysis, and deletion of the gene coding for subunit IV of cytochrome *c* oxidase in *Paracoccus denitrificans. J. Biol. Chem.* 272:5514–17

110. Witt H, Zickermann V, Ludwig B. 1995. Site-directed mutagenesis of cytochrome *c* oxidase reveals two acidic residues involved in the binding of cytochrome *c*. *Biochim. Biophys. Acta* 1230:74–76

111. Witt SN, Blair DF, Chan SI. 1986. Chemical and spectroscopic evidence for the formation of a ferryl Fe_{a3} intermediate during turnover of cytochrome *c* oxidase. *J. Biol. Chem.* 261:8104–7

112. Witt SN, Chan SI. 1987. Evidence for a ferryl Fe_{a3} in oxygenated cytochrome *c* oxidase. *J. Biol. Chem.* 262:1446–48

113. Woodruff WH. 1993. Coordination dynamics of heme-copper oxidases. The ligand shuttle and the control and coupling of electron transfer and proton translocation. *J. Bioenerg. Biomembr.* 25:177–88

114. Woodruff WH, Einarsdottir O, Dyer RB, Bagley KA, Palmer G, et al. 1991. Nature and functional implications of the cytochrome a_3 transients after photodissociation of CO-cytochrome oxidase. *Proc. Natl. Acad. Sci. USA* 88:2588–92

115. Wrigglesworth JM. 1984. Formation and reduction of a "peroxy" intermediate of cytochrome *c* oxidase by hydrogen peroxide. *Biochem. J.* 217:715–19

116. Yanamura W, Zhang YZ, Takamiya S, Capaldi RA. 1988. Tissue-specific differences between heart and liver cytochrome *c* oxidase. *Biochemistry* 27:4909–14

117. Yonetani T. 1961. Studies on cytochrome oxidase. III: improved preparation and some properties. *J. Biol. Chem.* 236:1680–88

118. Zickermann V, Verkhovsky M, Morgan J, Wikström M, Anemüller S, et al. 1995. Perturbation of the Cu_A site in cytochrome-c oxidase of *Paracoccus denitrificans* by replacement of Met227 with isoleucine. *Eur. J. Biochem.* 234:686–93

Annu. Rev. Biophys. Biomol. Struct. 1998. 27:357–406
Copyright © 1998 by Annual Reviews. All rights reserved

THE USE OF ^{2}H, ^{13}C, ^{15}N MULTIDIMENSIONAL NMR TO STUDY THE STRUCTURE AND DYNAMICS OF PROTEINS

Kevin H. Gardner and Lewis E. Kay

Protein Engineering Network Centres of Excellence and Departments of Medical Genetics and Microbiology, Biochemistry, and Chemistry, University of Toronto, Toronto, Ontario, Canada, M5S 1A8; e-mail: gardner@bloch.med.utoronto.ca; kay@bloch.med.utoronto.ca

KEY WORDS: protein deuteration, triple resonance NMR, amino acid-specific isotopic labeling, structure determination, sidechain dynamics

ABSTRACT

During the past thirty years, deuterium labeling has been used to improve the resolution and sensitivity of protein NMR spectra used in a wide variety of applications. Most recently, the combination of triple resonance experiments and ^{2}H, ^{13}C, ^{15}N labeled samples has been critical to the solution structure determination of several proteins with molecular weights on the order of 30 kDa. Here we review the developments in isotopic labeling strategies, NMR pulse sequences, and structure-determination protocols that have facilitated this advance and hold promise for future NMR-based structural studies of even larger systems. As well, we detail recent progress in the use of solution ^{2}H NMR methods to probe the dynamics of protein sidechains.

CONTENTS

357

1056-8700/98/0610-0357$08.00

INTRODUCTION

Background: Deuteration prior to 1993

Over the past thirty years deuterium labeling methods have played a critical
role in solution NMR studies of macromolecules, in many cases improving the
quality of spectra by both a reduction in the number of peaks and concomitant
narrowing of linewidths. Deuteration was initially used in a set of elegant
experiments by the groups of Crespi and Jardetzky to reduce the complexity of
one-dimensional (1D) ^{1}H spectra of proteins (19, 20, 100). To this end, highly
deuterated proteins were produced by growing algae or bacteria in D_2O media
supplemented either with uniformly or selectively protonated amino acids. By
monitoring the chemical shifts of the few remaining protons, conformational
changes that occurred upon ligand binding (100) or oligomerization (19) were
investigated. Since these initial experiments, the preparation of proteins with
amino acid selective protonation in a deuterated environment (or conversely,
selective deuteration in an otherwise protonated molecule) has been regularly
used for spectral simplification and residue type assignment (3, 4, 12, 120).

In the 1980s, random fractional deuteration was employed to improve the
quality of homonuclear proton two-dimensional (2D) NMR spectra. Because of
the significantly lower gyromagnetic ratio of ^{2}H compared to ^{1}H ($\gamma[^2H]/\gamma[^1H]$
= 0.15), replacement of protons with deuterons removes contributions to proton
linewidths from proton-proton dipolar relaxation and ^{1}H-^{1}H scalar couplings.
At deuteration levels between 50–75%, the expected decrease in sensitivity
resulting from the limited number of protons is offset to a large extent by a
reduction in peak linewidths. Sensitivity gains were initially demonstrated in
1D ^{1}H spectra of the 43 kDa *Escherichia coli* EF-Tu protein (61) and subsequently in 2D homonuclear spectra of *E. coli* thioredoxin used for chemical shift assignment (94). Significant improvements have also been noted in

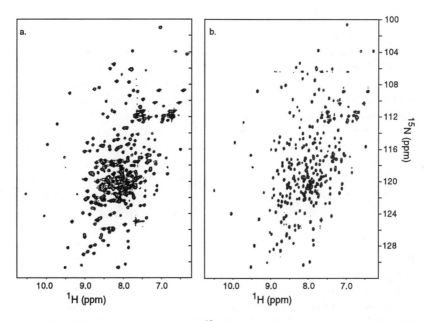

Figure 1 Effect of perdeuteration on the 2D ^{15}N-NH HSQC spectrum of the 30 kDa N-terminal domain of Enzyme I from the *E. coli* phosphoenolpyruvate-sugar phosphotransferase system. Both proteins are uniformly ^{15}N labeled, while the deuterated protein is approximately 90% uniformly deuterated. (33, by permission.)

many heteronuclear experiments. This is demonstrated for the case of a ^{15}N-^{1}H HSQC experiment in Figure 1 where spectra recorded on fully protonated and perdeuterated samples (all nonexchangeable hydrogens substituted with deuterons) of a 30 kDa N-terminal domain of Enzyme I of the *E. coli* phospho-enolpyruvate:sugar phosphotransferase system (EIN) are illustrated (33). As observed for the 14 kDa villin 14T protein (101), deuterating all nonexchangeable sites to levels of 80–90% decreases amide proton transverse relaxation rates by approximately twofold. The improvement in sensitivity and resolution in the NH-detected dimension is particularly important since many classes of experiments record the amide proton chemical shift during acquisition (16).

Deuteration can also improve the quality of NOESY experiments. In particular, substitution of aliphatic/aromatic protons with deuterons results in impressive sensitivity gains in NOESY spectra that record NH-NH correlations (94, 156). Initially demonstrated in perdeuterated systems, similar benefits have also been observed for proteins and peptides that are protonated at specific positions in an otherwise highly deuterated background (5, 124, 132, 158). The sensitivity gains in these NOESY data sets are largely the result of reduced NH linewidths, as described above. However, the decrease in spin diffusion pathways and concomitant increase in selective T_1 values of the diagonal resonances also result in improvements. Moreover, it is possible to employ longer mixing times and, because of reduced spin diffusion rates, relate cross-peak intensities to internuclear distances more accurately than is possible from data recorded on highly protonated samples. This is of particular significance for longer-range distance restraints. Finally, it is important to note that even in highly deuterated molecules, the effects of spin diffusion cannot be neglected. In the case of highly deuterated proteins containing protonated amino acids, NOE spectra have been recorded with long mixing times specifically to promote intra-residue spin diffusion. In this way sidechain protons for several dimeric proteins with molecular weights above 20 kDa have been assigned (4, 5, 133).

Scope of This Review: Deuteration since 1993

As described above, deuteration can result in substantial improvements in NMR spectra used to study the structures of proteins and protein complexes. An alternative powerful strategy is triple-resonance, multi-dimensional NMR spectroscopy of uniformly ^{15}N, ^{13}C labeled proteins (9, 16). In this approach, sets of intra- and interresidue chemical shifts are correlated by transferring magnetization from one nucleus to another through one- or two-bond scalar couplings. Data analysis from several of these experiments in combination facilitates the assignment of nitrogen, carbon, and proton chemical shifts of proteins with molecular weights of approximately 25 kDa or less. For systems larger than this, long molecular correlation times result in very efficient relaxation of the participating spins, especially ^{13}C nuclei, attenuating signal intensity and degrading spectral resolution.

A straightforward approach to decrease the relaxation rates of many of the nuclei that are key players in triple resonance experiments is to substitute carbon-bearing protons with deuterons. At the field strengths currently in use, the major contribution to relaxation of carbon magnetization, for example, derives from one-bond ^{13}C-^1H dipolar interactions (2, 13). In the case of a ^{13}C-^1H spin-pair attached to a macromolecule, replacement of the proton with a deuteron attenuates the dipolar interaction by a factor of approximately 15. This results in a substantial lengthening of carbon relaxation times leading to improvements in the sensitivity of experiments relying on scalar coupling based transfers of magnetization involving carbon nuclei (38, 82, 159, 170, 171).

The first demonstration of the utility of deuteration in concert with triple resonance spectroscopy was in 1993 when Bax and coworkers described the 4D HN(COCA)NH experiment for correlating sequential amides (38). Subsequently a suite of triple-resonance experiments for assignment of backbone

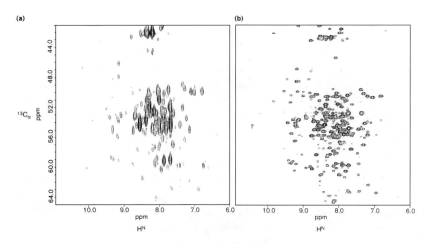

Figure 2   Comparison of 2D (^{13}Cα, NH) projections from 3D HNCA spectra recorded of a 23 kDa Shc PTB domain/phosphotyrosine peptide complex. (*a*) ^{15}N, ^{13}C, ^{1}H uniformly labeled Shc PTB domain. (*b*) ^{15}N, ^{13}C, 75% ^{2}H uniformly labeled Shc PTB domain. (136, by permission.)

chemical shifts of deuterated proteins was developed and demonstrated on a 37 kDa protein/DNA complex (170, 171) and later extended for use on a 64 kDa version of this system (142). The dramatic improvement in both the sensitivity and the resolution of triple resonance spectra that deuteration provides is illustrated in Figure 2 by comparing 2D ^{13}C/^{1}H projections of 3D HNCA spectra recorded on a fully protonated ^{15}N, ^{13}C labeled 23 kDa Shc PTB domain/peptide complex (*a*) and a 75% deuterated version of the same complex (*b*). The decrease in ^{13}C linewidth allows individual peaks to be resolved in the crowded center of these spectra and the improved signal-to-noise facilitates the observation of weaker cross-peaks.

Many triple resonance pulse sequences have since been optimized for use on deuterated proteins (see "Backbone Chemical Shift Assignment" below). The application of many of these methods to high molecular weight proteins (40 kDa and beyond) will require significant levels of deuteration. For example, complete assignment of ^{15}N, ^{13}C^α, ^{13}C^β and NH chemical shifts was achieved for a 37 kDa trp repressor/DNA ternary complex (170, 171) where the protein component was labeled at approximately 70%. However, a 90% deuteration level was required for similar studies on a 64 kDa trp repressor/DNA complex (142). Regrettably, the advantages associated with deuteration are not without compromise. The substitution of deuterons for protons depletes the number of protons available for NOE-based interproton distance restraints. In the limiting case of perdeuteration, only exchangeable protons remain, resulting in a drastic reduction in both numbers and types of NOEs that can be measured in relation to fully protonated samples. It is not surprising, therefore, that structures determined from NOEs between backbone NH protons only have very low precision and accuracy (32, 146, 161). This has stimulated the development of several different methods for the production of proteins that are selectively protonated at key positions in the molecule, allowing additional distance restraints to be measured, while maintaining a high level of deuteration at other sites so that experiments for sidechain and backbone assignment can enjoy the sensitivity gains that accompany deuteration.

To this point we have introduced the use of deuterium as an approach to improve the efficacy of large classes of triple resonance experiments that would otherwise suffer significantly from relaxation losses. Outside of the low gyromagnetic ratio of the deuteron, no other properties of ^{2}H are exploited in these experiments. In contrast to the relatively recent use of deuterium in this role, the utility of ^{2}H NMR spectroscopy for the study of molecular dynamics has been recognized for several decades. Most of the work focused primarily on liquid crystal samples, samples in the solid state, or solution state samples with deuterium labeling restricted to a small number of sites (58, 60, 74, 75, 139, 141, 162). Methods have emerged more recently for the measurement of sidechain dynamics properties of uniformly ^{13}C-labeled, fractionally deuterated proteins through the indirect measurement of deuterium relaxation times, T_1 and $T_{1\rho}$ (68, 114, 131).

In this review, recent developments in the use of deuterium for studying protein structure and dynamics will be described. This includes the preparation of highly deuterated proteins, optimization of triple resonance NMR experiments for use on highly deuterated samples, prospects for the structure determination of highly deuterated proteins and the use of ^{2}H relaxation for the study of protein dynamics. The interested reader should consult previous reviews (38, 8–90) for a more thorough coverage of work in these fields prior to 1993.

DEUTERIUM LABELING METHODS

Proteins used for NMR studies can be labeled using a number of different protocols that produce molecules with different patterns of deuterium incorporation. One labeling strategy results in deuterium incorporation throughout a protein in a roughly site-independent manner (uniform or random labeling) while a second approach produces a high level of deuteration (or protonation) at a restricted number of sites (site-specific labeling). The optimal labeling pattern for a particular sample, is of course, determined by the intended application(s). In what follows, a number of methods are described for the generation of proteins deuterated on aliphatic/aromatic carbon sites. Although considerable progress has been realized in the past several years in the production of uniformly deuterated (8) or site-specifically deuterated (1, 28, 123, 153) nucleotides for use in NMR studies of RNA and DNA molecules, the present discussion will exclusively focus on protein applications.

Uniform Deuteration

As mentioned above, the optimal level of deuteration for a specific application, ranging from the complete substitution of protons with deuterons to moderate levels of fractional replacement, will very much depend on the experiments that are planned. Completely deuterated proteins have been used to eliminate contributions to spectra from one component of a macromolecular complex, as demonstrated in studies of a complex of fully deuterated calmodulin with a protonated peptide (140) and deuterated cyclophilin with protonated cyclosporin (51). However, a wider range of applications have made use of samples of (random) fractionally deuterated molecules. For example, random fractionally deuterated proteins were initially used to improve the sensitivity of 2D ^{1}H-^{1}H homonuclear spectra by reducing dipolar relaxation pathways, spin-diffusion and passive scalar couplings (94, 156). Fractional deuteration also significantly improves the sensitivity of many triple resonance (^{15}N, ^{13}C, ^{1}H) experiments (26, 27, 38, 117, 142, 170, 171), as will be discussed in greater detail below in "Triple Resonance Methods." In addition, the sidechain dynamics of proteins prepared in this manner can be studied using a number of new ^{13}C and ^{2}H spin relaxation experiments (81, 92, 114, 131) as addressed below in "Use of Deuteration to Study Protein Dynamics."

To a first approximation, randomly deuterated proteins can be generated in a straightforward manner. A culture of bacteria containing an overexpression vector for the protein of interest is grown in minimal media with the D_2O/H_2O ratio chosen to reflect the desired level of deuterium incorporation. Proteins generated will be composed of amino acids containing approximately the same deuterium content as in the overexpression media (see below). Cultures of simple eukaryotes such as algae and yeast can also grow in media containing up to 100% D_2O, facilitating the use of these organisms for the biosynthetic production of highly deuterated proteins (20, 62).

Expression of deuterated proteins in higher eukaryotic cells (plant and animal) is more challenging because these cells will not grow in media containing more than 30–50% D_2O (62). This problem can be partially circumvented by culturing these cells in H_2O media supplemented with commercially available ^{2}H-labeled algal amino acid extracts, analogous to previously established methods for expressing uniformly ^{15}N, ^{13}C, ^{1}H-labeled proteins in these systems (45). Proteins produced in this manner will be highly deuterated at most carbon positions, although significant levels of potentially undesired protonation can still occur through ^{2}H/^{1}H exchange with solvent protons, most notably at Cα sites.

Note that several factors can lead to a nonuniform distribution of deuterium throughout "randomly" fractionated proteins. In this regard, the carbon compounds used as growth substrates for *E. coli* are particularly important since protons from these molecules can be efficiently retained at specific sites within several amino acids. For example, proteins produced in bacteria grown in deuterated media containing ^{1}H-glucose typically have relatively high levels of protonation in sidechains of the aromatic amino acids. This results from the fact that aromatic groups are synthesized from glucose-derived carbohydrates (90). In certain cases, specific retention of protons from a protonated carbon source can be exploited to generate useful patterns of site-specific protonation within a highly deuterated background (See "Protonated Methyl Groups in a Deuterated Background: Pyruvate," below). For applications requiring perdeuterated proteins, bacteria can be grown on deuterated carbon sources [e.g. ^{2}H-glucose or ^{2}H-succinate (94)] or simple protonated carbon sources where the carbon-bound protons are replaced by solvent deuterons prior to or during amino acid biosynthesis [e.g. ^{1}H-sodium acetate (160)].

Nonuniform deuteration can still be significant even when deuterated carbon sources exclusively are employed. Kinetic and thermodynamic isotope effects can alter the activity of metabolic and biosynthetic enzymes to the point of significantly biasing the distribution of deuterium in partially deuterated samples (29, 102). For example, a protein overexpressed in *E. coli* grown in an 80:20% D$_2$O:H$_2$O media supplemented with deuterated succinate and 75% ^{2}H, DL-alanine was deuterated on average to a level of approximately 75% (91). However, specific sites within the protein had significantly lower ^{2}H incorporation, including the Ile γ1 methylene positions (<50% deuterated). In another case, nonuniform type-specific deuterium incorporation has been observed in the CH$_3$:CH$_2$D:CHD$_2$ isotopomer distribution of methyl groups of an SH2 domain overexpressed in *E. coli* grown in 65:35% D$_2$O:H$_2$O media (68).

Site-Specific Protonation in a Highly Deuterated Environment

PROTONATED AMINO ACID SIDECHAINS IN A DEUTERATED BACKGROUND   In contrast to the approaches described above for producing proteins with deuterium substituted at an approximately uniform level throughout most of the aliphatic sites, proteins can also be generated where only specific sites are protonated in an otherwise highly deuterated background. Proteins can be labeled in this manner by overexpression in bacterial cultures grown in minimal D$_2$O media supplemented with protonated small organic molecules such as amino acids, amino acid precursors or carbon sources (89, 90). Alternatively, bacteria can also be cultivated in H$_2$O-based media supplemented with deuterated algal cell lysates that have been chemically or enzymatically treated to promote site-specific protonation.

Some of the earliest ^{2}H-based NMR studies of proteins made use of deuterated, site-protonated molecules isolated from organisms grown in minimal media with high levels of D$_2$O and supplemented with fully or partially protonated amino acids (19, 20, 100). The resulting simplified 1D ^{1}H NMR spectra of these proteins facilitated the observation of well-separated peaks reporting on sites dispersed throughout the primary sequence of the molecule. Initial studies focused on the incorporation of leucine (20). Subsequently, most of the twenty natural amino acids have been successfully incorporated in this manner, either alone or in combination with other residues (12, 109, 120, 146). In general, wild-type strains of bacteria and algae can be used for amino acid specific labeling so long as the growth media is supplemented with relatively high concentrations (>30 mg/liter) of protonated compounds. In cases where it is necessary to use smaller amounts of these potentially expensive labeled compounds or to limit undesirable labeling of amino acids derived from the labeled compound, amino acid-specific auxotrophic strains have been employed (89, 120). Similar approaches have also been used in the context of specific ^{15}N and ^{13}C labeling (106, 165).

As mentioned previously, proteins produced by bacteria in highly deuterated media containing a number of fully protonated amino acids usually retain most of the sidechain protons on these residues. In a typical D$_2$O-based growth media, deuterons will replace between 30–80% of the Hα protons of the protonated amino acids (20, 109, 146), while the sidechains remain almost entirely protonated. On one hand, this high level of residual protonation is beneficial for the sensitivity of many proton-detected experiments. However, the presence of these spins can lead to rapid transverse relaxation rates for sidechain ^{13}C nuclei (109, 146), reducing the sensitivity of triple resonance experiments designed to assign sidechain chemical shifts, such as the HCC(CO)NH TOCSY (see "Sidechain Chemical Shift Assignment," below). As well, protons located on the sidechain provide effective intraresidue spin diffusion pathways in NOE-based experiments, complicating the quantitation of cross-peak intensities in terms of internuclear distances (124).

PROTONATED METHYL GROUPS IN A DEUTERATED BACKGROUND: PYRUVATE
To circumvent the problems associated with the use of fully protonated amino acids in the production of deuterated site-protonated proteins, Rosen and coworkers have developed a method that produces molecules with a more limited number of highly protonated sites (134). The approach involves growing bacteria in D$_2$O-based minimal media with a protonated nonglucose carbon

source. As discussed above in "Uniform Deuteration," for the case of glucose, the use of a protonated carbon source introduces protons at specific positions in various amino acids in a manner dependent on the details of the metabolism of the compound. Rosen et al have taken advantage of the fact that the methyl group of pyruvate is the metabolic precursor of the methyls of Ala, Val, Leu, and Ile (γ_2 only) to produce proteins that are highly deuterated at all positions with the exceptions of the methyl groups mentioned above. In this approach, proteins are overexpressed in *E. coli* grown in D_2O-based minimal media with protonated pyruvate as the sole carbon source. The utility of this approach is demonstrated in Figure 3, which presents a comparison of ^{13}C-^1H HSQC spectra of ^{15}N, ^{13}C, fully protonated (*a*) and ^{15}N, ^{13}C, methyl-protonated, highly deuterated samples (*b*) of the C-terminal SH2 domain of bovine phospholipase $C_{\gamma 1}$ (PLCC). The figure shows that the majority of the aliphatic sites in the pyruvate-derived protein are completely deuterated, while the methyl groups of Ala, Val, Leu,

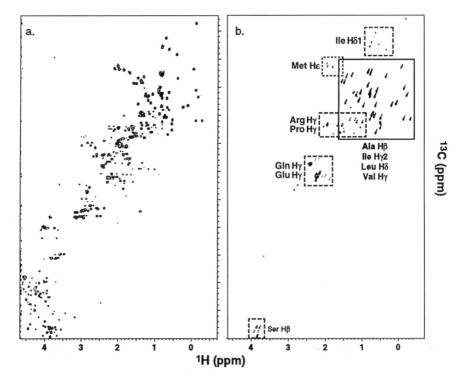

Figure 3 Constant-time ^{13}C-^1H HSQC spectra of the PLCC SH2 domain prepared from (*a*) a fully protonated, H_2O medium with a ^{13}C-glucose carbon source and (*b*) a D_2O-based medium with ^{13}C, ^1H pyruvate the sole carbon source.

and Ile (γ2) are significantly protonated. However, the methylene groups of several amino acids identified in Figure 3b are also protonated to a lower extent.

It is noteworthy that the methyl peaks in the spectrum of the deuterated sample are highly asymmetric. This is the result of the production of CH_3, CH_2D, and CHD_2 isotopomers coupled with the significant one-bond deuterium isotope shift for both ^{13}C (-0.3 ppm per ^{2}H) and ^{1}H (-0.02 ppm per ^{2}H) (32). The extent of protonation for the pyruvate-derived methyl groups ranges from 40% (Ala) to 60% (Val and Ile) to 80% (Leu), as established on the basis of both mass spectrometry and NMR studies (134). These levels can be further increased by shortening the induction step during growth (31). The moderately high levels of protonation at Ala, Ile (γ2), Val and Leu methyl groups and the significant deuteration at most other sites (most notably, C$\alpha > 95\%$ and C$\beta > 80\%$ deuterated) ensures that high sensitivity triple resonance spectra for both backbone assignment and for correlation of sidechain ^{13}C and ^{1}H chemical shifts with backbone ^{15}N-^{1}H spin pairs can be obtained (31).

PROTONATED METHYL GROUPS IN A DEUTERATED BACKGROUND: SPECIFICALLY PROTONATED AMINO ACIDS AND AMINO ACID PRECURSORS   Despite the utility of the pyruvate strategy described above, the presence of methyl isotopomers is limiting, both in terms of resolution and sensitivity. In addition, the level of protein produced in *E. coli* cultures grown in pyruvate-based media is approximately two-fold reduced relative to cultures that use glucose as the carbon source. It is therefore necessary to develop an alternative approach in which proteins are overproduced in bacteria grown in a highly deuterated, glucose media supplemented with amino acid precursors and amino acids that have useful patterns of protonation and deuteration. Both the precursors and the amino acids can be prepared in vitro using a combination of synthetic and enzymatic approaches with the conversion of the amino acid precursors to the appropriate amino acids occurring in vivo once the compounds are provided to *E. coli*. Intermediates can be chosen based on several criteria, including the ability to enter a biosynthetic pathway without complications from subsequent ^{1}H/^{2}H exchange reactions, the extent of *E. coli* assimilation and the ease of preparation. An example of this approach is illustrated in the production of proteins with high levels of deuteration at all positions with the exception of methyl positions of Val, Leu, and Ile (δ1 only) (30). Proteins are overexpressed in *E. coli* grown in minimal ^{15}N, ^{13}C, ^{2}H media containing deuterated glucose as the carbon source and supplemented with [2,3-^{2}H$_2$]-^{15}N, ^{13}C Val (available commercially) and [3,3-^{2}H$_2$]-^{13}C 2-ketobutyrate. Addition of [2,3-^{2}H$_2$]-Val to the growth media (50 mg/liter, see below) results in the production of proteins where both Val and Leu are highly deuterated at all nonmethyl positions, and where the only protonated methyl produced is the CH_3 isotopomer ($\gtrsim$90% CH_3,

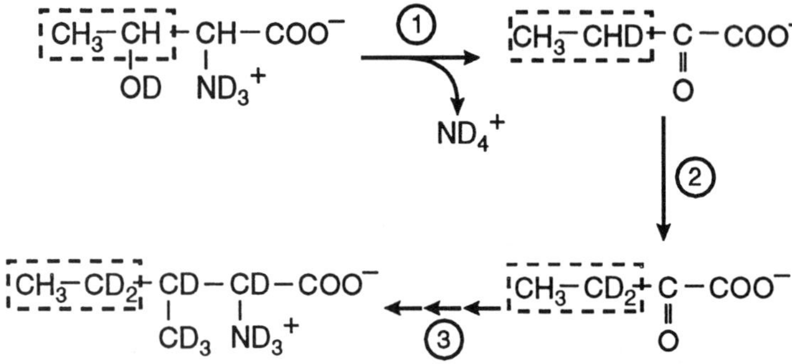

Figure 4 Generation of protein labeled with ^{13}C, ^{2}H (^{1}H-$\delta 1$ methyl) Ile. Step 1: In vitro conversion from Thr into [3-^{2}H] 2-ketobutyrate, catalyzed by *E. coli* biosynthetic threonine deaminase (24). Step 2: In vitro conversion of [3-^{2}H] 2-ketobutyrate into [3,3-$^{2}H_2$] 2-ketobutyrate by proton/deuterium exchange at C3 using pH* 10.2, 45°C. Step 3: In vivo conversion of [3,3-$^{2}H_2$] 2-ketobutyrate into Ile and eventual incorporation into overexpressed protein, carried out by *E. coli* metabolism. All steps performed in 99.5% D_2O. (30, by permission.)

$\leq 10\%$ CD_3). Ile, protonated only at the C$\delta 1$ position, is generated using the set of reactions illustrated in Figure 4. Commercially available ^{15}N, ^{13}C-labeled Thr is the starting compound and is stoichiometrically converted to [3-^{2}H]-^{13}C 2-ketobutyrate in a process catalyzed by *E. coli* biosynthetic threonine deaminase. Note that because this reaction is carried out in D_2O one of the two methylene hydrogens of 2-ketobutyrate becomes deuterated. Substitution of the remaining methylene proton with a deuteron is achieved via base-catalyzed exchange. The resultant product is sterile filtered and added without any further purification to a D_2O-based minimal medium supplemented with [2,3-$^{2}H_2$]-^{15}N, ^{13}C Val.

A ^{13}C-^{1}H HSQC spectrum of the methyl region of the PLCC SH2 domain expressed from *E. coli* grown in this supplemented medium is shown in Figure 5. Despite the fact that a prototrophic strain has been employed in the overexpression, over 90% of Val, Leu, and Ile in the protein is derived from the added Val and 2-ketobutyrate (30). The nonmethyl Ile sidechain positions are highly deuterated and, as is the case with Val and Leu, only the CH_3 protonated isotopomer is produced. In this particular example, fully protonated ^{15}N, ^{13}C Val has been used and therefore Val and Leu retain some protonation at the methine (Val β, Leu γ) positions. The undesired protonation can be eliminated by replacing the ^{15}N, ^{13}C Val added to the growth media in the production of the SH2 domain with [2,3-$^{2}H_2$]-^{15}N, ^{13}C Val, as discussed above. In this context, we have recently obtained a sample of the 40 kDa maltose binding protein by overexpression in *E. coli* grown in minimal media (D_2O) using ^{2}H, ^{13}C glucose

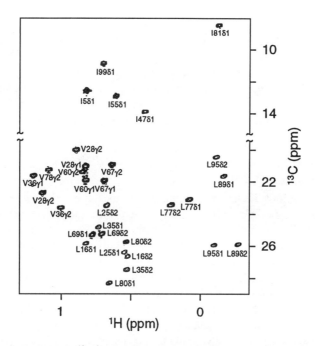

Figure 5 Methyl region of a ^{13}C-^{1}H constant time HSQC spectrum of a highly deuterated, methyl-protonated PLCC SH2 domain, labeled using D$_2$O media supplemented with ^{15}N, ^{13}C Val and [3,3-^{2}H$_2$]-^{13}C 2-ketobutyrate (30). This protein is highly deuterated at all aliphatic sites except for the Val Cβ and Leu Cγ methine positions; these sites can be deuterated by the substitution of [2,3-^{2}H$_2$]-^{15}N, ^{13}C Val in place of ^{15}N, ^{13}C Val. Over 90% of Val, Ile, and Leu derive from the added 2-ketobutyrate or Val. (30, by permission.)

and ^{15}NH$_4$Cl as the sole carbon and nitrogen sources and supplemented with [2,3-^{2}H$_2$]-^{15}N, ^{13}C Val and [3,3-^{2}H$_2$]-^{13}C 2-ketobutyrate. ^{13}C-^{1}H HSQC spectra have established the high level of protonation at methyl groups of Val, Leu, and Ile (δ1) and the very significant extent of deuteration at other carbon positions.

PROTONATED Cα IN A DEUTERATED BACKGROUND   While significant emphasis has been placed on producing highly deuterated proteins with protonation at select sidechain positions, methods have also emerged that place protons at specific backbone sites. Recently Yamazaki and coworkers (173) have produced a sample of the α subunit of *E. coli* RNA polymerase that is ^{15}N, ^{13}C, ^{2}H, ^{1}Hα labeled. By acetylating a ^{15}N, ^{13}C, ^{2}H-labeled amino acid mixture and hydrolyzing the resulting esters in H$_2$O under highly acidic conditions, the deuterons at the Cα positions of most amino acids are efficiently replaced by solvent protons. The sidechain positions, however, remain highly deuterated during this procedure. The resulting mixture of ^{2}H, ^{1}Hα amino acids was added to *E. coli* growing in an H$_2$O-based minimal media immediately prior to protein overexpression. Ten of the amino acid types in RNA polymerase produced in this manner were over 80% protonated at the Cα position and most sidechain positions retained high levels of deuteration. One drawback to this methodology in terms of cost effectiveness is that the ester hydrolysis step racemizes the Cα position; in principle this could be circumvented by the use of enzyme-based approaches (49).

Practical Aspects of Producing Deuterated Proteins in Escherichia coli

Although many of the labeling methods described above can be readily performed in any laboratory that routinely overexpresses proteins in bacterial systems, several aspects deserve special commentary. Figure 6 outlines the approach that we have used to generate both randomly deuterated and deuterated, site-protonated proteins.

At the outset of each growth, we use freshly transformed *E. coli* [typically, but not exclusively, strain BL21(DE3)] that has been plated onto solid H$_2$O-based rich medium. This is in contrast to approaches that utilize bacteria that have been previously adapted to growth in deuterated media by culturing through steps with progressively higher percentages of D$_2$O [e.g. (160)] and then stored as glycerol stabs in a high-level D$_2$O medium. Because the culture is manipulated through multiple liquid media steps (Figure 6), we rely on several basic guidelines to ensure robust growth. All of the cultures are maintained at subsaturating cell densities, with optical densities measured at 600 nm (A$_{600}$) typically below 0.6. When the culture reaches this level the media is briefly centrifuged and removed and the cells resuspended in an amount of fresh media to bring the A$_{600}$ to 0.05–0.1. In this manner, the culture is kept essentially in log-phase growth without significant lag periods. Note that the D$_2$O used during protein production can be recycled by flash chromatography to minimize the cost of this process (111).

It is extremely important that the composition of media used in each step of the growth process be carefully regulated to ensure a constantly high growth rate. In particular, only one variable of the growth media is changed (e.g. solvent or carbon source) between subsequent steps. As a result, we have found that we can completely change many variables (e.g. H$_2$O to D$_2$O or glucose to pyruvate) over the course of multiple steps without causing the bacterial culture to enter growth lag phases of longer than 1 to 2 h. Note that at least two D$_2$O growth steps occur prior to induction in each of the paths illustrated in Figure 6, significantly minimizing the level of residual protonation in overexpressed proteins. With the typical doubling times indicated on the figure for bacterial cultures grown at 37°C, a usual growth requires between 18 to 60 hours.

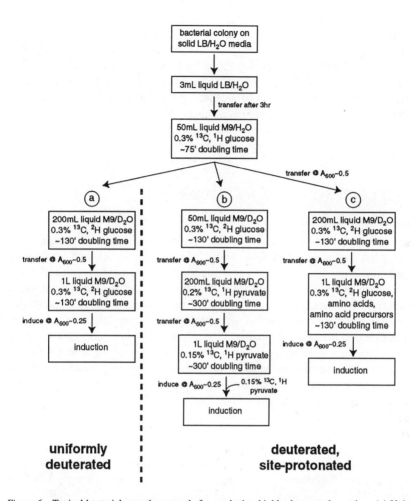

Figure 6 Typical bacterial growth protocols for producing highly deuterated proteins. (*a*) Uniformly deuterated protein production achieved by growing bacteria in D$_2$O medium (see text: "Uniform Deuteration"). (*b*) Production of deuterated, methyl-protonated protein at Ala, Val, Ile (γ2), and Leu sites using ^{1}H-pyruvate as a carbon source in a D$_2$O medium (see text: "Protonated Methyl Groups in a Deuterated Background. Pyruvate"). A total concentration of 0.3% ^{1}H-pyruvate is used in the final induction culture, added incrementally as described in (134). (*c*) Production of deuterated, methyl-protonated protein at Val, Ile (δ1), and Leu sites using protonated amino acids and amino acid precursors in a D$_2$O media (see above: "Protonated Methyl Groups in a Deuterated Background: Specifically Protonated Amino Acids and Amino Acid Precursors"). In all cases, ^{2}H-labeled glucose should be used for steps in D$_2$O media to obtain as uniform a level of deuteration as possible. M9 is defined as the medium without the carbon source.

The purification of a highly deuterated protein is essentially unchanged relative to procedures used for the corresponding protonated versions of the molecule. It is important to recognize that proteins synthesized in D_2O will typically retain deuterons at a significant fraction of backbone amide sites even though purification takes place in H_2O-based buffers. Introduction of protons at labile sites can be achieved by a denaturation/renaturation cycle of the protein in an H_2O-containing buffer using chemical denaturants such as guanidine hydrochloride or urea (18, 159). Alternatively, thermostabile proteins can be incubated at high temperatures for extended periods of time to catalyze NH exchange.

TRIPLE-RESONANCE METHODS

General Comments

Despite the demonstrated utility of triple-resonance (^{15}N, ^{13}C, ^1H) methods for structural studies of proteins, a number of significant limitations occur when these techniques are applied to proteins or protein complexes with molecular weights in excess of approximately 20 kDa. The first problem relates to the rapid relaxation rates of many of the nuclei that participate in the magnetization transfer steps that occur during the course of these complex pulse sequences. The situation is particularly acute in the case of ^{13}C spins, where, for example, $^{13}C\alpha$ transverse relaxation times are on the order of 16 ms for a protein tumbling with a correlation time of 15 ns (171). The second limiting feature is the lack of resolution in spectra (in particular in carbon dimensions), to a large extent the product of short acquisition times that are necessitated by rapid transverse relaxation rates. As described in the introduction to this paper and illustrated in Figure 7 for the case of a $^{13}C\alpha$ carbon with a single attached hydrogen, deuteration of carbon sites provides a solution to these problems.

The figure displays a comparison of carbon linewidths for a carbon-hydrogen spin pair as a function of molecular correlation time. Relaxation contributions to the ^{13}C spin from chemical shift anisotropy, $^{13}C\alpha$-$^1H\alpha$ or $^{13}C\alpha$-$^2H\alpha$ dipolar interactions are considered. It is clear in the case of a ^{13}C-^1H pair that the dominant interaction is dipolar and that this effect can be largely suppressed through deuteration. For example, for a molecular correlation time of 14.5 ns, deuteration is predicted to increase the carbon transverse relaxation time from 16.8 ms (^{13}C-^1H) to 257 ms (^{13}C-^2H), where only one-bond ^{13}C-^1H/^{13}C-^2H dipolar effects have been considered. When contributions from additional dipolar interactions involving the adjacent carbonyl, $^{13}C\beta$ and ^{15}N spins as well as chemical shift anisotropy are included, the predicted carbon transverse relaxation time decreases from 257 to approximately 160 ms. Experimentally, transverse relaxation times were found to increase from 16.5 ± 3 ms to 130 ± 12 ms in

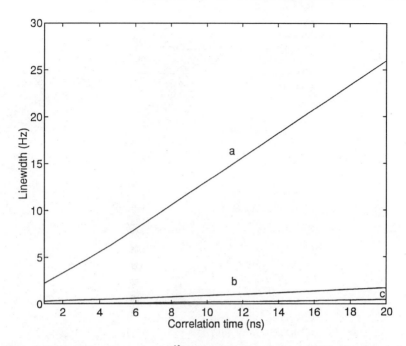

Figure 7 Expected contributions to the ^{13}Cα line-width from dipolar and CSA relaxation mechanisms assuming an isolated ^{13}Cα-^{1}Hα or ^{13}Cα-^{2}Hα spin pair as part of an isotropically tumbling molecule in solution. (*a*) Contribution to the ^{13}Cα line-width from ^{13}Cα-^{1}Hα dipolar interactions (assuming a 1.10 Å carbon-proton separation) (*b*) Contribution from ^{13}Cα-^{2}Hα dipolar interactions. (*c*) Contribution from ^{13}Cα CSA (assuming an axially symmetric ^{13}Cα CSA tensor, $\Delta\sigma =$ 34 ppm). (170, by permission.)

the case of a ^{15}N, ^{13}C, ~70% ^{2}H-labeled 37 kDa trpR/unlabeled DNA complex (correlation time of 14.5 ± 0.9 ns) (170). The discrepancy between calculated and experimental values (160 ms vs. 130 ms) is likely the result of the residual 30% protonation.

Substitution of deuterons for protons has a second major benefit as well. The significant decrease in carbon linewidths in deuterated proteins facilitates the use of constant-time carbon acquisition periods (135, 163). For many experiments, such as the CT-HNCA and CT-HN(CO)CA, this period is set to $1/J_{CC}$, where J_{CC} is the one-bond ^{13}C-^{13}C homonuclear scalar coupling (170, 171). Besides improving resolution by allowing significantly longer acquisition times than would otherwise be possible, the deleterious effects of passive one-bond carbon couplings on spectral resolution and sensitivity can be eliminated (see "Backbone Chemical Shift Assignment," below).

Table 1 Triple resonance NMR methods with versions optimized for use with highly deuterated proteins

Method	Reference
Backbone	
Out-and-back	
3D CT-HNCA	(171)
3D CT-HN(CO)CA	(170)
3D HN(COCA)CB	(170)
3D HN(CA)CB	(170)
4D HNCACB	(170)
3D CT-HN(COCA)CB	(142)
3D CT-HN(CO)CA	(142)
3D HN(CA)CO	(103, 104)
3D HACAN	(173)
3D HACACO	(173)
3D HACACB	(173)
3D HACA(N)CO	(173)
Straight-through	
3D, 4D HN(COCA)NH	(38, 103, 143)
4D HN(CA)NH	(54)
4D HBCB/HACANNH	(117)
4D HBCB/HACA(CO)NNH	(117)
Sidechain	
Out-and-back	
2D H_2N-HSQC	(27)
3D H_2N(CO)$C_{\gamma/\beta}$	(27)
3D H_2N(CO$C_{\gamma/\beta}$)$C_{\beta/\alpha}$	(27)
2D H($N_{\varepsilon/\eta}$)$C_{\delta/\varepsilon}$	(27)
2D H($N_{\varepsilon/\eta}C_{\delta/\varepsilon}$)$C_{\gamma/\delta}$	(27)
2D H(N_ε)C_ξ	(27)
2D H($N_{\varepsilon/\eta}$)C_ξ	(27)
Straight-through	
3D C(CC)(CO)NH	(26)
4D HCC(CO)NH	(117)
3D (H)C(CO)NH-TOCSY	(31)

A wide variety of triple resonance pulse schemes have been modified to take advantage of reduced ^{13}C relaxation rates in highly deuterated proteins. Table 1 provides a listing of many of these experiments.

In general, only minor changes are required to adapt a pulse sequence for use on deuterated proteins. Primarily these changes include the use of deuterium decoupling (see below) and, in some cases, the incorporation of various elements such as constant time indirect detection periods, that likely would result in unacceptable sensitivity losses in experiments on protonated proteins. Specific modifications tailored to particular samples are also possible, such as pulse schemes developed for use on highly deuterated, site-protonated proteins including deuterated, methyl-protonated (31, 134) and deuterated, Hα-protonated (173) molecules.

The fact that it is possible, at least in principle, to generate deuterated samples with high occupancy of protons at the labile sites in the molecule has resulted in the design of many experiments that are of the "out-and-back" variety where magnetization both originates and is detected on NH spins (170, 171). These experiments are performed on samples dissolved in H$_2$O and benefit by the relatively good dispersion of cross-peaks in ^{15}N, NH correlation spectra. Alternatively, a different strategy is required for samples in which the Hα site is protonated in proteins that are otherwise highly deuterated. In this case "out-and-back" experiments have been developed where the role of the NH spin discussed above is replaced by the Hα nucleus (173). Experiments of this type are best conducted in D$_2$O. It must be noted that a drawback of deuteration in all experiments is that the T$_1$ relaxation times of the remaining protons are significantly increased, requiring the use of longer recycle delays than typically employed in experiments performed with protonated molecules (101, 117, 170).

Backbone Chemical Shift Assignment

Many experiments for assignment of backbone chemical shifts have been developed for use on deuterated proteins, with many of these pulse schemes analogous to versions used for protonated samples. Besides the 4D HN(COCA)NH described first by Bax and coworkers (38) and the suite of experiments for correlating backbone ^{13}Cα, ^{15}N, NH and sidechain ^{13}Cβ chemical shifts designed by Yamazaki et al (170, 171), several other groups have published pulse schemes optimized for use on deuterated molecules. Experiments include the HN(CA)CO (103, 104), HN(CA)NH (54), alternative HN(COCA)NH sequences (103, 143), as well as schemes providing backbone correlations with residue-selective editing (23).

To illustrate a number of the features that are particular to pulse schemes optimized for use on deuterated samples, we provide a brief description of the CT-HNCA (171). This experiment correlates the chemical shifts of intraresidue ^{15}N-NH spin pairs of residue i with the ^{13}Cα shifts of residues i and (i − 1). Figure 8 presents the pulse sequence of the CT-HNCA experiment (171).

It is clear that many of the magnetization transfer steps are identical to those employed in the HNCA experiment developed for ^{15}N, ^{13}C, ^{1}H samples (39, 55, 66). Schematically, these steps can be diagrammed as:

$$\text{NH(i)} \xrightarrow{\text{J}_{\text{NH}}} {}^{15}\text{N(i)} \xrightarrow{\text{J}_{\text{NC}}} {}^{13}\text{C}\alpha\text{(i, i − 1)[t}_1\text{]} \xrightarrow{\text{J}_{\text{NC}}} {}^{15}\text{N(i)[t}_2\text{]} \xrightarrow{\text{J}_{\text{NH}}} \text{NH(i)[t}_3\text{]}$$

where t$_1$, t$_2$, and t$_3$ are acquisition periods, and the active couplings involved

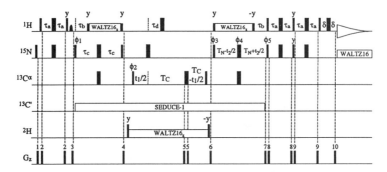

Figure 8   Pulse sequence for the CT-HNCA experiment for use on uniformly ^{15}N, ^{13}C, fractionally ^{2}H-labeled proteins. Correlations linking ^{15}N,NH spin pairs with intra- (i) and inter-residue (i − 1) ^{13}Cα chemical shifts are provided by this experiment. (171, by permission, with the addition of 90° pulses on both sides of the ^{2}H WALTZ-16 decoupling field.)

in each transfer step are indicated above the arrows. Fourier transformation of the resultant time domain data set gives a frequency domain map with both intra- (one bond) and interresidue (two bond) correlations of the form (^{13}Cα, ^{15}N, NH).

It is noteworthy that both ^{13}Cα and ^{15}N chemical shifts are recorded in a constant-time manner. During the carbon constant time period, evolution of magnetization owing to the passive one-bond ^{13}C-^{13}C scalar coupling proceeds according to the relation, $\cos^N(2\pi J_{CC}T_C)$, where N = 0 for Gly and 1 for all other amino acids. Because J_{CC} values connecting aliphatic carbons are essentially uniform, it is possible to refocus the effects of such couplings by choosing $2T_C$ to be a multiple of $1/J_{CC}$ (135, 163). In practice, $2T_C$ is set to $1/J_{CC}$ (28 ms) in order to minimize signal attenuation caused by relaxation. In this regard, deuteration is critical, since in proteins of even modest size transverse relaxation of ^{13}Cα carbons can become limiting. For example, consider a protein with a correlation time of 14.5 ns, such as the 37 kDa trpR/DNA complex studied by Jardetzky and coworkers (4, 176) and Yamazaki et al (170, 171). Assuming average ^{13}Cα T_2 values of 16 ms and 130 ms for protonated and deuterated samples, respectively, relaxation during the constant time period correspondingly attenuates the final signal by factors of 5.8 and 1.2. In the case of the trpR/DNA complex described above, deuteration was critical for the complete assignment of backbone chemical shifts using triple resonance methods.

Several additional features relating to the sensitivity of the pulse scheme of Figure 8 are worthy of comment. First, signal-to-noise can be improved by minimizing saturation and/or dephasing of the water signal (40, 72, 148). This is achieved by ensuring that water magnetization is placed along the +z axis prior to the application of homospoil gradients and immediately prior to signal detection. Maintaining a reservoir of water magnetization is critical, especially in experiments performed on highly deuterated proteins where magnetization originates on NH spins. In this case, exchange between water and labile sites can increase the rate at which NH magnetization is replenished (148), circumventing to some extent the limitations imposed by long T_1 values on repetition delays. Second, as described in some detail later in this review, it is essential that deuterium decoupling be employed during periods in which transverse carbon magnetization is present. The deuterium decoupling element is sandwiched between ^{2}H 90° pulses that place ^{2}H magnetization collinear with the decoupling field (26, 114). In this manner, the magnetization is restored to the +z axis after decoupling, minimizing lock instability. Note the analogous use of ^{1}H 90° pulses flanking the WALTZ-16 decoupling elements in the CT-HNCA sequence, which minimizes scrambling of water caused by nonintegral multiples of the WALTZ scheme (72). Third, an enhanced sensitivity pulsed field gradient approach is employed to select for ^{15}N magnetization during the nitrogen constant time period. The use of gradients to select for coherence transfer pathways and a discussion of the classes of experiments and the molecular weights for which the enhanced sensitivity method is beneficial is deferred until later in this review (see below: "The Use of Enhanced Sensitivity Pulsed Field Gradient Coherence Transfer Methods for Experiments on Large Deuterated Proteins").

As a final point of interest, it is noteworthy that a ^{1}H 180° pulse is applied at a time of $t_1/2 + \tau_d$ after the start of the carbon constant-time period. By choosing τ_d to be $1/(4J_{CH})$, where J_{CH} is the magnitude of the one-bond ^{13}C-^{1}H scalar coupling, carbon magnetization from ^{13}C-^{1}H spin pairs evolves for a net duration of $1/(2J_{CH})$ during this constant-time interval and is not refocused into observable signal by the application of the remaining pulses in the sequence. In the case where the experiment is performed on perdeuterated molecules this pulse is not necessary. However, in applications to fractionally deuterated proteins it may be possible to observe signals from both ^{13}C-^{1}H and ^{13}C-^{2}H pairs, arising from residues with high levels of mobility and hence decreased carbon relaxation rates. The doubling of signals degrades resolution in the carbon dimension of the HNCA spectrum and application of this pulse is thus recommended in these cases.

As described above, many of the triple resonance pulse schemes that are currently employed for the assignment of deuterated proteins record backbone and sidechain carbon chemical shifts and in these cases deuterium decoupling during carbon evolution is necessary. However, in special classes of experiments it is possible to eliminate deuterium decoupling through the use of magnetization transfer schemes which rely on carbon cross-polarization. For example, in a version of the HN(COCA)NH experiment proposed by Shirakawa and coworkers (143) magnetization is transferred from ^{13}CO to ^{13}Cα spins and subsequently from $^{13}C\alpha$ to ^{15}N using cross-polarization sequences. This circumvents the need for deuterium decoupling which would otherwise be necessary during the relay from carbon to nitrogen if INEPT-based magnetization transfer methods had been employed (38).

Recently Yamazaki and coworkers have described a suite of pulse sequences for use with highly deuterated, $C\alpha$-protonated samples (173). The experiments are of particular value in cases where rapid exchange with water precludes the use of NH-based schemes. In a manner analogous to the CT-HNCA sequence described above, carbon chemical shift is recorded in a constant time manner. In order to minimize the rapid decay of carbon magnetization during this period, double- and zero-quantum ^{13}C, ^{1}H coherences are established. It is straightforward to show that in the macromolecule limit the relaxation of these two-spin coherences proceeds in a manner that is independent of the large ^{13}C-^{1}H one-bond dipolar interaction (36). In the case of a protonated sample the advantages of using double/zero quantum coherences are offset to some extent by relaxation of the participating proton with proximal proton spins. Additionally, homonuclear proton couplings that evolve during the constant time carbon evolution period further attenuate the signal (42). Because the molecules prepared by Yamazaki et al are deuterated at all non-$C\alpha$ positions, pulse schemes that make use of this approach enjoy benefits that are seldom realized in applications involving protonated samples. For example, increases in relaxation times of approximately a factor of 4.5 (double/zero quantum vs. carbon single quantum) have been realized for the carboxy-terminal domain of the α-subunit of *E. coli* RNA polymerase at 10°C (correlation time of 17 ns).

Sidechain Chemical Shift Assignment

Two of the most often used experiments for the assignment of aliphatic sidechain chemical shifts in protonated, ^{15}N, ^{13}C labeled proteins are the (H)C(CO)NH- and H(CCO)NH-TOCSY (37, 96, 97, 110). In these pulse schemes magnetization originating on sidechain protons is relayed via a carbon TOCSY step to the backbone $C\alpha$ position and finally transferred to the ^{15}N, NH spins of the subsequent residue. These experiments provide correlations linking either aliphatic protons or carbons with backbone amide shifts, or in the case of a 4D sequence developed by Fesik and coworkers (96), connectivities are established between all four groups of spins (^{13}C, ^{1}H, ^{15}N, NH). The large number of transfer steps involved in the relay of magnetization from sidechain to backbone sites in these experiments limits their utility to proteins or protein complexes with molecular weights on the order of 20 kDa or less. Nietlispach et al (117) have developed a number of experiments for sidechain assignment in fractionally deuterated proteins and suggest that deuteration levels on the order of 50% provide a good balance between the need for aliphatic protons and the requirement of decreased carbon relaxation rates.

Farmer and Venters have developed a number of experiments for sidechain assignment in highly deuterated proteins. In one such scheme, a simple modification to the original (H)C(CO)NH-TOCSY is made allowing magnetization to originate on (deuterated) aliphatic carbon sites (26). The utility of this sequence has been demonstrated in spectacular fashion on a perdeuterated sample of human carbonic anhydrase (HCA II, 29 kDa) allowing essentially complete assignment of sidechain carbon chemical shifts. A number of experiments for assignment of sidechain ^{15}N/NH resonances in highly deuterated samples have also been published by this group (27). These triple resonance sequences rely on correlating sidechain ^{15}N-NH pairs with carbon shifts that have been previously assigned using the experiment(s) discussed above. Because deuteration limits the number of available NOEs for structure determination, it is important that as many of the remaining protons in the molecule as possible be assigned. In this context, the assignment of Arg, Gln, and Asn labile sidechain protons is crucial.

Deuterium Decoupling

In the extreme narrowing limit, the ^{13}C spectrum of an isolated ^{13}C-^{2}H spin pair consists of a triplet, with each multiplet component separated from its nearest neighbor by J_{CD}, where J_{CD} is the magnitude of the one-bond ^{13}C-^{2}H scalar coupling. As the tumbling time of the molecule to which the ^{13}C-^{2}H pair is attached increases, the ^{2}H T_1 relaxation time decreases, and the multiplet structure collapses in the vicinity of the T minimum. In the slow correlation time limit, linewidths of the components narrow and the multiplet component structure becomes decidedly asymmetric as a result of cross correlation between ^{13}C-^{2}H dipolar and ^{2}H quadrupolar relaxation interactions (41, 82, 98, 115). Finally, at very long correlation times the outer components disappear completely.

The deleterious effects of deuterium spin flips on ^{13}C spectra of deuterated proteins were recognized over two decades ago by Browne and coworkers (13), who suggested the use of high power deuterium decoupling as a means of reducing carbon linewidths. However, at that time the power levels required for efficient decoupling could not be achieved. The increase in ^{2}H T_1 relaxation times at the magnetic field strengths typically in use today coupled with the higher decoupling power levels that are available on commercial spectrometers have led to the successful use of deuterium decoupling in triple resonance NMR applications, first demonstrated by Bax and coworkers in 1993 (38).

The Use of Enhanced Sensitivity Pulsed Field Gradient Coherence Transfer Methods for Experiments on Large Deuterated Proteins

It has long been recognized that pulsed field gradients could be used both to select for desired coherence transfer pathways and reject others (10, 105) and to reduce the artifact content in spectra (73). However, the use of this technology in high resolution NMR spectroscopy had to await the development of probes with actively shielded gradient coils in the early 1990s; since this time the use of gradients has become widespread. Many of the initial applications to macromolecules employed gradients to select for coherence transfer pathways (11, 22, 154), following on the pioneering work of Ernst and coworkers (105) and Bax et al (10). A significant limitation associated with these early experiments is that only one of the two paths that normally contribute to the observed signal in nongradient based experiments was observed, reducing sensitivity (63, 64). More recently, building on the enhanced sensitivity nongradient methods of Rance and coworkers (14, 126), gradient-based pulse schemes with pathway selection that do not suffer from the above mentioned sensitivity losses have been developed (67, 112, 137, 138). In the absence of relaxation and pulse imperfections the proposed methods are a full factor of 2 more sensitive than their counterparts that employ gradients for coherence transfer selection but do not make use of enhanced sensitivity, and a factor of $\sqrt{2}$ more sensitive than nongradient experiments.

The sensitivity advantages associated with enhanced sensitivity pulsed field gradient coherence transfer selection in triple resonance-based NH detected spectroscopy have been described for applications to fully protonated, ^{15}N, ^{13}C labeled molecules ranging in molecular weight from approximately 10–20 kDa (112). On average, gains of approximately 15–25% were noted in relation to nongradient methods. The decrease in sensitivity relative to the expected theoretical enhancement of $\sqrt{2}$ is largely the result of relaxation losses that occur during the increased number of delays in these experiments. Because these losses are most severe for large molecules, it is important to establish the molecular weight limit above which the sensitivity advantages of this method are marginal. In this regard Shan et al have compared signal-to-noise ratios of HNCO spectra recorded both with and without enhanced sensitivity methods (142). A ^{15}N, ^{13}C, $\sim$80% ^{2}H sample of the PLCC SH2 domain was prepared in either 0%, 15%, or 30% glycerol; the steep viscosity dependence of glycerol with temperature allows convenient manipulation of the overall correlation time of the SH2 domain, allowing spectra to be recorded as a function of "effective molecular weight." Statistically significant sensitivity gains were observed for correlation times as large as 21 ns. It is noteworthy that the enhancements in triple-resonance based spectra are likely to be larger than in ^{15}N-NH HSQC spectra, since the ^{15}N chemical shift is not recorded in a constant-time manner in the latter experiment. Thus, additional delays must be included during ^{15}N evolution to allow for the application of coherence transfer selection gradients without the introduction of phase distortions resulting from chemical shift evolution.

Finally, signal-to-noise advantages mentioned above in the context of highly deuterated proteins will be larger than for protonated molecules. As discussed in this paper's introduction, deuteration increases transverse relaxation times of NH protons by approximately a factor of two (101, 159). This has a particularly significant effect on the efficiency of sensitivity enhanced-based experiments that, relative to other classes of experiments, rely on increased delay times during which NH magnetization evolves. It must be emphasized that even in the absence of notable sensitivity gains there are advantages in gradient based coherence transfer selection methods, including artifact and solvent suppression and minimization of phase cycling.

Deuterium Isotope Effects on ^{13}C and ^{15}N Chemical Shifts

With the benefits that deuterium substitution provides in the reduction of heteronuclear transverse relaxation rates comes the not-so-desired perturbation of the chemical shifts of ^{15}N and ^{13}C nuclei. These so-called deuterium isotope shifts are significant for ^{15}N and ^{13}C spins located within at least three bonds of the site of deuteration (46). In an effort to measure the magnitude of one $[^1\Delta\ ^{13}C(^2H)]$, two $[^2\Delta\ ^{13}C(^2H)]$ and three bond $[^3\Delta\ ^{13}C(^2H)]$ deuterium isotope effects on ^{13}C chemical shifts, Venters et al (159) and Gardner et al (32) have compared chemical shifts of ^{13}Cα and ^{13}Cβ carbons in protonated and highly deuterated versions of the same molecule. Based on results from HCA II (159), a single ^{1}H $\rightarrow$ ^{2}H substitution produces chemical shift changes of -0.29 ± 0.05, -0.13 ± 0.02 and -0.07 ± 0.02 ppm for a ^{13}C nucleus one, two, or three bonds away, respectively. Gardner et al have measured average values for $^1\Delta\ ^{13}C(^2H)$ and $^2\Delta\ ^{13}C(^2H)$ of -0.25 and -0.1 ppm, respectively. These effects are additive, resulting in total shifts of over 1 ppm for ^{13}C nuclei at sites with many proximal deuterons, such as is the case for sidechains of long aliphatic amino acids. Slightly smaller changes are typical for backbone nuclei, on the order of -0.3 ppm (^{15}N) and -0.5 ppm (^{13}Cα) for highly deuterated proteins dissolved in H_2O (30, 33, 38, 82, 159). The ^{13}Cα deuterium isotope shifts are weakly dependent on secondary structure (93).

In a recent study of the EIN protein, ^{13}Cα resonances were shifted upfield by an average of 0.50 ± 0.08 ppm for residues in α-helical regions of the protein compared to 0.44 ± 0.08 ppm for amino acids in β-strands (33). In contrast to the ^{2}H-isotope shift observed for aliphatic carbon resonances, no significant changes were observed between NH or carbonyl chemical shifts in a comparison between protonated and highly deuterated PLCC SH2 domains.

Given the additivity and only weak structural dependence of deuterium isotope effects, one can reliably transfer chemical shift assignments between fully protonated and perdeuterated molecules (159). This facilitates the use of "secondary shift" based identification of secondary structure elements (167) from the ^{13}C chemical shifts of deuterated proteins (18, 32, 159). Note that transferability of carbon chemical shifts (i.e. the ability to calculate ^{13}C shifts in a protonated molecule from assignments obtained in a perdeuterated system and visa versa) is a prerequisite for combining data from deuterated and protonated proteins where chemical shifts obtained from a highly deuterated sample are used to assign NOE cross-peaks recorded on a highly protonated molecule (18, 33, 159, 175).

In the case of partially deuterated systems the presence of multiple deuterium-containing isotopomers at each site can significantly complicate spectra. Recall that in the case of the CT-HNCA experiment recorded on fractionally deuterated proteins, correlations involving $^{13}C\alpha$ sites that are protonated can be removed from spectra in a straightforward fashion by insertion of a single ^1H pulse. Signals from deuterated sites are unaffected by this pulse (See "Backbone Chemical Shift Assignment" above). In the case of fractionally deuterated aliphatic sidechain sites the situation is somewhat more complex. Consider, for example, the high resolution ^{13}C-^1H constant time HSQC spectrum of a deuterated, methyl-protonated sample of the PLCC SH2 domain produced using pyruvate as a carbon source (see above: "Protonated Methyl Groups in a Deuterated Background: Pyruvate") shown in Figure 9a. Three peaks are observed for each Ala and Val methyl group, corresponding to the three possible proton-containing methyl isotopomers: CH_3, CH_2D, and CHD_2. Each methyl component is separated by deuterium isotope shifts of approximately 0.3 ppm for ^{13}C and 0.02 ppm for ^1H (32). A smaller number of isotopomers are observed for Met (two) and Thr (one), reflecting differences between these amino acids in the biosynthetic incorporation of protons from the protonated pyruvate carbon source.

Many of the multidimensional experiments that are used for assignment of chemical shifts and for measuring distance restraints are recorded with relatively short acquisition times in the indirect-detection dimensions (4–5 ms in carbon dimensions, for example), principally because of the lengthy acquisition times associated with collecting large (nD) data sets. In addition, in some applications acquisition times are constrained further by evolution involving passive homonuclear couplings. As such, these experiments are chiefly limited by poor digital resolution and cross-peaks from individual isotopomers are usually not resolved (32, 117). However, in higher resolution spectra it is readily apparent that the deuterium isotopomers do significantly degrade spectral resolution, even in a well-dispersed spectrum recorded on a 12 kDa protein (Figure 9a). As discussed in detail previously (32) the best solution to the problem is to eliminate all but CH_3 isotopomers during protein expression and in this regard Gardner and Kay have developed a strategy for producing highly deuterated, (Val, Leu, Ile δ1-methyl protonated proteins using appropriately labeled amino

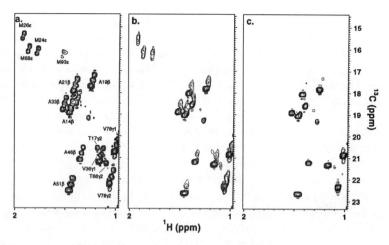

Figure 9 Removal of ^{13}CH$_2$D and ^{13}CHD$_2$ cross-peaks in ^{13}C-^{1}H correlation spectra. All panels show a section of the methyl region from ^{13}C-^{1}H constant-time HSQC spectra recorded on a ^{15}N, ^{13}C, ^{2}H, ^{1}H-methyl (from ^{1}H-pyruvate)-labeled sample of the PLCC SH2 domain bound to a phosphotyrosine-containing peptide (32). (*a*) ^{2}H decoupling applied throughout the constant-time ^{13}C chemical shift evolution period (set to 1/J$_{CC}$ ~ 28 ms) for maximum resolution of each methyl isotopomer (CH$_3$:CH$_2$D:CHD$_2$ from downfield to upfield for Ala and Val; CH$_2$D:CHD$_2$ for Met; CHD$_2$ for Thr). (*b*) Minimizing cross-peak intensities from deuterium-containing isotopomers by eliminating ^{2}H decoupling during ^{13}C chemical shift evolution. (*c*) Elimination of cross-peaks from deuterium-containing isotopomers by removing deuterium decoupling as in (*b*) and application of the purging scheme described in the text. (32, by permission.)

acids and amino acid precursors (see above: "Protonated Methyl Groups in a Deuterated Background: Specifically Protonated Amino Acids and Amino Acid Precursors").

It is also possible to remove CH$_2$D and CHD$_2$ groups from ^{13}C-^{1}H correlation spectra using multi-pulse NMR methods although regrettably the spin alchemy employed does not restore the full complement of protons to the methyl groups that the biosynthetic approach described by Gardner & Kay (30) provides. Nevertheless the filtering schemes that have been used to suppress CH$_2$D and CHD$_2$ signals illustrate a number of important features regarding deuterium decoupling and purging of unwanted coherences that the reader may find of interest, and with this in mind a brief description of the approach that we have developed for retaining only CH$_3$ isotopomers is in order.

Earlier sections of this review described the importance of deuterium decoupling during the evolution of carbon magnetization (see "Backbone Chemical Shift Assignment" and "Deuterium Decoupling"). In the absence of decoupling, deuterium spin flips mix carbon multiplet components associated with different deuterium spin states, leading to significant broadening and hence attenuation of cross-peaks. This feature can be put to good use in the separation of CH_3 isotopomers from CH_2D and CHD_2 groups in the present application. By eliminating deuterium decoupling during the constant time delay period where carbon chemical shift is recorded, cross-peaks originating from deuterium containing methyl groups are significantly attenuated, as illustrated in Figure 9b. It is clear that in most experiments recorded on deuterated molecules where the idea is to maximize signal intensity from CD_n groups deuterium decoupling is essential. To further reduce the intensity of cross-peaks from CH_2D methyl types, it is possible to actively purge magnetization from these groups. This is achieved by allowing carbon magnetization to evolve for a period of $1/(2J_{CH})$ from the start of the carbon constant-time period. At this point magnetization from CH_3, CH_2D, and CHD_2 groups is given by terms of the form, $C_{TR}I_Z^i I_Z^j$ ($i \neq j$), $C_{TR}I_Z^i$, C_{TR}, respectively, where C_{TR} is transverse carbon magnetization and I_Z^k refers to the z component of magnetization associated with methyl proton k. Application of a ^1H $90_x 90_\phi$ pulse pair where the phase ϕ is cycled (x, −x) with no change in the receiver phase eliminates magnetization from CH_2D methyl groups. Additional purging of signals arising from partially deuterated methyls occurs by applying a ^2H purge (90°) pulse at a time of $1/(4J_{CD})$ after the start of the constant time carbon evolution period, where J_{CD} is the one-bond ^{13}C-^2H coupling constant. As described in some detail previously (32), the outer components of a CD triplet evolve at a rate of $\pm 2\pi J_{CD}$, while in the case of a CD_2 spin system the lines closest to and farthest from the center line evolve with frequencies of $\pm 2\pi J_{CD}$ and $\pm 4\pi J_{CD}$, respectively (neglecting ^2H spin flips). Note that the central lines do not evolve. Given the range of frequencies over which different multiplet components evolve it is not possible to eliminate all lines completely with a single purge pulse. In Figure 9c a compromise delay of $1/(4J_{CD})$ has been employed and it is clear that excellent purging of CH_2D and CHD_2 groups has been achieved.

IMPACT OF DEUTERATION ON STRUCTURE DETERMINATION

Structure Determination of Perdeuterated Proteins

Current NMR solution structure determination methods rely heavily on both NOE-based interproton distance restraints and on scalar-coupling based dihedral angle restraints (169a). The quality of any given structure is, of course, heavily influenced by both the total number and the accuracy and precision of the input restraints (17, 50, 56, 95, 177). Because the number of restraints can vary significantly with deuteration levels and with the type of deuterium strategy employed, it is important to evaluate how each of the different deuteration approaches affects the quality of protein structures determined by NMR.

On a positive note the use of relatively high levels of deuteration (>75%) can improve the accuracy of NOE-derived interproton distance measurements, achieved largely through a reduction of spin diffusion. That is, by eliminating proton C that relays magnetization between protons A and B, the A–B separation can be measured more accurately. In addition, because the linewidths of the remaining protons in a deuterated molecule can be significantly narrowed (see Introduction), overlap is reduced and, in the case of NH-NH cross-peaks, in particular, appreciable gains in sensitivity have been noted (94, 124, 156, 157). This leads to further improvements in the accuracy of distance measurements. Recently, 4D ^{15}N-, ^{15}N-edited NOESY experiments were developed (43, 161) and data sets with high ^{15}N sensitivity and resolution can be recorded using samples of modest protein concentrations (1 mM). Deuteration also facilitates the use of longer NOE mixing times, allowing the measurement of larger distances than would be possible in protonated systems (161).

However, these benefits do come at a cost. Deuteration reduces the concentration of protons that would normally be available for providing NOE-based distance restraints, decreasing the total amount of structural information that can be used for analysis. In the most extreme case of a fully deuterated protein, the remaining protons derive exclusively from exchangeable sites such as amides and hydroxyls and only a subset of these will have sufficiently slow exchange rates and well-dispersed chemical shifts for analysis in NOESY experiments.

To investigate the impact of perdeuteration on the number of distance restraints that can be obtained from NOE experiments we have used a database of crystal structures solved to better than 2.5 Å that includes over 200 non-homologous proteins (48), and tabulated the number of protons within 5 Å of each backbone amide proton. In the case of a fully protonated molecule, on average, 15.7 ± 2.0 protons are located within a 5 Å radius of each backbone NH. In contrast, only 2.5 ± 0.4 protons are within 5 Å of a backbone amide proton in the case of a fully deuterated molecule dissolved in H_2O. Two factors contribute to the six-fold reduction in the number of potential internuclear distance restraints involving backbone NHs that are available in a perdeuterated protein. Most obvious, the decrease in NOEs simply reflects the loss of protons that accompanies deuteration, as illustrated in Figure 10 where a comparison of the distribution and numbers of protons within protonated and perdeuterated PLCC SH2 domains is provided. Perdeuteration leads to a five-fold reduction in the number of protons in this molecule, from over 750 to approximately 60 sidechain and 90 backbone NHs. In addition, the spatial location of the majority of the remaining protons further lowers the number of possible NOE-based

a.

b.

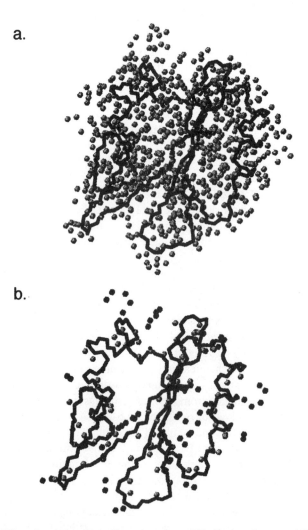

Figure 10 Effect of perdeuteration on the total number and distribution of protons within a protein. *Gray spheres*: Protons from residues 10–100 in the PLCC SH2 domain. *Heavy black line*: protein N, Cα, C backbone. (SM Pascal, AU Singer, LE Kay, JD Forman-Kay, unpublished results). (*a*) Fully protonated protein, containing a total of 756 protons. (*b*) Perdeuterated protein, containing 87 backbone amide and 62 sidechain amide protons on Arg, Asn, Gln, and Trp residues. *Light gray* and *dark gray* spheres: Backbone and sidechain amide protons, respectively. Figures generated by MOLMOL (77).

distance restraints. Many backbone and sidechain amide protons are involved in hydrogen-bonding networks in the core of secondary structure elements and are thus separated by distances of greater than 5 Å from protons on other α-helices or β-sheets. This is particularly problematic for α-helices, given the clustering of backbone NH protons in the centers of these structures (32).

Studies using either experimentally derived distance restraints or distances obtained on the basis of previously determined structures have established that backbone NH-NH distances of 5 Å or less will not, in general, be sufficient for calculating accurate global folds (32, 146, 161). Structures generated in this manner typically have backbone heavy atom root-mean-square (rms) deviations on the order of 8 Å relative to reference structures. In addition, the precision of these folds is also quite poor, especially for proteins containing a high percentage of α-helix. It is noteworthy that Venters, Farmer, and coworkers have calculated well defined global folds of HCA II using data sets generated from the known structure of the molecule where all backbone and sidechain NH NOEs within 7 Å are included (161). Unfortunately, with the current generation of spectrometers and with limitations imposed on sample concentration due to issues of solubility, aggregation, viscosity, or expense of production, it seems unlikely that large numbers of NH-NH distances beyond 5 Å will be observed for most systems. For example, only a small fraction (4%) of the possible NOEs connecting NH backbone protons separated by more than 5 Å were measured in a study of a highly deuterated PLCC SH2 domain (1.9 mM) in complex with target peptide (32). In general, therefore, additional NOE restraints are required to obtain overall folds of proteins.

Improving the Quality of Structures from Perdeuterated Systems: Additional Distance Restraints

As discussed above, the generation of accurate global folds of perdeuterated proteins requires that backbone NH-NH NOEs be supplemented by additional restraints. One obvious source of distance information derives from sidechain amide protons of Arg, Asn, and Gln. Note that these sidechain positions can, in principle, be fully protonated in a perdeuterated protein dissolved in H_2O. In addition to developing experiments for the site-specific assignment of sidechain amides, Farmer and Venters have also demonstrated the utility of sidechain NOEs in improving both the precision and accuracy of global fold determination from a limited NOE restraint set (27). Figure 11a illustrates the distribution of sidechain NH protons from Arg, Asn, Gln, and Trp in the PLCC SH2 domain. Many of these protons are located in the interior of the molecule where they are sufficiently close to other NH protons to provide measurable distance restraints. However, a significant percentage are located on the exterior of the protein where they are likely prone to rapid exchange with solvent and poor chemical

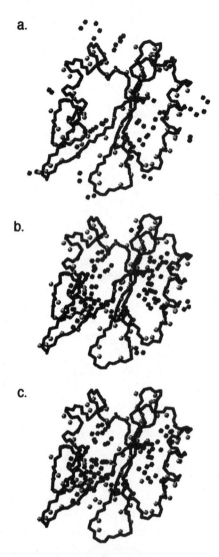

Figure 11 Distribution of sidechain protons in the PLCC SH2 domain obtained from different methods used to produce site-protonated, highly deuterated proteins. *Light gray spheres*: Backbone amide protons. *Dark gray spheres*: Additional protons. (*a*) Sidechain amide protons of Arg, Asn, Gln, and Trp available using any of the labeling strategies described in the text. (*b*) The 108 methyl protons of Ala, Val, Leu, and Ile ($\gamma 2$ methyl only) produced using ^{1}H-pyruvate-based labeling (134). (*c*) Labeling scheme obtained using the method of Gardner and Kay (30) based on the addition of [2,3-^{2}H$_2$] ^{15}N, ^{13}C-Val, and [3,3-^{2}H$_2$] ^{13}C 2-ketobutyrate to D$_2$O medium with ^{2}H, ^{13}C glucose as the carbon source. This approach produces 90 methyl protons. Graphics generated by MOLMOL (77).

shift dispersion. Nevertheless, in the case of perdeuterated HCA II, Farmer and Venters were able to assign sidechain amide ^{1}H and ^{15}N chemical shifts for over 80% of the Asn and Gln residues and all of the Arg ε positions.

A second and more important source of additional NOE restraints derives from protonated methyl sites in otherwise highly deuterated proteins (see section above: "Site-Specific Protonation in a Highly Deuterated Environment"). Several important factors enter into the choice of methyl groups as sites of protonation. First, the methyl region of ^{13}C-^{1}H correlation spectra is often reasonably well resolved and fast rotation about the methyl symmetry axis leads to narrow ^{13}C and ^{1}H linewidths, even in cases of large proteins (65). Analysis of the distribution of methyl-containing amino acids in proteins establishes that Ala, Val, Ile and Leu are the most common residues in protein interiors and that Val and Leu are two of the three most abundant amino acids at molecular interfaces (57). Therefore, protonated methyl groups are often within 5 Å of methyl or NH protons of other residues on different secondary structure elements. Figure 11b highlights the distribution of the methyl groups of Ala, Val, Ile (γ_2 only), and Leu in the PLCC SH2 domain. Recall that this pattern of protonation is produced using D$_2$O-based media supplemented with ^{1}H-pyruvate (see "Protonated Methyl Groups in a Deuterated Background: Pyruvate," below) (134). A similar distribution of methyl groups is observed for other patterns of site-specific protonation using deuterated, site-protonated or fully protonated forms of these amino acids (30, 109, 146). For example, in Figure 11c the aliphatic proton distribution in a sample generated by the procedure of Gardner & Kay (30) where methyls from Val, Leu, and Ile ($\delta 1$ only) are protonated is illustrated.

The utility of methyl site-specific protonation in providing additional distance restraints is readily appreciated by analyzing distances in a large set of nonhomologous proteins solved to high resolution by x-ray diffraction techniques (48). For example, an average of 5.1 ± 1.9 backbone amide protons and a total of 2.8 ± 1.5 Val γ, Ile $\delta 1$ (i, i $\neq$ j) and Leu δ methyl groups are within 6 Å of a given Ile $\delta 1$ (j) methyl. NOEs between methyl protons in highly deuterated molecules where only the Val γ, Ile $\delta 1$, and Leu δ methyl groups are protonated (see above: "Protonated Methyl Groups in a Deuterated Background: Specifically Protonated Amino Acids and Amino Acid Precursors") involve residues with a median separation of 30 amino acids, as opposed to 2 and 3 for amide-amide and amide-methyl NOEs, respectively.

Given that inter-methyl NOEs contain information constraining the location of residues that are so widely separated in the primary sequence, it is not surprising that they can significantly improve the quality of structures in relation to those calculated using distance restraints solely between backbone amide protons. Figure 12 illustrates this clearly by comparing several sets of structures of the PLCC SH2 domain generated using different subsets of NOE information.

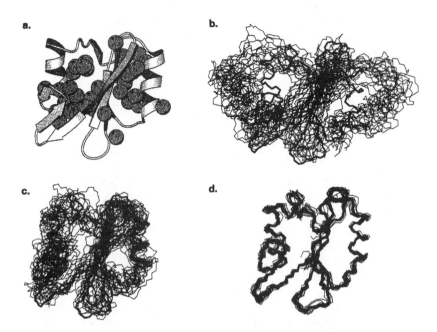

Figure 12   Structures of the PLCC SH2 domain obtained using different sets of distance restraints. (*a*) Schematic view showing ordered secondary structure elements identified by Pascal et al (129). Pyruvate-derived methyl groups are shown in a space-filling representation, highlighting their position between the central β-sheet and flanking α-helices. (*b*) Structures obtained on the basis of NH-NH NOEs and dihedral angle restraints established from $^{13}C\alpha$ and $^{13}C\beta$ chemical shifts (1.1 distance, 0.7 dihedral restraints/residue). (*c*) Structures generated by including methyl-methyl and NH-methyl restraints as well as the restraints in *b*) (2.7 distance, 0.7 dihedral restraints/residue). (*d*) Reference structures, generated using an average of 16.0 distance and 1.7 dihedral angle restraints per residue, obtained from data recorded on a fully protonated sample (SM Pascal, AU Singer, LE Kay, JD Forman-Kay, unpublished results). Each bundle has 18 independently refined structures (*thin lines*) and is fit to the mean reference structure (*thick line*) using the backbone atoms of the secondary structure elements shown in (*a*). (*a*) drawn using MOLSCRIPT (79); all other figures generated using MOLMOL (77). (32, by permission.)

Figure 12*a* is a schematic representation of the secondary structure of this domain, highlighting the location of the methyl groups of Ala, Val, Ile (γ2 only) and Leu at the interfaces between the central β-sheet and the two flanking α-helices. Figure 12*b* shows structures determined using only experimentally observed backbone NH-NH distances and loose (φ, ψ) dihedral angle restraints established from experiments performed on a ^{15}N, ^{13}C, ^2H [^1H-methyl Ala, Val, Ile(γ2), Leu] sample of this protein (32). Structures produced from such limited data are poorly defined as evidenced by the 3.5 Å RMSD of the 18 structures in Figure 12*b* to the mean structure. More importantly, the experimentally-determined structures have a different shape than the high precision reference structure (*bold line* in Figure 12*b*), owing to the lack of long-range structural restraints and the use of a repulsive-only van der Waals potential. This distorts the overall fold, resulting in a 7.7 Å RMSD between the experimental structures and the reference structure derived from data recorded on a fully protonated sample!

The accuracy and precision of the experimentally determined PLCC SH2 structures can be significantly improved by including distance restraints involving methyl groups obtained from 4D ^{13}C, ^{13}C-edited (164) and ^{13}C, ^{15}N-edited (113) NOESY experiments recorded on the ^{15}N, ^{13}C, ^{2}H, methyl protonated sample described above. An additional 175 methyl-NH and methyl-methyl distance restraints are obtained from these two data sets and in combination with the NH-NH and dihedral angle restraints used to produce the structures of Figure 12*b*, generate the folds illustrated in Figure 12*c*. The experimentally determined structures in Figure 12*c* superimpose on the average and the reference structures with backbone RMSD values of 2.4 Å and 3.1 Å, respectively. Note that the precision of the structures of Figure 12*c* is considerably lower than for the reference structures determined from a fully protonated sample of the PLCC SH2 domain complexed with a 12-residue phosphopeptide (Figure 12*d*). Similar conclusions regarding the importance of methyl NOEs have been noted in the case of simulations where tables of suitable interproton distances derived from crystal structures are constructed and used to generate global folds of proteins (30, 32, 109, 146).

To date, most attention regarding potential sites of protonation in highly deuterated proteins has focused on methyl groups. From a structural perspective, aromatic residues are excellent candidates for protonation as well, since these amino acids are frequently important components of hydrophobic protein cores. However, the poor dispersion of aromatic ^{1}H and ^{13}C chemical shifts, the strong coupling between aromatic carbons and the efficient transverse relaxation of aromatic ring spins complicates the use of these residues in a manner analogous to the use of methyl containing amino acids described above. In addition, the large pseudoatom corrections required for aromatic-based distance restraints significantly lowers the precision of the structural data available using these sites. In lieu of these problems Smith et al (146) have suggested the use of ambiguously assigned NOEs (118, 119) involving protonated aromatic residues in determining the global folds of highly deuterated proteins.

Improving the Quality of Structures from Highly Deuterated Systems

NOE-DERIVED DISTANCE RESTRAINTS   As of mid 1997, the largest monomeric protein structures that have been determined by NMR are of systems of approximately 30 kDa in molecular weight and include the 259-residue

EIN protein (33) and the 245-residue ErmAm rRNA methyltransferase (175). In both cases, highly ($\geq$75%) deuterated samples were used for backbone and sidechain assignment as well as for the identification of proximal NH pairs from ^{15}N, ^{15}N-edited 4D NOESY experiments. The high sensitivity and resolution of this experiment, in particular, facilitates the rapid assignment of secondary structural elements. Despite the utility of deuteration in the assignment stages, the majority of interproton distances and all of the dihedral angle restraints used in structure determination were derived from experiments recorded on fully protonated samples.

Applications involving still larger proteins will likely be compromised by severe overlap and low signal intensity in spectra recorded on protonated molecules, necessitating the use of highly deuterated, amino acid proton-ated proteins (109, 146) ("Protonated Amino Acid Sidechains in a Deuter-ated Background," above), or site protonated proteins (31, 32, 134) ("Proto-nated Methyl Groups in a Deuterated Background: Pyruvate," and "Protonated Methyl Groups in a Deuterated Background: Specifically Protonated Amino Acids and Amino Acid Precursors," above). However, as demonstrated so far (32, 109, 146), at best global folds of only moderate (2–3 Å) precision and accuracy can be obtained from a combination of methyl-methyl, methyl-NH, NH-NH NOEs, and loose backbone dihedral angle restraints. Unfortunately, addition of sidechain NH-NH and sidechain NH-methyl restraints is unlikely to significantly improve the precision of structures beyond the 2–3 Å limit. Clearly, more information is required to improve the quality of structures de-rived from data collected exclusively on samples of highly deuterated proteins.

DIHEDRAL ANGLE RESTRAINTS   As briefly described above, backbone dihedral angle restraints can be indirectly obtained from the chemical shifts of nuclei that are assigned during the initial stages of the structure determi-nation process. The difference ($\Delta\delta$) between the chemical shifts of backbone proton and carbon nuclei from their random coil values is secondary structure dependent (147, 168). In a highly deuterated, ^{13}C labeled protein the $\Delta\delta$ values calculated from ^{13}Cα, ^{13}Cβ and ^{13}CO chemical shifts can be used to quickly and qualitatively identify whether a residue is in an α-helix or β-strand conforma-tion using the Chemical Shift Index (CSI) method (167) after suitable correction for deuterium isotope effects on ^{13}C chemical shifts (see above: "Deuterium Isotope Effects on ^{13}C and ^{15}N Chemical Shifts"). Recently Metzler, Farmer, Venters, and coworkers have suggested using a function of the form [$\Delta\delta$ (^{13}Cα) $- \Delta\delta(^{13}$C$\beta)$] to identify secondary structural elements (107, 108, 159). A re-cent evaluation of the use of ^{13}Cα and ^{13}Cβ chemical shifts for secondary structure element identification based on a study of fourteen proteins suggests that this approach can be used to correctly identify approximately 75% of

α-helical and 50% of β-strand residues (99). However, in our experience the CSI method is a much more reliable indicator of secondary structure than this study suggests.

Chemical shift information can also be incorporated more quantitatively and directly into the structure determination process. For example, it is possible to perform direct structure refinement against ^{13}Cα and ^{13}Cβ chemical shifts (86) or against (ϕ, ψ) dihedral angle restraints derived from ^{13}Cα shifts (15). It may also be possible, in the case of partially protonated proteins, to refine against proton chemical shifts (84). It is noteworthy that improvements in quantum mechanical calculations of chemical shifts as a function of (ϕ, ψ) will allow the use of tighter restraints than presently possible, significantly improving the quality of structures derived from sparse data sets (87, 121).

The NOE-derived distance restraints and the loose (ϕ, ψ) restraints available from ^{13}Cα and ^{13}Cβ chemical shifts can be supplemented by additional dihedral angle restraints from measured coupling constants defining sidechain torsion angles. Recently Konrat et al (76) and Bax and coworkers (52, 53) have developed triple resonance pulse schemes for measuring χ_1 angles based on recording ^{15}N-^{13}Cγ and ^{13}CO-^{13}Cγ three bond scalar couplings. Hennig et al (47) have described an experiment for measuring homonuclear three bond couplings correlating ^{13}Cα and ^{13}Cδ spins in highly deuterated proteins, allowing determination of trans, gauche, or averaged χ_2 rotameric states.

BOND VECTOR RESTRAINTS FROM DIPOLAR COUPLINGS AND DIFFUSION ANISOTROPY   A major shortcoming of NOE- and dihedral angle-based structural restraints is that they provide information only on local features such as short range (≤ 5 Å) distances and angles between bonds that are proximal in sequence. Restraints between nuclei separated by distances in excess of 5 Å are difficult to obtain. In many cases, macromolecules consist of discrete domains or other structural elements separated by distances that are longer than those that can be measured using NOE methods. Recently a number of approaches have been described that address this limitation by providing restraints describing the relative orientation of domains in a manner that is independent of the distance between these modules (long-range order).

One method for measuring long range order in macromolecules is based on the well-known result that molecules with anisotropic magnetic susceptibilities will orient in an external magnetic field, B_o, with the degree of orientation a function of B_o^2 (7). Thus, the dipolar interaction between two spins, which in the high field limit scales as ($3\cos^2\theta - 1$) (where θ is the angle between the vector joining these spins and B_o), no longer averages to zero (155). As a result, small residual splittings are observed. In the case of an axially symmetric susceptibility, these splittings depend on B_o^2, the size of the susceptibility anisotropy and the angle between the dipole vector and the unique axis of the molecular susceptibility tensor. It is clear that the size of these splittings will be largest in molecules with large anisotropic magnetic susceptibility tensors including proteins with paramagnetic centers (155) or duplex DNA where smaller contributions to the susceptibility from each base pair add coherently (80).

Residual dipolar contributions to splittings of ^{15}N resonances of ^{15}N-NH spin-pairs and ^{13}C resonances of ^{13}Cα-^{1}Hα pairs in a number of proteins and protein-DNA complexes have been measured (149, 151, 152, 155). Because the measured splittings are comprised of a field invariant scalar coupling term, a dynamic frequency shift contribution that can be calculated, and a dipolar term that scales quadratically with field, dipolar contributions are readily obtained from a field dependent study. Differences in ^{15}N-NH splittings of between 0.0 and approximately -0.2 Hz have been measured for ubiquitin from spectra recorded at 600 and 360 MHz (151). In contrast, dipolar couplings ranging from 1 Hz to -5 Hz have been measured at 750 MHz in the case of the paramagnetic protein cyanometmyoglobin (155). The orientational dependence of the dipolar couplings with respect to the components of the susceptibility tensor can be exploited in structure refinement. In this regard a pseudoenergy potential has recently been developed for direct refinement against observed dipolar couplings during restrained molecular dynamics calculations and used in the structure determination of a GATA-1/DNA complex (152).

A second approach for obtaining long-range order in macromolecules is based on the measurement of ^{15}N relaxation times, T_1 and T_2. In the case of an isotropically tumbling molecule without internal motions, the ^{15}N T_1/T_2 ratio is uniform. In contrast, for a molecule with an axially symmetric diffusion tensor the T_1/T_2 ratio is a function of the angle between the N-NH bond vector and the unique axis of the diffusion tensor. In cases where the diffusion tensor is axially symmetric, therefore, it is possible to measure the orientation of each amide bond vector with respect to the diffusion frame and to use this information as an additional structural restraint, in an analogous manner to the use of dipolar couplings described above. Tjandra et al (150) have shown that in the case of EIN ($D_{\parallel}/D_{\perp} \sim 2$, where $D_{\parallel}$ and $D_{\perp}$ are the parallel and perpendicular components of the diffusion tensor), ^{15}N T_1/T_2 data are important in defining the relative orientation of the two domains in the molecule.

OTHER STRUCTURAL INFORMATION   Besides the experiments described above, studies involving deuterium exchange (169b), paramagnetic perturbation of either chemical shifts (35, 44) and/or relaxation rates (34, 78), and chemical crosslinking (21) can also provide useful distance restraints. Further information can be obtained from statistical analyses of databases of previously determined protein structures. Residue-dependent preferences of various structural parameters, such as the values of backbone and sidechain dihedral angles or distances between pairwise combinations of amino acid residues, have been quantified and tables of these preferences converted into "knowledge-based" potentials of mean force to provide an energy scale to assign to values of these distances or dihedral angles (59, 144). Such knowledge-based potentials have been used in a wide variety of applications, including error detection in experimentally-determined structures, refinement of protein structures in combination with experimentally determined restraints (6, 83, 85, 145) and *ab initio* structure prediction. One major advantage of knowledge-based potentials lies in their representation of structural information that is dependent on the entire range of molecular forces, including solvation effects. These potentials are thus better able to discriminate between favorable and unfavorable protein conformations than the commonly utilized potentials for van der Waals interactions. This, in turn, results in more efficient searches of conformational space and the generation of final structures with improved packing (85). A number of recent applications involving the use of knowledge-based dihedral angle potentials in structure calculations include studies of a specific GAGA factor-DNA complex (122) and the EIN protein (33).

In combination, the use of NOE and dihedral angle restraints, chemical shift deviations from random coil values, dipolar couplings, and protein structure data bases will facilitate structure determination of higher molecular weight proteins using ^{2}H-based strategies with improved precision and accuracy.

USE OF DEUTERATION TO STUDY PROTEIN DYNAMICS

NMR spectroscopy can provide a wealth of information about molecular dynamics extending over a wide range of motional timescales. Studies to date have focused mostly on backbone dynamics, largely through measurement of backbone ^{15}N relaxation properties in uniformly ^{15}N labeled proteins (116, 125). An attractive feature of backbone ^{15}N relaxation studies relates to the fact that the data can be easily analyzed. For example, the relaxation of a two-spin ^{15}N-NH spin pair can be described simply in terms of the ^{15}N-NH dipolar interaction and to a smaller extent by the ^{15}N chemical shift anisotropy (71). While interference between these two relaxation mechanisms does occur, methods have been developed that can effectively remove this complication (70, 127).

The situation is, in general, more complex for the study of motional properties of sidechains. Although the use of carbon relaxation to probe sidechain dynamics appears to be an obvious approach, ^{13}C relaxation methods are not without some rather significant problems. First, most sidechain positions are either of the CH_2 or CH_3 variety and cross correlation between ^{13}C-^1H dipolar interactions can be significant in these cases (65, 128). Although the interpretation of such effects provides powerful insight into molecular dynamics (166) several experiments must often be performed where the relaxation behavior of the individual multiplet components is monitored. In addition, relaxation contributions from neighboring spins can complicate the extraction of accurate dynamics parameters. Second, differential relaxation of multiplet components occurring during the course of the pulse sequences used to measure ^{13}C relaxation times results in the transfer of magnetization from ^{13}C to ^1H in a manner that may not reflect the equilibrium intensity of each carbon multiplet component. While pulse sequences that minimize this effect in the case of methyl groups have been described (65) they do not eliminate the problem completely. Third, in the case of applications involving uniformly ^{13}C labeled samples both scalar and dipolar ^{13}C-^{13}C couplings must be taken into account (25, 172). Although this problem is eliminated through the use of molecules where only a select number of sites are labeled the information content available in such systems is, of course, much less.

A recent series of papers by LeMaster and Kushlan have addressed many of the above mentioned limitations in the use of ^{13}C spectroscopy to study sidechain dynamics (81, 92). Using a suitable strain of *E. coli* grown on media containing either [2-^{13}C]-glycerol or [1,3-$^{13}C_2$]-glycerol, LeMaster and Kushlan have shown that it is possible to produce proteins in which isotopic enrichment is largely restricted to alternating carbon sites and in this manner eliminate the deleterious effects of carbon-carbon couplings. In addition, complications arising from the presence of more than one proton attached to a given ^{13}C spin are removed through the use of approximately 50% random fractional deuteration in concert with pulse schemes that select for ^{13}C-^1H two-spin spinsystems. The method has been applied to investigate the dynamics of *E. coli* thioredoxin, a small protein of 108 residues (92).

To this point in the review all applications discussed have made use of deuteration simply as a method for removing proton spins, thereby improving the relaxation properties of the remaining NMR active nuclei (prior sections), or simplifying analysis of ^{13}C relaxation times in terms of molecular dynamics (this section). These deuterons can be thought of as passive participants in the experiments in that none of their spectroscopic properties are recorded. It is possible, however, to make use of fractionally deuterated protein samples in quite a different way than has been previously described to obtain information about protein dynamics. In this regard, it is noteworthy that ^2H NMR has enjoyed a rich history in the study of biomolecular motion through measurement of deuterium relaxation and line shape parameters (58, 75, 141, 162). Applications have largely focused on liquid crystalline and solid-state samples (74).

The low sensitivity of ^{2}H direct detect spectra coupled with broad linewidths and poor chemical dispersion has, until recently, restricted the application of high resolution solution-state ^{2}H NMR methods to a few relaxation studies of site-specifically deuterated proteins for estimate of molecular rotational correlation times (60, 139). However, the power of ^{2}H relaxation as a probe of molecular dynamics, largely the result of the fact that the relaxation is dominated by the well understood quadrupolar interaction, has stimulated interest in developing solution state based methods for measuring ^{2}H relaxation rates that do not suffer from the problems mentioned above.

Recently a triple resonance method has been described for the measurement of ^{2}H spin relaxation times, T_1 and $T_{1\rho}$, in fractionally deuterated ^{15}N, ^{13}C labeled proteins (114). The idea is to select for methylene or methyl groups with only a single attached deuteron, allow relaxation of magnetization proportional to either D_z (T_1) or D_y ($T_{1\rho}$) to proceed for a delay time, T, during the course of the experiment and encode this decay in cross-peak intensities measured in ^{13}C-^{1}H constant time correlation spectra. Thus, the approach makes use of a series of magnetization transfer steps in which signal originating on a sidechain [^{13}CHD (LE Kay, unpublished results); ^{13}CH$_2$D, (114)] proton is transferred to the attached carbon and subsequently to the deuteron bound to the same carbon. At this point the relaxation proceeds for a defined time, T, and the signal is subsequently returned to the originating proton for detection.

The flow of magnetization during the course of experiment can be represented by:

$$^1\text{H} \xrightarrow{J_{CH}} {}^{13}\text{C} \xrightarrow{J_{CD}} {}^2\text{H}(T) \xrightarrow{J_{CD}} {}^{13}\text{C}(t_1) \xrightarrow{J_{CH}} {}^1\text{H}(t_2),$$

where the active couplings involved in each INEPT-based transfer are indicated above each arrow and t_1 and t_2 denote periods during which ^{13}C and ^{1}H chemical shifts are recorded. A set of 2D (^{13}C, ^{1}H) correlation spectra are obtained where the time profile of the intensity of a cross-peak arising from a ^{13}CH$_2$D methyl, for example, is related to the relaxation time (T_1 or $T_{1\rho}$) of the attached deuteron. In practice, because of the magnetization transfer steps that are involved, the decay of operators of the form $I_zC_zD_z$ (T_1) or $I_zC_zD_y$ ($T_{1\rho}$) is measured during the relaxation time, T. T_1 and $T_{1\rho}$ values of pure deuterium magnetization can be obtained by recording an additional experiment in which the decay of the two-spin order, I_zC_z, is measured and subtracting this rate from the decay rates of $I_zC_zD_z$ and $I_zC_zD_y$ according to

$$1/T_1(D_z) = 1/T_1(I_zC_zD_z) - 1/T_1(I_zC_z)$$

$$1/T_{1\rho}(D_y) = 1/T_{1\rho}(I_zC_zD_y) - 1/T_1(I_zC_z).$$

Cross-correlation between the many different relaxation mechanisms that could potentially complicate the decay of the triple spin terms described above has been examined in detail and shown not to contribute in a measurable way to the decay of the magnetization (174).

The deuterium relaxation methods described above have been applied to study the sidechain dynamics of the PLCC SH2 domain, both in the presence and absence of target peptide (68). Remarkably, certain residues in the hydrophobic binding region of this SH2 domain that are important for the specificity of its interaction with peptide, are highly mobile in both peptide free and complexed states. A comparison of the dynamics of the PLCC SH2 domain with the amino-terminal SH2 domain from the Syp phosphatase has provided insight into the origin of the very different peptide binding properties of these two highly homologous structures (LE Kay, DR Muhandiram, JD Forman-Kay, unpublished results).

Recently Pervushin et al (131) have described 2D heteronuclear experiments for measuring transverse and longitudinal ^{2}H relaxation rates in ^{15}NHD groups (Asn and Gln) in uniformly ^{15}N labeled proteins. Samples are dissolved in a 1:1 mixture of H_2O/D_2O to give maximal concentrations of ^{15}NHD groups with deuteration at either E or Z positions. These pulse sequences are closely related to the ^{13}C-^{2}H relaxation experiments described above. Interestingly, because the direction of the bond connecting the amide nitrogen and the ^{2}H^Z deuteron is nearly parallel to the Cβ-Cγ or Cγ-Cδ bond in Asn and Gln, respectively, rotation about χ_2 (Asn) or χ_3 (Gln) affects the transverse relaxation of ^{2}H^Z much less than ^{2}H^E. Thus, the relaxation rates for ^{2}H^Z are predicted to be larger than for ^{2}H^E; this has been observed in relaxation studies of the 70-residue fushi-tarazu (ftz) homeodomain and its complex with a 14 base-pair DNA.

CONCLUDING REMARKS

This review highlighted many of the important current advances in the use of deuteration, both for structural and dynamics studies of proteins and protein complexes. Outstanding areas of investigation include (a) the further development of labeling schemes for site-specific incorporation of protons in highly deuterated proteins, (b) new pulse sequence methodology customized for the labeling methods that will be introduced, and (c) the design of new classes of experiments that provide structural parameters complementary to the existing NOE- and scalar-coupling–based classes of restraints. It is also clear that future improvements in spectrometer hardware and further increases in magnetic fields, resulting in gains in dispersion and sensitivity for multi-dimensional NMR applications, will also have a significant impact on the scope of problems that can be studied. The future promises to be exciting indeed.

ACKNOWLEDGMENTS

The authors would like to thank Julie Forman-Kay (Hospital for Sick Children, Toronto) for helpful discussions and a critical reading of the manuscript and Drs. Dan Garrett (NIH) and Steve Fesik (Abbott Laboratories) for providing preprints. This work was supported by a grant from the Medical Research Council of Canada. KHG gratefully acknowledges a postdoctoral fellowship from the Helen Hay Whitney Foundation.

> Visit the *Annual Reviews* home page at
> http://www.AnnualReviews.org.

Literature Cited

1. Agback P, Maltseva TV, Yamakage S-I, Nilson FPR, Földesi A, Chattopadhyaya J. 1994. The differences in the T_2 relaxation rates of the protons in the partially deuterated and fully protonated sugar residues in a large oligo-DNA ('NMR-window') gives complementary structural information. *Nucl. Acids Res.* 22:1404–12

2. Allerhand A, Doddrell D, Glushko V, Cochran DW, Wenkert E, et al. 1971. Conformational and segmental motion of native and denatured ribonuclease A in solution. Application of natural abundance carbon-13 partially relaxed Fourier transform nuclear magnetic resonance. *J. Am. Chem. Soc.* 93:544–6

3. Anglister J. 1990. Use of deuterium labelling in NMR studies of antibody combining site structure. *Q. Rev. Biophys.* 23:175–203

4. Arrowsmith CH, Pachter R, Altman RB, Iyer SB, Jardetzky O. 1990. Sequence-specific ^{1}H NMR assignments and secondary structure in solution of *Escherichia coli trp* repressor. *Biochemistry* 29:6332–41

5. Arrowsmith CH, Treat-Clemons L, Szilágyi L, Pachter R, Jardetzky O. 1990. The use of selective deuteration for the sequence-specific ^{1}H NMR assignment of larger proteins. *Die Makromol. Chem., Macromol. Symp.* 34:33–46

6. Aszódi A, Gradwell MJ, Taylor WR. 1995. Global fold determination from a small number of distance restraints. *J. Mol. Biol.* 251:308–26

7. Bastiaan EW, Maclean C, Van Zijl PCM, Bothner-By AA. 1987. High-resolution NMR of liquids and gases: effects of magnetic-field-induced molecular align-ment. *Annu. Rep. NMR. Spec.* 19:35–77

8. Batey RT, Cloutier N, Mao H, Williamson JR. 1996. Improved large scale culture of *Methylophilus methylotrophus* for ^{13}C/^{15}N labeling and random fractional deuteration of ribonucleotides. *Nucl. Acids Res.* 24:4836–37

9. Bax A. 1994. Multidimensional nuclear magnetic resonance methods for protein studies. *Curr. Opin. Struct. Biol.* 4:738–44

10. Bax A, De Jong DE, Mehlkopf AF, Smidt J. 1980. Separation of the different orders of NMR multiple-quantum transitions by the use of pulsed field gradients. *Chem. Phys. Lett.* 69:567–70

11. Boyd J, Soffe N, John B, Plant D, Hurd R. 1992. The generation of phase-sensitive 2D ^{15}N-^{1}H spectra using gradient pulses for coherence-transfer-pathway selection. *J. Magn. Reson.* 98:660–64

12. Brodin P, Drakenberg T, Thulin E, Forsén S, Grundström T. 1989. Selective proton labelling of amino acids in deuterated bovine calbindin D9k. A way to simplify NMR spectra. *Prot. Eng.* 2:353–58

13. Browne DT, Kenyon GL, Packer EL, Sternlicht H, Wilson DM. 1973. Studies of macromolecular structure by ^{13}C nuclear magnetic resonance. II. A specific labeling approach to the study of histidine residues in proteins. *J. Am. Chem. Soc.* 95:1316–23

14. Cavanagh J, Rance M. 1988. Sensitivity improvement in isotropic mixing (TOCSY) experiments. *J. Magn. Reson.* 88:72–85

15. Celda B, Biamonti C, Arnau MJ, Tejero R, Montelione GT. 1995. Combined use

of ^{13}C chemical shift and $^{1}H\alpha$-$^{13}C\alpha$ heteronuclear NOE data in monitoring a protein NMR refinement. *J. Biomol. NMR* 5:161–72

16. Clore GM, Gronenborn AM. 1994. Multidimensional heteronuclear nuclear magnetic resonance of proteins. *Meth. Enz.* 239:349–63

17. Clore GM, Robien MA, Gronenborn AM. 1993. Exploring the limits of precision and accuracy of protein structures determined by nuclear magnetic resonance spectroscopy. *J. Mol. Biol.* 231:82–102

18. Constantine KL, Mueller L, Goldfarb V, Wittekind M, Metzler WJ, et al. 1997. Characterization of NADP+ binding to perdeuterated MurB: backbone atom NMR assignments and chemical-shift changes. *J. Mol. Biol.* 267:1223–46

19. Crespi HL, Katz JJ. 1969. High resolution proton magnetic resonance studies of fully deuterated and isotope hybrid proteins. *Nature* 224:560–62

20. Crespi HL, Rosenberg RM, Katz JJ. 1968. Proton magnetic resonance of proteins fully deuterated except for ^{1}H-leucine side chains. *Science* 161:795–96

21. Das M, Fox CF. 1979. Chemical cross-linking in biology. *Annu. Rev. Biophys. Bioeng.* 8:165–93

22. Davis AL, Keeler J, Laue ED, Moskau D. 1992. Experiments for recording pure-absorption heteronuclear correlation spectra using pulsed field gradients. *J. Magn. Reson.* 98:207–16

23. Dötsch V, Matsuo H, Wagner G. 1996. Amino-acid-type identification for deuterated proteins with a β-carbon-edited HNCOCACB experiment. *J. Magn. Reson. B* 112:95–100

24. Eisenstein E. 1991. Cloning, expression, purification, and characterization of biosynthetic threonine deaminase from *Escherichia coli*. *J. Biol. Chem.* 266:5801–7

25. Engelke J, Rüterjans H. 1995. Determination of $^{13}C\alpha$ relaxation times in uniformly $^{13}C/^{15}N$-enriched proteins. *J. Biomol. NMR* 5:173–82

26. Farmer BT II, Venters RA. 1995. Assignment of side-chain ^{13}C resonances in perdeuterated proteins. *J. Am. Chem. Soc.* 117:4187–88

27. Farmer BT II, Venters RA. 1996. Assignment of aliphatic side-chain $^{1}H_N/^{15}N$ resonances in perdeuterated proteins. *J. Biomol. NMR* 7:59–71

28. Földesi A, Yamakage S-I, Nilsson FPR,

Maltseva TV, Chattopadhyaya J. 1996. The use of non-uniform deuterium labelling ["NMR-window"] to study the NMR structure of a 21mer RNA hairpin. *Nucl. Acids Res.* 24:1187–94

29. Galimov EM. 1985. *The Biological Fractionation of Isotopes*, p. 261. Orlando: Academic

30. Gardner KH, Kay LE. 1997. Production and incorporation of ^{15}N, ^{13}C, ^{2}H (^{1}H-δ_1 methyl) isoleucine into proteins for multidimensional NMR studies. *J. Am. Chem. Soc.* 119:7599–7600

31. Gardner KH, Konrat R, Rosen MK, Kay LE. 1996. A (H)C(CO)NH-TOCSY pulse scheme for sequential assignment of protonated methyl groups in otherwise deuterated ^{15}N, ^{13}C-labeled proteins. *J. Biomol. NMR* 8:351–56

32. Gardner KH, Rosen MK, Kay LE. 1997. Global folds of highly deuterated, methyl protonated proteins by multidimensional NMR. *Biochemistry* 36:1389–1401

33. Garrett DS, Seok Y, Liao D, Peterkofsky A, Gronenborn AM, Clore GM. 1997. Solution structure of the 30 kDa N-terminal domain of enzyme I of *Escherichia coli* phosphoenolpyruvate: sugar phosphotransferase system by multidimensional NMR. *Biochemistry* 36:2517–30

34. Gillespie JR, Shortle D. 1997. Characterization of long-range structure in the denatured state of staphylococcal nuclease. I. Paramagnetic relaxation enhancement by nitroxide spin labels. *J. Mol. Biol.* 268:158–69

35. Gochin M, Roder H. 1995. Protein structure refinement based on paramagnetic NMR shifts: applications to wild-type and mutant forms of cytochrome c. *Prot. Sci.* 4:296–305

36. Griffey RH, Redfield AG. 1987. Proton-detected heteronuclear edited and correlated nuclear magnetic resonance and nuclear Overhauser effect in solution. *Q. Rev. Biophys.* 19:51–82

37. Grzesiek S, Anglister J, Bax A. 1993. Correlation of backbone amide and aliphatic side-chain resonances in $^{13}C/^{15}N$-enriched proteins by isotropic mixing of ^{13}C magnetization. *J. Magn. Reson. B* 101:114–19

38. Grzesiek S, Anglister J, Ren H, Bax A. 1993. ^{13}C line narrowing by ^{2}H decoupling in $^{2}H/^{13}C/^{15}N$-enriched proteins. Application to triple resonance 4D J connectivity of sequential amides. *J. Am. Chem. Soc.* 115:4369–70

39. Grzesiek S, Bax A. 1992. Improved 3D triple-resonance NMR techniques applied to a 31 kDa protein. *J. Magn. Reson.* 96:432–40

40. Grzesiek S, Bax A. 1993. The importance of not saturating H$_2$O in protein NMR: application to sensitivity enhancement and NOE measurements. *J. Am. Chem. Soc.* 115:12593–94

41. Grzesiek S, Bax A. 1994. Interference between dipolar and quadrupolar interactions in the slow tumbling limit: a source of line shift and relaxation in ^{2}H-labeled compounds. *J. Am. Chem. Soc.* 116:10196–201

42. Grzesiek S, Bax A. 1995. Spin-locked multiple quantum coherence for signal enhancement in heteronuclear multidimensional NMR experiments. *J. Biomol. NMR* 6:335–39

43. Grzesiek S, Wingfield P, Stahl S, Kaufman JD, Bax A. 1995. Four-dimensional ^{15}N-separated NOESY of slowly tumbling perdeuterated ^{15}N-enriched proteins. Application to HIV-1 Nef. *J. Am. Chem. Soc.* 117:9594–95

44. Guiles RD, Sarma S, DiGate RJ, Banville D, Basus VJ, et al. 1996. Pseudocontact shifts used in the restraint of the solution structures of electron transfer complexes. *Nat. Struct. Biol.* 3:333–39

45. Hansen AP, Petros AM, Mazar AP, Pederson TM, Rueter A, Fesik SW. 1992. A practical method for uniform isotopic labeling of recombinant proteins in mammalian cells. *Biochemistry* 31:12713–18

46. Hansen PE. 1988. Isotope effects in nuclear shielding. *Prog. NMR Spec.* 20:207–55

47. Hennig M, Ott D, Schulte P, Löwe R, Krebs J, et al. 1997. Determination of homonuclear ^{13}C-^{13}C J couplings between aliphatic carbon atoms in perdeuterated proteins. *J. Am. Chem. Soc.* 119:5055–56

48. Heringa J, Sommerfeldt H, Higgins D, Argos P. 1992. OBSTRUCT: A program to obtain largest cliques from a protein sequence set according to structural resolution and sequence similarity. *CABIOS* 8:599–600

49. Homer RJ, Kim MS, LeMaster DM. 1993. The use of cystathionine γ-synthase in the production of α and chiral β deuterated amino acids. *Anal. Biochem.* 215:211–15

50. Hoogstraten CG, Markley JL. 1996. Effects of experimentally achievable improvements in the quality of NMR distance constraints on the accuracy of calculated protein structures. *J. Mol. Biol.* 258:334–48

51. Hsu VL, Armitage IM. 1992. Solution structure of cyclosporin A and a nonimmunosuppressive analog bound to fully deuterated cyclophilin. *Biochemistry* 31:12778–84

52. Hu J-S, Bax A. 1997. Determination of ϕ and χ_1 angles in proteins from ^{13}C-^{13}C three-bond J couplings measured by three-dimensional heteronuclear NMR: How planar is the peptide bond? *J. Am. Chem. Soc.* 119:6360–68

53. Hu J-S, Grzesiek S, Bax A. 1997. Two-dimensional NMR methods for determining χ_1 angles of aromatic residues in proteins from three-bond J$_{C'C}$ and J$_{NC}$ couplings. *J. Am. Chem. Soc.* 119:1803–4

54. Ikegamí T, Sato S, Wälchli M, Kyogoku Y, Shirakawa M. 1997. An efficient HN(CA)NH pulse scheme for triple-resonance 4D correlation of sequential amide protons and nitrogen-15 in deuterated proteins. *J. Magn. Reson.* 124:214–17

55. Ikura M, Kay LE, Bax A. 1990. A novel approach for sequential assignment of ^{1}H, ^{13}C and ^{15}N spectra of proteins: heteronuclear triple-resonance three-dimensional NMR spectroscopy. Application to calmodulin. *Biochemistry* 29:4659–67

56. James T. 1994. Assessment of quality of derived macromolecular structures. *Meth. Enz.* 239:416–39

57. Janin J, Miller S, Chothia C. 1988. Surface, subunit interfaces and interior of oligomeric proteins. *J. Mol. Biol.* 204:155–64

58. Jelinski LW, Sullivan CE, Torchia DA. 1980. ^{2}H NMR study of molecular motion in collagen fibrils. *Nature* 284:531–34

59. Jernigan RL, Bahar I. 1996. Structure-derived potentials and protein simulations. *Curr. Opin. Struct. Biol.* 6:195–209

60. Johnson RD, La Mar GN, Smith KM, Parish DW, Langry KC. 1989. Solution deuterium NMR quadropolar relaxation study of heme mobility in myoglobin. *J. Am. Chem. Soc.* 111:481–85

61. Kalbitzer HR, Leberman R, Wittinghofer A. 1985. ^{1}H-NMR spectroscopy on elongation factor Tu from *Escherichia coli*. *FEBS Lett.* 180:40–42

62. Katz JJ, Crespi HL. 1966. Deuterated

organisms: cultivation and uses. *Science* 151:1187–94

63. Kay LE. 1995. Pulsed field gradient multi-dimensional NMR methods for the study of protein structure and dynamics in solution. *Prog. Biophys. Mol. Biol.* 63:277–99

64. Kay LE. 1995. Field gradient techniques in NMR spectroscopy. *Curr. Opin. Struct. Biol.* 5:674–81

65. Kay LE, Bull T, Nicholson LK, Griesinger C, Schwalbe H, et al. 1992. The measurement of heteronuclear transverse relaxation times in AX_3 spin systems via polarization transfer techniques. *J. Magn. Reson.* 100:538–58

66. Kay LE, Ikura M, Tschudin R, Bax A. 1990. Three-dimensional triple-resonance NMR spectroscopy of isotopically enriched proteins. *J. Magn. Reson.* 89:496–514

67. Kay LE, Keifer P, Saarinen T. 1992. Pure absorption gradient-enhanced heteronuclear single quantum correlation spectroscopy with improved sensitivity. *J. Am. Chem. Soc.* 114:10663–65

68. Kay LE, Muhandiram DR, Farrow NA, Aubin Y, Forman-Kay JD. 1996. Correlation between dynamics and high affinity binding in an SH2 domain interaction. *Biochemistry* 35:362–68

69. Deleted in proof.

70. Kay LE, Nicholson LK, Delaglio F, Bax A, Torchia DA. 1992. Pulse sequences for removal of the effects of cross correlation between dipolar and chemical-shift anisotropy relaxation mechanisms on the measurement of heteronuclear T_1 and T_2 values in proteins. *J. Magn. Reson.* 97:359–75

71. Kay LE, Torchia DA, Bax A. 1989. Backbone dynamics of proteins as studied by ^{15}N inverse detected heteronuclear NMR spectroscopy: application to staphylococcal nuclease. *Biochemistry* 28:8972–79

72. Kay LE, Xu GY, Yamazaki T. 1994. Enhanced-sensitivity triple-resonance spectroscopy with minimal H_2O saturation. *J. Magn. Reson. A* 109:129–33

73. Keeler J, Clowes RT, Davis AL, Laue ED. 1994. Pulsed-field gradients: theory and practice. *Meth. Enz.* 239:145–207

74. Keniry MA. 1989. Solid-state deuterium nuclear magnetic resonance spectroscopy of proteins. *Meth. Enz.* 176:376–86

75. Keniry MA, Rothgeb TM, Smith RL, Gutowsky HS, Oldfield E. 1983. Nuclear magnetic resonance studies of amino acids and proteins. Side-chain mobility of methionine in the crystalline amino acid and in crystalline sperm whale (*Physeter catodon*) myoglobin. *Biochemistry* 22:1917–26

76. Konrat R, Muhandiram DR, Farrow NA, Kay LE. 1997. Pulse schemes for the measurement of $^3J_{C'C_\gamma}$ and $^3J_{NC_\gamma}$ scalar couplings in ^{15}N, ^{13}C uniformly labeled proteins. *J. Biomol. NMR.* 9:409–22

77. Koradi R, Billeter M, Wüthrich K. 1996. MOLMOL: a program for display and analysis of macromolecular structures. *J. Mol. Graphics* 14:51–55

78. Kosen PA, Scheck RM, Nadevi H, Basus VJ, Manogaran S, et al. 1986. Two-dimensional ^1H NMR of three spin labeled derivatives of bovine pancreatic trypsin inhibitor. *Biochemistry* 25:2356–64

79. Kraulis PJ. 1991. MOLSCRIPT: a program to produce both detailed and schematic plots of protein structures. *J. Appl. Cryst.* 24:946–50

80. Kung HC, Wang KY, Goljer I, Bolton PH. 1995. Magnetic alignment of duplex and quadruplex DNAs. *J. Magn. Reson. B* 109:323–25

81. Kushlan DM, LeMaster DM. 1993. ^1H-detected NMR relaxation of methylene carbons via stereoselective and random fractional deuteration. *J. Am. Chem. Soc.* 115:11026–27

82. Kushlan DM, LeMaster DM. 1993. Resolution and sensitivity enhancement of heteronuclear correlation for methylene resonances via ^2H enrichment and decoupling. *J. Biomol. NMR* 3:701–8

83. Kuszewski J, Clore GM, Gronenborn AM. 1997. Improvements and extensions in the conformational database potential for the refinement of NMR and X-ray structures of proteins and nucleic acids. *J. Magn. Reson.* 125:171–77

84. Kuszewski J, Gronenborn AM, Clore GM. 1995. The impact of direct refinement against proton chemical shifts on protein structure determination by NMR. *J. Magn. Reson. B* 107:293–97

85. Kuszewski J, Gronenborn AM, Clore GM. 1996. Improving the quality of NMR and crystallographic protein structures by means of a conformational database potential derived from structure databases. *Prot. Sci.* 5:1067–80

86. Kuszewski J, Qin J, Gronenborn AM, Clore GM. 1995. The impact of direct refinement against $^{13}C\alpha$ and $^{13}C\beta$ chemi-

cal shifts on protein structure determination by NMR. *J. Magn. Reson. B* 106:92–6

87. Le H, Pearson JG, de Dios AC, Oldfield E. 1995. Protein structure refinement and prediction via NMR chemical shifts and quantum chemistry. *J. Am. Chem. Soc.* 117:3800–7

88. LeMaster DM. 1989. Deuteration in protein proton magnetic resonance. *Meth. Enz.* 177:23–43

89. LeMaster DM. 1990. Deuterium labelling in NMR structural analysis of larger proteins. *Q. Rev. Biophys.* 23:133–73

90. LeMaster DM. 1994. Isotope labeling in solution protein assignment and structural analysis. *Prog. NMR Spec.* 26:371–419

91. LeMaster DM. 1997. Assessment of protein solution versus crystal structure determination using spin-diffusion-suppressed NOE and heteronuclear relaxation data. *J. Biomol. NMR* 9:79–93

92. LeMaster DM, Kushlan DM. 1996. Dynamical mapping of *E. coli* thioredoxin via ^{13}C NMR relaxation analysis. *J. Am. Chem. Soc.* 118:9255–64

93. LeMaster DM, LaIuppa JC, Kushlan DM. 1994. Differential deuterium isotope shifts and one-bond ^{1}H-^{13}C scalar couplings in the conformational analysis of protein glycine residues. *J. Biomol. NMR* 4:863–70

94. LeMaster DM, Richards FM. 1988. NMR sequential assignment of *Escherichia coli* thioredoxin utilizing random fractional deuteration. *Biochemistry* 27:142–50

95. Liu Y, Zhao D, Altman R, Jardetzky O. 1992. A systematic comparison of three structure determination methods from NMR data: dependence upon quality and quantity of data. *J. Biomol. NMR* 2:373–88

96. Logan TM, Olejniczak ET, Xu RX, Fesik SW. 1992. Side chain and backbone assignments in isotopically labeled proteins from two heteronuclear triple resonance experiments. *FEBS Lett.* 314:413–18

97. Logan TM, Olejniczak ET, Xu RX, Fesik SW. 1993. A general method for assigning NMR spectra of denatured proteins using 3D HC(CO)NH-TOCSY triple resonance experiments. *J. Biomol. NMR* 3:225–31

98. London RE, LeMaster DM, Werbelow LG. 1994. Unusual NMR multiplet structures of spin-1/2 nuclei coupled to spin-1 nuclei. *J. Am. Chem. Soc.* 116:8400–1

99. Luginbühl P, Szyperski T, Wüthrich K. 1995. Statistical basis for the use of ^{13}Cα chemical shifts in protein structure determination. *J. Mag. Reson. B* 109:229–33

100. Markley JL, Putter I, Jardetzky O. 1968. High-resolution nuclear magnetic resonance studies of selectively deuterated staphylococcal nuclease. *Science* 161:1249–51

101. Markus MA, Kayie KT, Matsudaira P, Wagner G. 1994. Effect of deuteration on the amide proton relaxation rates in proteins. Heteronuclear NMR experiments on villin 14T. *J. Magn. Reson. B* 105:192–95

102. Martin ML, Martin GJ. 1990. Deuterium NMR in the study of site-specific natural isotope fractionation. In *NMR: Basic Principles and Progress*, ed. P Diehl, E Fluck, H Günther, R Kosfeld, J Seelig, 23:1–61. Berlin: Springer-Verlag. 263 pp.

103. Matsuo H, Kupce E, Li H, Wagner G. 1996. Use of selective Cα pulses for improvement of HN(CA)CO-D and HN(COCA)NH-D experiments. *J. Magn. Reson. B* 111:194–98

104. Matsuo H, Li H, Wagner G. 1996. A sensitive HN(CA)CO experiment for deuterated proteins. *J. Magn. Reson. B.* 110:112–15

105. Maudsley AA, Wokaun A, Ernst RR. 1978. Coherence transfer echoes. *Chem. Phys. Lett.* 55:9–14

106. McIntosh LP, Dahlquist FW. 1990. Biosynthetic incorporation of ^{15}N and ^{13}C for assignment and interpretation of nuclear magnetic resonance spectra of proteins. *Q. Rev. Biophys.* 23:1–38

107. Metzler WJ, Constantine KL, Friedrichs MS, Bell AJ, Ernst EG, et al. 1993. Characterization of the three-dimensional solution structure of human profilin: ^{1}H, ^{13}C, and ^{15}N NMR assignments and global folding pattern. *Biochemistry* 32:13818–29

108. Metzler WJ, Leiting B, Pryor K, Mueller L, Farmer BT II. 1996. Three-dimensional solution structure of the SH2 domain from p55$_{blk}$ kinase. *Biochemistry* 35:6201–11

109. Metzler WJ, Wittekind M, Goldfarb V, Mueller L, Farmer BT II. 1996. Incorporation of ^{1}H/^{13}C/^{15}N-{Ile, Leu, Val} into a perdeuterated, ^{15}N-labeled protein: potential in structure determination

of large proteins by NMR. *J. Am. Chem. Soc.* 118:6800–1

110. Montelione GT, Lyons BA, Emerson DS, Tashiro M. 1992. An efficient triple resonance experiment using carbon-13 isotropic mixing for determining sequence-specific resonance assignments of isotopically enriched proteins. *J. Am. Chem. Soc.* 114:10974–5

111. Moore PB. 1979. The preparation of deuterated ribosomal materials for neutron scattering. *Meth. Enz.* 59:639–55

112. Muhandiram DR, Kay LE. 1994. Gradient-enhanced triple resonance three-dimensional NMR experiments with improved sensitivity. *J. Magn. Reson. B* 103:203–16

113. Muhandiram DR, Xu GY, Kay LE. 1993. An enhanced-sensitivity pure absorption gradient 4D ^{15}N, ^{13}C-edited NOESY experiment. *J. Biomol. NMR* 3:463–70

114. Muhandiram DR, Yamazaki T, Sykes BD, Kay LE. 1995. Measurement of ^{2}H T_1 and $T_{1\rho}$ relaxation times in uniformly ^{13}C-labeled and fractionally ^{2}H-labeled proteins in solution. *J. Am. Chem. Soc.* 117:11536–44

115. Murali N, Rao BDN. 1996. Lineshape variations of a spin-1/2 nucleus coupled to a quadrupolar spin subjected to RF irradiation. *J. Magn. Reson. A* 118:202–13

116. Nicholson LK, Kay LE, Torchia DA. 1996. Protein dynamics as studied by solution NMR techniques. In *NMR Spectroscopy and its Application to Biomedical Research*, ed. SK Sarkar, pp. 241–80. Amsterdam: Elsevier. 387 pp.

117. Nietlispach D, Clowes RT, Broadhurst RW, Ito Y, Keeler J, et al. 1996. An approach to the structure determination of larger proteins using triple resonance NMR experiments in conjunction with random fractional deuteration. *J. Am. Chem. Soc.* 118:407–15

118. Nilges M. 1995. Calculation of protein structures with ambiguous distance restraints: automated assignment of ambiguous NOE crosspeaks and disulphide connectivities. *J. Mol. Biol.* 245:645–60

119. Nilges M, Macias MJ, O'Donoghue SI, Oschkinat H. 1997. Automated NOESY interpretation with ambiguous distance restraints: the refined NMR solution structure of the pleckstrin homology domain from β-spectrin. *J. Mol. Biol.* 269:408–22

120. Oda Y, Nakamura H, Yamazaki T, Nagayama K, Yoshida M, et al. 1992. ^{1}H NMR studies of deuterated ribonuclease HI selectively labeled with protonated amino acids. *J. Biomol. NMR* 2:137–47

121. Oldfield E. 1995. Chemical shifts and three-dimensional protein structures. *J. Biomol. NMR* 5:217–25

122. Omichinski JG, Pedone PV, Felsenfeld G, Gronenborn AM, Clore GM. 1997. The solution structure of a specific GAGA factor-DNA complex reveals a modular binding mode. *Nat. Struct. Biol.* 4:122–32

123. Ono A, Makita T, Tate S, Kawashima E, Ishido Y, Kainosho M. 1996. C5α methylene proton signal assignment of DNA/RNA oligomers labeled with C5′-monodeuterated nucleosides by ^{1}H-^{31}P HSQC spectroscopy. *Mag. Res. Chem.* 34:S40-46

124. Pachter R, Arrowsmith CH, Jardetzky O. 1992. The effect of selective deuteration on magnetization transfer in larger proteins. *J. Biomol. NMR* 2:183–94

125. Palmer AG III. 1993. Dynamic properties of proteins from NMR spectroscopy. *Curr. Opin. Biotechnol.* 4:385–91

126. Palmer AG III, Cavanagh J, Wright PE, Rance M. 1991. Sensitivity improvement in proton-detected two dimensional heteronuclear correlation spectroscopy. *J. Magn. Reson.* 93:151–70

127. Palmer AG III, Skelton NJ, Chazin WJ, Wright PE, Rance M. 1992. Suppression of the effects of cross-correlation between dipolar and anisotropic chemical shift relaxation mechanisms in the measurement of spin-spin relaxation rates. *Mol. Phys.* 75:699–711

128. Palmer AG III, Wright PE, Rance M. 1991. Measurement of relaxation time constants for methyl groups by proton-detected NMR spectroscopy. *Chem. Phys. Lett.* 185:41–6

129. Pascal SM, Singer AU, Gish G, Yamazaki T, Shoelson SE, et al. 1994. Nuclear magnetic resonance structure of an SH2 domain of phospholipase c-γ1 complexed with a high affinity binding peptide. *Cell* 77:461–72

130. Deleted in proof

131. Pervushin K, Wider G, Wüthrich K. 1997. Deuterium relaxation in a uniformly ^{15}N-labeled homeodomain and its DNA complex. *J. Am. Chem. Soc.* 119:3842–43

132. Reisman J, Jariel-Encontre I, Hsu VL, Parello J, Guiduschek EP, Kearns DR. 1991. Improving two-dimensional ^{1}H NMR NOESY spectra of a large protein by selective deuteration. *J. Am. Chem. Soc.* 113:2787–89

133. Reisman JM, Hsu VL, Jariel-Encontre I,

Lecou C, Sayre MH, et al. 1993. A ^{1}H-NMR study of the transcription factor 1 from *Bacillus subtilis* phage SPO1 by selective ^{2}H-labeling. *Eur. J. Biochem.* 213:865–73

134. Rosen MK, Gardner KH, Willis RC, Parris WE, Pawson T, Kay LE. 1996. Selective methyl group protonation of perdeuterated proteins. *J. Mol. Biol.* 263:627–36

135. Santoro J, King GC. 1992. A constant-time 2D Overbodenhausen experiment for inverse correlation of isotopically enriched species. *J. Magn. Reson.* 97:202–7

136. Sattler M, Fesik SW. 1996. Use of deuterium labeling in NMR: overcoming a sizeable problem. *Structure* 4:1245–49

137. Schleucher J, Sattler M, Griesinger C. 1993. Coherence selection by gradients without signal attenuation: application to the three-dimensional HNCO experiment. *Angew. Chem. Int. Ed. Engl.* 32:1489–91

138. Schleucher J, Schwendinger M, Sattler M, Schmidt P, Schedletzky O, et al. 1994. A general enhancement scheme in heteronuclear multidimensional NMR employing pulsed field gradients. *J. Biomol. NMR* 4:301–6

139. Schramm S, Oldfield E. 1983. Nuclear magnetic resonance studies of amino acids and proteins. Rotational correlation times of proteins by deuterium nuclear magnetic resonance spectroscopy. *Biochemistry* 22:2908–13

140. Seeholzer SH, Cohn M, Putkey JA, Means AR, Crespi HL. 1986. NMR studies of a complex of deuterated calmodulin with melittin. *Proc. Natl. Acad. Sci. USA* 83:3634–38

141. Seelig J. 1977. Deuterium magnetic resonance: theory and application to lipid membranes. *Q. Rev. Biophys.* 10:363–418

142. Shan X, Gardner KH, Muhandiram DR, Rao NS, Arrowsmith CH, Kay LE. 1996. Assignment of ^{15}N, ^{13}Cα, ^{13}Cβ and HN resonances in a ^{15}N, ^{13}C, ^{2}H labeled 64 kDa *trp* repressor-operator complex using triple resonance NMR spectroscopy and ^{2}H decoupling. *J. Am. Chem. Soc.* 118:6570–79

143. Shirakawa M, Wälchli M, Shimizu M, Kyogoku Y. 1995. The use of heteronuclear cross-polarization for backbone assignment of ^{2}H-, ^{15}N- and ^{13}C-labeled proteins: a pulse scheme. *J. Biomol. NMR* :323–26

144. Sippl M. 1995. Knowledge-based potentials for proteins. *Curr. Opin. Struct. Biol.* 5:229–35

145. Skolnick J, Kolinski A, Ortiz AR. 1997. MONSSTER: A method for folding globular proteins with a small number of distance restraints. *J. Mol. Biol.* 265:217–41

146. Smith BO, Ito Y, Raine A, Teichmann S, Ben-Tovim L, et al. 1996. An approach to structure determination using limited NMR data from larger proteins selectively protonated at specific residue types. *J. Biomol. NMR* 8:360–68

147. Spera S, Bax A. 1991. Empirical correlation between protein backbone conformation and Cα and Cβ ^{13}C nuclear magnetic resonance chemical shifts. *J. Am. Chem. Soc.* 113:5490–92

148. Stonehouse J, Shaw GL, Keeler J, Laue ED. 1994. Minimizing sensitivity losses in gradient-selected ^{15}N-^{1}H HSQC spectra of proteins. *J. Mag. Reson. A* 107:178–84

149. Tjandra N, Bax A. 1997. Measurement of dipolar contributions to $^1J_{CH}$ splittings from magnetic-field dependence of J modulation in two-dimensional NMR spectra. *J. Magn. Reson.* 124:512–15

150. Tjandra N, Garrett DS, Gronenborn AM, Bax A, Clore GM. 1997. Defining long range order in NMR structure determination by diffusion induced relaxation anisotropy. *Nat. Struct. Biol.* 4:443–49

151. Tjandra N, Grzesiek S, Bax A. 1996. Magnetic field dependence of nitrogen-proton J splittings in ^{15}N-enriched ubiquitin resulting from relaxation interference and residual dipolar coupling. *J. Am. Chem. Soc.* 118:6264–72

152. Tjandra N, Omichinski JG, Gronenborn AM, Clore GM, Bax A. 1997. Use of dipolar ^{1}H-^{15}N and ^{1}H-^{13}C couplings in the structure determination of magnetically oriented macromolecules in solution. *Nat. Struct. Biol.* 4:732–38

153. Tolbert TJ, Williamson JR. 1996. Preparation of specifically deuterated RNA for NMR studies using a combination of chemical and enzymatic synthesis. *J. Am. Chem. Soc.* 118:7929–40

154. Tolman JR, Chung J, Prestegard JH. 1992. Pure-phase heteronuclear multiple quantum spectroscopy using field gradient selection. *J. Magn. Reson.* 98:462–67

155. Tolman JR, Flanagan JM, Kennedy MA, Prestegard JH. 1995. Nuclear magnetic dipole interaction in field-oriented proteins: information for structure determi-

nation in solution. *Proc. Natl. Acad. Sci. USA* 92:9279–83

156. Torchia DA, Sparks SW, Bax A. 1988. Delineation of α-helical domains in deuterated staphylococcal nuclease by 2D NOE NMR spectroscopy. *J. Am. Chem. Soc.* 110:2320–21

157. Torchia DA, Sparks SW, Bax A. 1988. NMR signal assignments of amide protons in the α-helical domains of staphylococcal nuclease. *Biochemistry* 27:5135–41

158. Tsang P, Wright PE, Rance M. 1990. Specific deuteration strategy for enhancing direct nuclear Overhauser effects in high molecular weight complexes. *J. Am. Chem. Soc.* 112:8183–85

159. Venters RA, Farmer BT II, Fierke CA, Spicer LD. 1996. Characterizing the use of perdeuteration in NMR studies of large proteins: ^{13}C, ^{15}N, and ^{1}H assignments of human carbonic anydrase II. *J. Mol. Biol.* 264:1101–16

160. Venters RA, Huang C-C, Farmer BT II, Trolard R, Spicer LD, Fierke CA. 1995. High-level ^{2}H/^{13}C/^{15}N labeling of proteins for NMR studies. *J. Biomol. NMR* 5:339–44

161. Venters RA, Metzler WJ, Spicer LD, Mueller L, Farmer BT II. 1995. Use of ^{1}H$_{N}$-^{1}H$_{N}$ NOEs to determine protein global folds in perdeuterated proteins. *J. Am. Chem. Soc.* 117:9592–93

162. Vold RR, Vold RL. 1991. Deuterium relaxation in molecular solids. In *Advances in Magnetic and Optical Resonance*, ed. WS Warren, 16:85–171. San Diego: Academic Press. 277 pp.

163. Vuister GW, Bax A. 1992. Resolution enhancement and spectral editing of uniformly ^{13}C-enriched proteins by homonuclear broadband ^{13}C decoupling. *J. Magn. Reson.* 98:428–35

164. Vuister GW, Clore GM, Gronenborn AM, Powers R, Garrett DS, et al. 1993. Increased resolution and improved spectral quality in four-dimensional ^{13}C/^{13}C-separated HMQC-NOESY-HMQC spectra using pulsed field gradients. *J. Magn. Reson. B* 101:210–13

165. Waugh DS. 1996. Genetic tools for selective labeling of proteins with α-^{15}N-amino acids. *J. Biomol. NMR* 8:184–92

166. Werbelow LG, Grant DM. 1977. Intramolecular dipolar relaxation in multispin systems. *Adv. Magn. Reson.* 9:189–299

167. Wishart DS, Sykes BD. 1994. The ^{13}C chemical-shift index: a simple method for the identification of protein secondary structure using ^{13}C chemical-shift data. *J. Biomol. NMR* 4:171–80

168. Wishart DS, Sykes BD, Richards FM. 1991. Relationship between nuclear magnetic resonance chemical shift and protein secondary structure. *J. Mol. Biol.* 222:311–33

169a. Wüthrich K. 1986. NMR of Proteins and Nucleic Acids, pp 117–202. New York: Wiley. 292 pp.

169b. Wüthrich K. 1986. See Ref. 169a, pp. 168–169

170. Yamazaki T, Lee W, Arrowsmith CH, Muhandiram DR, Kay LE. 1994. A suite of triple resonance NMR experiments for the backbone assignment of ^{15}N, ^{13}C, ^{2}H labeled proteins with high sensitivity. *J. Am. Chem. Soc.* 116:11655–66

171. Yamazaki T, Lee W, Revington M, Mattiello DL, Dahlquist FW, et al. 1994. An HNCA pulse scheme for the backbone assignment of ^{15}N, ^{13}C, ^{2}H-labeled proteins: application to a 37 kDa *trp* repressor-DNA complex. *J. Am. Chem. Soc.* 116:6464–65

172. Yamazaki T, Muhandiram DR, Kay LE. 1994. NMR experiments for the measurement of carbon relaxation properties in highly enriched, uniformly ^{13}C, ^{15}N-labeled proteins: application to ^{13}Cα carbons. *J. Am. Chem. Soc.* 116:8266–78

173. Yamazaki T, Tochio H, Furui J, Aimoto S, Kyogoku Y. 1997. Assignment of backbone resonances for larger proteins using the ^{13}C-^{1}H coherence of a ^{1}Hα-, ^{2}H-, ^{13}C- and ^{15}N-labeled sample. *J. Am. Chem. Soc.* 119:872–80

174. Yang D, Kay LE. 1996. The effects of cross correlation and cross relaxation on the measurement of deuterium T_1 and $T_{1\rho}$ relaxation times in ^{13}CH$_2$D spin systems. *J. Magn. Reson. B* 110:213–18

175. Yu L, Petros AM, Schnuchel A, Zhong P, Severin JM, et al. 1997. Solution structure of an rRNA methyltransferase (ErmAm) that confers MLS antibiotic resistance. *Nat. Struct. Biol.* 4:483–89

176. Zhang H, Zhao D, Revington M, Lee W, Jia X, et al. 1994. The solution structures of the *trp* repressor-operator DNA complex. *J. Mol. Biol.* 238:592–614

177. Zhao D, Jardetzky O. 1994. An assessment of the precision and accuracy of protein structures determined by NMR. *J. Mol. Biol.* 239:601–7

Annu. Rev. Biophys. Biomol. Struct. 1998. 27:407–45

RNA RECOGNITION BY RNP PROTEINS DURING RNA PROCESSING

Gabriele Varani and Kiyoshi Nagai

MRC Laboratory of Molecular Biology, Hills Road, Cambridge CB2 2QH, United Kingdom; e-mail: gv1@mrc-lmb.cam.ac.uk; kn@mrc-lmb.cam.ac.uk

ABSTRACT

The ribonucleoprotein (RNP) domain is one of the most common eukaryotic protein folds. Proteins containing RNP domains function in important steps of posttranscriptional regulation of gene expression by directing the assembly of multiprotein complexes on primary transcripts, mature mRNAs, and stable ribonucleoprotein components of the RNA processing machinery. The diverse functions performed by these proteins depend on their dual ability to recognize RNA and to interact with other proteins, often utilizing specialized auxiliary domains. Crystallographic and NMR structures of several RNP domains and a handful of structures of RNA-protein complexes have begun to reveal the molecular basis for RNP-RNA recognition.

CONTENTS

407

1056-8700/98/0610-0407$08.00

PERSPECTIVES AND OVERVIEW

Mature mRNAs are produced in the cell nucleus from primary transcripts of coding genes (pre-mRNAs or hnRNAs, heterogeneous nuclear RNAs) by a series of processing events that include capping of the 5'-end with a methylated guanosine analogue, removal of noncoding regions (pre-mRNA splicing), and cleavage and polyadenylation at the 3'-end. Mature mRNAs are transported to the cytoplasm; the transport, stability, intra-cellular localization, and efficiency of translation of individual mRNAs are subject to regulation. These processes are mediated by numerous RNA-binding proteins and ribonucleoprotein complexes that recognize specific features of primary transcripts or mature mRNAs. These complexes, rather than isolated proteins or RNAs, constitute structural and functional units during gene expression.

Proteins involved in posttranscriptional regulation of gene expression have modular structure, being composed of RNA-binding domain(s) and additional domains that perform essential functions, for example in mediating protein-protein interactions. RNA-binding modules provide specificity for certain mRNAs or certain components of the RNA-processing apparatus, allowing functional multiprotein complexes to assemble on specific mRNAs. The RNP domain (also called RRM, RNA recognition motif) is the most common eukaryotic RNA-binding module and mediates RNA recognition in hundreds of proteins from the RNA processing machinery (14, 69, 78). Animal, plant, fungal, and prokaryotic cells contain RNP proteins in virtually all organelles, suggesting that this is an ancient protein fold associated with essential functions. Analysis of the sequence database indicates that this is one of the most common eukaryotic protein sequence motifs, providing an RNA-binding counterpart to zinc-finger or homeobox motifs for DNA.

RNP domains are found in single or multiple copies in individual proteins (up to four, Figure 1) and function primarily in targeting specific RNAs. Sometimes a single domain is sufficient to specify the RNA recognition ability of a given protein, but very often single RNP domains do not function as independent RNA recognition units. Sequences immediately N- or C-terminal to the domain are often required for RNA recognition. In many cases of proteins containing multiple domains, two or more domains contribute to define the specificity of the protein. Besides this primary ability to recognize RNA, RNP proteins also interact with other proteins. These interactions may either modulate or affect the specificity of the domain and are critical in the assembly of multiprotein complexes that carry out various RNA processing events.

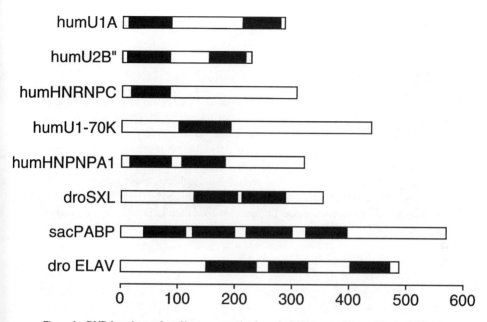

Figure 1   RNP domains are found in many proteins from the RNA processing machinery. Different proteins contain variable numbers of domains, ranging between 1 (e.g. hnRNP C) and 4 (e.g. Poly(A) binding protein).

The RNP domain is identified by two highly conserved stretches of 6 and 8 amino acids separated by approximately 30 amino acids, named RNP-2 and RNP-1, respectively. The motif was first identified as a repeated sequence within the polyadenylate binding protein and in hnRNP A1 (2, 90). Sequence conservation outside these two repeats is low, but structure-based alignment of members of this family demonstrate the conservation of hydrophobic residues that stabilize the protein structure (11). Structural analysis of RNP domains from several different proteins (7, 31, 45, 64, 79, 127) has demonstrated that the domain folds in a compact $\alpha\beta$ structure, with a four-stranded β-sheet packed against two α-helices through an extensive hydrophobic core. Biochemical (50, 79) and NMR studies (34, 46, 51) identified the surface of the β-sheet as the primary site of RNA recognition. A crystallographic structure (84) and a subsequent NMR structure (3) of complexes between the N-terminal RNP domain of human U1A protein and distinct RNA targets have revealed the structural basis for RNP-RNA recognition.

This review describes how RNP proteins function to mediate RNA recognition during diverse RNA processing events and summarizes our current knowledge of the structure of the RNP domain and the molecular basis for RNA recognition.

DIVERSITY OF FUNCTIONS OF RNP PROTEINS

RNP proteins are involved in most if not all steps of posttranscriptional regulation of gene expression. Immediately after transcription, primary transcripts are associated with a set of very abundant factors (hnRNP proteins), many of which contain RNP domains. Components of stable ribonucleoprotein particles involved in pre-mRNA splicing and many regulators of splicing contain RNP domains. Formation of mature 3′-ends by polyadenylation involves several RNP proteins, and the mature poly(A) tail is recognized by the poly(A) binding protein. RNP domains can also be found within factors involved in initiation of protein synthesis (72).

hnRNP Proteins

Newly transcribed mRNAs (pre-mRNAs or hnRNAs) are associated with hnRNP proteins. hnRNP proteins localize throughout the nucleus and are abundant; in a growing cell, the nuclear concentration of hnRNP A1 exceeds 10 μM, corresponding to $\gg 10^8$ copies of the protein. hnRNPs remain associated with pre-mRNA until processing is complete and with mature mRNAs during nucleocytoplasmic transport (48, 73). By associating with pre-mRNAs, hnRNP proteins affect the interactions of pre-mRNAs with components of the RNA processing apparatus (28). A subset of hnRNP proteins shuttle continuously between the nucleus and the cytoplasm, and at least hnRNP A1 remains associated with polyadenylated mRNAs throughout this process. This activity is mediated by a noncanonical nuclear localization signal that provides a nuclear export signal as well (73), suggesting that shuttling hnRNPs may also function as carriers of mRNAs to the cytoplasm.

hnRNP proteins share structural and functional features with protein components of stable spliceosomal particles (e.g. snRNPs) or splicing regulators, in that they contain common RNA-binding and auxiliary domains and affect RNA splicing. Unlike snRNPs, hnRNP complexes are heterogeneous, labile, and composed of large numbers of different proteins. At least 20 major hnRNP proteins exist in human cells, ranging in molecular weight between 34 and 120 kDa (28). Multiple isoforms of hnRNP proteins are produced by alternative processing of the genes coding for these proteins. This diversity is further increased by posttranslational modification of potential physiological significance, including dimethylation of arginine side chains and phosphorylation. Most hnRNP proteins have RNA-binding ability, attributable in many cases to RNP domains or other RNA-binding motifs. The structure of individual members of this family varies considerably: (a) hnRNP I (also known as the polypyrimidine-tract-binding protein), L and M contain four RNP domains; (b) hnRNP A/B proteins contain two RNP domains at the N-terminus and a Gly-rich auxiliary domain at the carboxy end; (c) hnRNP C proteins contain a single RNP domain at the N-terminus.

Most hnRNP proteins have general RNA-binding activity, but individual proteins display preference for specific sequences. However, hnRNP proteins generally do not bind specific sites exclusively but recognize different RNAs with a wide spectrum of affinities (1, 15). Preferred sequences tend nevertheless to coincide with sites of functional importance in pre-mRNA processing, suggesting that hnRNP proteins may form specialized complexes or indirectly recruit other factors to such sites. RNA binding is further modulated by cooperative protein-protein interactions, which are particularly important because of the fact that the physiological concentration of these proteins is far in excess of that of high-affinity binding sites. Whether through direct protein-RNA interactions or through cooperativity, the array of hnRNP proteins bound to a given hnRNA is determined by the RNA sequence (28). Under conditions of competition for distinct binding sites, each mRNA will associate with a unique set of hnRNP proteins, and the composition of these complexes is likely to change during the processing and transport of hnRNAs.

hnRNP proteins function in early processing events by associating with nascent transcripts. hnRNP A1 modulates splice site selection by antagonizing the activity of serine-arginine–rich splicing factors (SR proteins, see below) (19, 70). Alternative splicing is a major mechanism to control the expression of viral and cellular genes, and variations in the intracellular concentration of antagonistic splicing factors may affect tissue-specific and developmental regulation of gene expression. The amount of hnRNP A1 varies during the cell cycle, but the physiological significance of this variation remains unclear. Splicing regulation by hnRNP A1 requires both RNP domains; both domains are also required in vitro for specific RNA recognition (15).

Spliceosomal Components and Splicing Factors

Noncoding sequences are removed from primary mRNA transcripts (premRNAs) in a process called pre-mRNA splicing (103). Catalysis takes place in the spliceosome, a dynamic assembly of pre-mRNA, five small nuclear RNP particles (snRNPs), and numerous protein factors (58). Although catalytic activity is almost certainly RNA-based, protein components of snRNPs and other protein factors play essential functions in the recognition, selection, and regulation of spliceosome assembly and catalysis. Coding regions (exons) are generally relatively short, almost always less than 100 nucleotides in length, but noncoding regions (introns) can be as large as 200,000 nucleotides. A

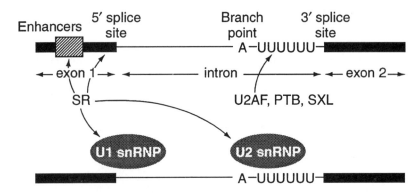

Figure 2   RNA signals essential for pre-mRNA splicing include the exon-intron junctions (5′ and 3′ splice sites) and the branch point. Critical regulatory functions are provided by the polypyrimidine-tract within introns and by exonic enhancer sequences.

remarkable feature of pre-mRNA splicing is that the splicing apparatus can excise introns with widely diverse size. Furthermore, signals essential for intron removal are relatively poorly conserved in sequence and clustered over just a few nucleotides at the exon-intron border and at the so-called branch sites and polypyrimidine tracts (Figure 2). Despite the limited information content, these signals are recognized effectively across a long distance. It is the function of snRNP particles and other protein components of the spliceosome to assure accuracy and specificity in the cleavage reaction and to regulate utilization of alternative splice sites present in most eukaryotic genes. Many spliceosomal components and regulators contain RNP domains that are essential to the function of these factors. In this context, RNP proteins recognize specific RNA signals and establish intricate networks with other protein and RNA components of the spliceosome.

Five RNP particles, U1, U2, U4, U5, and U6 snRNP, play major roles in the formation of the catalytic core during splicing and presumably provide the catalytically active residues. Protein components of snRNPs modulate and stabilize the three-dimensional structure of these particles and establish protein-protein interactions during spliceosome assembly (57). U1 snRNPs function primarily in recognizing the 5′ (upstream) site of cleavage by direct base pairing between U1 snRNA and the exon-intron junction (Figure 2). Mammalian splice sites are highly divergent in sequence, making it unlikely that base-pairing alone is sufficient for recognition of the cleavage site with high fidelity. U1 snRNP contains U1 70K, a protein that recognizes stem-loop I of U1 snRNA via the RNP domain (87). However, this region of the protein is dispensable for growth in yeast: protein-protein interactions between the N-terminal part of U1 70K and "core" components of U1 snRNP overcome the need for direct RNA-protein interactions (43, 80). U1 70K promotes recognition of the 5′-splice site through a direct interaction with ASF/SF2 (and possibly other SR proteins) mediated by its C-terminal RS domain (57). ASF/SF2 binds the pre-mRNA first, then recruits U1 snRNP to the 5′-splice site through this interaction with U1 70K. The tripartite complex of ASF/SF2, U1 snRNP, and pre-mRNA appears to be sufficient to define the 5′-splice site in the commitment complex, the first functional pre-spliceosomal complex in which the RNA cannot be competed off by exogenous pre-mRNAs. In analogy with transcription, specific protein-protein interactions between RNA-bound activators and components of the general RNA processing machinery regulate the formation of productive splicing complexes.

The spliceosomal cycle involves interconversion of snRNAs between distinct conformational states at precise steps of the cycle itself. Spliceosomal snRNAs undergo numerous conformational rearrangements during the splicing cycle involving formation and disruption of numerous base pairs within themselves and with pre-mRNAs. U4 and U6 snRNAs are base-paired to each other in a single particle and are incorporated in the spliceosome in association with U5 snRNP. The U4/U6 interaction is destabilized during catalysis and U4 is released from the spliceosome, but the U4/U6 complex must be reformed for the next cycle of splicing to occur. This process is mediated by a U6-associated RNP protein (prp24 in yeast), one of the factors that mediate RNA conformational changes during spliceosome assembly (49a,b, 102). Mutations within the RNP domain of prp24 suppress the effect of mutations in RNA sequence that destabilize the U4/U6 interaction.

Most introns of higher eukaryotic genes contain a regulatory region rich in pyrimidines between the branch site and the 3′ splice site (polypyrimidine tract, or PPT) (Figure 2). This region plays an essential role in the identification of the 3′-splice site at early stages in spliceosome assembly, a function mediated by several protein factors that recognize such sites. The best-characterized polypyrimidine-tract binding factor is U2AF, an essential component of the spliceosome. Mammalian U2AF contains two subunits of 35 and 65 kDa; the larger subunit contains three C-terminal RNP domains that mediate binding to the polypyrimidine tract (52, 85, 132), while the N-terminal RS domain mediates protein-protein interactions. All three RNP domains of U2AF are essential for RNA binding and splicing activity, while the RS domain is dispensable for RNA binding but essential for spliceosome formation (132). The large subunits of U2AF are >80% identical from yeast to humans in the RNA-binding region, emphasizing the importance of RNA recognition for the function of this protein in splicing. The 35 kDa subunit is encoded by an essential gene in *Drosophila*, interacts with the RS domain of the larger subunit, and may function with other proteins in bridging 5'- and 3'- splice sites (115, 128). The small subunit of U2AF may also promote utilization of weak splice sites that depend on the function of enhancer elements, as a critical component of a network of RNA-binding proteins that link splicing enhancer and 3'-splice site sequences through multiple weak protein-protein interactions (134).

A second RNP protein involved in recognition of the polypyrimidine tract is PTB, the polypyrimidine-tract-binding protein, probably involved in regulation of alternative splicing. PTB has four RNP domains that match the consensus rather poorly but nonetheless mediate RNA recognition. A third protein essential for constitutive splicing, the polypyrimidine-associated splicing factor (PSF), also contains two RNP domains and a typical auxiliary domain (RGG box) at the C-terminus (58).

The polypyrimidine tract and its associated proteins perform important regulatory functions. *Sxl* is the master regulator of a cascade of events required to maintain female cell fate in *Drosophila*. *Sxl* regulates use of two different splicing pathways (male-specific and female-specific) for the *tra* protein by specifically recognizing the polypyrimidine-rich tract on *tra* pre-mRNA, just upstream of the 3'-splice site of the second exon of this gene. Binding is to the polypyrimidine tract of the non-sex–specific 3'-splice site of the *tra* pre-mRNA (47). This interaction disrupts the interaction between U2AF and the polypyrimidine tract, which is necessary to recruit U2 snRNP to the branch site early during spliceosome assembly, thereby activating a female-specific splice site recognized by U2AF with lower affinity (118). *Sxl* directs early events during somatic and germline sexual development and maintains the female-specific expression pattern through an autoregulatory feedback loop. Thus, *Sxl* is a positive regulator of the female-specific *transformer* gene. Sexual differentiation and maintenance of female cell fate in *Drosophila* are directly linked to the ability of *Sxl* to bind the polypyrimidine tract (51).

PTB, U2AF, and *Sxl* share a general preference for pyrimidine-rich sequences, but these proteins have significantly divergent RNA targets (105). (*a*) U2AF binds a U-rich sequence that closely matches polypyrimidine tracts found in natural metazoan pre-mRNAs; (*b*) *Sxl* binds preferentially a highly specific sequence similar to the PPT of the regulated *Tra* Pre-mRNA; (*c*) PTB does not recognize typical PPTs, but rather specialized sequences involved in negative regulation of splicing. However, *Sxl* binds with roughly equal affinity in vitro polypyrimidine-tracts that it does not regulate in vivo: The selectivity of *Sxl* observed in vitro is insufficient to explain the selectivity in regulation of pre-mRNA splicing observed in vivo (51). An attractive explanation would invoke interactions between *Sxl* and other proteins to modulate *Sxl*-RNA binding and allow regulation of splicing in vivo.

SR Proteins and the Control of Alternative Pre-mRNA Splicing

SR proteins are a family of pre-mRNA splicing factors sharing a common structure comprising one or two RNP domains at the N-terminus and a domain rich in arginine-serine dipeptides at the C-terminus (RS domain, Figure 3). Other proteins (for example snRNP associated factors such as U1 70K and splicing regulators such as *Drosophila Tra*) share this structural organization. However, the term SR proteins refers to eight major polypeptides ranging between 20 and 75 kDa in size that share the ability to modulate splice-site choice and complement deficient extracts in splicing reconstitution assays.

SR proteins are essential pre-mRNA splicing factors and critical regulators of the selection of alternative splice sites. They are present in all eukaryotes except yeast, where true alternative splicing does not occur. SR proteins have been implicated in many steps of spliceosome assembly, from recognition of the 5′-splice site at the earliest step of splicing (57, 136) to binding and regulation of so-called exonic-enhancer sequences that stimulate use of suboptimal splice sites. SR proteins are distinguished by the presence or absence of the second RNP domain and by the length of the RS domain; when present, the sequence of the second domain is often divergent from the canonical consensus sequence (30, 66). Individual proteins display a remarkable sequence conservation across metazoan species (11), suggesting that the activity of at least one essential gene is regulated by each SR protein. Consistent with this, the gene coding for ASF/SF2 is essential in vertebrates, human ASF/SF2 can functionally substitute its chicken analogue (123), and deletion, mutation, or overexpression of *Drosophila* B52 (equivalent to human SRp55) prevents normal development.

SR proteins have overlapping but not identical function. Different SR proteins commit distinct pre-mRNAs to splicing in vitro, suggesting that the function of these proteins in the earliest steps of spliceosome assembly involves, at least in part, sequence-specific binding to distinct pre-mRNAs (29, 66, 108). Interactions between SR proteins and pre-mRNAs may be critical to determine whether a pre-mRNA is spliced or not. The RNA-binding specificities observed for different SR proteins are likely to be physiologically significant and may provide a mechanism to regulate alternative and tissue-specific splicing (29, 42, 107, 108, 122). The RNP domain(s) are essential for the activity of all members of this family (18, 24, 135) and define the RNA-binding specificity of individual proteins. The RS domains at the C-terminal end function primarily as protein-protein recognition units (57, 128) as well as regulatory domains (26, 36, 75, 76). RS domains can be interchangeable in vitro, although the high conservation across species suggests that this may not be true in vivo (24). The highly basic character of RS domains masks and modulates specific

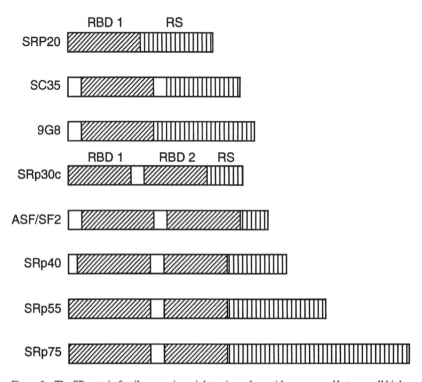

Figure 3 The SR protein family comprises eight major polypeptides conserved between all higher eukaryotes, containing one or two RNP domains at the N-terminus and an RS domain of various length and sequence composition at the C-terminus.

RNA binding: Sequence-specific binding of ASF/SF2 to RNA is observed only when the RS domain is absent or phosphorylated (107, 108, 129).

The primary function of SR proteins appears to be regulation of alternative splice sites, which are present in the vast majority of higher eukaryotic pre-mRNAs. Alternative splicing is a common mechanism to regulate gene expression in a cell-type specific manner, because it allows the synthesis of different proteins from the same gene. It is also an essential aspect of the biology of retroviruses, permitting expression of numerous reading frames from a single pre-mRNA. ASF/SF2 (SRp30a in humans) controls splice site utilization in a concentration-dependent manner both in vitro and in vivo (19), suggesting that the physiological concentration of competing splicing factors may be important for regulation of splice site selection. Intriguingly, SR proteins are ubiquitously expressed, yet cell-type specific differences are observed in their distribution, suggesting that each cell type may have distinct patterns of concentration of

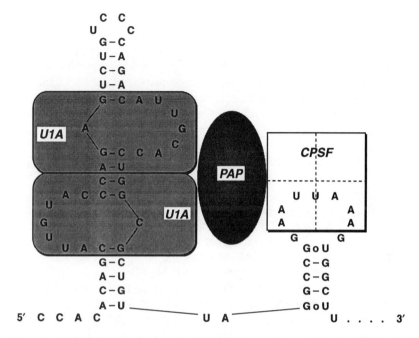

Figure 4 Regulation of gene expression of U1A protein requires recognition by U1A itself of a conserved element within the 3′-untranslated region of the mRNA coding for U1A itself; upon binding RNA, U1A interacts directly with the poly(A) polymerase enzyme and inhibits its activity.

each SR protein (29, 117). The activity of SR proteins in regulation of alternative splicing is closely connected with the role of exonic enhancer sequences, purine-rich RNA sequences that stimulate splicing activity and regulate alternative splice site utilization. A primary property of enhancer elements is their location within a pre-mRNA: An ASF/SF2-responsive enhancer element can be transformed in a repressor of splicing when placed within an intron (53).

The structural organization of SR proteins and their ability to interact with other proteins suggest a model for their function, where the RNA-binding domain(s) provide specificity for certain mRNAs (or classes of mRNAs) by recognizing specific RNA signals, while the RS domain may recruit other factors during spliceosome assembly by protein-protein interactions (117). The dual ability of SR proteins to establish highly specific RNA-protein and protein-protein interactions raises the unanswered question of how splicing control is achieved. Enhancer sequences may differ in their requirements for cooperativity in binding SR proteins, and a wide spectrum of enhancers may exist in vivo, ranging from high-affinity sites requiring a single SR protein to function (107, 108, 131) to low-affinity sites recognized by multiple SR proteins.

High-affinity sites may allow alternative splicing to be regulated by specific SR proteins, while pre-mRNA splicing that does not rely on such sites may rely instead on multiple weak interactions with RNA and other proteins. Among the potential targets for protein-protein interactions are RS domains from other SR proteins, splicing regulators, and spliceosomal components. Despite the limited sequence diversity of these regions, interactions mediated by the RS domains are highly specific: RS domains are not generic protein recognition units, but rather mediators of specific protein-protein interactions that are critical for spliceosome assembly and regulation (6, 41, 114, 128).

SR proteins are phosphorylated in vivo at multiple serine residues within the RS domain, and their activity is regulated by phosphorylation. At least four kinases have been implicated in the phosphorylation of SR proteins, although the physiological role of these enzymes remains to be firmly established (26, 36, 88). Relatively little is known about the functional consequences of phosphorylation and the specific signal transduction pathways that may regulate splicing activity, but it is known that the phosphorylation state of SR proteins varies during the cell cycle; at least one SR kinase is regulated by the cell cycle (26, 36). Cycles of phosphorylation and dephosphorylation may define the organization of splicing within the cell nucleus by affecting the RNA-binding activity and subnuclear localization of RS-domain containing proteins (76). Phosphorylation is important for specific RNA recognition, since the high positive charge of unphosphorylated RS domains masks the specificity of the RNP domains and enhances nonspecific binding (107, 129). Protein-protein interactions are instead enhanced by phosphorylation (129), which also affects the subnuclear localization of splicing factors, causing their release from storage sites of splicing components (75, 36).

Formation of Mature 3'-Ends of mRNAs

RNP proteins are also found among factors involved in the formation of the mature 3'-end of mRNAs. In higher eukaryotes, the primary signal for polyadenylation is represented by the AAUAAA sequence. This signal is recognized by a multisubunit complex (cleavage and polyadenylation specificity factor, CPSF), and RNA binding is enhanced by an additional multiprotein complex (cleavage and stimulation factor, CstF) (65, 121). The pre-mRNA is cleaved 20 to 30 nucleotides downstream of the AAUAAA signal and subsequently polyadenylated by the poly(A) polymerase enzyme associated with the CPSF complex. CstF interacts directly with downstream GU-rich enhancer elements through its CstF-64 component and substantially enhances binding of the cleavage specificity factor to the AAUAAA signal.

The CstF-64 component of the CstF complex has an RNP domain at its N-terminus that mediates recognition of GU-rich sequences that function as downstream stimulatory elements in polyadenylation reactions (109, 110). The RNP domain of CstF-64 suffices to define the specificity of the entire CstF multiprotein complex, but strong cooperativity between CPSF and CstF allows GU-rich elements that bind CstF-64 with different affinity to function equally well in in-vitro–reconstituted polyadenylation reactions. CstF-GU recognition may be more important in vivo, where CstF factors compete with many more proteins and RNAs for the same site than in a simplified reconstituted system (110). The strong cooperativity observed in the reconstituted reaction suggests nevertheless that sequence-specific recognition by a single domain or protein may be less important in 3'-end formation than interactions between protein factors.   Because protein-protein interactions diminish the need for highly specific RNA-protein recognition, even partially conserved and highly variable sequence elements can effectively direct all mRNAs to general processing pathways such as polyadenylation.

Regulation of polyadenylation can occur either at the level of protein-protein interaction or through highly specific RNA-protein interactions. The yeast homologue of CstF-64 itself (the product of the RNA-15 gene) provides an example of regulation of polyadenylation by protein-protein interactions. RNA-15 protein interacts in vitro and in vivo with the poly(A) binding protein Pab1p (5); this interaction appears to control the length of the poly(A) tail, an important determinant of mRNA stability (8). On the other hand, U1A autoregulates its own expression by interacting directly with the poly(A) polymerase enzyme, upon recognizing a conserved secondary structure within the 3'-untranslated region (3'-UTR) of its own pre-mRNA (Figure 4) (13, 37, 38, 120). Two U1A proteins must be bound for regulation to occur, and formation of a specific protein-RNA complex on the U1A 3'-UTR is enhanced by cooperative interactions between U1A proteins mediated by the C-terminal end of the first RNP domain of U1A. However, specificity for the U1A pre-mRNA is achieved primarily through direct protein-RNA contacts. These two examples illustrate different mechanisms by which RNA processing events are regulated. When general sequence elements such as GU-rich enhancers provide primary regulatory signals, protein-RNA recognition cannot provide specificity for a given pre-mRNA and regulation depends on multiple weak interactions. On the other hand, RNP domains allow very effective recognition of signals that are unique to certain mRNAs or subset of mRNAs and allow the assembly of regulatory multiprotein complexes to occur only on such mRNAs.

The Poly(Adenylate) Binding Protein

Among the most interesting RNP proteins is the polyadenylate binding protein (PABP-I, or Pab1p in yeast), one of the most abundant mRNA-binding proteins in the cell (2). Poly(A) binding proteins from all organisms share the same conserved structure, with four RNP domains (2, 90) plus a carboxy-terminal Pro-rich region that is dispensable for poly(A) binding (16, 89). The sequence of individual domains and of the linker regions is highly conserved across species, each domain being much more similar to the corresponding domain from other species than to any of the other RNP domain in the same protein (16). Specific poly(A) binding activity is localized within the two amino terminal domains, while domains 3 and 4 may cooperate with the C-terminal Pro-rich domain to organize a ribonucleoprotein particle with multiple copies of regularly spaced proteins on the poly(A) tail (60).

mRNA stability and translatability are primary mechanisms of regulation of gene expression, and the poly(A) tail of mRNAs and its associated protein functions ubiquitously in eukaryotes to regulate mRNA turnover and stimulate its translation. The 5′-cap and poly(A) tail regulate stability and translational initiation in a close functional connection mediated by the poly(A) binding protein. The primary mechanism of mRNA degradation (at least in yeast) requires shortening of the poly(A) tail, followed by decapping and subsequent degradation by 5′-3′ endonucleases (8, 20). The poly(A) tail protects the mRNA from decapping, an activity that requires the poly(A) binding protein. The primary signal for translational initiation is represented by the cap structure, but the poly(A) tail is also required for efficient protein synthesis. In fact, uncapped mRNAs can be translated as efficiently as capped mRNAs in some cell extracts, because the poly(A) tail and poly(A) binding protein recruit the 40S ribosomal subunit to the mRNA just as effectively as the cap-eIF-4E complex (91, 111, 113). Pab1p is also involved in the regulation of the length of the poly(A) tail, through association with the cleavage and polyadenylation apparatus (74).

STRUCTURE OF RNP PROTEINS

RNP Proteins Have Modular Structures

Many RNA-binding proteins have modular structures, being composed of structured and well-conserved RNA-binding domains, linked to divergent, generally unstructured auxiliary domains (Figure 5) (10, 11). hnRNP C contains an acidic C-terminal domain analogous to those observed in transcription factors, while Gly-rich domains are observed in hnRNP proteins and in the pre-ribosomal RNA-binding protein nucleolin; in some cases, the Gly-rich region is found in the context of RGG-type repetitions (RGG box). Other classes of auxiliary motifs are so-called RS domains found in SR proteins (see above), spliceosomal components such as U2AF and U1 70K, and splicing regulators such as *Drosophila tra* and *tra*-2. Although the specificity of a protein is largely or completely determined by RNA-binding domains, some auxiliary domains are involved in RNA binding as well. For example, the Gly-rich C-terminal domain

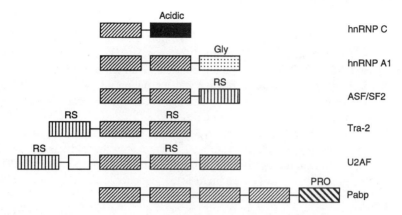

Figure 5   RNP proteins have modular structure and include auxiliary domains that are often essential for their function.

of hnRNP A1 promotes RNA binding through cooperative protein-protein interactions (25). However, these interactions are generally nonspecific and may just enhance the specific recognition mediated by the RNA-binding domains (10).

Although not essential for RNA binding, auxiliary domains are nonetheless often essential for function (123). Determinants of many essential functions such as protein-protein recognition and nuclear localization often reside within the auxiliary domains. The clearest example of the function of auxiliary domains of RNP proteins in protein-protein recognition is provided by RS domains, as described above; protein-protein interactions independent of RNA binding have also been demonstrated for the Gly-rich domain of hnRNP A1 (22). The activity of RNA-binding proteins containing auxiliary domains is subjected to regulation by posttranslational modifications such as phosphorylation or dimethylation of arginine side chains (14).

RNA-binding domains are generally highly conserved and cluster within a small number of structural motifs, of which the RNP motif is by far the most common. In contrast, auxiliary domains of RNA-binding proteins have low sequence complexity and are difficult to identify from the primary sequence (11), yet these regions are not simply interchangeable. For example, a chimeric hnRNP A1 construct, where the RS domain of ASF/SF2 is fused to the C-terminal of hnRNP A1 in place of its Gly-rich tail, is nonfunctional. The precise size and sequence composition of individual domains are also important: The alternative splicing and RNA-binding activities of hnRNP A/B proteins depend on the precise composition of the Gly-rich domains (70).

Structure of the RNP Domain

The three-dimensional structure of the RNP domain was first determined by X-ray crystallography for an N-terminal fragment of U1A protein containing residues 2–95 (79). The RNP domain consists of an $\alpha\beta$ sandwich structure with a four-stranded antiparallel β-sheet with a pronounced right-handed twist, packed by an extensive hydrophobic core against two nearly perpendicular α helices on the opposite surface (Figure 6a).

The topology of the fold is a repeated $\beta\alpha\beta$ arrangement with the strands of the β-sheet arranged in the order $\beta4$-$\beta1$-$\beta3$-$\beta2$. Remarkably, the fold was correctly predicted from the homology with acylphosphatase (32). The conserved RNP1 and RNP2 motifs that identify the domain at the sequence level are juxtaposed in

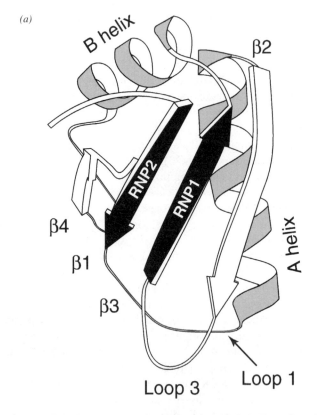

(a)

B helix

$\beta2$

RNP2

RNP1

$\beta4$

$\beta1$

A helix

$\beta3$

Loop 3   Loop 1

Figure 6 (*a*) Three-dimensional structure of the RNP domain (79). (*b*) Three-dimensional structure of hnRNP A1 (101, 130); two contiguous RNP domains separated by a flexible linker region interact via several salt bridges.

(b)

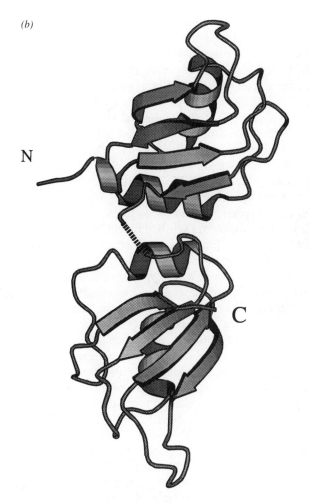

N

C

Figure 6   (Continued)

the two middle β-strands. The side chains of Tyr-13, Gln-54, and Phe-56, corresponding to the three highly conserved aromatic residues of RNP1 and RNP2 motifs, project on the surface of the β-sheet. Aromatic residues are exposed on β-sheet surfaces in single-stranded DNA-binding proteins, and sequences analogous to RNP-1 and RNP-2 have also been found in adjacent strands of antiparallel β-sheets for Y-box proteins, but the Y-box fold differs from the RNP structure (95, 96). The N- and C-terminal regions, outside the RNP domain defined by sequence alignment, are poorly ordered; loop3 connecting β2 and $\beta 3$ also appears to be flexible (63, 79). Strong binding of RNA to the RNP domain generally requires additional sequences at the N- and C-terminal ends of the domain, or two or more consecutive RNP domains in tandem. Loop3 constitutes the region of greatest genetic diversity among RNP proteins (11) and plays an important role in determining substrate specificity (14, 54).

The conserved architecture of the domain was confirmed by NMR studies of the N- and C-terminal RNP domains of U1A protein (45, 64), the first and second RNP domains of *Drosophila* Sxl (63), hnRNP C (127), and the second RNP domain of human hnRNP A1 (31). The two other most common eukaryotic RNA-binding folds, KH domain and double-stranded RNA-binding domain, are also $\alpha \beta$ proteins (17, 55, 77). This similarity may imply that the $\alpha \beta$ structure is an optimal structure for RNA recognition. However, the split $\alpha \beta$ fold of RNP proteins is very common among proteins with diverse function: It is a particularly stable fold able to satisfy different functional requirements (83). The β-sheet surface may provide a large surface for binding single-stranded nucleotides, as also observed in single-stranded DNA-binding proteins and in other examples of RNA-protein recognition, namely the MS2 phage capsid coat protein (119) and the β-barrel domain of aspartyl-tRNA synthetase (23). However, β-sheets are not the only way to define extensive exposed surfaces for RNA recognition; the 4-helix bundle protein *rop* accomplishes the same goal through a completely different architecture (86).

RNP proteins display subtle structural variations that may be important for RNA recognition. It is not surprising that differences in structure and degree of order are observed in loop3, given its diversity in sequence and length. The shortest loop3 of a known RNP domain is in hnRNP protein C, and the longest in the first RNP domain of *Drosophila* ELAV protein (11). Sxl and U1A contain β-bulges within $\beta 2$ (63, 79), while hnRNP C has β-bulges in both $\beta 1$ and $\beta 4$ (127). The length and relative orientation of the two α-helices at the back of the domain also differ among RNP proteins. The N-terminal RNP domains of U1A and U2B" proteins have an insertion of four residues in the loop 1 region (between $\beta 1$ and helix A), compared with other RNP domains. As a result, helices A in these two proteins are one turn longer than in other RNP domains. The most singular structural feature observed so far is the presence of an additional helix (helix C) directly following the N-terminal RNP domain in U1A (residues 92 to 98). The helix was first noted in NMR studies of a fragment of U1A comprising residues 2 to 102 (46), and its position relative to the RNP domain was revealed by the crystal structure of the complex between U1A protein and a hairpin RNA (84). In the complex, helix C extends from the domain along the direction of $\beta 2$. In the structure of an unbound fragment of U1A comprising residues 2–117, it lies instead across the β-sheet, with residues Ile93, Ile94, and Met97 making hydrophobic contacts with Leu44, Phe56, and

Ile58 (7). The position of helix C in the RNA-bound form is stabilized by alternative hydrophobic interaction involving Ile93, Ile94, Met97, and Ile58, His10 and Val62, and a hydrogen bond between Thr11 and Ser91 (3, 84). The Thr11 → Val mutation reduces RNA binding substantially (50, 133), showing that this amino acid plays a crucial role in stabilizing helix C in the RNA-bound position. Helix C is likely to be a distinct feature of U1A and U2B'' proteins and therefore probably important for specificity: With the exception of U2B'', the similarity in amino acid sequence with other RNP proteins does not extend beyond residue 87 (11).

Interdomain Interactions in Multidomain Proteins

Many RNP proteins contain multiple copies of the RNP domain (Figure 1). Poly(A) binding proteins contain four copies of the RNP domains and the amino acid sequence homology between the corresponding domains of human and yeast proteins is higher than that between the domains within the protein from a given species (16). Because the amino acid sequences of the linkers between the RNP domains are also conserved, each domain and linker must have retained a distinct function during evolution. It is likely that RNP domains within a given protein have a distinct geometric relationship that is critical for RNA binding. However, multiple domains are not always required for RNA binding. The second RNP domains of U1A and U2B'' proteins apparently fail to bind RNA (64), while the two C-terminal RNP domains of poly(A) binding protein are dispensable for poly(A) binding (81). Because the domain structure of these proteins is highly conserved across species, it is likely that these RNP domains are involved in functions other than RNA binding.

The crystal structure of a fragment of hnRNP A1 protein containing its two RNP domains, determined independently by two groups (101, 130), revealed how tandemly arranged RNP domains interact with each other (Figure 6b). The regions between Pro7 and Arg92 and between Gly99 and Ser182 fold independently into domains similar to the RNP domain of U1A; six residues between Glu93 and Gly98 are poorly ordered in the crystal, consistent with the sensitivity of this linker region to proteases. The two RNP domains interact through an antiparallel arrangement of helices B from each domain; as a result, the four-stranded antiparallel β-sheets are on the same side of the protein, forming a large exposed surface for RNA recognition.

The domain interface buries 840 Å^2 of protein surface and is stabilized by water-mediated hydrogen bonds and two salt-bridges between Arg74 and Asp156 and between Arg87 and Asp154 [note: residue numbering differs between (101) and (130)]. The conservation of the residues involved in the interdomain salt-bridges within the hnRNP protein A/B family and the effect of salt on its function suggest that the interdomain interactions seen in the crystal play important roles in RNA binding and in the formation of A1/B2 protein tetramers. However, there must be alternative ways to arrange multiple RNP domains: Not all four RNP domains of poly(A) binding protein can interact with each other in the way seen in the hnRNP A1 protein crystal.

The conservation of key amino acid residues between the two RNP domains and UV cross-linking experiments show that both RNP domains of hnRNP A1 interact directly with RNA. Phe17 and Phe59 of the first RNP domain and Phe108 and Phe150 of the second RNP domain can be UV-cross-linked to $d(T)_8$ (71). Phe17 and Phe108 correspond to Tyr13, while Phe 59 and Phe150 correspond to Phe5 of U1A protein, respectively. Tyr13 and Phe56 stacks onto C10 and A11 of hairpin II of U1 snRNA, respectively (84), and Tyr13 can be cross-linked with iodo-U at position 10 of hairpin II RNA in which C10 is substituted with iodo-U (106) [note: different numbering for RNA residues is used in (106)]. The Phe residues of hnRNP A1 protein cross-linked to $d(T)_8$ are likely to stack with the bases. The third conserved aromatic residues of the RNA consensus sequence in hnRNP A1 protein, Phe56 and Phe147, were not cross-linked to RNA. Gln54, the corresponding residue in U1A, forms a hydrogen bond with Tyr13 and plays an important role in determining the orientation of Tyr13. Phe56 and Phe147 do not cross-link with RNA and may also play a role in orienting the other Phe side chains for optimal base stacking. The structures suggest various ways in which RNA can interact with hnRNP A1 (101, 130). When four nucleotides of hairpin II of U1 snRNA are overlaid onto the two RNP domains of hnRNP A1 protein, a sequence of 4 to 5 nucleotides is necessary to link the 5′ end of one RNA to the 3′ end of the other RNA. A sequence longer than 12 nucleotides would be necessary to bind to the two RNP domains simultaneously.

RNP-RNA RECOGNITION

The diversity of biological functions associated with RNP proteins requires the RNP motif to recognize a disparate range of RNA structures and sequences with diverse affinity and specificity. In some cases, RNP proteins bind RNA very tightly [$K_d \gg 10^{-9}$ or less (40, 61)] and with exquisite specificity (e.g. U1A or U1 70K) to form stable ribonucleoprotein particles. In other cases (e.g. many hnRNP proteins) binding to RNA is much weaker ($K_d \sim 10^{-6}$ M) and the proteins discriminate poorly between different RNAs. A weak direct interaction between an RNP protein and RNA does not necessarily imply lack of a specific intracellular target for that protein; specificity can be provided by multiple weak protein-protein interactions, often mediated by auxiliary domains. Generalized low-affinity binding may also accelerate binding to high-affinity sites (14). The diversity of RNA structures recognized by RNP proteins is an outstanding feature of RNA recognition that stands in sharp contrast with

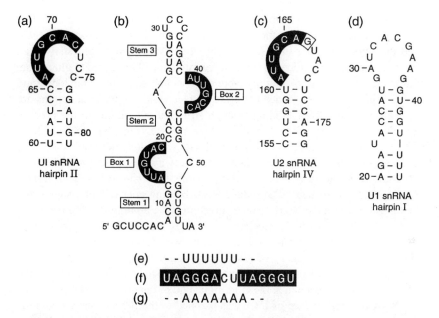

Figure 7 RNP proteins recognize RNAs widely divergent in structure. U1A protein recognizes hairpin (*a*) and internal loop (*b*) sites on different RNAs; U2B'' (*c*) and U170K (*d*) also bind hairpin structures; many RNP proteins [e.g. hnRNP C (*e*), hnRNP A1 (*f*), and Pab1p (*g*)] bind single-stranded RNAs with diverse sequences.

DNA recognition and with the conservation of the structure of the domain itself (Figure 7). (*a*) U1A and U1 70K bind hairpin structures, stem loop II (93) and stem loop I (87) within U1 snRNA, respectively; (*b*) U1A also binds an internal loop (120); (*c*) *Sxl* binds tightly and fairly specifically a single-stranded pyrimidine-rich sequence with strong homology to the polypyrimidine tract found upstream of the branch point in many pre-mRNAs (51); (*d*) hnRNP C recognizes a consensus U-rich single-stranded sequence with strong homology to polypyrimidine tracts (33). However, there is no example of recognition of purely double-stranded RNA by an RNP protein. Investigators must understand the molecular determinants of the affinity and specificity of RNP proteins.

RNA Recognition Occurs on the β-Sheet Surface

Extensive biochemical experiments have been carried out to investigate how RNP domains interact with RNA. Direct involvement of RNP1 and RNP2 motifs in RNA binding was predicted from their high sequence conservation, and the first experimental evidence for the direct interaction between the RNP consensus sequence and nucleic acid ligands was obtained by UV cross-linking experiment of hnRNP A1 protein with $d(T)_8$ (71). The crystal structure of U1A protein allowed the identification of surface residues likely to interact with RNA, and their possible roles in RNA binding were tested by mutagenesis. When lysine and arginine residues in U1A were systematically mutated to glutamine, mutations affecting RNA binding were mostly clustered around the loop1 and loop3 regions (50, 79). Since these are surface residues, these mutations are unlikely to affect RNA binding through structural alterations in the protein. The first residue of the RNP1 motif is either Arg or Lys in the majority of RNP domains, and a substitution of Arg52 with Gln was highly detrimental to RNA binding, although the Arg-Lys mutation has only a small effect (50). Mutation of residues on the surface of the β-sheet (Phe56, Gln54 in RNP1, or Tyr13, Asn15, and Asn16 in RNP2) reduce RNA binding considerably, suggesting that these residues are likely to be involved in RNA binding (50, 93, 106).

The conclusion of these biochemical studies that the β-sheet surface represents the primary site of RNA recognition was supported by several NMR studies. When NMR spectra of RNA-bound and uncomplexed hnRNP C were compared, changes were observed predominantly for residues located on the surface of the β-sheet and at the C-terminal end of the domain (34). Similarly, the RNA binding surface of U1A was mapped to the β-sheet surface and the C-terminal extension of the domain (46), and extensive NMR spectral changes were also observed on the β-sheet surface for the complex between the second RNP domain of *Sxl* and a U-rich oligonucleotide (51). The RNA binding surface mapped by NMR for U1A was in good agreement with the mutagenesis experiments (50) and supported a model based on mutagenesis data as well as chemical protection experiments carried out to map regions of RNA that are in contact with U1A. The backbone phosphate groups of free hairpin II RNA were uniformly ethylated by ethylnitrosourea, whereas the phosphate backbone of the 5' stem strand and the 3' region of the loop were protected from ethylation in the complex (50). Although the protrusion of loop3 of U1A through the RNA loop was not predicted, the conclusion that the major groove side of the loop interacts with the surface of the β-sheet and the 5' strand of the stem faces the loop1 and loop3 regions of the protein was proved correct by the crystal structure of the complex (84).

One of the most intriguing conclusions of the biochemical and NMR studies was the involvement of regions beyond the RNP domain in RNA recognition. U1A protein constructs comprising the entire domain but without the C-terminal tail (residues 1–91) fail to bind U1 snRNA effectively (50, 92, 94). Progressive shortening of the tail reduces binding: A truncation at residue 95 binds ~50-fold less well than the fully active protein, while truncation at residue 93 binds approximately 400-fold less well (133). The N- and C-terminal extensions of the domain are often important not only for high-affinity binding, but also to determine the specificity of RNP-RNA recognition. A fragment of hnRNP C containing the entire RNP domain but without the C-terminal addition failed to discriminate between oligonucleotides selected for high-affinity binding and oligonucleotides that did not contain specific target sequences. The ability to discriminate was restored when a region of 10 amino acids immediately C-terminal to the domain was added to the construct (33). Disruption of the structure of the C-terminus of U1A (for example by mutating Thr11) eliminates the ability to discriminate between nucleotides within the target RNA sequence (133).

Structure of the U1A-Hairpin Complex

The complexes of human U1A with stem-loop II of U1 snRNA and with an internal loop regulatory element within the 3'-UTR of the mRNA coding for U1A itself have come to represent paradigms to understand RNA recognition by RNP proteins. A fragment of U1A protein containing residues 2 to 98 was crystallized with a 21-nucleotide RNA (Figure 8b) representing hairpin II of U1 snRNA; this crystal structure, determined at 1.9 Å resolution, revealed the stereochemical basis of RNP-RNA recognition (84). The 10-nucleotide loop of the RNA binds to the surface of the β-sheet as an open structure and loop3 of U1A protrudes through the RNA loop (Figure 8a). The bases of the first seven loop nucleotides, AUUGCAC, lie in the groove formed by the C-terminal region and loop3 of the protein, but the last three nucleotides of the loop extend into solution and are much less ordered. As predicted (50), the major groove side of the RNA loop and the 5' strand of the stem are in contact with the protein. Arg52 from the RNP1 sequence forms hydrogen bonds with the loop-closing G·C base pair and with the first base of the loop, A6. Base stacking interactions and the helical geometry of the phosphate backbone continue to the first two single-stranded nucleotides, A6 and U7. U8 is packed against the side chain of Gln54 and the base of G9 stacks on the base of U8.

A similar interaction was observed between a Glu side chain and an RNA base in the complex of elongation factor Tu with tRNA (82). The base of C10 stacks on the aromatic side chain of Tyr13 (Figure 8c), and continuous stacking interactions are observed between the side chain of Phe56, the bases of A11 and C12, and the side chain of Asp92 (Figure 8d). Stacking interactions dominate the energetics of RNA folding, and all bases of the AUUGCAC sequence stack onto either an adjacent base, protein side chain, or both. The seven unpaired bases form an intricate network of direct and water-mediated hydrogen bonds with protein side chains and with main chain carbonyl and amide groups, satisfying nearly all hydrogen bonding donors and acceptors on the RNA bases. The majority of intermolecular contacts observed in the stem-loop II complex are to RNA bases, while the MS2 hairpin, which binds its cognate protein as a

(a)

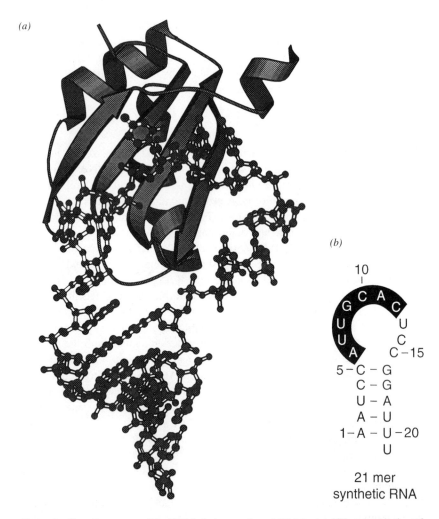

(b)

Figure 8   Crystal structure of the U1A-hairpin complex.   (*a*) Molscript (59) representation of the structure of the complex; (*b*) sequence of the hairpin RNA used for crystallization; (*c*) stacking interaction between C10 and Tyr13; (*d*) stacking of Phe56, A11, C12, and Asp92 (84, by permission).

(c)

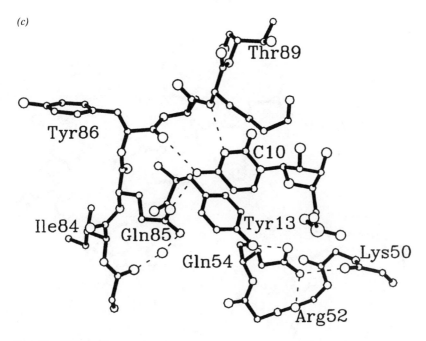

Figure 8   (Continued)

relatively rigid structure, is predominantly recognized through contacts to the phosphodiester backbone (119). The hydrogen bonding network extends into the loop3 region, which becomes more ordered upon RNA binding. Helix C lies on the surface of the β-sheet in the free protein but rotates away like a cat-flap from the β-sheet surface to extend along the β2 strand upon RNA binding (3). The hydrophobic interactions between Ile93, Ile94, Met97, Leu44, Phe56, and Ile58 in free protein (7) are replaced by the hydrophobic interactions between Ile93, Ile94, Leu41, Val62 and His10, and a hydrogen bond between Thr11 and Ser91. The repositioning of helix C buries this hydrophobic patch, exposes the surface of the β-sheet for recognition, and presents the loop connecting β4 and helix C to the RNA (3, 7). The side chains of Lys20 and Lys22 extend towards the phosphate backbone of the stem, and the RNA phosphodiester backbone generally follows the positive electrostatic potential along the protein surface.

Intermolecular interactions involving the surface of the β-sheet and the seven common single-stranded nucleotides are very similar between the crystal structure of the U1A hairpin complex and the NMR structure of the internal loop complex (4). In this common region, differences between solution and crystal structures are most likely due to intrinsically greater flexibility in solution and

(d)

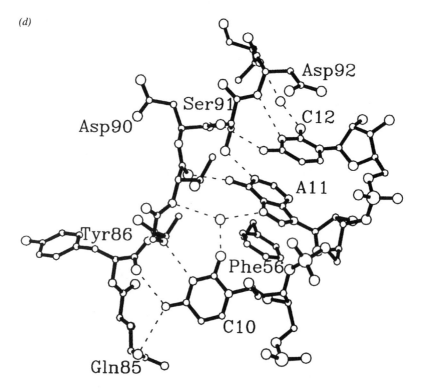

Figure 8   *(Continued)*

to difficulties in detecting by NMR bound water molecules, which mediate several interactions in the crystal structure. However, significant differences are observed in interactions between the variable loops of the domain (loop1 and loop3) and the RNA, owing to the presence of an extra stem in the internal loop RNA. Electrostatic interactions from Arg47, Lys23, and Lys96 side chains to the RNA phosphates in the internal loop complex appear to be analogous to the interactions of loop1 observed in the hairpin complex. The most significant differences are observed for loop3 residues, which appear to be involved in many more intermolecular interactions in the internal loop structure. These differences are most likely due to the fact that U13, C14, and C15 in stem-loop II are poorly ordered in the hairpin complex, but roughly corresponding nucleotides are highly ordered and interact directly with loop3 residues in the internal loop complex.

The importance of the identity of the single-stranded nucleotides involved in intermolecular contacts in the crystal structure was emphasized by in vitro selection experiments (116). The AUUGCAC sequence, found in hairpin II of U1 snRNA and in one of the internal loops of the polyadenylation inhibition element, was selected in the first seven positions of the loop, but all four bases were almost equally represented in the last three positions of the loop. The seven nucleotides in the loop are involved in extensive interactions with the protein, whereas the bases of the last three nucleotides are not in contact with the protein in the crystal structure (84). These last three loop nucleotides can even be substituted with ethylene glycol linkers of various length without altering binding significantly, although deletion of the last three loop nucleotides progressively reduces the binding constant (126).

The integrity of the double helical stem is another important element of recognition: Mutation of the Watson-Crick pairs to abolish the double helical region reduces binding very severely. The structures suggest several roles for the double helical stem in protein binding (78): (a) It restricts the conformation of the RNA loop to reduce entropy losses upon complex formation; (b) it provides the terminal G·C base pair recognized by Arg52; and (c) it provides electrostatic interactions between exposed basic side chains and the phosphodiester backbone (4, 84).

Intermolecular stacking interactions involving three highly conserved heteroaromatic amino acids from RNP-1 and RNP-2 are a distinctive feature of U1A-RNA recognition, probably common to all RNP-RNA complexes. Although rare in protein complexes with double-stranded DNA, planar stacking interactions have been observed in complexes of nucleic acids with aspartyl (23) and lysyl tRNA synthetases (27), single-stranded DNA-binding proteins (12, 100), proteins that recognize the methylated guanosine cap of eukaryotic mRNAs (44, 67, 68), and in the MS2 bacteriophage coat protein complex with the operator RNA hairpin (119). In aspartyl- and lysyl-tRNA synthetase complexes, U35 in the anticodon loop stacks onto Phe-127 and Phe-71, respectively, and forms base-specific hydrogen bonds with the synthetases. In the MS2 coat-protein–RNA complex, the C at position −5 stacks onto Tyr85 and forms a hydrogen bond with Asn87. Stacking interactions between aromatic side chain and RNA bases restrict the conformation of the RNA bases (3, 35) and facilitate the formation of base-specific hydrogen bonds, making a significant contribution to the binding energy. Replacement of these aromatic residues in the MS2 coat protein, U1A protein, and hnRNP A1 protein significantly reduces the RNA affinity, although it is not easy to estimate the relative contributions of stacking, hydrogen bonding, and conformational entropy accurately (50, 62, 106).

Stacking interactions can contribute to the specificity of binding as well, as illustrated by the cap complexes (44, 67, 68). Because RNA bases differ in their electronic structure, stacking energies are likely to differ between nucleotides. Stacking interactions are also important in the U1A complex to define the packing of RNA and protein side chains at the RNA-protein interface: A mutation of Gln54 to Tyr or Phe (the residues generally found at that position of RNP-2 in other RNP proteins) causes a very large reduction in affinity because a larger side chain cannot be accommodated.

The U1A-RNA structures have revealed many aspects of RNP-RNA recognition but have also raised intriguing questions concerning the molecular origin of the ability of these proteins to discriminate between substrates. The observation of so many hydrogen bonds and van der Waals contacts between single-stranded RNA nucleotides and protein residues would seem to imply that recognition of unpaired bases determines the specificity of RNP protein. However, several single-stranded nucleotides can be mutated with small effects in binding energy, despite their involvement in extensive intermolecular interactions. Although the recognition of the identity of RNA base functionalities exposed in single-stranded loops is an important element of molecular discrimination, other elements of the RNA structure/sequence must be critical as well. One way to look at RNP-RNA complexes is to consider that the U1A complexes produce buried interfaces that resemble the interior of a protein (3, 4, 84). As observed in studies of protein stability, the intermolecular interface may readily adjust to mitigate the effects of potentially deleterious substitutions. Thus, although the sequence of the single-stranded nucleotides provides optimal intermolecular contacts and is therefore well conserved, some mutations are well tolerated. In contrast, inclusion of bulky amino acid side chains at the intermolecular interface (50), extensive disruption of Watson-Crick pairing in the helical stems, or changes in the size of the single-stranded loop (39, 116) reduce binding substantially. Because different RNA targets vary enormously in their overall structural features, it is likely that the overall three-dimensional shape and charge distribution of different RNA substrates are critical features of discrimination.

Modulation of RNA Recognition by Protein-Protein Interactions

Many RNP proteins bind RNA without needing protein cofactors. However, modulation of RNA recognition by protein-protein interactions is an essential aspect of RNP protein function. The best-understood example of modulation of RNA recognition by protein-protein interactions is provided by U2B" protein, a component of U2 snRNP, the ribonucleoprotein complex that recognizes the branch point within pre-mRNAs. The architectures of U1A and U2B" proteins are very similar, both containing RNP domains at their N and C termini connected by long, flexible linkers. The N- and C-terminal RNP domains of U2B" proteins are nearly identical in sequence to the corresponding domains of U1A protein, but the sequence of the linker region has diverged substantially. U1A protein binds to hairpin II of U1 snRNA on its own, while U2B″ protein binds to hairpin IV of U2 snRNA only when it is complexed with U2A′ protein (9, 92). U2A′ contains five copies of a Leu-rich repeat motif found in over 100 proteins, many of which interact with other proteins. The first protein structure in the Leu-rich repeat family to be solved was porcine ribonuclease inhibitor (56). This protein contains 16 copies of the Leu-rich repeat, each forming a β strand and α helix, and the conserved leucine residues point to the inside to form the protein hydrophobic core. The protein forms a horseshoe-shaped solenoid with inner circumference made up of a parallel β-sheet and the outer circumference composed of α helices.

A fragment of U2B″ protein corresponding to the minimal RNA-binding fragment of U1A protein (residues 2 to 98) retains the abilities to bind both U2A′ protein and RNA (92). There are only 25 amino acid replacements between U1A and U2B″ proteins within this region, and the two RNA hairpin targets share the same seven nucleotides that are the primary site of U1A-RNA recognition (84), yet these two proteins bind specifically only their cognate RNA hairpins. A variety of chimeric constructs of these two proteins were compared to identify residues that stabilize the interactions between U2B″ and U2A′ proteins or that allow discrimination between hairpin II of U1 snRNA and hairpin IV of U2 snRNA (9, 92). Two mutations, Lys28-Arg, Asp24-Glu, are sufficient to allow U1A protein to bind U2A′ protein. The LVSRSL sequence on loop 2 of U1A is replaced by the VALKTM sequence in U2B″. These six consecutive amino acid replacements as well as the Glu19-Asp and Met17-Leu replacements are important to discriminate between the two RNAs (92, 94). U2A′ protein increases the affinity for hairpin IV of U2 snRNA and reduces the affinity for hairpin II of U1 snRNA. A U1A protein phage display library in which the nine residues (39 to 41 and 44 to 49) were randomly chosen from either U1A or U2B″ sequences was constructed, and clones that bind hairpin II of U1 snRNA tightly were selected (61). Ser46 and Leu49 were found to be important for binding of U1 RNA hairpin II. The crystal structure of a ternary complex of U2B″ and U2A′ proteins bound to a fragment of hairpin IV of U2 snRNA was recently determined (S Price, P Evans, and K Nagai, manuscript in preparation); this structure accounts for the RNA-binding specificity of the U2B″/U2A′ protein complex. The switch in RNA-binding specificity is achieved by a small number of amino acid residues in key positions that induce the formation of an alternative hydrogen bond network and by the interaction between the RNA stem and U2A′ protein.

Conformational Adaptation in RNP-RNA Recognition

A further level of complexity in RNP-RNA interaction is provided by the extensive conformational changes observed in both protein and RNA components in the U1A complexes (Figure 9; 3, 7, 35). Structural rearrangements have been observed for all RNA complexes with proteins and peptides for which structural data exist for both free and bound components, suggesting that it is a general feature of RNA recognition. RNA-protein recognition is clearly a dynamic event: RNA structure defines distinct protein binding surfaces, which are then reorganized upon interaction to optimize surface complementarity and functional group recognition. This flexibility of RNA structure has been exploited by proteins that regulate the activity of RNA enzymes (21, 124, 125). An intriguing question yet to be addressed is to what extent these conformational changes are sequence-sensitive.

The major difference between the free and bound U1A protein structures is in the position of helix C (Figure 9a), spanning residues 92 to 98 in both free and bound forms. In the free structure, helix C points towards loop3 and covers part of the β-sheet surface directly involved in RNA binding (7). In the complex, helix C is instead directed away from the β-sheet surface and the RNA. Residues immediately preceding helix C (88–92) are involved in extensive interactions with three single-stranded nucleotides, but almost all intermolecular contacts from this region of the protein involve main-chain functionalities. Although residues from helix C do not contact RNA directly, mutations of some of the amino acids involved in positioning helix C (for example Thr11 to Val) reduce RNA binding significantly (50). The formation of helix C and its positioning in the complex through hydrophobic interactions with the rest of the domain are likely to be specific to U1A and U2B''. A second mechanism by which helix C may contribute to molecular discrimination is related to its position in the free protein. Since helix C lies across the surface of the β-sheet and covers a large part of the RNA-binding surface, interactions between U1A and noncognate RNAs may provide insufficient energy to drive the conformational change in the protein, thereby reducing the affinity for noncognate RNAs.

The RNA substrates also differ significantly in structure and degree of order between free and bound states (Figure 9b). Five of seven single-stranded nucleotides from the internal loop complex are highly flexible in the free RNA but are much more highly ordered in the complex (35). Distinct changes between free and bound RNA are also observed in the pattern of base-stacking interactions. Protein binding essentially opens up the RNA loop: In the free RNA, the A39, U40, U41, A44, C45, and A24 bases are oriented toward the inside of the loop, filling the cavity created by the sugar-phosphate backbone of G23-G25 and C38-C46; only G42 and C43 are solvent-exposed (35). The space in the cavity occupied by U41, A44, and C45 in the free RNA is filled instead in the complex by protein residues from loop3, while the bases of A24, A39, U40, U41, A44, and C45 are directed towards the protein.

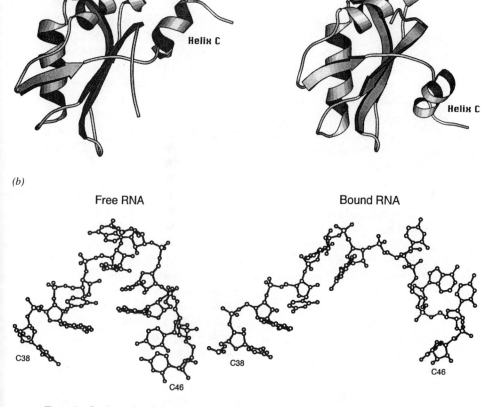

(a)

(b)

Figure 9 Conformational adaptation in RNP-RNA recognition. Binding of U1A to the polyadenylation inhibition element requires a conformational change at the C-terminal end of the protein domain (3, 7). Free protein (*right*, in *a*) [Molscript representation (59)] reorders the structure of the RNA single-stranded nucleotides (*b*) (3, 35).

Interdomain Interactions Are Critical for Recognition in Multidomain Proteins

In proteins containing multiple RNP domains, two or more domains are often required for specific RNA recognition (15, 51, 97, 98, 104, 107, 108, 132). In such cases, multiple domains define RNA binding cooperatively and function together as a single RNA-binding unit. Interactions between domains may fix the domains in the spatial orientation required to achieve efficient substrate binding (101, 130).

When multiple RNP domains are present, the affinity is not simply the product of the affinity of individual proteins and the specificity of the intact protein is generally different from that of individual domains. For example, the specificity of functional two-domain constructs of hnRNP A1 (15) and of several SR proteins (107, 108) is different from that of individual domains derived from the same protein. Although individual domains retain general RNA-binding activity (98, 108, 135), biologically active two-domain constructs bind RNA much more tightly and with different specificity (15, 18, 24, 108, 135). In many cases, these effects are due to interdomain interactions that contribute to cooperativity. However, even if multiple domains were binding RNA in a completely independent manner, the energies of binding would not simply add up. The affinity of a protein containing two identical domains separated by an infinitely long and flexible linker would simply be twice the affinity of each individual domain, while domains separated by shorter, more rigid linkers contribute various amounts to the cooperativity of binding (99). Thus, even without direct RNA-linker contacts or the linker defining the relative position of two domains, the length and rigidity of the linker region is an important determinant of the affinity of multidomain RNP proteins.

In many cases where multiple domains cooperatively contribute to define the specificity of RNP proteins, the linker region between RNP domains is highly conserved phylogenetically, suggesting that domain spacing is critical for proper binding geometry. For example, the loop connecting the first and second RNP domain of poly(A) binding proteins contains 13 amino acids that are absolutely conserved from yeast to humans (16). However, the linker sequence is not always important: It can be deleted in ASF/SF2 without loss of function (135). A majority of proteins that bind RNA through multiple domains recognize single-stranded RNA. However, the preribosomal RNA-binding protein nucleolin (97) and the SR proteins *Drosophila* B52 (104) and human SRp40 (107) recognize stem-loop structures through two contiguous RNP domains.

The function of multidomain proteins as a single RNA-binding unit has clear physiological significance. *Sxl* binds specifically to the polypyrimidine tract of the regulated 3′-splice site of the *tra* pre-mRNA. This interaction disrupts recognition of the polypyrimidine tract by the essential splicing factor U2AF, which is necessary to recruit U2 snRNP to the branch site during spliceosome assembly (118). Both RNP domains of *Sxl* are required for specific RNA binding to sequences that are very similar to regulated polypyrimidine tracts: Individual domains do not discriminate between wild-type and mutant polypyrimidine tracts (51). Intact *Sxl* binds a wild-type polypyrimidine tract approximately 700-fold more tightly than a mutated PPT, but individual RNP domains of *Sxl* bind mutant RNAs indistinguishably from wild-type sequences. Similarly, the contiguous pair of the two N-terminal RNP domains of poly(A) binding protein confers specificity for poly(A) (16, 81), and these two domains are also necessary and sufficient for one of the primary functions of this protein, stimulation of translational initiation (112, 113).

CONCLUSIONS AND FUTURE DIRECTIONS

Proteins containing RNP domains play crucial roles in all aspects of the post-transcriptional regulation of gene expression. The biological function of RNP proteins resides in their dual ability to interact with RNA as well as with other proteins, often through auxiliary domains present in many of these proteins. When general sequence elements provide primary regulatory signals, protein-RNA recognition cannot provide specificity for a given pre-mRNA, and regulation depends on multiple weak interactions, allowing for combinatorial control of RNA-processing events. On the other hand, RNP domains allow very effective recognition of signals that are unique to certain mRNAs or subset of mRNAs, and allow the assembly of regulatory multiprotein complexes to occur only on such mRNAs.

The attention of the biochemical community has so far been focused on RNA recognition: A variety of biochemical and genetic studies and the first structures of RNP-RNA complexes have begun to clarify how the RNP domain functions as a ubiquitous RNA-binding element. The diversity of biological functions associated with RNP proteins requires the RNP domain to bind many different RNA structures and sequences. The diversity of RNA substrates of RNP proteins is an outstanding feature of RNP-RNA recognition, which stands in sharp contrast with the conservation of the structure of the domain itself. It is far less clear how RNP proteins interact with other proteins. Specific protein-protein interactions between RNA-bound activators or repressors and components of the general RNA processing machinery facilitate the formation of productive RNA processing complexes. In many cases, interactions of RNP proteins with other proteins are even more important than direct RNA-protein interactions in defining the substrate specificity of components of the RNA-processing machinery. The recently completed structure of the ternary U2A'-U2B''–RNA complex (S Price, P Evans, and K Nagai, manuscript in preparation) provides a first insight into this new example of biomolecular recognition. It is likely that the focus of biochemical and structural investigations will settle much more on RNA-dependent protein-protein interactions in the future.

ACKNOWLEDGMENTS

It is a pleasure to thank Drs. Phil Evans and Chris Oubridge for critical reading of the manuscript.

Literature Cited

1. Abdul-Manam N, O'Malley SM, Williams KR. 1996. Origins of the binding specificity of the A1 heterogeneous ribonucleoprotein. *Biochemistry* 35:3545–54

2. Adam SA, Nakagawa T, Swanson MS, Woodruff TK, Dreyfuss G. 1986. mRNA polyadenylate-binding protein: gene isolation and sequencing and identification of a ribonucleoprotein consensus sequence. *Mol. Cell. Biol.* 6:2932–43

3. Allain FH-T, Gubser CC, Howe PWA, Nagai K, Neuhaus D, Varani G. 1996. Specificity of ribonucleoprotein interaction determined by RNA folding during complex formation. *Nature* 380:646–50

4. Allain FH-T, Howe PWA, Neuhaus D, Varani G. 1997. Structural basis of the RNA binding specificity of human U1A protein. *EMBO J.* 16:5764–74

5. Amrani N, Minet M, Le Gouar M, Lacroute F, Wyers F. 1997. Yeast Pab1 interacts with RNA15 and participates in the control of the poly(A) tail length in vitro. *Mol. Cell. Biol.* 17:3694–3701

6. Amrein H, Hedley ML, Maniatis T. 1994. The role of specific protein-RNA and protein-protein interactions in positive and negative control of pre-mRNA splicing by *Transformer 2*. *Cell* 76:735–46

7. Avis J, Allain FH-T, Howe PWA, Varani G, Neuhaus D, Nagai K. 1996. Solution structure of the N-terminal RNP domain of U1A protein: the role of C-terminal residues in structure stability and RNA binding. *J. Mol. Biol.* 257:398–411

8. Beelman CA, Parker R. 1995. Degradation of mRNA in eukaryotes. *Cell* 81:179–83

9. Bentley RC, Keene JD. 1991. Recognition of U1 and U2 small nuclear RNAs can be altered by a 5-amino-acid segment in the U2 small nuclear ribonucleoprotein particle (snRNP) B" protein and through interactions with U2 snRNP-A' protein. *Mol. Cell. Biol.* 11:1829–39

10. Biamonti G, Riva S. 1994. New insights into the auxiliary domains of eukaryotic RNA binding proteins. *FEBS Lett.* 340:1–8

11. Birney E, Kumar S, Krainer AR. 1993. Analysis of the RNA-recognition motif and RS and RGG domains: conservation in metazoan pre-mRNA splicing factors. *Nucleic Acids Res.* 21:5803–16

12. Bochkarev A, Pfuetzner RA, Edwards AM, Frappier L. 1997. Structure of the single-stranded-DNA-binding domain of replication protein A bound to DNA. *Nature* 385:176–81

13. Boelens WC, Jansen EJR, van Venrooij WJ, Stripecke R, Mattaj IW, Gunderson SI. 1993. The human U1 snRNP-specific U1A protein inhibits polyadenylation of its own pre-mRNA. *Cell* 72:881–92

14. Burd CG, Dreyfuss G. 1994. Conserved structures and diversity of functions of RNA-binding proteins. *Science* 265:615–21

15. Burd CG, Dreyfuss G. 1994. RNA binding specificity of hnRNP A1: significance of hnRNP A1 high-affinity binding sites in pre-mRNA splicing. *EMBO J.* 13:1197–1204

16. Burd CG, Matunis EL, Dreyfuss G. 1991. The multiple RNA-binding domains of the mRNA poly(A)-binding protein have different RNA-binding activities. *Mol. Cell. Biol.* 11:3419–24

17. Bycroft M, Grünert S, Murzin AG, Proctor M, St Johnston D. 1995. NMR solution structure of a dsRNA binding domain from *Drosophila* staufen protein reveals homology to the N-terminal domain of ribosomal protein S5. *EMBO J.* 14:3563–71

18. Cáceres JF, Krainer AR. 1993. Functional analysis of pre-mRNA splicing factor ASF/SF2 structural domains. *EMBO J.* 12:4715–26

19. Cáceres JF, Stamm S, Helfman DM, Krainer AR. 1994. Regulation of alternative splicing in vivo by overexpression of antagonistic splicing factors. *Science* 265:1706–9

20. Caponigro G, Parker R. 1995. Multiple functions for the poly(A)-binding protein in mRNA decapping and deadenylation in yeast. *Genes Dev.* 9:2421–32

21. Caprara MG, Mohr G, Lambowitz AM. 1996. A tyrosyl-tRNA synthetase protein induces tertiary folding of the group I intron catalytic core. *J. Mol. Biol.* 257:512–31

22. Cartegni L, Maconi M, Morandi E, Cobianchi F, Riva S, Biamonti G. 1996.

hnRNP A1 selectively interacts through its Gly-rich domain with different RNA-binding proteins. *J. Mol. Biol.* 259:337–48

23. Cavarelli J, Rees B, Ruff M, Thierry J-C, Moras D. 1993. Yeast tRNA^{Asp} recognition by its cognate class II aminoacyl-tRNA synthetase. *Nature* 362:181–84

24. Chandler SD, Mayeda A, Yeakley JM, Krainer AR, Fu X-D. 1997. RNA splicing specificity determined by the coordinated action of RNA recognition motifs in SR proteins. *Proc. Natl. Acad. Sci. USA* 94:3596–3601

25. Cobianchi F, Karpel RL, Williams KR, Notario V, Wilson SH. 1988. Mammalian heterogeneous nuclear ribonucleoprotein A1: large-scale overproduction in *Escherichia coli* and cooperative binding to single-stranded nucleic acids. *J. Biol. Chem.* 263:1063–71

26. Colwill K, Pawson T, Andrews B, Prasad J, Manley JL, et al. 1996. The Clk/Sty protein kinase phosphorylates SR splicing factors and regulates their intranuclear distribution. *EMBO J.* 15:265–75

27. Cusack S, Yaremchuk A, Tukalo M. 1996. The crystal structures of *T. thermophylus* lysyl-tRNA synthetase complexed with *E. coli* tRNA^{Lys} and a *T. thermophylus* tRNA^{Lys} transcript: anticodon recognition and conformational changes upon binding of a lysyl-adenylate analogue. *EMBO J.* 15:6321–34

28. Dreyfuss G, Matunis MJ, Piñol-Roma S, Burd CG. 1993. hnRNP and the Biogenesis of mRNA. *Annu. Rev. Biochem.* 62:289–321

29. Fu X-D. 1993. Specific commitment of different pre-mRNAs to splicing by single SR proteins. *Nature* 365:82–85

30. Fu X-D. 1995. The superfamily of arginine/serine-rich splicing factors. *RNA* 1:663–80

31. Garrett DS, Lodi PJ, Shamoo Y, Williams KR, Clore GM, Gronenborn AM. 1994. Determination of the secondary structure and folding topology of an RNA binding domain of mammalian hnRNP A1 protein using three-dimensional heteronuclear magnetic resonance spectroscopy. *Biochemistry* 33:2852–58

32. Ghetti A, Padovani C, Di Cesare G, Morandi C. 1989. Secondary structure prediction for RNA binding domain in RNP proteins identifies $\beta\alpha\beta$ as the main structural motif. *FEBS Lett.* 257:373–76

33. Görlach M, Burd CG, Dreyfuss G. 1994. The determinants of RNA-binding specificity of the heterogeneous nuclear

ribonucleoprotein C proteins. *J. Biol. Chem.* 269:23074–78

34. Görlach M, Wittekind M, Beckman RA, Mueller L, Dreyfuss G. 1992. Interaction of the RNA-binding domain of the hnRNP C proteins with RNA. *EMBO J.* 11:3289–95

35. Gubser CC, Varani G. 1996. Structure of the polyadenylation regulatory element of the human U1A pre-mRNA 3′-untranslated region and interaction with the U1A protein. *Biochemistry* 35:2253–67

36. Gui J-F, Lane WS, Fu X-D. 1994. A serine kinase regulates intracellular localization of splicing factors in the cell cycle. *Nature* 369:678–82

37. Gunderson SI, Beyer K, Martin G, Keller W, Boelens WC, Mattaj IW. 1994. The human U1A snRNP protein regulates polyadenylation via a direct interaction with poly(A) polymerase. *Cell* 76:531–41

38. Gunderson SI, Vagner S, Polycarpou-Schwarz M, Mattaj IW. 1997. Involvement of the carboxy terminus of vertebrate poly(A) polymerase in U1A autoregulation and in the coupling of splicing and polyadenylation. *Genes Dev.* 11:761–73

39. Hall KB. 1994. Interaction of RNA hairpins with the human U1A N-terminal RNA binding domain. *Biochemistry* 33:10076–88

40. Hall KB, Stump WT. 1992. Interaction of N-terminal domain of U1A protein with an RNA stem-loop. *Nucleic Acids Res.* 20:4283–90

41. Headly ML, Maniatis T. 1991. Sex-specific splicing and polyadenylation of dsx pre mRNA requires a sequence that binds specifically to tra–2 protein in vitro. *Cell* 65:579–86

42. Heinrichs V, Baker BS. 1995. The *drosophila* SR protein RBP1 contributes to the regulation of doublesex alternative splicing by recognizing RBP1 RNA target sequences. *EMBO J.* 14:3987–4000

43. Hileren PJ, Kao H-Y, Siciliano PG. 1995. The amino terminal domain of yeast U1–70K is necessary and sufficient for function. *Mol. Cell. Biol.* 15:6341–50

44. Hodel AE, Gershon PD, Shi X, Wang S-M, Quiocho FA. 1997. Specific protein recognition of an mRNA cap through its alkylated base. *Nat. Struct. Biol.* 4:350–54

45. Hoffman DW, Query CC, Golden BL, White SW, Keene JD. 1991. RNA-binding domain of the A protein component of the U1 small nuclear ribonucleopro-

tein analyzed by NMR spectroscopy is structurally similar to ribosomal proteins. *Proc. Natl. Acad. Sci. USA* 83:2495–99

46. Howe PWA, Nagai K, Neuhaus D, Varani G. 1994. NMR studies of U1 snRNA recognition by the N-terminal RNP domain of the human U1A protein. *EMBO J.* 13:3873–81

47. Inoue K, Hoshijima K, Sakamoto H, Shimura Y. 1990. Binding of the *Drosophila* sex-lethal gene to the alternative splice site of the transformer primary transcript. *Nature* 344:461–63

48. Izaurralde E, Mattaj IW. 1995. RNA export. *Cell* 81:153–59

49. Jandrositz A, Guthrie C. 1995. Evidence for a Prp24 binding site in the U6 snRNA and in a putative intermediate in the annealing of U6 and U4 snRNAs. *EMBO J.* 14:820–32

50. Jessen TH, Oubridge C, Teo CH, Pritchard C, Nagai K. 1991. Identification of molecular contacts between the U1A small nuclear ribonucleoprotein and U1 RNA. *EMBO J.* 10:3447–56

51. Kanaar R, Lee AL, Rudner DZ, Wemmer DE, Rio DC. 1995. Interaction of the sex-lethal RNA binding domains with RNA. *EMBO J.* 14:4530–39

52. Kanaar R, Roche SE, Beall EL, Green MR, Rio DC. 1993. The conserved pre-mRNA splicing factor U2AF from *Drosophila*: requirements for viability. *Science* 262:569–73

53. Kanopka A, Mühlemann O, Akusjäevi G. 1996. Inhibition by SR proteins of splicing of a regulated adenovirus pre-mRNA. *Nature* 381:535–38

54. Kenan DJ, Query CC, Keene JD. 1991. RNA recognition: towards identifying determinants of specificity. *TIBS* 16:214–20

55. Kharrat A, Macias MJ, Gibson TJ, Nilges M, Pastore A. 1995. Structure of the dsRNA binding domain of *E. coli* RNAse III. *EMBO J.* 14:3572–84

56. Kobe B, Deisenhofer J. 1993. Crystal structure of porcine ribonuclease inhibitor, a protein with leucine-rich repeats. *Nature* 366:751–56

57. Kohtz JD, Jamison SF, Will CL, Zuo P, Lührmann R, et al. 1994. Protein-protein interactions and 5′-splice-site recognition in mammalian mRNA precursors. *Nature* 368:119–24

58. Krämer A. 1996. The structure and function of proteins involved in mammalian pre-mRNA splicing. *Annu. Rev. Biochem.* 65:367–409

59. Kraulis PJ. 1991. MOLSCRIPT: a program to produce both detailed and schematic plots of protein structures. *J. Appl. Crystallogr.* 24:946–50

60. Kühn U, Pieler T. 1996. *Xenopus* poly(A) binding protein: functional domains in RNA binding and protein-protein interactions. *J. Mol. Biol.* 256:20–30

61. Laird-Offinga IA, Belasco JG. 1995. Analysis of RNA-binding proteins by in vitro genetic selection: identification of an amino acid residue important for locking U1A onto its RNA target. *Proc. Natl. Acad. Sci. USA* 92:11859–63

62. LeCuyer KA, Behlen LS, Uhlenbeck OC. 1996. Mutagenesis of a stacking contact in the MS2 coat protein-RNA complex. *EMBO J.* 15:6847–53

63. Lee AL, Kanaar R, Rio DC, Wemmer DE. 1994. Resonance assignments and solution structure of the second RNA-binding domain of sex-lethal determined by multidimensional heteronuclear magnetic resonance. *Biochemistry* 33:13775–86

64. Lu J, Hall KB. 1995. An RBD that does not bind RNA: NMR secondary structure determination and biochemical properties of the C-terminal RNA binding domain from the human U1A protein. *J. Mol. Biol.* 247:739–52

65. Manley JL. 1995. A complex protein assembly catalyzes polyadenylation of mRNA precursors. *Curr. Op. Gen. Develop.* 5:222–28

66. Manley JL, Tacke R. 1996. SR proteins and splicing control. *Genes Dev.* 10:1569–79

67. Marcotrigiano J, Gingras A-C, Sonenberg N, Burley SK. 1997. Cocrystal structure of the messenger RNA 5′ cap-binding protein (eIF–4E) bound to 7-methyl-GDP. *Cell* 89:951–61

68. Matsuo H, Li H, McGuire AM, Fletcher CM, Gingrass A-C, et al. 1997. Translational initiation factor eIF–4e: solution structure and interactions with mRNA cap and 4E-BP. *Nat. Struct. Biol.* 4:717–24

69. Mattaj IW. 1993. RNA recognition: a family matter? *Cell* 73:837–40

70. Mayeda A, Munroe SH, Cáceres JF, Krainer AR. 1994. Function of conserved domains of hnRNP A1 and other hnRNP A/B proteins. *EMBO J.* 13:5483–95

71. Merrill BM, Stone KL, Cobianchi F, Wilson SH, Williams KR. 1988. Phenylalanines that are conserved among several RNA-binding proteins form part of a nucleic-acid binding pocket in the A1 heterogeneous nuclear ribonucleoprotein. *J. Biol. Chem.* 263:3307–13

72. Méthot N, Pickett G, Keene JD, Sonenberg N. 1996. In vitro RNA selection identifies RNA ligands that specifically bind

to eukaryotic translation initiation factor 4B: the role of the RNA recognition motif. *RNA* 2:38–50

73. Michael WM, Choi M, Dreyfuss G. 1995. A nuclear export signal in hn-RNP A1: a signal-mediated, temperature-dependent nuclear protein export pathway. *Cell* 83:415–22

74. Minvielle-Sebastia L, Preker PJ, Wiederkher T, Strahm Y, Keller W. 1997. The major yeast poly(A)-binding protein is associated with cleavage factor IA and functions in premessenger RNA 3′-end formation. *Proc. Natl. Acad. Sci. USA* 94: 7897–7902

75. Misteli T, Cáceres JF, Spector DL. 1997. The dynamics of a pre-mRNA splicing factor in living cells. *Nature* 387:523–27

76. Misteli T, Spector DL. 1997. Protein phosphorylation and the nuclear organization of pre-mRNA splicing. *TICB* 7: 135–38

77. Musco G, Stier G, Joseph C, Castiglione Morelli MA, Nilges M, et al. 1996. Three-dimensional structure and stability of the KH domain: molecular insight into the fragile X syndrome. *Cell* 85:237–45

78. Nagai K, Oubridge C, Ito N, Avis J, Evans P. 1995. The RNP domain: a sequence-specific RNA-binding domain involved in processing and transport of RNA. *TIBS* 20:235–40

79. Nagai K, Oubridge C, Jessen TH, Li J, Evans PR. 1990. Structure of the RNA-binding domain of the U1 small nuclear ribonucleoprotein A. *Nature* 348:515–20

80. Nelissen RLH, Will CL, van Venrooij WJ, Lührmann R. 1994. The association of the U1-specific 70K and C proteins with U1 snRNPs is mediated in part by common U snRNP proteins. *EMBO J.* 13:4113–25

81. Nietfeld W, Mentzel H, Pieler T. 1990. The *Xenopus laevis* poly(A) binding protein is composed of multiple functionally independent RNA binding domains. *EMBO J.* 9:3699–3705

82. Nilsen P, Kjeldgaard M, Thirup S, Polekhina G, Reshetnikova L, et al. 1995. Crystal structure of the ternary complex of the phe-tRNA^{Phe}, EF-TU and a GTP analog. *Science* 270:1464–72

83. Orengo CA, Thornton JM. 1993. Alpha plus beta folds revisited: some favoured motifs. *Structure* 1:105–20

84. Oubridge C, Ito N, Evans PR, Teo C-H, Nagai K. 1994. Crystal structure at 1.92 Å resolution of the RNA-binding domain of the U1A spliceosomal protein complexed with an RNA hairpin. *Nature* 372:432–38

85. Potashkin J, Naik K, Wentz-Hunter K.

1993. U2AF homolog required for splicing in vivo. *Science* 262:573–75

86. Predki PF, Nayak LM, Gottlieb MBC, Regan L. 1995. Dissecting RNA-protein interactions: RNA-RNA recognition by Rop. *Cell* 80:41–50

87. Query CC, Bentley RC, Keene JD. 1989. A common RNA recognition motif identified within a defined U1 RNA binding domain of the 70K U1 snRNP protein. *Cell* 57:89–101

88. Rossi F, Labourier E, Forné T, Divita G, Derancourt J, et al. 1996. Specific phosphorylation of SR proteins by mammalian DNA topoisomerase I. *Nature* 381:80–82

89. Sachs AB, Davis RW, Kornberg RD. 1987. A single domain of yeast poly(A) binding protein is necessary and sufficient for RNA binding and cell viability. *Mol. Cell. Biol.* 7:3268–76

90. Sachs AB, Kornberg RD. 1986. A single gene from yeast for both nuclear and cytoplasmic polyadenylate binding proteins: domain structure and expression. *Cell* 45:827–35

91. Sachs AB, Sarnow P, Hentze MW. 1997. Starting at the beginning, middle and end: translation initiation in eukaryotes. *Cell* 89:831–38

92. Scherly D, Boelens W, Dathan NA, van Venrooij WJ, Mattaj I. 1990. Major determinants of the specificity of interaction between small nuclear ribonucleoproteins U1A and U2B″ and their cognate RNAs. *Nature* 345:502–6

93. Scherly D, Boelens W, van Venrooij WJ, Dathan NA, Hamm J, Mattaj IW. 1989. Identification of the RNA binding segment of human U1A protein and definition of its binding site on U1 snRNA. *EMBO J.* 8:4163–70

94. Scherly D, Kambach C, Boelens W, van Venrooij WJ, Mattaj IW. 1991. Conserved amino acid residues within and outside of the N-terminal ribonucleoprotein involved in U1 RNA binding. *J. Mol. Biol.* 219:577–84

95. Schindelin H, Marahiel MA, Heinemann U. 1993. Universal nucleic acid binding domain revealed by crystal structure of the *B. subtilis* major cold-shock protein. *Nature* 364:164–68

96. Schnuchel A, Wiltscheck R, Czisch M, Herrier M, Willimsky G, et al. 1993. Structure in solution of the major cold-shock protein from *Bacillus subtilis*. *Nature* 364:169–71

97. Serin G, Joseph G, Ghisolfi L, Bauzan M, Erard M, et al. 1997. Two RNA-binding domains determine the RNA binding

specificity of nucleolin. *J. Biol. Chem.* 272:13109–16

98. Shamoo Y, Abdul-Manam N, Patten AM, Crawford JK, Pellegrini MC, Williams KR. 1994. Both RNA-binding domains in heterogeneous nuclear ribonucleoprotein A1 contribute toward single-stranded-RNA binding. *Biochemistry* 33:8272–81

99. Shamoo Y, Abdul-Manan N, Williams KR. 1995. Multiple RNA binding domains (RBDs) just don't add up. *Nucleic Acids Res.* 23:725–28

100. Shamoo Y, Friedman AM, Parsons MR, Konigsberg WH, Steitz TA. 1995. Crystal structure of a replication fork single-stranded DNA binding protein (T4 gp32) complexed to DNA. *Nature* 376:362–66

101. Shamoo Y, Krueger U, Rice LM, Williams KR, Steitz TA. 1997. Crystal structure of the two RNA binding domains of human hnRNP A1 at 1.75 Å resolution. *Nat. Struct. Biol.* 4:215–22

102. Shannon KW, Guthrie C. 1991. Suppressors of a U4 snRNA mutation define a novel U6 snRNP protein with RNA-binding motifs. *Genes Dev.* 5:773–85

103. Sharp PA. 1994. Split genes and RNA splicing. *Cell* 77:805–15

104. Shi H, Hoffman BE, Lis JT. 1997. A specific RNA hairpin loop structure binds the RNA recognition motifs of the *Drosophila* SR protein B52. *Mol. Cell. Biol.* 17:2649–57

105. Singh R, Valcarél J, Green MR. 1995. Distinct binding specificities and functions of higher eukaryotes polypyrimidine tract-binding proteins. *Science* 268:1173–76

106. Stump WT, Hall KB. 1995. Crosslinking of an iodo-uridine-RNA hairpin to a single site on the human U1A N-terminal RNA binding domain. *RNA* 1:55–63

107. Tacke R, Chen Y, Manley JL. 1997. Sequence-specific RNA binding by an SR protein requires RS domain phosphorylation: creation of an SRp40-specific splicing enhancer. *Proc. Natl. Acad. Sci. USA* 94:1148–53

108. Tacke R, Manley JL. 1995. The human splicing factors ASF/SF2 and Sc35 possess distinct, functionally significant RNA binding specificities. *EMBO J.* 14:3540–51

109. Takagaki Y, MacDonald CC, Shenk T, Manley JL. 1992. The human 64-kDa polyadenylation factor contains a ribonucleoprotein-type RNA binding domain and unusual auxiliary motifs. *Proc. Natl. Acad. Sci. USA* 89:1403–7

110. Takagaki Y, Manley JL. 1997. RNA recognition by the human polyadenyla-

tion factor CstF. *Mol. Cell. Biol.* 17:3907–14

111. Tarun SZ Jr, Sachs AB. 1995. A common function for mRNA 5' and 3' ends in translational initiation in yeast. *Genes Dev.* 9:2997–3007

112. Tarun SZ, Wells SE, Deardorff JA, Sachs AB. 1997. Translation initiation factor eIF–4G mediates poly(A) tail dependent translation initiation. *Proc. Natl. Acad. Sci. USA* 94:9046–51

113. Tarun SZJ, Sachs AB. 1996. Association of the yeast poly(A) tail binding protein with translation initiation factor eIF–4G. *EMBO J.* 15:7168–77

114. Tian M, Maniatis T. 1993. A splicing enhancer complex controls alternative splicing of doublesex pre-mRNA. *Cell* 74:105–14

115. Tronchére H, Wang J, Fu X-D. 1997. A protein related to splicing factor U2AF[35] that interacts with U2AF[65] and SR proteins in splicing of pre-mRNA. *Nature* 388:397–400

116. Tsai DE, Harper DS, Keene JD. 1991. U1-snRNP-A protein selects a ten-nucleotide consensus sequence from a degenerate RNA pool presented in various structural contexts. *Nucleic Acids Res.* 19:4931–36

117. Valcárel J, Green MR. 1996. The SR protein family: pleiotropic functions in pre-mRNA splicing. *TIBS* 21:296–301

118. Valcárel J, Singh R, Zamore PD, Green MR. 1993. The protein sex-lethal antagonizes the splicing factor U2AF to regulate alternative splicing of transformer pre-mRNA. *Nature* 362:171–75

119. Valegárd K, Murray JB, Stockley PG, Stonehouse NJ, Liljas L. 1994. Crystal structure of an RNA bacteriophage coat protein-operator complex. *Nature* 371:623–26

120. van Gelder CWG, Gunderson SI, Jansen EJR, Boelens WC, Polycarpou-Schwartz M, et al. 1993. A complex secondary structure in U1A pre-mRNA that binds two molecules of U1A protein is required for regulation of polyadenylation. *EMBO J.* 12:5191–5200

121. Wahle E, Keller W. 1996. The biochemistry of polyadenylation. *TIBS* 21:247–50

122. Wang J, Manley JL. 1995. Overexpression of the SR proteins ASF/SF2 and Sc35 influences alternative splicing in vivo in diverse ways. *RNA* 1:335–46

123. Wang J, Takagaki Y, Manley JL. 1996. Targeted disruption of an essential vertebrate gene: ASF/SF2 is required for cell viability. *Genes Dev.* 10:2588–99

124. Weeks KM, Cech TR. 1995. Protein facilitation of group I intron splicing by assembly of the catalytic core and the 5' splice site domain. *Cell* 82:221–30

125. Weeks KM, Cech TR. 1996. Assembly of a ribonucleoprotein catalyst by tertiary structure capture. *Science* 271:345–48

126. Williams DJ, Hall KB. 1996. RNA hairpins with non-nucleoside spacers bind efficiently to the human U1A protein. *J. Mol. Biol.* 257:265–75

127. Wittekind M, Görlach M, Friedrichs M, Dreyfuss G, Mueller L. 1992. 1H, 13C, and 15N NMR assignments and global folding pattern of the RNA-binding domain of the human hnRNP C proteins. *Biochemistry* 31:6254–65

128. Wu JY, Maniatis T. 1993. Specific interactions between proteins implicated in splice site selection and regulated alternative splicing. *Cell* 75:1061–70

129. Xiao S-H, Manley JL. 1997. Phosphorylation of the ASF/SF2 RS domain affects both protein-protein and protein-RNA interactions and is necessary for splicing. *Genes Dev.* 11:334–44

130. Xu R-M, Jokhan L, Cheng X, Mayeda A, Krainer AR. 1997. Crystal structure of human UP1, the domain of hnRNP A1 that contains two RNA-recognition motifs. *Structure* 5:559–70

131. Yeakley JM, Morfin J-P, Rosenfeld MG, Fu X-D. 1996. A complex of nuclear proteins mediate SR proteins binding to a purine-rich splicing enhancer. *Proc. Natl. Acad. Sci. USA* 93:7582–87

132. Zamore PD, Patton JG, Green MR. 1992. Cloning and domain structure of the mammalian splicing factor U2AF. *Nature* 355:609–14

133. Zeng Q, Hall KB. 1997. Contribution of the C-terminal tail of U1A RBD1 to RNA recognition and protein stability. *RNA* 3:303–14

134. Zuo P, Maniatis T. 1996. The splicing factor U2AF^{35} mediates critical protein-protein interactions in constitutive and enhancer-dependent splicing. *Genes Dev.* 10:1356–68

135. Zuo P, Manley JL. 1993. Functional domains of the human splicing factor ASF/SF2. *EMBO J.* 12:4727–37

136. Zuo P, Manley JL. 1994. The human splicing factor ASF/SF2 can specifically recognize pre-mRNA 5' splice sites. *Proc. Natl. Acad. Sci. USA* 91:3363–67

Annu. Rev. Biophys. Biomol. Struct. 1998. 27:447–74
Copyright © 1998 by Annual Reviews. All rights reserved

ON THE CHARACTERISTICS OF FUNCTIONAL MAGNETIC RESONANCE IMAGING OF THE BRAIN

S. Ogawa

Biological Computation Research, Bell Laboratories, Lucent Technologies, Murray Hill, New Jersey 07974; e-mail: so@physics.bell-labs.com

R. S. Menon

Laboratory for Functional Magnetic Resonance Research, The John P. Robarts Research Institute, London, Ontario, Canada N6A 5K8;
e-mail: rmenon@irus.rri.uwo.ca

S.-G. Kim and K. Ugurbil

Center for Magnetic Resonance Research, Department of Radiology, University of Minnesota Medical School, Minneapolis, Minnesota 55455;
e-mail: kim@geronimo.drad.umn.edu; kamil@geronimo.drad.umn.edu

KEY WORDS: functional activation, hemodynamics, metabolic load, BOLD, perfusion

ABSTRACT

In this review we discuss various recent topics that characterize functional magnetic resonance imaging (fMRI). These topics include a brief description of MRI image acquisition, how to cope with noise or signal fluctuation, the basis of fMRI signal changes, and the relation of MRI signal to neuronal events. Several observations of fMRI that show good correlation to the neurofunction are referred to. Temporal characteristics of fMRI signals and examples of how the feature of real time measurement is utilized are then described. The question of spatial resolution of fMRI, which must be dictated by the vascular structure serving the functional system, is discussed based on various fMRI observations. Finally, the advantage of fMRI mapping is shown in a few examples. Reviewing the vast number of recent fMRI application that have now been reported is beyond the scope of this article.

447

1056-8700/98/0610-0447$08.00

CONTENTS

INTRODUCTION

In the years since its introduction in 1992 (4, 58, 75), functional magnetic resonance imaging (fMRI) of the human brain has been well received as a noninvasive modality for studying human brain function and has rapidly become probably the widest-used method in investigating human brain function. The method is based on MRI signal changes due to hemodynamic and metabolic responses at the sites of neuronal activation induced by external and internal stimuli to the brain. Using this methodology, it is possible to construct whole brain activation maps for sensory and mental functions with high spatial resolution.

The most important role of fMRI in investigating human brain function arises from the fact that brain function is spatially segmented and compartmentalized. This functional specialization can be defined and mapped by fMRI utilizing secondary hemodynamic and metabolic responses to alterations in neuronal activity; in this sense, it is similar to positron emission tomography (PET) (78) where the most common approach for detecting brain activation is to measure regional cerebral blood flow (rCBF) by O^{15} water injection (97). An important additional feature of fMRI is its capability to follow signal changes in real time, even though the temporal (67) as well as spatial resolution (69) of fMRI is dictated by the characteristics of the hemodynamic response. While the time-constants of electrical activity of neuronal systems are shorter than some hundreds of msec, the hemodynamic response time is characterized by several seconds. Modalities such as EEG (electroencephalography) and MEG (magnetic encephalography) that can measure electrical and magnetic responses of the brain to evoking stimuli, on the other hand, encounter difficulties in accurately locating the sites of activation. Although the response time is on the order of seconds, fMRI can still take advantage of real-time data acquisition and follow the time course of the signal change associated with mental activity that can evolve over seconds for particular cognitive tasks or specially designed paradigms. This is difficult to achieve in PET experiments.

Another modality of studying brain function—optical measurements of so-called "intrinsic signals" in visible wave length (63) to near infrared regions (50, 62, 96)—is also based on the hemodynamic and the metabolic responses. The chromophore monitored in these studies is mostly hemoglobin and the signal characteristics are very similar to those of fMRI.

The emergence of fMRI methodology is fundamentally based on the fortuitous presence of an endogenous contrast agent, paramagnetic deoxyhemoglobin, circulating in the brain and the tight coupling between neuronal activation and hemodynamic/metabolic responses. In addition, however, the rapidly developing MRI technology, largely driven by clinical applications and needs, has been a crucial factor that has made fMRI possible. This noninvasive technology has evolved to a point where relatively small regional signal changes can be detected and imaged over the whole brain with high reliability in localizing the sites of signal changes, and thus the sites of increased neuronal activity. There are already several published articles reviewing this rapidly growing field (17, 25, 55, 85). In this article, we discuss topics that characterize this modality and we focus mainly on our experiences.

METHOD

In fMRI, a large number of images—tens to several hundreds—are measured consecutively in a single experiment lasting anywhere from a few minutes to a quarter of an hour. The collected data are a time series of signal intensity from small volume elements or "voxels" covering regions of interest or the whole brain. During the data acquisition period, inputs for brain activation are presented to the subject in the magnet at appropriate periods. The input can be sensory stimulation, sensory input–guided cognitive tasks, subject-initiated mental activity, or even spontaneous brain activity the subject may not be aware of. Images taken during the absence of these inputs are used as a control. Image signals responding to the input are then compared with the control image signal (3).

It is preferable to image the whole brain simultaneously so that all the relevant activation patterns can be captured at once. Therefore, ultrafast imaging techniques, which may require extra MRI hardware, are indispensable. With echoplanar imaging (EPI) (89) or spiral k-space scan imaging (65), the magnetization induced from a slice in the brain by a single excitation can be measured at 64×64 2-D complex datapoints in as short as 30 msec to produce one image. In this acquisition time, the brain is virtually standing still. Within a few seconds, the whole brain area can be covered and the same image acquisition sequence is repeated until the desired time series data are collected. Progress has been made to deal with some difficulties such as image distortion and signal losses in areas with severe phase dispersion (especially at high magnetic fields) in these fast imaging methods (43, 47, 103). Because there is a limit in the available time to measure the magnetization in the single-shot acquisition owing to the T_2^* signal decay, the in-plane spatial resolution is limited to a few mm. For higher spatial resolution, image acquisition is segmented to cover larger numbers of k-space data points in separate spin excitations. The FLASH (fast low-angle shot) imaging method, much slower in imaging, can acquire higher resolution fMRI images (31) at the expense of time.

Signal changes in fMRI are small and are typically only 1-to-several percent of the average image signal intensity. The signal change is larger at higher static fields. In a well-controlled comparison of signal activation by visual simulation with FLASH measurements at three field strengths, the fractional signal change in cortical gray matter was found to increase as 1.6 power of the static field (36). Although the instrumental noise in modern MRI instruments is getting below 1% peak-to-peak as measured in a phantom, the signal fluctuation in fMRI images of the brain is much larger. Even when head-motion is minimized by restraining the head, there are signal fluctuations of physiological origin. Cardiac and respiratory motions are the most notable ones. Even with fast imaging, the interimage signal fluctuation is substantial and induces signal alterations that exceed a few percent. When physiological signals are collected concurrently during MRI measurements, some retrospective signal correction can remove the signal fluctuation (44) to a useful degree. When MRI image acquisition is carried out faster, so that the Nyquist frequency is higher than the heart rate and therefore the respiration rate, the physiological fluctuations can be visualized in the power spectrum of the time series data (7, 70, 98). Such physiological oscillations present in the time series can be filtered out by postprocessing (5, 7, 70).

In the postprocessing of MRI data to extract functionally relevant signals, averaging over adjacent voxels with activated signals and also averaging in time are implicitly performed in various statistical analyses to generate activation maps (3, 33, 90, 101). All activation maps represent signal changes above a threshold. How to select this threshold in the statistical analysis is controversial, considering that the noise in MRI data is obviously not white as mentioned above. One way to improve confidence in selecting the threshold is to make the same experiment without the input task and to select the threshold on the basis of the dry run (70).

Choosing appropriate paradigms for fMRI experiments is probably the most important part of the experiment. Here, neuroscientists, neurologists, and psychologists play crucial roles, because it is important to clarify which elementary neural substrates are involved in a given task. Although the MRI environment is not so friendly and there are limitations in implementing some tasks, one advantage of fMRI is that a few tasks in a paradigm can be nested with the control state and can easily be modified. An example where this feature was fully utilized is the mapping of the visual system in the human brain, where the input stimulus was varied in the visual field (space) with time continuously to activate the corresponding visual areas (26, 83).

FMRI SIGNAL

MRI Signal Response to Brain Function

Any direct effect of the electrical activity of neurons on water proton MRI has not been observed. There are extracranial magnetic fields generated by some concerted neuronal activities in localized areas of the brain. They are detected and used for functional studies by MEG. However, their magnetic effect at the site of the activity appears very small for water spins to sense and has eluded detection by MRI.

When there are moving water spins, they can be detected by MRI. The major part of the moving spins detected in the brain arise from blood water flowing in arteries and veins (angiography). Recently, however, blood-water perfusion in the capillary bed has been imaged to yield maps of rCBF and rCBF alteration coupled to functional activation. Water diffusion in the brain tissue has been measured to study the brain cell swelling in cases such as stroke (95) and spreading depression (61). If there is appreciable water movement into or out of brain cells associated with functional activation, some change in the apparent water diffusion constant could be expected. This effect seems to have been detected, but for some reason the response time is very slow in minutes (106).

In optical experiments, changes in light reflection or scattering by brain activation have been reported (38, 63) as a fast-response phenomenon associated with neuronal activation. There have been no reports of detectable MRI changes related to these phenomena except a small but fast decaying signal in functional MR spectroscopy of water (42).

Because deoxyhemoglobin in red blood cells is paramagnetic, there are susceptibility-induced field variations in and around blood vessels, and water spins sense the local field distortion. The hemodynamic and metabolic changes associated with brain functional activation influence the deoxyhemoglobin content in the tissue, and the induced signal change in MRI can represent the functional activation. This deoxyhemoglobin effect has been called the blood oxygenation level dependent (BOLD) effect (73).

Regional hemodynamics and metabolic load are tightly coupled to the regional neuroactivation and therefore BOLD as well as perfusion measurements are the main part of fMRI. The MRI signal of an image voxel is a sum of the water signals from components such as tissue, blood, or bulk cerebrospinal fluid (CSF), and has T_1^* dependent (flow sensitive) and T_2^* dependent parts as expressed in Equation 1 for one component (labeled as x).

$$S_x = v_x \cdot S_{0x}(T_{1x}^*) \cdot A_x(T_{2x}^*) \cdot \exp(i\phi_x) \tag{1}$$

where v_x is the volume fraction of the component and A is the attenuation factor due to the T_2^* decay $(1/T_2^* = R_2^*)$ during the echo time (t_e) of the signal acquisition $[\sim \exp(-t_e/T_2^*)]$. As a part of $1/T_2^*$ signal decay, the blood susceptibility effect contributes to the $1/T_2^*$ decay and $A = A_0 \cdot A_{sus}$. The residual phase ϕ_x of the signal, if any, mostly comes from a small off-resonance frequency of the component, including the field shift by red cells with deoxyhemoglobin. Signal changes occur when these relaxation parameters follow the hemodynamic and metabolic changes.

The total signal S is a sum of the contribution from the component S_x, $S = \Sigma S_x$. In usual fMRI analysis, the fractional signal change from control state is taken as a difference in the signal magnitude, $\Delta S/|S| = \Delta|S|/|S|$, instead of the phased difference $\Delta S/|S| = \Sigma \Delta S_x/|S|$ due to the phase instability of the signal which tends to increase noise more in the latter value. When the residual phases, ϕ_x's, are small, the two values of signal changes are essentially the same. When a vein occupies a large portion of an image voxel, the phase ϕ differs from the nearby voxels with tissue only. This has been used to generate a high-resolution venogram image (16, 60).

Inflow Effect and Perfusion

When signal acquisition is performed rapidly to cause T_1 saturation of the water signal (S_{0x} term in Equation 1 is reduced from 1), the extent of saturation is less in blood water because the fresh blood-water spins flow in from the neighboring region outside of the RF excitation. Thus, the relaxation rate is no longer determined by $1/T_1$ but by a faster rate defined as $1/T_1^*$, which contains the flow effect. This $1/T_1^*$ by flow is further enhanced by functional activation, especially at larger vessels where the flow velocity is high. Most of the signal activation with the inflow effect occurs in veins but not in arteries. In the latter, the flow is so fast (tens of cm/sec) that all blood-water content is replaced within the RF repetition. When a large vein shows activation by the inflow effect, it gets the fresh blood water from the neighboring area and not from the area in the observing image slice. This means that the corresponding neuroactivation sites are fairly away from the vein. Strategies in signal acquisition to avoid or to increase the inflow effect have been discussed in various papers (32, 35, 55, 56).

Recently, it has become possible to make quantitative measurements of the above inflow signal to capillary beds where blood water perfuses through the tissue. The change in the perfusion signal by functional activation is an rCBF change and an important element of fMRI. Many methods aiming to make perfusion measurements use spin-tagging, by preinversion or presaturation of either inflowing spins (21, 23, 99) or the spins in the zone of observation (52, 58); in both cases, spins coming into the area of observation are then examined by comparing to data obtained with no tagging (52). The simplest and probably cleanest among these methods is the flow-sensitive alternating-inversion-recovery (FAIR) method (52, 53, 59). Here, spins in the observing slice are first inverted (local inversion), and after a period of about $T_1(1 \sim 2 \text{ sec})$ during which uninverted fresh blood water spins flow into the slice, sampling pulses are given to get the slice image. As a control to the local inversion recovery imaging, a global inversion of spins is made. In this case, the flow-in spins do not have any distinction from the local spins and take the same inversion recovery course as the latter. From the difference of the two cases, one can estimate the amount of blood flow into the voxel during the period of the "incubation." The inflow signal in capillary beds gets stronger, with an incubation time longer than the transit time of flowing blood from arterioles through capillaries to venules. The uninverted blood water spins following into the capillaries is not simply refilling the vascular space but exchanging with the tissue water (perfusion). The perfusion or the exchange of the water molecules between capillary and the surrounding tissue is a fast process (99) as compared with the "incubation" time of a second or two. When the blood flow gets very high, however, the exchange becomes incomplete (24, 99).

The estimated quantity from these perfusion measurements is essentially the CBF (ml of blood/gram of tissue/min) at each voxel in the image. Thus, these perfusion methods provide easily interpretable quantities for functional activation, namely the regional CBF change.

BOLD Effect

Blood water $1/T_2$ has been known to increase with blood deoxygenation because of the susceptibility effect from red cells (91). This susceptibility effect due to deoxyhemoglobin has also been observed in brain MR images (73). The enhancement of the apparent relaxation rate constant $1/T_2^*$ (in gradient echo images) occurs not only in the blood water but also in the tissue water around blood vessels. The BOLD effect changes with the physiological conditions of the brain under which the deoxyhemoglobin content varies (73). A temporal ischemic episode was followed by the $1/T_2^*$ change in time (94).

The signal attenuation, A_x in Equation 1, is caused by intravoxel dispersion of the signal phase ($\phi = \delta\omega \cdot t_e$) resulting from the local field ($\delta\omega$) induced by the red cell susceptibility. This is expressed by the voxel average of the water signal phase factor $\langle \exp(i\phi) \rangle_{\text{voxel}}$ in space and time (movement of water molecules).

The extent of this averaging, $\langle \exp(i\phi) \rangle_{voxel}$, differs among the water molecules in intra- and extravascular spaces of capillary and venule compartments as well as areas containing large veins (1, 8, 9, 28, 51, 74, 102). For the blood-water, the water exchange between red cells and plasma—where the susceptibility-induced fields differ—is an important process for the averaging (105). By spin echo data acquisition, the relaxation rate $1/T_2^*$ is smaller than the rate $1/T_2^*$ appears in gradient echo because of the refocusing effect of the phase inversion pulse in the former on the averaging. The susceptibility-dependent $1/T_2^*$ of the blood-water is much larger than that of the extravascular tissue-water, but the volume fraction v_b is small ($0.02 \sim 0.04$).

Song et al (88) showed that fMRI BOLD signals from the motor cortex during a finger-tapping task at 1.5 Tesla disappeared when a relatively small dipolar diffusion gradient (b-factor of 42 sec/mm^2) was applied during the signal acquisition. With this diffusion gradient, intravascular signals from non-capillary vessels with blood flow velocities of above several mm/sec would be dispersed out. This indicated that these fMRI signals were intra-vascular and mostly contributed by noncapillary vessels.

A further study at 1.5 Tesla (8) showed that two-thirds of fMRI signals in visual stimulation experiments were from moving spins and were lost with diffusion gradient of b $= 600$ sec/mm^2. These signals, acquired by asymmetric spin echo (165 msec echo time t_e for spin echo with 20 msec gradient echo contribution), were inside homogeneous gray matter regions without the presence of any obvious large vessels. At higher B_0 fields of 3 Tesla (87) and 4 Tesla, however, substantial fMRI signals in gradient echo acquisition persisted even with diffusion gradient of b $= 400$ sec/mm^2, showing that the extravascular contribution becomes more important at higher B_0 field.

When a voxel contains a large vein, the signal activation is very large (several to 20 percent). The signal change $\Delta S/S$ has contributions

$$\Delta(S_{0,blood} \cdot v_b \cdot A_{0,blood} \cdot A_{sus,blood})$$

from blood water as seen from Equation 1. It will be enhanced by a large blood volume fraction v_b in the voxel and high $S_{0,blood}$ resulting from inflow effect, if any. The anisotropic orientation dependence of the susceptibility effect is not averaged for a large vein. Therefore, $A_{sus,blood}$ itself can vary sharply with the oxygenation and similarly the extravascular contribution (72) also can be large.

In a venule compartment of gray matter, if a CBF increase of 60% raises the venous blood oxygenation Y from 0.6 to 0.75, the signal change contributed by the blood water, $\Delta(v_b \cdot A_{sus,blood})$, at 1.5 Tesla would be 0.8% with an echo time of 40 msec, taking the susceptibility dependent $1/T_2^*$ of the blood water at Y $= 0.7$ to be 11 sec^{-1} (8, 15). At higher B_0, the $1/T_2^*$ of the blood and also the sensitivity to the oxygenation increase, but the signal change does not necessarily become larger, because at the basal physiological condition $A_{sus,blood}$ itself is diminishing strongly with t_e (more attenuated blood water signal). At 4 Tesla with the same hemodynamic condition as above and $1/T_2^*$ of $31 \ sec^{-1}$, $\Delta(v_b \cdot A_{sus,blood})$ would be 0.7%. On the other hand, the extravascular contribution increases with B_0 field linearly or with a higher power up to 2.

The measurement of the BOLD effect is simple with gradient echo or spin echo imaging. However, the quantitative aspect of the signal change is not clear because it could be influenced by many unknown parameters of the vasculature and hemodynamics. The expression for the signal change appears to be not as simple as

$$\Delta S/S \sim \Delta(1/T_2^*) \cdot t_e \sim a \cdot t_e \cdot \Delta\{(1-Y) \cdot v_b\},$$

predicted some time ago (72). Efforts are being made to calibrate BOLD signals empirically in terms of measurable hemodynamic and vascular parameters, $\Delta S/S = func(Y, \Delta Y, v_b, \Delta v_b)$, by using a hypercapnia condition that allows investigators to vary CBF, and therefore cerebral blood volume (CBV) (40) and blood oxygenation without changing the oxygen consumption rate (2, 20, 82). Although there may be some difference in vascular responses between the conditions of functional activation and hypercapnia, the latter is so far the only approach easily accessible for this calibration. An empirical fit such as

$$\Delta S/S = a(\Delta Y) + b(\Delta v_b/v_b) + c(\Delta Y)(\Delta v_b/v_b)$$

or in other functional forms of these parameters (20) has to be found for the quantitative analysis of the BOLD effect.

Physiological Connection of fMRI Signal

Fick's principle for arteriovenous oxygen balance relates oxygen extraction (or oxygen consumption) to CBF and venous blood oxygenation level (Y), and the latter is a relevant parameter to determine BOLD signal changes. Under normoxic conditions,

$$(oe) = CBF \cdot C_h \cdot (1-Y),$$

where (oe) is the rate of oxygen extraction and C_h is the heme concentration in unit volume of blood. Oxygen extraction factor OEF (the fraction of oxygen extracted from arterial blood oxygen), an often used parameter, is

$$OEF = (oe)/(CBF \cdot C_h) = 1 - Y.$$

When there are changes in the metabolic load and hemodynamics, Equation 2 describes the changes in the above balance between the two steady states.

Assuming the hematocrit does not vary,

$$1 + \Delta(OEF)/OEF = (1 + \Delta(oe)/(oe))/(1 + \Delta CBF/CBF)$$

$$= 1 - (\Delta Y)/(1 - Y). \tag{2}$$

The knowledge of CBF increase and ΔY can lead to $\Delta(oe)$ estimate from the equation. If one can analyze the BOLD signal quantitatively to estimate ΔY, then CBF and BOLD measurements could lead to characterize the metabolic load associated with the functional neuroactivation (2, 20, 54).

If the hemodynamic response to neuronal activation proceeds without OEF change, $\Delta(OEF) = 0$, or $\Delta(oe)/(oe) = \Delta CBF/CBF$. With this complete coupling of $\Delta CBF/CBF$ to $\Delta(oe)/(oe)$, a BOLD signal will not show any appreciable positive increase in the presence of a CBF increase ($\Delta Y = 0$ and $\Delta v_b > 0$). With photic stimulation, $\Delta CBF/CBF$ ($\sim 50\%$) has been shown to far exceed $\Delta(oe)/(oe)$ ($\sim 5\%$) in the visual area in the human brain (29, 30). With these changes in Equation 2, then $\Delta(OEF)/(OEF) - (\Delta Y)/(1 - Y)$ is -0.3. At $Y \sim 0.6$ for the resting state, ΔY becomes 0.12 in this uncoupled hemodynamic change from the oxygen extraction change. Most fMRI (BOLD) signals observed in functional activation are positive and show very similar activation maps as CBF measurements by PET or perfusion measurements by MRI. The disparity of the CBF increase over (oe) increase is a common phenomenon in functional activation.

An early attempt to correlate BOLD and perfusion measurements with a visual stimulation paradigm is shown in Figure 1 (54). The two measurements (FAIR and BOLD) are alternately made in a time series of one experiment. The data are from a total of 29 measurements in 12 subjects and each point is a spatial average in the common ROI covering most of the primary visual cortical ribbon seen in a slice image. The average value of $\Delta CBF/CBF$ is 43%, consistent with previous PET measurements (30). There the points are scattered widely in CBF as well as BOLD signal percent changes even though the paradigm was the same for all subjects. There is a scant correlation that the CBF increase is accompanied with BOLD increase. One would argue that the comparison has to be made at a pixel-by-pixel level for the common activation sites in a single subject with a multitrial average to establish the quantitative relation between the two measurements.

Neuronal Activation and fMRI Signal

Although the quantitative aspect is still to be clarified, the BOLD signal has been shown to reflect neuronal events. The dependence of a BOLD response on the flashing frequency of red and black or black and white checkerboard stimulation is—as in the case of rCBF in the visual area—quite consistent with the known neuronal response to this stimulation (58). When the evoked

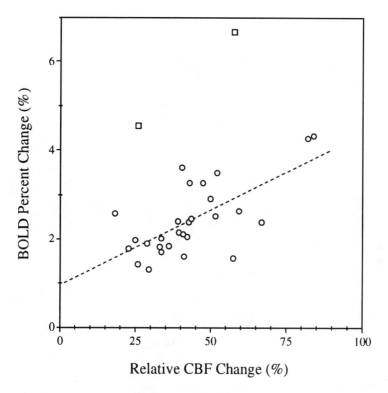

Figure 1 Relationship between BOLD and CBF changes during visual stimulation at a frequency of 8 Hz using goggles. BOLD with a gradient echo time of 30 msec and FAIR images were acquired at 4 Tesla in an alternative manner. A total of 29 measurements were performed in 12 subjects. The region of interest is the gray matter area in the primary visual cortex, chosen from anatomic images. To correlate CBF and BOLD changes, two points with the *square symbol* were not included. The best fitted line is that BOLD(%) = 0.028*CBF(%) + 1.3 (r2 = 0.26).

potential induced by electrical stimulation at the frontal paws is monitored by an intracranial electrode in the sensorimotor area in the rat brain, the electrical activity peaks at the stimulating frequency of 3 Hz and decreases above that frequency. The corresponding BOLD signal also shows quite similar frequency dependence, indicating it is reflecting the neuronal events very well (41).

Figure 2 shows a comparison of fMRI responses to a motor task in human subjects (79) with electrophysiological measurements in a trained monkey (L Shen, GE Alexander, private communication) having a very similar motor task paradigm. Using a visual input, the subject was instructed how to move his right hand fingers in a finger sequence and told to refrain from executing

(a)

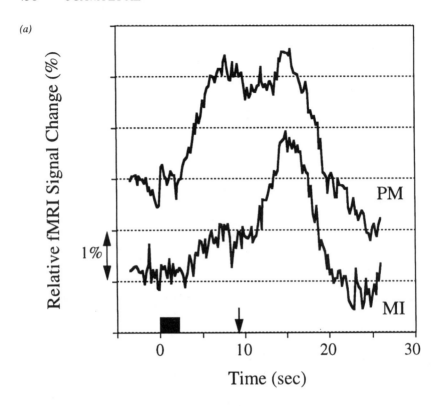

(b)

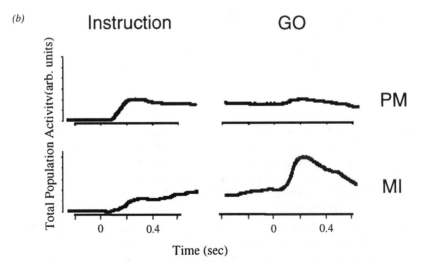

the task until a "GO" command appeared on the screen. The responses in the primary motor (M1) and premotor (PM) areas are shown in Figure 2a,b (80). In the M1 area, the signal increased slightly after visual instruction and much more after a GO cue in both human fMRI and monkey single-neuron recording studies. Further, in the PM, magnitudes of signal changes before and after the GO cue are similar in both studies. Although hemodynamic response is delayed and could be blurred, temporal patterns of fMRI and total population activity are extremely similar. The electrical activities in the plots (Figure 2b) are averages from single-electrode intracellular recordings at more than 100 of output neurons in each area and the activities occur as subsecond time scale events. It is interesting that the fMRI response pattern follows the population activity of the areas and not necessarily some peak activity of certain cells observable in the intracellular recording (L Shen, GE Alexander, private communication).

The aforedescribed observations support the validity of numerous BOLD-based functional maps of the human brain already acquired and indicate that these maps actually represent the sites of the brain activation of interest.

COUPLING OF HEMODYNAMICS AND METABOLISM TO NEURONAL EVENTS

Recently, Jueptner and Weiller (48) reviewed issues concerning the relationship of synaptic activity to rCBF and metabolic load. Most of relevant questions with respect to this problem can also be found in Raichle's earlier review (78). Many of these questions remain unanswered today.

Although the induced rCBF increase is a well recognized indicator for elevation of electrical activity, the mechanism of activation-related rCBF control is not yet established. There are many candidates for mediating the control, such as K^+, NO, adenosine, CO_2, direct electrical connection to vasculature, and so on. None of them has been shown to be the sole controlling factor, but several may be involved (100). It is not clear that CBF control is from the spike-generating neuronal cell bodies or from the neuropils (areas of synaptic

---

Figure 2 Dynamic BOLD-based fMRI signal changes in humans (*a*) and population activities in a trained monkey (*b*) during a delayed motor task. The primary motor area (*M1*) and premotor (*PM*) are shown. The task consists of instruction, delay, GO cue, and movements. Instruction is given visually for movements (shown as *box* in A; time = 0 at instruction in *a*), and subjects move after a GO cue (*arrow* in *a*; time = 0 at GO in *b*). The delay time between instruction and GO is 7 s for humans and 1.0–1.5 s for monkey studies, during which subjects are supposed not to move. In both studies, movements were monitored during performance of a task using electromyography. Because a delay time in *b* is randomized, averaging was performed to lock (time = 0) either the visual presentation (*left* time courses) or GO cue (*right*) (79, 84).

endings at dendrites) participating in the activation and consuming with oxidative metabolism most of the energy for the increased activity. In the high-resolution fMRI maps of whisker-barrel activation in the rat brain shown by Yang et al (104), the layer IV of the activated cortex appears as the major site of CBF increases. The layer in this cortical area is well vascularized and contains these barrels characterized by the high population of cytochrome oxidase (19). However, this does not necessarily indicate that the neuropil activity triggers the CBF increase. On the other hand, the intracellular recordings, from which Figure 2b is obtained, are from spiking neurons in the output-generating layer of the motor cortices. Because the temporal response patterns of the population activity in these neuronal cells and the fMRI are so much alike except in time scale (Figure 2a and 2b), they may suggest the possibility that the neuronal cells contributing to the population spiking have some role in triggering or sustaining the hemodynamic response.

The larger fractional CBF increase relative to the fractional oxygen consumption elevation with neuroactivation leads to the possibility that the elevated glucose use that occurs together with the increased CBF following heightened neuronal activity is quite anaerobic. Lactate production in visual areas during photic stimulation has been observed in fMR spectroscopy (77). Recently, a new scheme for the anaerobic glucose metabolism has been presented. Anaerobic glucose metabolism in astrocytes is promoted by the increased synaptic activity in the neuropil to take up excess released glutamate, which is the major transmitter in mammalian CNS (76, 93). Some portion of lactate produced is used oxidatively at the neurophil to support the energy demand.

In contrast to the anaerobic glucose use mentioned above, a highly oxidative cerebral metabolic rate of glucose ($CMR_{glucose}$) increase has been reported in C^{13} MR spectroscopy study of sensorimotor cortex activation in α-chloralose anaesthetized rats. Following the C^{13} labels from injected glucose to glutamate, the Yale group (46) has measured a significant and large increase in the tricarboxylic acid cycling rate that is linked directly to $CMR_{glucose}$ and also related to the recycling of transmitter glutamate. If this is the case, the uncoupling of CBF and oxidative metabolism has a different meaning from the one described above. The appearance of lactate has to be a temporary phenomenon and quantitatively not meaningful. In this scheme of metabolism, the activation-induced changes in CBF and $CMR_{glucose}$ will lose their strong linkage (37, 81). Buxton et al (12) have presented a model to make the disparity between oxygen extraction and CBF increases [$\Delta(oe)/(oe) \ll \Delta CBF/CBF$] consistent for a completely oxidative metabolism. There, the $CMRO_2$ increase dictates the CBF that is required to increase disproportionately in order to elevate the O_2 concentration gradient from the blood to the tissue. In this model, however, the increased "available" oxygen in the tissue observed with oxygen electrodes in

situ during sensory and motor activation in the human brain is not explained
(78, 86).

TEMPORAL CHARACTERISTICS

Figure 3 shows temporal response patterns of tissue BOLD signal at 4 Tesla in
the primary visual area during and following a series of brief photic stimuli of
different durations (45).

All time courses display initial small signal decreases, or "dips," reaching
their minimum (average 1.2%) within a few seconds after the onset of the stimuli, followed by much larger positive signal increases. After the termination
of the stimuli, the signal decays in several seconds. The time up to ten seconds and the undershoot of the decay response depend on the length of the
stimulation period. The initial dip as observed by Menon et al (67) is small
and difficult to detect in a BOLD signal. It has been reported so far only in

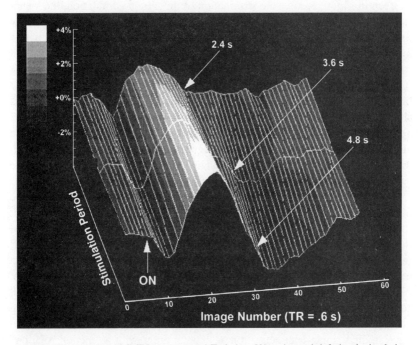

Figure 3 Time courses of fMRI response at 4 Tesla in a V1 region to brief visual stimulation.
The three time courses correspond to stimulus duration (8 Hz flashing LED) of 2.4, 3.6, and
4.8 seconds. Four segmented EPI with TR/TE = 600/30 (msec) was used and retrospective
physiological fluctuation correction was applied (45).

high-field measurements of photic stimulation (45, 66, 67). The negative dip has been attributed to an increase of the deoxyhemoglobin content in the tissue caused by the increase of the metabolic load as shown by optical imaging data (39) on an awake monkey. More recently, an optical imaging spectroscopy study of the cat brain by Malonek and Grinvald (63) showed that despite the increase of deoxyhemoglobin, oxyhemoglobin content did not change much. This indicates that in this early response period there is some blood-volume increase in addition to the decrease in the blood oxygenation. The fMRI signal decrease could be due to the extravascular $1/T_2^*$ contribution, which is more pronounced in high field as described before (13). The initial dip is presumably due to the increased metabolic load and should be well localized at the site of activation and free from the large-vessel contribution often seen in the later period. The subsequent increase in rCBF makes the area hyperoxygenated and the signal becomes positive ($1/T_2^*$ decrease owing to deoxyhemoglobin decrease) and large. In most cases, the activated signal levels last during the stimulation period. This signal increase in the period is usually used for functional mapping. As seen in Figure 3, after the termination of the photic stimulation, the signal stays up for some seconds and then decays. The "undershoot" in the decay time course, which is observable with longer duration of stimuli, is likely due to the unbalanced metabolic energetics yet to settle (the oxygen consumption rate is still elevated) or the slow return of the increased blood volume fraction (CBV) to the basal state. The latter delayed vascular response has been shown in animal models (64). It is interesting to note that this undershoot, which is slightly larger than the initial dip, has been observed relatively easily by 1.5 Tesla field measurements too. Since the major component of the signal change at 1.5 T appears to be the blood water signal, the vascular volume decrease in this recovery process should lead the signal from high to low. Therefore, the vascular recovery alone cannot explain the observed undershoot.

The temporal response of fMRI signals as mentioned above is dictated by the hemodynamic response of the vascular system and is slow with a time constant of many seconds. However, fMRI is a modality of real-time measurements and the period of the signal activation tracks the period of stimulation very well if the latter lasts long enough for fMRI detection. This tracking of activation extends to brain areas of cognitive functions. For studying cognitive function, a single run–single trial experiment is often highly desirable. As a recent trend, such single-trial activation studies have been drawing interest (11, 80), taking advantage of this real-time tracking feature. For example, Richter et al (80) have studied single-trial activation at parietal areas with a "mental rotation" task. The areas are known to be involved in spatial information processing. The subject is first shown a picture of a block assembly that spans a reasonably complicated space. Later, a similar block assembly in different view is shown to the subject and the subject has to decide if the object is the same as the one first seen by mentally rotating the new object. When he/she reaches a decision, the subject presses an appropriate button to inform of the decision. The time required to reach the decision varies with the difficulty of the task. This reaction time (in many seconds) correlates extremely well with the period of the fMRI signal activation, indicating that the signal activation is following closely the on-going neuronal function. Similar results can be seen in Figure 2a, where behaviorally nonexplicit brain functions as well as explicit ones can be traced in the temporal response time course of fMRI.

Another type of temporal response pattern has been observed in hippocampus and cerebellar dentate nucleus (49) with a memory task. When a subject memorizes aurally given repeated words during a period of 50 s and then stops the effort of memorizing, the activation in these areas returns to the base line extremely slowly, taking one minute and a half to decay. In this period, the subject is not actively engaged in memorization. In auditory areas, the decay is immediate after the active task period. In Broca's area and Wernicke's area the decay is somewhat slow, with a decay time of 50 seconds. When a finger-tapping task is enforced during the slow decaying period of 90 s after the memorization task, the performance score of the original memory efforts deteriorates to an applicable degree. This observation of extra-slow retarded responses is unexpected and remains unexplained. Since the hippocampus is known to get easily sensitized for activation (81), some parts of memory activity (such as consolidation of memory) could last for some time without the subject's active participation.

When time-series data of fMRI are "denoised" (see Methods) and free from the contamination of irrelevant signal fluctuation, the data could reveal various types of spatiotemporal patterns; some are task-related and others may be spontaneous (70). MRI signals of resting human brain contain low-frequency oscillations at about 0.1 Hz. They are attributed to vasomotion, which is dependent on physiology but not necessarily on the electrical activity. Such vasomotion with several percent variation in CBF is known in experimental animals (71). It is interesting to note that a fairly early study of tissue oxygen in the human brain (18) showed a small fluctuation of O_2 level at about 0.1 Hz.

In denoised time-series data of the resting brain, Biswal et al (6, 7) has shown intra- and interhemispheric correlations among spontaneously varying signals of motor-related areas. They mapped the correlated areas to show a pattern of possible functional connectivity in those areas. Although it is yet to be shown that the origin of the correlation is neurophysiological, the observation is very exciting. This is a demonstration of the unique advantage of fMRI capable to gather spatiotemporal information of the brain function even without explicit input task to the subject.

SPATIAL RESOLUTION

There are various aspects to spatial resolution in fMRI. The signal activation can be seen at a large draining vein that may be several mm or more away from the activation site, local veins near the area of activation, and the tissue that contains capillaries and venules (32, 56, 69). These areas can be distinguished more or less by looking at the corresponding anatomical image at high resolution as well as the flow-sensitized image that depicts large vessels. Large veins often show large signal changes relative to tissue activation in gradient echo signal acquisition and therefore can be screened out from the activation map. As mentioned earlier, the fast-moving blood water signal from large vessels can be eliminated by imposing a weak bipolar diffusion gradient. In functional mapping by fMRI, the area of activation is often several mm or larger (a cluster of more than 2×2 pixels with 3 mm square pixel size). If one needs only the spatial resolution of these sizes, the mapping by tissue signals or even local vein signals serves the purpose.

Because the region served by the vasculature that controls the local hemodynamics is likely to be larger than the neuronal area of a functional unit, there is a limit in the spatial resolution of those methods based upon hemodynamics such as PET or fMRI. If the match between the area of a functional unit and the coverage of the local vasculature exists, however, the hemodynamic response will represent the area of neuronal activation for that function. This has been demonstrated in whisker barrels in the somatosensory cortex in the rodent brain. Stimulation of a single whisker induces a rCBF increase that is highly localized at the corresponding principal barrel (19). In high-resolution functional MRI of the rat brain, Yang et al (104) showed that a BOLD signal by a single whisker activation is well localized at the whisker-barrel location. Furthermore, the signal appears mostly at layer IV of the cortex. This layer is known to be the site of the input signal processing and with less lateral neural connection than other upper layers. It is $\sim$500 μm deep from the pial surface of the brain and hard to visualize by visible light optical reflectance imaging (22).

In optical imaging of ocular dominance columns in monkey visual cortex (34), the intrinsic signal resulting from hemoglobin absorption was shown to be poorly localized compared to the ocular dominance column structure (especially at the wavelength that represents the blood volume). In order to get the functional map that depicts ocular dominance columns, it was necessary to take the ratio of the two signals, one with left-eye-only and the other with right-eye-only stimulations. This (functional) mapping signal was a fraction of the global signal, the original one-sided signal, which did not show the spatial functional specificity. This distinction of the mapping signal from the global signal has been further demonstrated in the study of spectroscopic imaging of orientation columns in the cat brain by Malonek et al (63). The distinction comes from the change of the deoxyhemoglobin content associated with the increased metabolic load that should closely represent the area of functional activation. The spectral change caused by the induced CBF increase was not well localized in their experiments.

In the human brain, the size of an ocular dominance column is about 1×1 mm^2 in the cross-section normal to the cortical surface and several to 10 mm long parallel to the surface. Menon et al (68) examined the prospect to observe them by using-high resolution FLASH imaging at 4 Tesla. The size of the imaging voxel was $0.55 \times 0.55 \times 4$ mm^3. Observation of any monocular dominance specificity of these columns requires that their column axes be normal to the imaging slice plane; otherwise, voxels in V1 will be binocularly activated because of the partial-volume effect. When activated areas in V1 were selected in the postprocessing by a histogram analysis of left/right distributions, patchy activation maps could be obtained that were highly specific to the monocular dominance. The size of each area was estimated to be 0.9 mm. The time courses of the activation at these highly monocularly specific areas are shown in Figure 4 for a paradigm of binocular as well as the left and the right eye monocular stimulations in time series. In this global signal plot in time, the functional (ocular dominance) pattern is clearly seen. The signal increase by the monocular activation is as strong as with the binocular activation at these sites and the activation induced by the other eye stimulation is small.

The simplest interpretation of this result is that the hyperoxygenation induced by the activation (CBF increase dominant) is well localized at least in those patchy areas and the signal increase is in the area for the proper eye stimulation and the signal valley in the time course is due to the wrong eye stimulation, not vice versa. This result indicates the spatial resolution of fMRI could be as high as such functional units in ocular dominance columns, although it is necessary to use a difference mapping filter to select those functionally specific activation areas.

FUNCTIONAL MAPPING

Historically, the most compelling argument for the existence of regional specialization of human brain function was first presented by Pierre Paul Broca in the middle 19th century (10). Broca examined a patient who, as a result of a stroke, was unable to speak but was otherwise normal. Based on an autopsy performed subsequent to the patient's death, Broca concluded that the seat of the damage was an egg-size lesion located in the inferior frontal gyrus of the frontal lobe in the left hemisphere; this general area is now commonly referred to as Broca's area although its precise topographical extent remains somewhat

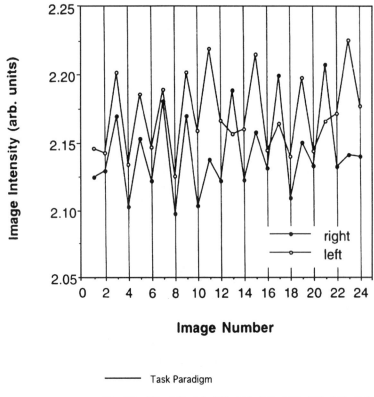

Image Number

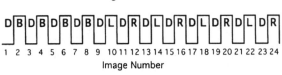

Image Number

Figure 4 Signal responses to binocular and left-right monocular visual simulation at 4 Tesla. The paradigm is shown at the bottom for 24 periods. *B*, binocular stimulation; *D*, dark; *L*, left-eye stimulation; *R*, right-eye stimulation. In each period of 15 seconds, one FLASH image of 256×256 complex data points with FOV of 14×14 cm^2 and 4 mm slice thickness was measured in sequence (68).

ambiguous. Such lesion studies and later intraoperative mapping efforts with electrodes have been until now the primary source of our current understanding of functional compartmentation in the human brain. The language area first identified by Broca can now be visualized with unprecedented spatial resolution using fMRI in data collection times that last only a few minutes.

As can be ascertained from the previous discussion in this review article, spatial specificity and resolution that can be achieved with fMRI remains one of the central questions in this new and rapidly evolving field. This question is particularly salient for methods such PET and fMRI, where functional maps are not based on monitoring neuronal activity directly but rather indirectly through the metabolic and hemodynamic response expressed by the cells and vasculature to the presence of increased transmission. With respect to fMRI, this indirect detection raises questions about the contributions of macrovascular inflow effects, macrovascular BOLD effects, and the spatial correspondence between the actual site of neuronal activity and the extent of the metabolic and hemodynamic response. While these issues can be addressed using specific experiments targeted to evaluate them directly, the deleterious consequences of these potential problems can also be evaluated by trying to map functionally distinct structures with well-defined organization and topography in the human brain. Early experiments introducing the methodology had employed such a strategy and demonstrated activation consistent with hemispheric lateralization in brain function. However, detection of functional specialization with respect to hemispheric laterality only reveals the existence of a very course level of spatial specificity, in the domain that can be characterized as several centimeters. On a much finer spatial scale, e.g. millimeter and submillimeter, it is possible to examine activation of small subcortical nuclei and even smaller level neuronal functional organizations such as ocular dominance columns.

The thalamus provides an excellent case for evaluating the question whether structures that are only a few millimeters in size can be accurately mapped by fMRI methodology, and if they can be mapped for tasks that are expected to generate rather weak stimulation. The thalamus contains several distinct, anatomically well defined regions or nuclei. These nuclei serve as a relay point for a remarkably large number of pathways and these various pathways utilize in general separate nuclei. For example, the lateral geniculate nucleus (LGN) is a small, subcentimeter size nucleus located posteriorly and ventrally within the thalamus. The LGN is a primary target of retinal afferents and, in turn, it projects to the primary visual cortex V1. A very strong back projection from V1 to LGN is also present. Therefore, LGN activation must be present during direct visual stimulation because of the retinal input. Because of the back-projection from V1, LGN activation may even be present under circumstances where V1 may be engaged even in the absence of direct photic stimulation, such as during visual mental imagery. Whether LGN activation in the human brain can be robustly detected during photic stimulation and resolved from activation that may be expected in adjacent structures within the thalamus, such as the pulvinar nucleus, was recently examined (14). These studies used high (4 Tesla) magnetic fields that provide advantages in sensitivity and specificity; the study was further extended subsequently to investigate if the V1 and the LGN activation are present together with activation in higher-order visual areas during visual mental imagery tasks. In this effort, the multislice capability of fMRI to generate a three-dimensional functional map of the whole brain was utilized so as to resolve the LGN from adjacent relevant structures. Figure 5 (see color insert) illustrates images of V1 and bilateral functional activation of the LGN in one participant in three different planes; these planes were extracted from the 3D data set by "reslicing."

In the axial image, the LGN in the two hemispheres are easily identified by their position relative to the optic tract; posteriorly from the optic chiasm, the optic tract runs adjacent to the cerebral peduncle in the midbrain and directly joins the LGN. In the axial image illustrated in Figure 5 (see color insert), the optic tract is seen clearly in both hemispheres near the optic chiasm, anterior to the midbrain. Proceeding posteriorly from the optic chiasm, it appears to merge with the midbrain, and is no longer visualized with clarity because it runs along the cerebral peduncle. Following this curved tract should directly lead to the LGN, which is where the activated loci identified as the LGN are located. In the coronal and parasagittal views, this activated area appears superior to the hippocampal formation as expected for LGN. While the main retinal afferents project to LGN and the geniculostriate projection forms the main pathway for transmission of visual information to the occipital cortex, a secondary pathway exists through the pulvinar nucleus of the thalamus that receives input from the retina and projects reciprocally to the parietal-occipital-temporal associa-tion cortex. The pulvinar nucleus in the thalamus, especially the inferior and adjacent lateral parts, must in principle be also activated in photic stimulation experiments; this was observed in these studies (14). The activated pulvinar regions were very close to the LGN neuroanatomically and the two areas could have been difficult to distinguish in most single-slice imaging studies; however, they were well resolved in the three dimensional reconstructed maps.

The specificity inherent in the fMRI data, as illustrated above, has already allowed detailed mapping of various functions in the human brain. One exam-ple is the set of studies performed on the visual cortex. Many specialized visual areas, i.e. V1, V2, VP (ventral-posterior), V3, and V4 were recently identified in the human brain for the first time within a short period as compared with laborious invasive animal studies. In fMRI studies, the investigators used the retinotopic organization of these early visual areas (27), but this in itself was not sufficient to identify boundaries of V1 and V2. Retinotopically organized regions of the cortex are divided into two categories when viewed from the cor-tical surface, those that contain a mirror-image representation of the visual field (e.g. V1), and those that contain a non-mirror-image representation (e.g. V2). Because adjoining areas have a different sign with respect to this representation, they can be and were used to define the borders (83, 92). Figure 6 (see color insert) illustrates images generated based on analysis of retinotopic mapping of the visual field for mirror and non-mirror-image representations where the boundaries of the early visual areas in the human brain are identified. Here, the advantage of the time-varying input capability of fMRI is used to highlight the neurophysiological characteristics of the activated areas.

SUMMARY AND CURRENT DIRECTIONS

We have reviewed various topics that characterize features of fMRI method and discussed the underlying physiological problem and the relation to neuronal events. The capability of measuring the CBF and BOLD signal on the same individual and within the same paradigm at essentially the same time will soon clarify the quantitative aspect of the BOLD signal. Once the two measurements are well established, then researchers can determine relatively easily the metabolic load associated with functional activation. These physiological parameters may be useful to further characterize the functional activation at a particular site with a particular task in greater detail.

With improvement in the reliability of fMRI measurements, studies with single-trial and short-stimulus presentation paradigms are now possible without the benefit of the multitrial temporal filter usually used in fMRI to improve the statistical reliability of the activation map. Such paradigms can be adjusted to be compatible with those used in other modalities such as MEG. The combination of fMRI and MEG will unite the strength of the two modalities, giving the high temporal resolution to fMRI and the precise locations of multiactivation sites to MEG, so that the uncertainty in solving the inverse problem for source localization is reduced (57). The ultimate goal is to find the functional connectivity among the activation sites at the time scale of neuroinformation transfer.

The field of fMRI is rapidly growing. Its application is already wide in areas of brain research. Further improvement in reliability will turn previously ignored small signal changes, positive or negative, into useful data. This will expand the scope of fMRI to detect more subtle neuronal events such as inhibition. The application of fMRI is expected to expand even further with the easier access to advanced MRI facilities by the brain-science community.

> Visit the *Annual Reviews home page* at
> http://www.AnnualReviews.org.

Literature Cited

1. Bandettini P. 1995. *Functional MRI*. PhD thesis. Medical College of Wisconsin
2. Bandettini P, Luh W, Davis T, Van Kylen J, Forster H, et al. 1997. Simultaneous measurement of cerebral perfusion and oxygenation changes during neuronal activation and hypercapnia. *Proc. Annu. Meet.* *Int. Soc. Magn. Reson. Med., 4th, Vancouver, BC,* p. 740
3. Bandettini PA, Jesmanowicz A, Wong EC, Hyde JS. 1993. Processing strategies for time-course data sets in functional MRI of the human brain. *Magn. Reson. Med.* 30:161–73

4. Bandettini PA, Wong EC, Hinks RS, Tikofsky RS, Hyde JS. 1992. Time course EPI of human brain function during task activation. *Magn. Reson. Med.* 25:390–97

5. Biswal B, DeYoe EA, Hyde JS. 1996. Reduction of physiological fluctuations in fMRI using digital filter. *Magn. Reson. Med.* 35:107–13

6. Biswal B, Hudetz AG, Yetkin FZ, Haughton VM, Hyde JS. 1997. Hypercapnia reversibly suppresses low frequency fluctuations in the human motor cortex during rest using echo planar MRI. *J. Cereb. Blood Flow Metab.* 17:301–8

7. Biswal B, Yetkin FZ, Haughton VM, Hyde JS. 1995. Functional connectivity in the motor cortex of resting human brain using echo-planar MRI. *Magn. Reson. Med.* 34:537–41

8. Boxerman JL, Bandettini PA, Kwong KK, Baker JR, Davis TL, et al. 1995. The intravascular contribution to fMRI signal change: Monte Carlo modeling and diffusion-weighted studies in vivo. *Magn. Reson. Med.* 34:4–10

9. Boxerman JL, Hamberg LM, Rosen BR, Weisskoff RM. 1995. MR contrast due to intravascular magnetic susceptibility perturbations. *Magn. Reson. Med.* 34:555–66

10. Broca P, Brown-Sequard CE. 1855. *Proprietes et fonctions de la moelle épinière: rapport sur quelques experiences de M. Brown-Sequard.* Lu à.la sociéte de biologie le 21 juillet, Bonaventure et Ducessois

11. Buckner RL, Bandettini PA, O'Craven KM, Savoy R, Petersen SE, et al. 1996. Detection of cortical activation during averaged single trials of a cognitive task using functional magnetic resonance imaging. *Proc. Natl. Acad. Sci. USA* 93: 14878–83

12. Buxton RB, Frank LR. 1997. A model for the coupling between cerebral blood flow and oxygen metabolism during neural stimulation. *J. Cereb. Blood Flow Metab.* 17:64–72

13. Buxton RB, Wong EC, Frank LR. 1997. Dynamics of perfusion and deoxyhemoglobin changes during brain activation. *NeuroImage* 5:S32

14. Chen W, Kato T, Zhu XH, Strupp J, Ogawa S, et al. 1997. Mapping of lateral geniculate nucleus activation during visual stimulation in human brain using fMRI. *Magn. Reson. Med.* In press

15. Chien D, Levin DL, Anderson CM. 1994. MR gradient echo imaging of intravascular blood oxygenation: T_2^* determination in the presence of flow. *Magn. Reson. Med.* 32:540–45

16. Cho Z-H, Ro Y-M, Park S-T, Chung S-C. 1996. NMR functional imaging using a tailored RF gradient echo sequence: A true susceptibility measurement technique. *Magn. Reson. Med.* 35:1–5

17. Cohen MS. 1996. Rapid MRI and functional applications. In *Brain Mapping: The Methods*, ed. AW Toga, JC Mazziotta, pp. 223–55. San Diego: Academic

18. Cooper R, Crow HJ, Walter WG, Winter AL. 1966. Regional control of cerebral vascular reactivity and oxygen supply in man. *Brain Res.* 3:174–91

19. Cox SB, Woolsey TA, Rovainen MC. 1993. Localized dynamic changes in cortical blood flow with whisker stimulation corresponds to matched vascular and neuronal architecture of rat barrels. *J. Cereb. Blood Flow Metab.* 13:899–913

20. Davis TL, Kwong KK, Bandettini PA, Weisskoff RM, Rosen BR. 1997. Mapping the dynamics of oxidative metabolism by functional MRI. *Annu. Meet. Int. Soc. Magn. Reson. Med.* 151. Vancouver

21. Detre JA, Leigh JS, Williams DS, Koretsky AP. 1992. Perfusion imaging. *Magn. Reson. Med.* 23:37–45

22. Dowling JL, Henegar MM, Liu D, Rovainen CM, Woolsey TA. 1996. Rapid optical imaging of whisker responses in the rat barrel cortex. *J. Neurosci. Methods* 66:113–22

23. Edelman RE, Siewer B, Darby DG, Thangaraj V, Nobre AC, et al. 1994. Quantitative mapping of cerebral blood flow and functional localization with echo-planar MR imaging and signal targeting with alternating radio frequency. *Radiology* 192:513–20

24. Eichling JO, Raichle ME, Grubb RL, Ter-Pogossian MM. 1974. Evidence of the limitations of water as a freely diffusible tracer in brain of the rhesus monkey. *Circ. Res.* 35:358–64

25. Ellerman J, Garwood M, Henderich K, Hinke R, Hu X, et al. 1994. Functional imaging of the brain by nuclear magnetic resonance. In *NMR in Physiology and Biomedicine*, ed. R Gillies. 137–50. San Diego: Academic

26. Engel SA, Glover GH, Wandell BA. 1997. Retinotopic organization in human visual cortex and the spatial precision of functional MRI. *Cereb. Cort.* 7:181–92

27. Engel SA, Rumelhart DE, Wandell BA, Lee AT, Glover GH, et al. 1994. fMRI of human visual cortex. *Nature* 369:525

28. Fisel CR, Ackerman JL, Buxton RB, Garrido L, Belliveau JW, et al. 1991. MR contrast due to microscopically heterogeneous magnetic susceptibility: numerical

simulations and applications to cerebral physiology. *Magn. Reson. Med.* 17:336–47

29. Fox PT, Raichle ME. 1986. Focal physiological uncoupling of cerebral blood flow and oxidative metabolism during somatosensory stimulation in human subjects. *Proc. Natl. Acad. Sci. USA* 83:1140–44

30. Fox PT, Raichle ME, Mintun MA, Dence C. 1988. Nonoxidative glucose consumption during focal physiologic neural activity. *Science* 241:462–64

31. Frahm J, Merboldt KD, W H. 1993. Functional MRI of human brain activation at high spatial resolution. *Magn. Reson. Med.* 29:139–44

32. Frahm J, Merboldt KD, Haenicke W, Kleinschmidt A, Boecker H. 1994. Brain or vein-oxygenation or flow? On signal physiology in functional MRI of human brain activation. *NMR Biomed.* 7:45–53

33. Friston KJ. 1996. Statistical parametric mapping and other analyses of functional imaging data. In *Brain Mapping: The methods*, ed. AW Toga, JC Mazziotta, pp. 363–86. San Diego: Academic

34. Frostig RD, Lieke EE, Ts'o DY, Grinvald A. 1990. Cortical functional architecture and local coupling between neuronal activity and the microcirculation revealed by in vivo high-resolution optical imaging of intrinsic signals. *Proc. Natl. Acad. Sci. USA* 87:6082–86

35. Gao J-H, Holland SK, Gore JC. 1988. Nuclear magnetic resonance signal from flowing nuclei in rapid imaging using gradient echo. *Med. Phys.* 15:809–14

36. Gati JS, Menon RS, Ugurbil K, Rutt BK. 1997. Experimental determination of the BOLD field strength dependence in vessels and tissue. *Magn. Reson. Med.* 38:296–302

37. Ginsberg MD, Dietrich WD, Rusto R. 1987. Coupled forebrain increases of local cerebral glucose utilization and blood flow during physiologic stimulation of a somatosensory pathway in the rat: demonstration by double-label autoradiography. *Neurology* 37:11–19

38. Gratton E. 1995. Rapid changes of optical parameters in the human brain during a tapping task. *J. Cogn. Neurosci.* 7:446–56

39. Grinvald A, Frostig RD, Siegel RM, Bartfeld E. 1991. High-resolution optical imaging of functional brain architecture in the awake monkey. *Proc. Natl. Acad. Sci. USA* 88:11559–63

40. Grubb RL, Raichle ME, Eichling JO, Ter-Pogossian MM. 1974. The effects of changes in $PaCO_2$ on cerebral blood volume, blood flow and vascular mean transit time. *Stroke* 5:630–39

41. Gyngell ML, Bock C, Schmitz B, Hoehn-Berlage M, Hossmann K-A. 1996. Variation of functional MRI signal in response to frequency of somatosensory stimulation in a-chloralose anesthetized rats. *Magn. Reson. Med.* 36:13–15

42. Henning J, Janz C, Speck O, Ernst T. 1995. Functional spectroscopy of brain activation following a single light pulse. *Int. J. Imag. Sys. Techol.* 6:203–8

43. Hu X, Le H. 1996. Artifact reduction in EPI with phase-encoded reference scan. *Magn. Reson. Med.* 36:166–71

44. Hu X, Le TH, Parrish T, Erhard P. 1995. Retrospective estimation and correction of physiological fluctuation in functional MRI. *Magn. Reson. Med.* 34:201–12

45. Hu X, Le TH, Ugurbil K. 1997. Evaluation of the early response in fMRI in individual subjects using short stimulus duration. *Magn. Reson. Med.* 37:877–84

46. Hyder F, Chase JR, Gehar KL, Mason GF, Siddeek M, et al. 1996. Increased tricarboxylic acid cycle flux in rat brain during forepaw stimulation detected with 1H[13C]NMR. *Proc. Natl. Acad. Sci. USA* 93:7612–17

47. Jezzard P, Balaban RS. 1995. Correction for geometric distortion in echo planar images from {B_0} field variation. *Magn. Reson. Med.* 34:65–73

48. Jueptner M, Weiller C. 1995. Does measurement of regional cerebral blood flow reflect synaptic activity?—implication for PET and fMRI. *NeuroImage* 2:148–56

49. Kato T. 1997. Monitoring of cerebral multiphasic sustained responses (CMSR) in memory processing using fMRI. *NeuroImage* 5:593

50. Kato T, Kamei A, Takashima S, Ozaki S. 1993. Human visual cortical function during photic stimulation monitored by means of near-infrared spectroscopy. *J. Cereb. Blood Flow Metab.* 13:516–20

51. Kennan R, Zhong J, Gore J. 1994. Intravascular susceptibility contrast mechanisms in tissues. *Magn. Reson. Med.* 31:9–21

52. Kim S-G. 1995. Quantification of relative blood flow change by flow-sensitive alternating inversion recovery (FAIR) technique: application to functional mapping. *Magn. Reson. Med.* 34:293–301

53. Kim S-G, Tsekos NV. 1997. Perfusion imaging by a flow sensitive alternating inversion recovery (FAIR) technique:

application to functional brain imaging. *Magn. Reson. Med.* 37:425–35

54. Kim S-G, Ugurbil K. 1997. Comparison of blood oxygenation and cerebral blood flow effects in fMRI: estimation of relative oxygen consumption change. *Magn. Reson. Med.* 38:59–65

55. Kim S-G, Ugurbil K. 1997. Functional magnetic resonance imaging of the human brain. *J. Neurosci. Meth.* 74:229–43

56. Kim S-K, Hendrich K, Hu X, Merkle H, Ugurbil K. 1994. Potential pitfalls of functional MRI using conventional gradient-recalled echo techniques. *NMR Biomed.* 7:69–74

57. Kuikka JT, Belliveau JW, Hari R. 1996. Future of functional brain imaging. *Eur. J. Nucl. Med.* 23:737–40

58. Kwong KK, Belliveau JW, Chesler DA, Goldberg IE, Weisskoff RM, et al. 1992. Dynamic magnetic resonance imaging of human brain activity during primary sensory stimulation. *Proc. Natl. Acad. Sci. USA* 89:5675–79

59. Kwong KK, Chesler DA, Weisskoff RM, Donahue KM, Davis TL, et al. 1995. MR perfusion studies with T1-weighted echo planar imaging. *Magn. Reson. Med.* 34:878–87

60. Lai S, Reichenbach JR, Haacke EM. 1996. Commutator filter: a novel technique for the identification of structure's significant susceptibility inhomogeneities and its application to functional MRI. *Magn. Reson. Med.* 36:781–87

61. Latour LL, Hasegawa Y, Formato JE, Fisher M, Sotak CH. 1994. Spreading waves of decreased diffusion coefficient after cortical stimulation in a rat. *Magn. Reson. Med.* 32:189–98

62. Liu H, Chance B, Hielscher AH, Jacques SL, Tittel FK. 1995. Influence of blood vessels on the measurement of hemoglobin oxygenation as determined by time resolved reflectance spectroscopy. *Med. Phys.* 22:1209–17

63. Malonek D, Grinvald A. 1996. Interaction between electrical activity and cortical microcirculation revealed by imaging spectroscopy: implication for functional brain mapping. *Science* 272:551–53

64. Mandeville J, Marota J, Keltner J, Kosovsky B, Burke J, et al. 1996. CBV functional imaging in rat brain using iron oxide agent at steady state concentration. *Proc. Annu. Meet. Int. Soc. Magn. Reson. Med., 3rd, New York,* p. 292

65. Mayer C, Nishimura D, Macovski A. 1992. Fast spiral coronary artery imaging. *Magn. Reson. Med.* 28:202–13

66. McIntosh J, Zhang Y, Kidambi S, Harsh-barger T, Mason G, et al. 1996. Echo-time dependence of the functional MRI "fast response". See Ref. 64, p. 284

67. Menon RS, Ogawa S, Hu X, Strupp JP, Anderson P, et al. 1995. BOLD based functional MRI at 4 Tesla includes a capillary bed contribution: Echo planar imaging correlates with previous optical imaging using intrinsic signals. *Magn. Reson. Med.* 33:453–59

68. Menon RS, Ogawa S, Strupp JP, Ugurbil K. 1997. Ocular dominance in human V1 demonstrated by functional magnetic resonance imaging. *J. Neurophysiol.* 77:2780–87

69. Menon RS, Ogawa S, Tank DW, Ugurbil K. 1993. 4 Tesla gradient recalled echo characteristics of photic stimulation-induced signal changes in the human primary visual cortex. *Magn. Reson. Med.* 30:380–86

70. Mitra PP, Ogawa S, Hu X, Ugurbil K. 1997. The nature of spatiotemporal changes in hemodynamics as manifested in functional MRI. *Magn. Reson. Med.* 37:511–18

71. Morita-Tsuzuki Y, Bouskella E, Hardebo JE. 1992. Vasomotion in the rat cerebral microcirculation recorded by laser-Doppler flowmetry. *Acta Physiol. Scand.* 146:431–39

72. Ogawa S, Lee TM, Barrere B. 1993. The sensitivity of magnetic resonance image signals of rat brain to changes in the cerebral venous blood oxygenation. *Magn. Reson. Med.* 29:205–10

73. Ogawa S, Lee TM, Kay AR, Tank DW. 1990. Brain magnetic resonance imaging with contrast dependent on blood oxygenation. *Proc. Natl. Acad. Sci. USA* 87:9868–72

74. Ogawa S, Menon RS, Tank DW, Kim SG, Merkle H, et al. 1993. Functional brain mapping by blood oxygenation level-dependent contrast magnetic resonance imaging. A comparison of signal characteristics with biophysical model. *Biophys. J.* 64:803–12

75. Ogawa S, Tank DW, Menon R, Ellermann JM, Kim S-G, et al. 1992. Intrinsic signal changes accompanying sensory stimulation: functional brain mapping with magnetic resonance imaging. *Proc.Natl. Acad. Sci. USA* 89:5951–55

76. Pellerin L, Magistretti PJ. 1994. Glutamate uptake into astrocytes stimulates arebic glycolysis: a mechanism coupling neuronal activity to glucose utilization. *Proc. Natl. Acad. Sci. USA* 91:10625–29

77. Prichard JW, Rothman DL, Novotny EJ,

Petroff OAC, Kuwabara T, et al. 1991. Lactate rise detected by 1H NMR in human visual cortex during physiologic stimulation. *Proc. Natl. Acad. Sci. USA* 88:5829–31

78. Raichle ME. 1987. Circulatory and metabolic correlates of brain function in normal humans. In *Handbook of Physiology—The Nervous System*, ed. F Plum. 5:643–74. Washington, DC: Am. Physiol. Soc.

79. Richter W, Anderson AP, Georgopoulos AP, Kim S-G. 1997. Sequential activity in human motor areas during delayed cued finger movement task studied by time resolved fMRI. *NeuroReport* 8:1257–61

80. Richter W, Georgopoulos AP, Ugurbil K, Kim S-G. 1997. Time-resolved fMRI of mental rotation. *NeuroReport* 8:3697–3702

81. Roland PE. 1993. *Brain Activation*. New York: Wiley-Liss

82. Rostrup E, Larsson HBW, Toft PB, Garde K, Thomsen C, et al. 1994. Functional MRI of CO_2- induced increase in cerebral perfusion. *NMR Biomed.* 7:29–34

83. Sereno MI, Dale AM, Reppas JB, Kwong KK, Belliveau JW, et al. 1995. Borders of multiple visual areas in humans revealed by functional magnetic resonance imaging. *Science* 268:889–93

84. Shen L, Alexander GE. 1997. Visualization of a sensory-to-motor transformation in motor and premotor cortex. Submitted

85. Shulman RG, Blamire AM, Rothman DL, McCarthy G. 1993. Nuclear magnetic resonance imaging and spectroscopy of human brain function. *Proc. Natl. Acad. Sci. USA* 90:3127

86. Silver A. 1978. Cellular microenvironment in relation to local blood flow. In *Cerebral Vascular Smooth Muscle and its Control*, ed. CF Symposium. 56:49–67. Amsterdam: Elsevier

87. Song A, Wong E, Jesmanowicz A, Tan S, Hyde JS. 1995. Diffusion weighted fMRI at 1.5 T and 3 T. *Annu. Meet. Soc. Magn. Reson. Med.*, Nice, p. 457.

88. Song A, Wong E, Tan S, Hyde J. 1996. Diffusion weighted fMRI at 1.5 T. *Magn. Reson. Med.* 35:155–58

89. Stehling MK, Turner R, Mansfield P. 1991. Echo-Planar imaging: magnetic resonance imaging in a fraction of a second. *Science* 254:43–49

90. Strupp J. 1996. Stimulate, a GUI-based fMRI analysis software package. *NeuroImage* 3:S607

91. Thulborn KR, Waterton JC, Matthews PM, Radda GK. 1982. Oxygenation dependence of the transverse relaxation time of water protons in whole blood at high field. *Biochim. Biophys. Acta* 714:265–70

92. Tootell RGH, Dale AM, Sereno MI, Malach R. 1996. New images from human visual cortex. *Trends Neurosci.* 19:481–89

93. Tsacopoulos M, Magistretti PJ. 1996. Metabolic coupling between glia and neurons. *J. Neuroscience* 16:877–85

94. Turner R, Le Bihan D, Moonen CTW, Frank J. 1991. Echo-planar time course MRI of cat brain oxygenation. *Magn. Reson. Med.* 22:159–66

95. van Gelderen P, de Vleeschouwer MHM, DesPres D, Pekar J, van Zijl PCM, et al. 1994. Water diffusion and acute stroke. *Magn. Reson. Med.* 31:154–63

96. Villringer A, Planck J, Hock C, Schleinkofer L, Dirnagl U. 1993. Near infrared spectroscopy (NIRS): a new tool to study hemodynamic changes during activation of brain function in human adults. *Neurosci. Lett.* 154:101–4

97. Volkow ND, Rosen B, Farde L. 1997. Imaging the living human brain: magnetic resonance imaging and positron emission tomography. *Proc. Natl. Acad. Sci. USA* 94:2787–88

98. Weisskoff RM, Baker J, Belliveau J, Davis TL, Kwong KK, et al. 1993. Power spectrum analysis of functionally-weighted MR data: What's in the noise? *Proc. Annu. Meet. Soc. Magn. Reson. Med. 1st, New York*, p. 7

99. Williams DS, Detre JA, Leigh JS, Koretsky AP. 1992. Magnetic resonance imaging of perfusion using spin inversion of arterial water. *Proc. Natl. Acad. Sci. USA* 89:212–16

100. Woolsey TA, Rovainen CM, Cox SB, Henegar MH, Liang GE, et al. 1996. Neuronal units linked to microvascular modules in cerebral cortex: response elements for imaging the brain. *Cereb. Cort.* 6:647–60

101. Worsley KJ, Marrett S, Neelen P, Vandal AC, Friston KJ. 1996. A unified statistical approach for determining significant signals in images of cerebral activation. *NeuroImage* 4:58–73

102. Yablonskiy DA, Haacke EM. 1994. Theory of NMR signal formation in magnetically inhomogeneous tissue: fast dephasing regime. *Magn. Reson. Med.* 32:749–63

103. Yang QX, Dardzinski BJ, Li S, Eslinger PJ, Smith MB. 1997. Multi-gradient echo with susceptibility inhomogeneity compensation (MGESIC): demonstration of

fMRI in the olfactory cortex at 3.0 T. *Magn. Reson. Med.* 37:331–35

104. Yang X, Hyder F, Shulman RG. 1996. Activation of single whisker barrel in rat brain localized by functional magnetic resonance imaging. *Proc. Natl. Acad. Sci. USA* 93:475–78

105. Ye FQ, Allen PS. 1995. Relaxation enhancement of the transverse magnetiza-tion of water protons in paramagnetic sus-pensions of red cells. *Magn. Reson. Med.* 34:713–20

106. Zhong J, Petroff OAC, Pleban LA, Gore JC, Prichard JW. 1997. Reversible, re-producible reduction of brain water ap-parent diffusion coefficient by cortical electroshocks. *Magn. Reson. Med* 37:1–6

Annu. Rev. Biophys. Biomol. Struct. 1998. 27:475–502

CRYSTALLOGRAPHIC STRUCTURES OF THE HAMMERHEAD RIBOZYME: Relationship to Ribozyme Folding and Catalysis

Joseph E. Wedekind and David B. McKay
Department of Structural Biology, Stanford University School of Medicine,
Stanford, California 94305-5126; e-mail: dave.mckay@stanford.edu;
wedekind@ribose.stanford.edu

KEY WORDS: x-ray crystallography, ribozyme, RNA, metalloenzyme, hammerhead

ABSTRACT

The hammerhead ribozyme is a small catalytic RNA that cleaves a target phosphodiester bond in a reaction dependent on divalent metal ions. Crystal structures of the hammerhead reveal the tertiary fold of an enzymatic "ground state" of the molecule; however, they do not clarify the catalytic mechanism of the ribozyme, presumably because a significant conformational rearrangement is required to reach an enzymatic transition state. The structural domains seen in the hammerhead can be related to sequence or structural motifs in transfer and ribosomal RNAs, suggesting that they represent tertiary building blocks that will be found in large, complex RNAs.

CONTENTS

475

PERSPECTIVES AND OVERVIEW

The hammerhead ribozyme is a small catalytic RNA motif first detected as a site-specific self-cleavage activity of concatenated linear RNA replicates from plant virusoids—small (~300–400 base pairs) circular RNA molecules that are encapsidated by some RNA viruses (6, 24, 40). Once sequences of several self-cleaving virusoids were available, a consensus sequence associated with the RNA cleavage activity emerged and was demonstrated to be sufficient for single-turnover cleavage in long RNAs (14, 15). The consensus [incorporating refinements by subsequent in vitro studies (42, 50)] has a conserved central core of thirteen nucleotides at the junction of three duplex stems (Figure 1a).

Emergence of the consensus sequence prompted a search for in vitro, multiple turnover cleavage activity by use of short, synthetic oligoribonucleotides. This was accomplished with two constructs having different connectivity; in one, the strands of stem III were connected with a loop (56), and in another, stem II was closed with a loop (18). Both designs resulted in constructs that catalyzed site-specific, multiple-turnover cleavage, establishing the hammerhead as a bona-fide RNA enzyme, or ribozyme.

The hammerhead was dwarfed in size by its ribozyme counterparts of the day, namely the group I intron, group II intron, and RNAse P, all of which require on the order of hundreds of nucleotides for activity. Only the small central core and three duplex stems are required for hammerhead activity. Additionally, there is substantial latitude in the lengths, sequence, and connectivity of the stems. Hammerhead variants could be synthesized readily by in vitro transcription, and more recently by chemical methods, and purified to homogeneity by gel electrophoresis. Thus as the "world's smallest ribozyme," the hammerhead became an attractive candidate for application and development of structural, mechanistic, and biophysical methods with which to study ribozyme activity. It was the first ribozyme to be crystallized (38) and to have its structure determined (37) (Figure 1b). In this review, we summarize the current understanding of the structure and mechanism of the hammerhead ribozyme from the perspective of its role as a prototype system for biophysical studies of how a particular RNA catalyzes a site-specific enzymatic reaction.

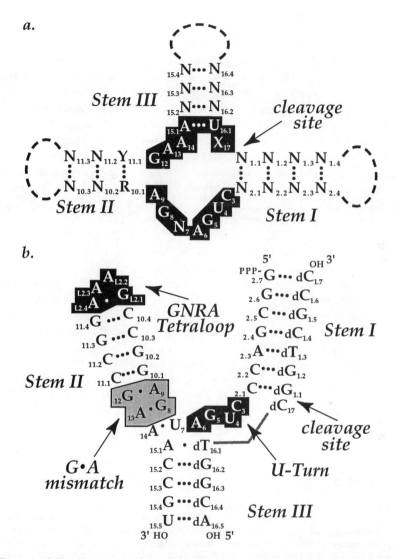

Figure 1 Schematic representations of the sequence and numbering scheme of the hammerhead ribozyme. Triply dotted lines represent Watson-Crick (WC) base pairs. (*a*) Predicted secondary structure of the hammerhead ribozyme. *Black boxes*, conserved bases within the core. X may be A, U, or C; N represents a nonconserved position. The substrate strand contains the cleavage site. (*b*) The global Y-shaped fold of the hammerhead ribozyme RNA-DNA complex solved by Pley et al (37). *Black boxes*, the uridine turn and GNRA tetraloops; *gray boxes*, the G•A mismatch; *single dotted lines*, non-WC base pairs.

HAMMERHEAD ACTIVITY

The Reaction and Its Requirements

The hammerhead ribozyme catalyzes the site specific cleavage of a phosphodiester bond to generate a free 5'-OH group and a 2',3'-cyclic phosphodiester (14, 56). The specificity of the cleavage site is dictated by WC base pairing in stems I and II as depicted in Figure 1a; any nucleotide except guanosine at position 17, 5' to the scissile bond, allows efficient cleavage. Alternative proposals for the general reaction scheme are summarized in Figure 2.

The ribose 2'-OH is absolutely essential for cleavage (11). Additionally, the reaction requires one or more divalent metal ions. Mg^{2+} is presumably the natural catalytic ion for the hammerhead, but it can be substituted by several others, including Mn^{2+}, Cd^{2+}, and Co^{2+}, which have several-fold more rapid cleavage rates than Mg^{2+} under similar conditions, and by Ca^{2+}, which has an order of magnitude slower cleavage rate (10, 12). Notably, Pb^{2+} does not promote efficient cleavage, despite its ability to catalyze cleavage of the phosphoribose backbone in other RNA systems. Higher cleavage rates appear to correlate with decreasing pKa of the solvated metal ion; one interpretation of this correlation is that a metal-coordinated hydroxide may participate in catalysis. Further, the logarithm of the rate increases linearly with pH, with a slope near unity, suggesting a single proton transfer. This has led to the proposal that a metal-bound hydroxide may serve as a general base that activates the essential 2'-OH at position 17 (10). An analogous role is played by a histidine in both the RNase A and RNase T1 mechanisms. Figure 2b depicts the general activation.

Several groups have independently demonstrated that the configuration of the reactive phosphate is inverted during catalysis (28, 53, 57). This observation strongly favors a reaction proceeding with in-line attack of the nucleophile on the phosphorus-oxygen bond, as shown in Figure 2b. The transesterification

---→

Figure 2   Two possible reaction mechanisms of hammerhead ribozyme catalysis. (*a*) The ground state conformation indicates the need for a conformation change. (*b–d*), one-metal mechanism (not necessarily concerted): (*b*) The 2'-hydroxyl is activated by a metal bound hydroxide at Site I. The nucleophile attacks the phosphorus, which is stabilized by an interaction with the Site I metal through an interaction at the *pro*-R_p phosphoryl oxygen. (*c*) The intermediate geometry is trigonal bipyramidal. The LG is most likely protonated. (*d*) The products are a stable 2',3' cyclic phosphodiester linkage and a free 5'-hydroxyl group from nucleotide 1.1. (*e* and *f*), two-metal mechanism: (*e*) Possible concerted two-metal mechanism proposed by Pontius et al (39). A free hydroxide abstracts the 2'-hydroxyl proton. Metals coordinate directly to the 2'-OH nucleophile, *pro*-R_p oxygen of G1.1, and the 5'-O LG. (*f*) The activated 2' oxyanion performs in-line attack on the phosphate, stabilized by divalent ions at Sites I and II. The intermediate geometry is trigonal bipyramidal. The LG is stabilized by direct association with a metal at Site II.

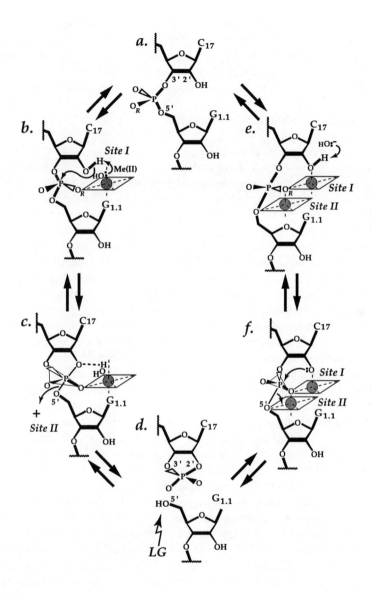

product is a stable 2′,3′ cyclic diester linkage and a free 5′ hydroxyl group from nucleotide 1.1, as illustrated in Figure 2d.

An area of continuing debate on the hammerhead mechanism involves a question of the number and location(s) of "catalytic" metal ions—those that are directly involved in the chemical steps of the reaction. Phosphorothioate labeling experiments have identified one site of probable direct (inner sphere) ligation for a catalytic divalent ion. When the *pro*-R_p oxygen at position 1.1 of the substrate strand is substituted with sulfur, the bond cleavage rate in the presence of ~10 mM Mg^{2+} is reduced at least two orders of magnitude (28, 52). Further, activity can be rescued only partially by Mg^{2+} concentrations approaching 1 M. In contrast, activity is readily rescued by Mn^{2+} (12). Since Mn^{2+} shows only a slight preference for oxo versus thiol inner sphere ligands, while Mg^{2+} has an apparent ~31,000-fold weaker affinity for sulfur as compared to oxygen (34), the rescue of cleavage activity for the thiophosphate-labeled substrate by Mn^{2+} but not Mg^{2+} argues that the *pro*-R_p atom contributes an essential ligand to the binding site of a catalytic ion [although recently this interpretation has been questioned by Zhou and colleagues (60)]. It is notable that a sulfur at the *pro*-S_p position of nucleotide 1.1 has minimal effect on activity (28, 52). Therefore, only one of the nonbridging phosphate oxygens at the cleavage site serves as a ligand for a divalent ion involved in catalysis.

The involvement of a second catalytic metal has been proposed as a means to stabilize the charge buildup on the 5′ oxyanion, since this would enhance its effectiveness as a leaving group (Figure 2f, Site II). Several investigations have been undertaken to scrutinize the existence of such a metal by use of deuterium solvent isotope effects. This experiment is based on the premise that oxyanions prefer protonation over deuteration, such that the ratio of k_H/k_D should be $\gg 1$ if a proton transfer occurs as the (sole) rate-limiting step of the reaction. In practice, such effects are difficult to interpret, especially if there is an isotope effect on the equilibrium constant in a step prior to the rate limiting step [for a review see Jencks (26)]. This was the conclusion put forth by Sawata and co-workers (47), who proposed that an isotope effect of 4.4 for the hammerhead reaction was attributable to an equilibrium shift in the effective Mg(II)OH versus Mg(II)OD concentrations, which suggests a proton transfer does not occur in the rate limiting step, implying participation of a second metal. (It should be noted that ΔpKa in question, has not been experimentally determined, but rather estimated for the Mg(II)-D_2O species). In contrast, Kuimelis & McLaughlin observed isotope effects of 3.6 and 2.3 for the Mg^{2+} and spermine-dependent (i.e. no metal) reactions (29). The latter observation is used as an argument in favor of a proton transfer in the rate limiting step, in which the metal-hydroxide equilibrium cannot be a significant factor. (Nonetheless, the isotope effect is diminished by 40%).

In order to address the question "What is the rate limiting step?" Zhou and coworkers (61) and, independently, Kuimelis and coworkers (29) performed an additional set of experiments. From a simplistic standpoint, the rate-limiting step must be either the activation of the nucleophile (e.g. Figure 2b) or departure of the leaving group (LG) (e.g. Figure 2c), both of which involve either proton transfer, or a second metal at Site II as shown Figure 2f. In order to evaluate effect of the LG on rate, both groups substituted sulfur for oxygen in the 5' position of nucleotide 1.1 and measured the rate of cleavage. By default, the superior LG ability of a thiol over an oxyanion translates into a significant rate acceleration if the rate of oxo LG departure is normally rate-limiting. In fact, the LG ability of a thiolate makes the substrate strand $\sim 10^6$-fold more reactive than its oxo counterpart, and as a consequence, it would be expected to need neither protonation nor a metal to function. The latter observations regarding lability were observed by both Zhou and co-workers (60), who saw a rate enhancement, and by Kuimelis and co-workers (29), who saw no rate enhancement, particularly in the presence of Mn^{2+} versus Mg^{2+}, which was offered as evidence supporting the participation of only one catalytic metal.

Pontius et al (39) offer a reinterpretation of existing data and suggest a pH dependent, concerted two metal mechanism in which a non-metal-bound hydroxide may activate the 2'-OH nucleophile, giving rise to the documented solvent isotope effect. A second metal coordinates directly to the LG oxyanion in the manner proposed by Sawata et al (47) (see Figure 2e-f). In summary, the number and exact role of catalytic divalent ion(s) required for hammerhead activity remains controversial at this time, and neither the single-metal nor the two-metal reaction scheme may be ignored in the interpretation of structural data on the molecule.

The Kinetic Scheme

A detailed kinetic and thermodynamic framework, giving rate constants and free energy changes for each step of the reaction, has been elucidated for the hammerhead (19). The kinetics of binding and release of substrate and product strands (steps labeled "a" in Figure 3) mimic what one anticipates for formation of canonical RNA duplexes in which stem regions engage in conventional WC base-pairing.

The bond cleavage rate (step "b", Figure 3), i.e. the rate of the chemical step, is ~ 1 min^{-1} under typical conditions (e.g. 10 mM Mg^{2+}, pH 7.5, 25 °C) (13). This rate generalizes to all hammerheads, and is influenced only modestly by length and sequence variations in the stems (13, 19, 20). In contrast, mutations in the conserved nucleotides of the central core, i.e. all nucleotides except the nonconserved nucleotide at position 7 (Fig. 1a), reduce activity two to three orders of magnitude (42). To a good approximation, substrate specificity is

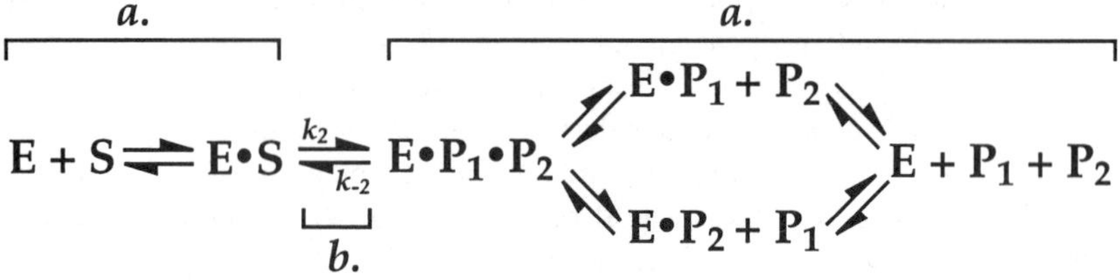

$$a. \qquad\qquad\qquad a.$$

$$E + S \rightleftharpoons E \cdot S \underset{k_{-2}}{\overset{k_2}{\rightleftharpoons}} E \cdot P_1 \cdot P_2 \begin{array}{c} \nearrow E \cdot P_1 + P_2 \searrow \\ \\ \searrow E \cdot P_2 + P_1 \nearrow \end{array} E + P_1 + P_2$$

$$b.$$

Figure 3 Kinetic scheme of the hammerhead ribozyme reaction. E, ribozyme; S, substrate; P_1 and P_2, products. (*a*) Binding and release of substrate and product follow kinetics of duplex formation. (*b*) Cleavage rate is ~ 1 min^{-1}; equilibrium is $\sim 10^2$-fold in favor of products.

relegated to the stems and the prerequisites for catalysis are sequestered in the central core of the hammerhead (Figure 1*a*).

The ground state to transition state activation energy is ~ 22 Kcal/mole for the bond cleavage reaction (21). The reaction is reversible, with the equilibrium strongly favoring product. In contrast, the intrinsic bond energy of a $2',3'$-cyclic phosphodiester (the product) is higher than that of a $3',5'$-phosphodiester (the substrate); the energetics of the chemical bonds, taken alone, favor ligated substrate over cleaved product. The discrepancy is accounted for by a substantial increase in entropy when the scissile bond is cleaved; qualitatively, the product complex is much more "floppy" than the substrate complex.

Both the hammerhead cleavage rate and the equilibrium ratio of substrate to product depend strongly on the concentration and species of divalent ion present. Higher metal ion concentration shifts the equilibrium toward uncleaved/religated substrate. For example, for saturating metal ion concentrations ($\gg 10$ mM) of the divalent metals Mg^{2+}, Mn^{2+} and Co^{2+}, the equilibrium lies 10-fold to 20-fold in favor of product, while for a concentration of 10 mM Mg^{2+}, which is typically present in hammerhead activity assays, product is favored 130-fold over substrate. The effective affinity for the catalytic ion(s) inferred from the metal ion concentration dependence of the substrate/product equilibrium is: 2.2, 4.0, and 13 mM for Co^{2+}, Mn^{2+}, and Mg^{2+} respectively; these values are essentially equal to the binding constants of these ions for $5'$-AMP, suggestive of an interaction with a single phosphate ligand at the cleavage site (30). These data reiterate the essential participation of catalytic metal ion(s) in the hammerhead reaction.

CRYSTALLOGRAPHIC STRUCTURES

Several x-ray crystallographic structures for the hammerhead ribozyme have been reported; they are summarized in Table 1.

Table 1 Crystallographic structures reported for hammerhead ribozymes

Construct (ribozyme; substrate/inhibitor)	Crystal stabilization conditions[a]	Resolution (Å)	PDB entry	Reference
1. 34-mer RNA; 13-mer DNA; GAAA tetraloop in stem II	2.4 M Li_2SO_4, 1 mM spermine, 10 mM Na-cacodylate, pH 6.0	2.6	1HMH	[b]
2. 16-mer RNA; 25-mer RNA with 2'-O-Me at cleavage site; GUAA tetraloop in stem III	23% PEG 6000, 100 mM NH_4OAc, 10 mM $Mg(OAc)_2$, 50 mM spermine, 5% glycerol, 10 mM NH_4-cacodylate, pH 6.5	3.1	1MME	[c]
3. 16-mer RNA; 25-mer RNA; GUAA tetraloop in stem III	1.8 M Li_2SO_4, 1.25 mM EDTA, 50 mM Na-cacodylate, pH 6.0	3.0	299D	[d]
4. Same as 3	1.8 M Li_2SO_4, Mn^{2+}, buffer, pH 5.0	3.0 / 3.0	300D / 300D	[d] / [d]
5. Same as 3	1.8 M Li_2SO_4, 100 mM $MgSO_4$, buffer, pH 8.5	3.1	301D	[d]

[a]To flash-cool crystals for data collection ($\sim 100°$K), a cryoprotectant of 20% glycerol was added to 1 and 3–5; 25% glycerol was added to 2.
[b]Pley et al 1994 (37).
[c]Scott et al 1995 (48).
[d]Scott et al 1996 (49).

The first crystallization and structure determination utilized a complex between a 34-nucleotide all-RNA "ribozyme" in which stem II was closed with a GAAA tetraloop, and a 13-nucleotide all-DNA inhibitor strand that left blunt ends for stems I and III (Figure 1b) (37). The use of a DNA inhibitor strand was justified by the fact that it differs from a substrate only by the lack of a 2'-OH at the cleavage site (position 17), and that mostly-DNA substrates with a single ribonucleotide at position 17 are cleaved efficiently by the ribozyme (11). Soon thereafter, an all-RNA hammerhead having a single 2'-O-methyl ribonucleotide at the cleavage site (to prevent self-cleavage) was crystallized and its structure determined (48). Work on this construct has been extended to an all-RNA hammerhead that is active in crystals under suitable conditions (49). Despite the differences in specific sequence, connectivity of stems, substitution of ribonucleotides with deoxyribonucleotides, and ionic strength of the crystallization conditions (low ionic strength versus 1.8–2.4 M Li_2SO_4), the three-dimensional structures and tertiary folds of hammerheads are strikingly similar. The primary difference in the structures of the ribozyme core is due to specific hydrogen bonding interactions of the 2′-OH of nucleotide 16.1 in the all-RNA hammerheads, which are absent from the RNA-DNA complex in which a deoxyribonucleotide occupies this position. These differences are compared elsewhere (48). In the following sections, we discuss the structural features that are conserved among hammerhead ribozymes and how they relate to hammerhead mechanism, as well as to the structure of biologically active RNAs in general.

Tertiary Fold

The hammerhead ribozyme is a "Y"-shaped molecule comprised of three A-form helical stems emerging from the conserved core that is essential for enzymatic activity; it is conventionally shown with stems I and II on the upper right and upper left respectively and stem III at the base (Figures 1*b* & 4) (37, 48). The molecule is flat, which is to say, the axes of the three stems are nearly coplanar. The core is comprised of two structural domains that were originally called

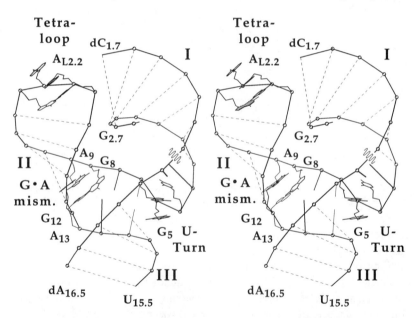

Figure 4   Schematic stereo representation of the hammerhead ribozyme.   Stems I, II, and III are labeled, as well as residues in the uridine turn (U Turn), G•A mismatch, and GNRA tetraloop. A portion of the ribose has been omitted for clarity. *Sticks*, residues in secondary structure motifs; *open circles*, phosphate backbone; *dashed lines*, bases involved in WC base-pairing; *solid lines*, core residues involved in non-WC pairing; *wavy line*, site of cleavage. Figures 5–9 maintain the perspective shown. Figures 4–9 utilized molecule 3 of Brookhaven Protein Data Bank (PDB) entry 1HMH.

domain 1 (C_3-A_6), which forms a sharp, "uridine" turn, and domain 2 (U_7-A_9 and G_{12}-A_{14}), which includes a tandem G·A mismatch; nucleotides within domain 2 form a continuous stack between stems II and III, so that these stems are almost (but not exactly) collinear (37). Nucleotides in the stems that were originally predicted from the primary structure to form WC base pairs do so, with the exception of $A_{15.1}$-$U_{16.1}$ at the beginning of stem III, where the bases share only a single hydrogen bond. Nucleotides within the core have non-WC interactions. The substrate/inhibitor strand is splayed between nucleotides 16.1 and 17 such that the former nucleotide is stacked with stem III, and the latter (which is 5' to the cleavage site) stacks in continuity with stem I (Figure 4).

The hammerhead ribozyme has a surprisingly simple tertiary structure, being composed essentially of two small structural domains, a uridine turn and a tandem G·A mismatch, at the junction of three helices. Additionally, the tetranucleotide loops ("tetraloops") of the constructs used in the crystallographic work, although not required for hammerhead function, are examples of a GNRA consensus sequence that is prevalent in large RNAs; these provide a third illustration of a small RNA structural domain, particularly one that is important for mediating tertiary or quaternary interactions. The hammerhead structures exemplify a theme that is emerging from structural studies of RNAs, *to wit*, that (both small and large) RNAs found in biological contexts, including ribozymes and ribosomal RNAs, are built from small structural motifs interlinked by A-form helices [see Holbrook & Kim, (23) for a review]. It is therefore of interest to consider the structural motifs of the hammerhead both from the perspective of their involvement in the enzymatic function, and from the perspective of their (demonstrated or hypothesized) recurrence elsewhere in RNA structures.

The Uridine Turn

Residues U_4, G_5, A_6 and the phosphate of U_7 compose a uridine turn (or π Turn) that is identical in conformation and stabilizing interactions to those found originally in the pseudouridine and anticodon loops of yeast tRNA[Phe] [for a review, see Quigley & Rich, (41)]. Two hydrogen bonds stabilize the turn (Figure 5): (*a*) that between N3 of U_4 and the *pro*-S_p phosphate oxygen of U_7, and (*b*) that between the 2'-OH of U_4 and N7 of the purine ring of A_6.

Additionally, the heterocyclic ring of U_4 and the phosphate group of A_6 are in van der Waals contact, which has been suggested to add further stability (41). The uridine turn results in an abrupt change in direction relative to an extended phosphoribose backbone; this is primarily due to changes in the torsion angles about P-O5' (α) and P-O3' (ζ) between U_4 and G_5, as noted previously for tRNA[Phe] (44). Consequently, the turn places a kink in stem I of the ribozyme strand, directly below the active site (See Figure 4). Beyond the structural role of the turn, there is substantial evidence that the exocyclic groups of the G_5 heterocycle are essential for hammerhead activity (31); however, these groups

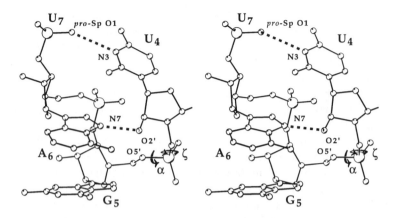

Figure 5   Ball-and-stick stereo representation of the uridine turn of the hammerhead ribozyme. *Arrows* around angles α and ζ indicate the torsional rotations responsible for the change in the course of the polyphosphate backbone (the result is a kink at the base of Stem I); *dashed lines*, hydrogen bonds.

are solvent-exposed and do not interact with the ribozyme in the crystallographic structures. This dilemma is readily apparent when one examines the functional group modification data (discussed in a later section).

As mentioned, the uridine turn is a conserved structural motif at two positions in tRNAs. The two hydrogen bonds shown in Figure 5 would suggest a consensus sequence of U_n, N_{n+1}, R_{n+2}, N_{n+3}, i.e. the first nucleotide must be uridine, (or pseudouridine in tRNA) any nucleotide may be at positions 2 and 4, and the third nucleotide must be a purine. However, in the anticodon stem of tRNA, nucleotides n+1 through n+3 form the anticodon, and hence sample all four nucleotides; in cases where nucleotide n+2 is not a purine, a hydrogen bond from the 2'-OH of the uridine is lost, apparently without disruption of the structural motif (33). The course of the phosphoribose backbone following the uridine turn is dictated by which of the two nonbridging phosphate oxygens at position n+3 is chosen by the uridine as a hydrogen bond partner; in the hammerhead, U_4 bonds the *pro-S$_p$* oxygen and the backbone emerges into the second structural domain of the core, while in tRNA, the initial uridine/pseudouridine of the turn bonds the *pro-R$_p$* oxygen, allowing the backbone to back-track upon the associated stem.

The GNRA Tetraloop

The GNRA tetraloop is the most prevalent hairpin element of ribosomal RNA (rRNA) structure. It accounts for between 38 to 55% of all hairpins observed in the predicted secondary structure of 16S and 23S rRNA (58). Its predominant role appears to be mediation of tertiary interactions through loops and stems in large RNAs (25, 32). Though not required for activity, GNRA tetraloops were incorporated into the hammerhead as a means to connect the strands of stems in RNA constructs used for crystallographic studies. In this context, and as a representative small RNA folding motif, this structural feature merits attention. To date, the structures of several GNRA loops have been described by both NMR (22), and crystallography (8, 36, 48). The respective structures superimpose remarkably well considering the variety of environments and conditions under which they have been characterized.[1] Figure 6a shows the structure of a tetraloop from the hammerhead ribozyme with sequence GAAA. In a manner reminiscent of the uridine turn, the 2'-OH of the initial $G_{L2.1}$ hydrogen bonds to the N7 of $A_{L2.3}$ and the exocyclic amino group of $G_{L2.1}$ hydrogen bonds both the pro-R_p phosphoryl oxygen and N7 of $A_{L2.4}$. Base stacking of the second, third and fourth nucleotides fortifies the structure.

Tetraloop interactions within the minor groove of RNA stems have been described in detail for both intra- and intermolecular complexes. Interestingly, the structure of the P4-P6 domain of the *Tetrahymena* Group I intron (7), and that of a hammerhead ribozyme (36) show many commonalities with respect to the spatial arrangement and molecular interactions observed between a tetraloop and its cognate "receptor," including extensive involvement of the 2'-OH's of the phosphoribose backbone mediated by hydrogen bonds (compare Figures 6b & 6c). At the same time, there are significant differences between the inter- and intramolecular complexes outside the A_3 and A_4 recognition interactions. In the crystal structure of the P4-P6 domain, the tetraloop recognizes an A-rich receptor element (J6a/6b) containing two side-by-side adenines (A_{225} & A_{226}) that form a single non-WC base pair. The stability of this A-platform arises through stacking upon adjacent non-WC duplex pairs. By maintaining the interactions at the A_3 & A_4 positions, the tetraloop and receptor dock on the platform to make a pseudocontinuous base stack (see Figure 6b). By analogy, a comparable "AG-platform" is observed in the hammerhead ribozyme intermolecular interaction, in which the half-sheared[2] $G_{L2.1}$ to $A_{L2.4}$ pair (Figure 6a) mimics the A-platform plane, fortified by two discontiguous triple-base stacks that include $A_{L2.2}$ to $A_{L2.4}$ from the respective tetraloops of molecules 1 & 2 (Figure 6c).

---

[1] The structures of five GAAA tetraloops from x-ray crystallographic Brookhaven Protein Data Bank (PDB) entries 1HMH and 1GID superimpose with an average rms deviation of 0.284 Å. The weighted rms average including 10 NMR structures from PDB entry 1ZIF is 0.493 Å (15 total structures).

[2] The GNRA structures of the respective hammerhead ribozymes as well as that of the P4-P6 structure do not maintain a hydrogen bond at the position equivalent to N3 of $G_{L2.1}$ to N6 of $A_{L2.4}$. This distance varies between ~3.7 to 5 Å; see Figure 6a. Thus the hydrogen bond configuration is only "half-sheared."

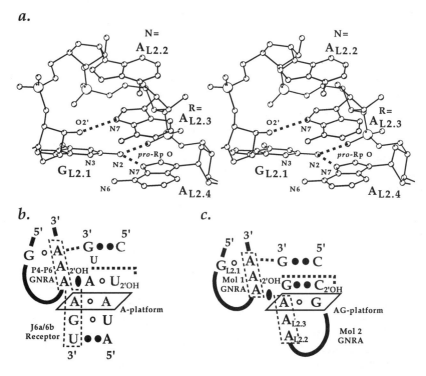

Figure 6 Schematic representations of the GNRA tetraloop. (*a*) Ball-and-stick stereo representation of the GAAA Tetraloop in Stem II. *Dashed lines*, hydrogen bonds. (*b*) Diagram of the J6a/6b tetraloop receptor of the P4-P6 domain of the Group I Intron (7). *Open circles*, non-WC pairs between bases. *Double closed circles*, WC base-pairs. *Dashed boxes*, stacked bases. *Dashed lines*, hydrogen bonds. *Ovals*, local nucleotide dyad. *Gray letters*, nucleotides on the same strand. Platforms fall in one plane. (*c*) Diagram of the intermolecular interface of the hammerhead ribozyme. See 6*b* for details of the interactions.

This spatial arrangement provides a "dock" for the tetraloop of molecule 1 in a manner markedly similar to that seen in P4-P6 (compare Figures 6*b* & 6*c*). This unexpected analogy between the docking of the inter- and intramolecular complexes is unlikely to be fortuitous and offers support to the intriguing suggestion of Costa & Michel (9) that tetraloop receptors have significant determinants of recognition beyond the two base pairs originally identified from sequence covariation (9, 32).

The Tandem G·A Mismatch

An additional structural motif is the tandem G·A mismatch, found in domain 2 of the hammerhead ribozyme core (Figure 4). Two layers of interactions within the G·A mismatch are shown in Figure 7.

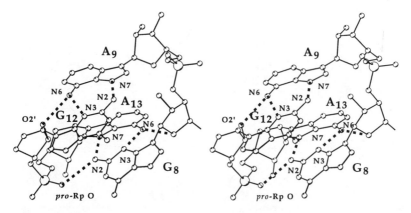

Figure 7   Ball-and-stick stereo representation of the tandem G•A mismatch in the core of the hammerhead ribozyme. Residues G_8:A_{13}, and A_9:G_{12} engage in sheared non-WC hydrogen bonds. *Dashed lines*, hydrogen bonds.

Both layers contain a "sheared" hydrogen bond pattern in which N7 and N6 of A interact with N2 and N3 of G, respectively. These interactions are seen in all hammerhead structures, and have also been observed previously in the NMR structure of the internal loop (rGGC$\underline{GA}$GCC)$_2$ (46). An additional hydrogen bond interaction within domain 2 occurs between the 2'-hydroxyl of G_{12} and N6 of A_9, which is not observed in the NMR model duplex. Mismatched bases in both the hammerhead and model duplex are in the *anti* conformation. In the hammerhead, the core bases extending from G_{12} through A_{14} stack uninterrupted with those of Stems II and III, leading to the near-collinearity of the stems. Non-conserved residue U_7 disrupts base stacking that is otherwise continuous from Stem II through A_9 and G_8 of the mismatch.

Phosphorothioate labeling experiments identify the *pro*-R_p phosphate oxygens of A_9, A_{13}, and A_{14} in domain 2 as probable divalent ion binding sites (27, 43). Divalent ion binding involving A_9 of the tandem G•A mismatch has been confirmed in independent x-ray structures of the hammerhead (37, 48). Anomalous difference electron density maps on crystals of the RNA-DNA complex soaked in either Mn^{2+} or Cd^{2+} demonstrated that either metal ion will bind as shown in Figure 8*a*; metal ligands are provided by the *pro*-R_p oxygen of phosphate A_9, in agreement with phosphorothioate labeling studies, and N7 of base $G_{10.1}$, explaining the preference for purines over pyrimidines at this position.

In all probability, the interaction with N7 would be mediated through a bridging H_2O molecule for Mg^{2+}, due to its high preference for oxygen over nitrogen ligands. This observation is corroborated by the residual difference electron density maps of Scott, which revealed a peak attributed to a hydrated

a.

b.

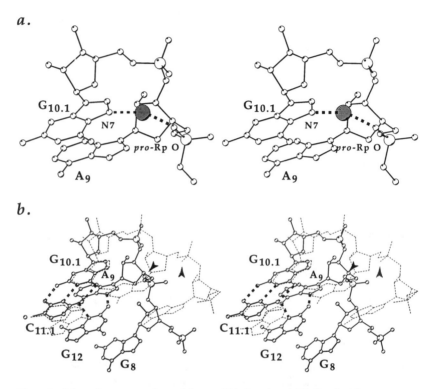

Figure 8 Schematic representations of the metal binding site. (*a*) Ball-and-stick stereo representation of the metal ligands observed with Mn^{2+} and Cd^{2+}. *Gray sphere*, (N7 of $G_{10.1}$ and the *pro*-R_p oxygen of phosphate A_9 are atoms in the first coordination sphere of the metal); *dashed lines*, interactions. (*b*) *Broken lines*, a least-squares[3] superposition of the metal binding site (8*a*) upon a model $\frac{5'-X-A-G-X-3}{3'-X-G-A-X-5}$ mismatch (59). The equivalent *pro*-R_p oxygens of the hammerhead (*black arrowhead*) and the model duplex (*gray arrowhead*) are separated by ~5Å. (*c*) Schematic drawing of the average O3'-to-P distances within the sheared G•A mismatch of the hammerhead. *Gray stripes*, G distances; *black stripes*, A distances; *asterisk*, site of metal coordination at the layer 1-to-2 interface of the mismatch structure. One layer represents one mismatch. (*d*) The imino-G mismatch of an A•G mismatch. See 8*c* for details.

magnesium. Interestingly, this site was modeled to interact with the *pro*-S_p oxygen of the A_9 phosphate. Although the significance of this difference in observed coordination is unclear, divalent ion binding at this location is essential for efficient hammerhead activity (35).

[3]A-form helices were minimized by the method of Kabsch as implemented in CCP4 (2) using over 85 atoms engaged in flanking Watson-Crick (WC) base-pair interactions (rms displacement 1.2 Å).

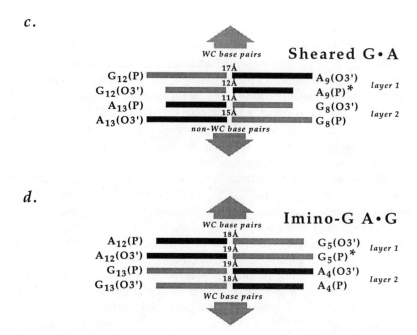

Figure 8 (*Continued*)

Tandem mismatches embedded in WC duplex stems, often referred to as "internal loops", occur frequently in large RNAs. The occurrence of such mismatches involving G·A pairs has been analyzed for 16S and 23S rRNA (17). Comparisons of phylogenetic sequence variation at sites where the presence of a tandem mismatch is conserved reveals a strong preference for the sequences $\frac{5'-G-A-3'}{3'-A-G-5'}$ and $\frac{5'-A-A-3'}{3'-A-G-5'}$ while the tandem mismatch $\frac{5'-A-G-3'}{3'-G-A-5'}$ is never observed. The prevalence of the former mismatches and exclusion of the latter cannot be rationalized on thermodynamic grounds, since the destabilization due to the insertion of the tandem mismatch into a WC duplex (i.e. the difference between the free energy of duplex formation with the mismatch versus without) is approximately the same for both $\frac{5'-G-A-3'}{3'-A-G-5'}$ and $\frac{5'-A-G-3'}{3'-G-A-5'}$, ~1.5–1.6 Kcal/mole (45). Therefore the preference for $\frac{5'-G-A-3'}{3'-A-G-5'}$ and $\frac{5'-A-A-3'}{3'-A-G-5'}$ over $\frac{5'-A-G-3'}{3'-G-A-5'}$ must be due to other factors.

Although a direct generalization from a single occurrence of the tandem G·A mismatch in domain 2 of the hammerhead to a structural and functional role in large RNAs is not warranted, it is provocative to consider what aspects of the structure of this small motif may correlate with the preference for this or closely related sequences in large RNAs. In particular, if we include all the contributors to the divalent ion binding activity (including $G_{10.1}$, whose N7 is a metal ligand), the consensus sequence required to retain the ion binding activity becomes $\frac{5'-Y-G-A^*R-3'}{3'-R-A-G-Y-5'}$, where an asterisk indicates the metal binding site, consistent with observations that a purine following the G·A mismatch is preferred for activity in the hammerhead (42, 54). In the sequences of internal loops of large RNAs, there is also a strong preference for a purine following a $\frac{5'-G-A-3'}{3'-A-G-5'}$ or a $\frac{5'-A-A-3'}{3'-A-G-5'}$ mismatch, while the sequences $\frac{5'-R-G-A-Y-3'}{3'-Y-A-G-R-5'}$ and $\frac{5'-X-A-G-X-3'}{3'-X-G-A-X-5'}$ (where X participates in a WC base pair) are rare (17, 59); the significance of this correlation remains an open question.

NMR studies of model duplexes have demonstrated significantly different structures for the $\frac{5'-G-A-3'}{3'-A-G-5'}$ and $\frac{5'-A-G-3'}{3'-G-A-5'}$ mismatches; $\frac{5'-G-A-3'}{3'-A-G-5'}$ forms tandem sheared G·A base pairs, while $\frac{5'-A-G-3'}{3'-G-A-5'}$ does not (59). The structural difference between these two mismatches is shown in Figure 8b, where the structure of the A·G mismatch determined by NMR in a model oligonucleotide, (rGGCAGGCC)$_2$, is superimposed on the G·A mismatch of the hammerhead ribozyme. It appears that the tandem A·G mismatch would be incapable of binding divalent ions in the manner similar to that of the G·A mismatch. In contrast to this, the $\frac{5'-A-A-3'}{3'-A-G-5'}$ mismatch has been modeled to have tandem sheared base pairs similar to $\frac{5'-G-A-3'}{3'-A-G-5'}$, and hence would be anticipated to have a similar conformation capable of binding divalent ions (17). In the hammerhead, domain 2 with the tandem G·A mismatch appears to have a divalent ion-dependent role in pulling stems II and III into alignment to form an active molecule (discussed in the section on solution structure); such mismatches may have similar roles in large RNAs.

A subtle but significant point regards the occurrence of the mismatches in tandem pairs, rather than, for example, as a single mismatch. The prevalence of pairs of mismatches is best explained by their capacity to form hydrogen bonds compatible with WC base pairing on both sides of the internal loop. The asymmetry inherent in a single layer of sheared G·A hydrogen bonds is demonstrated by the observations depicted in Figure 8c. For the hammerhead, the G(P)-A(O3') distances are long ($\sim$16 Å) compared to the shorter A(P)-G(O3') distances ($\sim$11.5 Å). The normal RNA values are closer to 17.5 Å. By placing a second G·A base pair in tandem with layer 1, a compensatory widening of the helix is achieved restoring the P-O3' distances to values representative of normal helical duplexes (Figure 8c). A similar phenomenon occurs for the imino-G A·G mismatch, although the duplex must be narrowed at the ends (Figure 8d). The significant widening of the duplex diameter readily accounts for the inability of the pro-R_p oxygen at G_5 to coordinate a metal, as seen for its G·A counterpart (position A_9) depicted in Figures 8b & c.

The Active Site

The most problematic feature of the crystallographic structures of the hammerhead is that the active site is not in a conformation that would allow bond cleavage consistent with the established chemistry of the reaction. Specifically, the scissile bond is not poised for in-line attack by the 2'-OH of nucleotide 17 (e.g. similar to Figure 2b or 2e); rather, the phosphoribose backbone is in a configuration similar to that shown in Figure 2a. Thus at a minimum, a substantial rearrangement of the phosphoribose backbone is required to position the catalytic moieties for bond cleavage. As discussed originally by Pley et al (37) this could be accomplished by nucleotide 17 unstacking and flipping outward, or by the target phosphate rotating inward in a manner similar to that shown in Figure 2, (or by an intermediate combination of both operations). Additionally, one or more divalent ions must be bound at the cleavage site. The "noncatalytic" conformations observed in the crystallographic structures can be reconciled as being relevant to the overall reaction pathway of the ribozyme if one accepts that they mimic the ground state enzyme-substrate complex of the reaction, and that a significant change (the exact nature of which is not obvious from the crystallographic structures) is required to ascend the ~22 Kcal/mole activation energy barrier (21) to the catalytic transition state.

In absence of the active site being poised for catalysis, efforts have been made to model plausible reaction pathways, extrapolating from the crystallographic structures, and also to experimentally trap catalytic conformations. Scott and colleagues have attempted to "freeze-trap" a catalytic intermediate of the reaction, by use of an active all-RNA ribozyme (49). In these studies, crystals of a ribozyme-substrate complex were grown at pH 6.0 in the absence of polyvalent metals. Activity of the complex was triggered through the addition of divalent metals soaked into crystals at pH 8.5, and the crystals were flash-cooled to liquid nitrogen temperatures before becoming disordered. Difference electron density maps from x-ray data collected before and after activation indicated a localized conformational change in the uridine turn and around the cleavage site. Further, a peak in an isomorphous difference electron density map was interpreted as a Mg^{2+} ion bound to the pro-R_p oxygen of $A_{1.1}$. Although the hammerhead was not in a conformation that would allow in-line attack (as in Figure 2c), the structure was judged to be a catalytic intermediate (possibly between Figure 2a and 2b) that was trapped on the reaction coordinate and allowed to accumulate to nearly full occupancy due to the constraints of the crystal lattice. Based upon this conformation, reaction pathways are proposed in which the Mg^{2+}, by binding the pro-R_p phosphate oxygen of nucleotide 1.1, induces the conformational change required for in-line attack on the scissile bond. Movements to reach the transition state would be small and localized, with the pre-catalytic Mg^{2+}-phosphate complex observed in the crystals rotating ~2 Å relative to the remainder of the ribozyme; no base unstacking or hydrogen bond breakage would be required. This would lead to a transition state structure consistent with a single metal ion cleavage mechanism.

Interaction with Divalent Metal Ions

Structural delineation of the interaction of the hammerhead ribozyme with divalent ions, which are crucial for its activity, has been hindered by both the modest diffraction limit, ~3 Å, of the crystals (whereas resolution approaching 2 Å is required for unequivocal definition of a metal ion and its surrounding ligands), and in the case of the RNA-DNA complex, also by interference with metal binding by the high salt conditions in which the crystals are stabilized (Table 1). Locating metal binding sites has relied on a combination of (a) residual difference electron density maps, where metal ions may show up as significant peaks in solvent regions, and (b) anomalous difference electron density maps using data from crystals soaked in Mn^{2+} or Cd^{2+}, which gives a signal specifically attributed to the heavier atoms, due to their K or L-edge x-ray absorption. Each method, although having the potential to contribute significant information on metal binding, comes with caveats; (a) residual peaks in difference electron density maps at ~3 Å resolution, if due to Mg^{2+} ions, do not resolve the ions from neighboring ligands, making detailed interpretation difficult, and (b) ions such as Mn^{2+} or Cd^{2+}, although their anomalous scattering signal is unambiguous, are not exact mimics of Mg^{2+} since they have different ligand preferences and larger atomic radii.

In summary, one divalent ion binding site in the tandem G·A mismatch has been documented in all the reported x-ray structures, as described above. Further, biochemical studies corroborate both the location of the binding site and its importance for activity. Additionally, Scott and colleagues have presented evidence for (a) a Mg^{2+} ion bound to the pro-Rp phosphate oxygen of the scissile bond in a reaction intermediate structure at pH 8.5, and (b) four additional sites in their hammerhead structures[4], three of which are in the catalytic core. Readers are referred to Scott et al (48, 49) for a discussion of details of the binding interactions of the latter ions. One of the unresolved issues regarding metal binding is the absence of divalent ions interacting with the phosphates of A_{13} and A_{14}, which have been identified by phosphorothioate labeling experiments as sites of interaction with one or more functionally significant Mg^{2+} ions (27, 43).

---

[4] Although 6 divalent metal binding sites have been identified, four sites (1, 3, 4, and 5) have been observed to have locations geometries, and environments consistent with those of fully hydrated metal ions, $Me(H_2O)_6^{2+}$, since the nearest hammerhead atoms are at distances ≥3.6 Å. Because these sites have been discussed elsewhere, [Scott et al (48), (49); see also PDB entries 300D and 301D], this review focuses upon metals engaged in first-sphere coordination.

Unanswered Questions

Despite progress made from the crystal structures of the ground state and reaction intermediate states of the hammerhead, there are still some obvious dilemmas regarding the correlation of structure with catalytic activity. First, the structures do not reflect catalytic transition state configurations, so that explicit suggestions for reaction pathways are predicated on significant extrapolation, which is inherently risky. Further, data regarding binding of essential structural and catalytic divalent metal ions are somewhat ambivalent (discussed in previous section). There is presently insufficient evidence, structural or otherwise, to support unambiguously the existence of a second metal ion in catalysis. There is no apparent means to protonate or otherwise stabilize the LG of the reaction. Most importantly, the conformational rearrangements of the active site that must occur for bond cleavage remain a conundrum. In the mind of the reader, these ambiguities may raise doubts regarding the relevance of the crystallographic structure data to hammerhead activity. In the next sections, we summarize data on site-specific chemical modification of the hammerhead and on the solution structure of the molecule, and analyze its correlation with the crystallographic structures.

FUNCTIONAL GROUP MODIFICATION DATA

In the context of the dilemma posed by the crystallographic structures of the hammerhead ribozyme, to wit that they show the overall tertiary structure, but do not readily reveal a catalytic configuration for the molecule, it is incumbent that some discretion is exercised in their interpretation. Therefore, it is instructive to ask how well the crystallographic data mesh with the results of chemical modification studies of the ribozyme. A detailed reiteration of the analysis of these data is outside the scope of this review, since it is available elsewhere (31); only the primary conclusions will be summarized.

Replacement of nucleotides within the central core of the hammerhead with other naturally occurring nucleotides has identified the consensus sequence that is required for activity (Figure 1a); typically, replacement of one nucleotide with another reduces catalytic activity two to three orders of magnitude (42). A methodology that allows a more specific delineation of the prerequisites for catalysis has been to incorporate modified nucleotides into the ribozyme, in which only one or two functional groups are modified, and to determine the consequent effect on activity. For example, many of the ribonucleotides of the ribozyme core have been individually substituted with either a deoxyribonucleotide, thereby "deleting" the 2'-hydroxyl, or with 2'-amino, 2'-fluoro, or 2'-O-methyl nucleotides, thereby changing both the hydrogen bonding pattern and the chemical reactivity of this site. In a similar vein, a spectrum of nucleotides with modified purine or pyrimidine rings has been incorporated to determine the consequence of deleting or altering specific exocyclic functional groups. Substitution of phosphates with thiophosphates has been used to identify sites of ligation for divalent metal ions. Most substitutions that have been reported either reduce hammerhead activity or leave it unaltered; however, a new type of modification which enhances activity has been reported; namely, replacing the non-conserved uracil ring of U_7 with a pyridine-4-one increases the bond cleavage rate approximately tenfold (5).

When the results from more than a hundred such modifications are assembled and mapped onto the three-dimensional structure, some general patterns emerge. Some of the main points are summarized in Figure 9; refer to (31) for a complete discussion.

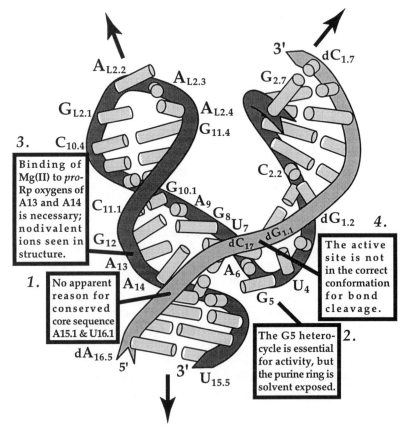

Figure 9 Ribbon model of the hammerhead ribozyme. *Light gray ribbon*, substrate; *dark ribbon*, ribozyme; *light cylinders*, bases; *boxed text* (1–4), features of the ground-state x-ray structures that cannot be reconciled with the current chemical modification data.

In some regions of the ribozyme core, and particularly in domain 2, many of the functional groups whose modification results in loss of activity are involved in specific tertiary interactions or in interactions with divalent metal ions. Arguably, modifications of these groups may destabilize the overall tertiary structure. However, there are other instances where the three-dimensional structure and the effects of functional group modification cannot be understood (Figure 9–1) or reconciled easily. For example, the greatest discrepancy involves nucleotide G_5 of domain 1; any alteration of the exocyclic groups of the guanosine base reduces hammerhead activity two to three orders of magnitude; this observation is confounded by the x-ray structures in which these groups are solvent-exposed and are completely devoid of intramolecular interactions (Figure 9–2). Additionally, the phosphates of A_{13} and A_{14} have been indicted as binding sites for essential divalent ions, yet no metal ion has been seen crystallographically at these positions (Figure 9–3). As discussed above, in the crystallographic structures the active site is not poised for catalysis (Figure 9–4). If the crystallographic structures of the hammerhead mimic a ground state enzyme-substrate complex, then the functional group modification data suggest a substantial conformational rearrangement involving both the cleavage site and the uridine turn must take place prior to reaching the transition state. By implication, significant intramolecular and metal ion binding interactions of the transition state must be absent, and hence not observed, in the crystallographic structures. However, evidence suggests that the ground to transition state rearrangement is localized to the ribozyme core region, and does not mandate a global conformational change of the stems; this will be discussed in the next section.

SOLUTION STRUCTURE AND FOLDING

At the same time efforts were under way to solve the crystallographic structure of the hammerhead ribozyme, several independent groups were using other methodologies to determine its structure in solution. Gel electrophoresis (3) and transient electric birefringence (TEB) (16) were used on constructs in which pairs of the three stems were extended—to 40 base pairs for gel electrophoresis and to ~70 base pairs for TEB—and the gel mobility or the rotational mobility inferred from the birefringence decay rate gave qualitative (for electrophoresis) or quantitative (for TEB) measures of the average angles between stems. Additionally, using RNA constructs in which the ends of stems were labeled pairwise with a fluorescence donor and acceptor, Tuschl and coworkers used fluorescence resonance energy transfer (FRET) to map distances between points on stems and constructed a model from an ensemble of distance constraints (55). All three of these methods converged upon similar models at nearly the same time, concluding that the hammerhead is Y-shaped in solution under ionic conditions where it is active. It is notable that these results are in complete agreement with, but were obtained independent of, the crystallographic structures.

Further evidence supports the suggestion that the Y-shaped conformation is the catalytically active form in solution. When stems I and II are tethered by crosslinking to a conformation close to that seen in the crystal structures, the molecules retain full activity under standard assay conditions (Figure 10c) (51). Likewise, TEB measurements on active hammerheads indicate no change of the average angle between stems I and II during the course of the reaction (1).

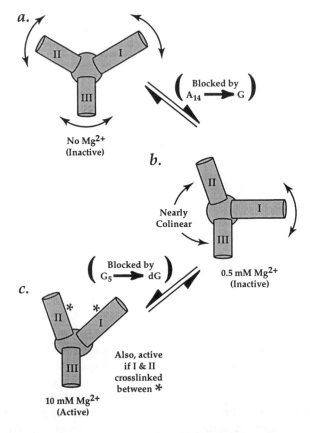

Figure 10 Schematic diagram of the hammerhead folding properties and stem conformations under various ionic conditions, based upon gel electrophoresis measurements. *Double arrows,* essentially random conformations for a given condition. (*a*) no Mg^{2+}, inactive; (*b*) 0.5 mM Mg^{2+}, inactive. (*c*) 10 mM Mg^{2+}, active; stems I and II may be crosslinked between positions marked with an *asterisk* and the hammerhead will remain active.

Gel electrophoresis measurements over a range of Mg^{2+} concentrations reveal a two-step folding path, where (a) in absence of divalent ion, all three stems have relatively random orientations (Figure 10a); (b) titrating to ~0.5 mM Mg^{2+}, stems II and III become approximately collinear while stem I remains randomized (Figure 10b); and (c) further titration to ~10 mM Mg^{2+} brings stem I into proximity of stem II, resulting in the Y-shaped conformation at Mg^{2+} concentrations where the hammerhead is active (Figure 10c) (3).

Modifications that affect both the global conformation and the catalytic activity of the hammerhead have been reported. The average angle between stems I and II measured by TEB shows some sequence dependence; two hammerheads differing in the sequence of four nucleotides adjacent to the core in stem I show a difference in inter-stem angle of 15°. Also, an approximate 5-fold difference in cleavage rate is observed between these molecules, such that the construct having a larger stem I–stem II angle (130° versus 115°) shows a lower cleavage rate (1). Further, specific alterations of the central core that affect the overall folding of the hammerhead have been characterized; A_{14} to G blocks the first step in the folding pathway (Figure 10a to b) and G_5 to deoxyG_5 blocks the second step (Figure 10b to c) (4).

Taken together, these solution studies show the hammerhead is flexible in solution in the absence of divalent ions, and that it has a two-step, Mg^{2+}-induced folding path leading to an active, Y-shaped conformation. If one accepts the premise that the crystallographic structures represent a ground state of the molecule and that a significant rearrangement around the cleavage site is required for bond cleavage, then the solution studies argue that catalysis does not require, and is probably accomplished in the absence of, a major global conformational change of the molecule.

SUMMARY

Crystallographic studies of the hammerhead ribozyme have given us our first look at the molecular structure of a catalytic RNA molecule. The hammerhead fold is deceptively simple, being composed of two small RNA motifs at the junction of three helices. Several structures on different hammerhead constructs, including fully active molecules, have the same fold. Further, the global conformation of the ribozyme in crystals agrees with the conformation found in solution by several independent methods. Hence there can be little doubt that the crystal structures are directly germane to the catalytic function of the molecule.

However, when our focus shifts from the overall tertiary structure of the molecule to the question of catalytic mechanism, we find that many questions are left unanswered. The active site is not poised for bond cleavage; we cannot unambiguously infer the transition state configuration from the available structures. On the contrary, the crystal structures mimic ground state enzyme-substrate complexes, and at a minimum, significant rearrangement must occur around the active site to climb the ~22 Kcal/mole activation barrier to the transition state of the cleavage reaction. Although progress has been made in the direction of trapping reaction intermediates, the precise nature of the rearrangements, and the locations where catalytic metal ion(s) bind throughout the course of the reaction, remain unresolved.

From a general perspective, we may ask whether our current dilemma suggests something about the hammerhead reaction in particular, and by implication, about the catalytic mechanisms of small ribozymes in general. What we fail to see in the structure is a "lock and key" fit between enzyme and substrate, or more precisely, between enzyme and the transition state of the bond cleavage reaction, a recurring paradigm in the structures of protein enzymes. This suggests that the hammerhead ribozyme, being a small structure and a rather inefficient catalyst, may rely less on static structural complementarity to a transition state of the substrate cleavage reaction, and more on dynamics or "induced-fit"—the ability to twist the active site into a conformation that is transiently poised for catalytic ion binding and bond cleavage—than we might have expected from prior experience with (larger and more efficient) protein enzymes.

ACKNOWLEDGMENTS

This work was supported by grant AI-30606 from the National Institutes of Health to DBM. JEW is a Burroughs Wellcome Fund Fellow of the Life Sciences Research Foundation.

Visit the *Annual Reviews* home page at
http://www.AnnualReviews.org.

Literature Cited

1. Amiri KM, Hagerman PJ. 1996. The global conformation of an active hammerhead RNA during the process of self-cleavage. *J. Mol. Biol.* 261:125–34
2. Bailey S. 1994. The CCP4 suite: programs for protein crystallography. *Acta Cryst.* D50:760–63
3. Bassi GS, Mollegaard NE, Murchie AI, von Kitzing E, Lilley DM. 1995. Ionic interactions and the global conformations of the hammerhead ribozyme. *Nat. Struct. Biol.* 2:45–55
4. Bassi GS, Murchie AI, Lilley DM. 1996. The ion-induced folding of the hammerhead ribozyme: core sequence changes that perturb folding into the active conformation. *RNA* 2:756–68
5. Burgin AJ, Gonzalez C, Matulic AJ, Karpeisky AM, Usman N, et al. 1996. Chemically modified hammerhead ribozymes with improved catalytic rates. *Biochemistry* 35:14090–97
6. Buzayan JM, Gerlach WL, Bruening G. 1986. Nonenzymatic cleavage and ligation of RNAs complementary to a plant virus satellite RNA. *Nature* 323:349–53
7. Cate JH, Gooding AR, Podell E, Zhou K, Golden BL, et al. 1996. Crystal structure of a group I ribozyme domain: principles of RNA packing. *Science* 273:1678–85

8. Cate JH, Gooding AR, Podell E, Zhou K, Golden BL, et al. 1996. RNA tertiary structure mediation by adenosine platforms. *Science* 273:1696–99
9. Costa M, Michel F. 1997. Rules for RNA recognition of GNRA tetraloops deduced by in vitro selection: comparison with in vivo evolution. *EMBO J.* 16:3289–302
10. Dahm SC, Derrick WB, Uhlenbeck OC. 1993. Evidence for the role of solvated metal hydroxide in the hammerhead cleavage mechanism. *Biochemistry* 32:13040–45
11. Dahm SC, Uhlenbeck OC. 1990. Characterization of deoxy- and ribo-containing oligonucleotide substrates in the hammerhead self-cleavage reaction. *Biochimie* 72:819–23
12. Dahm SC, Uhlenbeck OC. 1991. Role of divalent metal ions in the hammerhead RNA cleavage reaction. *Biochemistry* 30:9464–69
13. Fedor MJ, Uhlenbeck OC. 1992. Kinetics of intermolecular cleavage by hammerhead ribozymes. *Biochemistry* 31:12042–54
14. Forster AC, Symons RH. 1987. Self-cleavage of plus and minus RNAs of a virusoid and a structural model for the active sites. *Cell* 49:211–20
15. Forster AC, Symons RH. 1987. Self-cleavage of virusoid RNA is performed by the proposed 55-nucleotide active site. *Cell* 50:9–16
16. Gast FU, Amiri KM, Hagerman PJ. 1994. Interhelix geometry of stems I and II of a self-cleaving hammerhead RNA. *Biochemistry* 33:1788–96
17. Gautheret D, Konings D, Gutell RR. 1994. A major family of motifs involving G·A mismatches in ribosomal RNA. *J. Mol. Biol.* 242:1–8
18. Haseloff J, Gerlach WL. 1988. Simple RNA enzymes with new and highly specific endoribonuclease activities. *Nature* 334:585–91
19. Hertel KJ, Herschlag D, Uhlenbeck OC. 1994. A kinetic and thermodynamic framework for the hammerhead ribozyme reaction. *Biochemistry* 33:3374–85
20. Hertel KJ, Herschlag D, Uhlenbeck OC. 1996. Specificity of hammerhead ribozyme cleavage. *EMBO J.* 15:3751–57
21. Hertel KJ, Uhlenbeck OC. 1995. The internal equilibrium of the hammerhead ribozyme reaction. *Biochemistry* 34:1744–49
22. Heus HA, Pardi A. 1991. Structural features that give rise to the unusual stability of RNA hairpins containing GNRA loops. *Science* 253:191–94
23. Holbrook SR, Kim S-H. 1997. RNA Crystallography. *Biopolymers* 44:3–21
24. Hutchins CJ, Rathjen PD, Forster AC, Symons RH. 1986. Self-cleavage of plus and minus RNA transcripts of avocado sunblotch viroid. *Nucl. Acids Res.* 14:3627–40
25. Jaeger L, Michel F, Westhof E. 1994. Involvement of a GNRA tetraloop in long-range RNA tertiary interactions. *J. Mol. Biol.* 236:1271–76
26. Jencks WP. 1969. *Catalysis in Chemistry and Enzymology.* New York: McGraw-Hill
27. Knoll R, Bald R, Furste JP. 1997. Complete identification of nonbridging phosphate oxygens involved in hammerhead cleavage. *RNA* 3:132–40
28. Koizumi M, Ohtsuka E. 1991. Effects of phosphorothioate and 2-amino groups in hammerhead ribozymes on cleavage rates and Mg^{2+} binding. *Biochemistry* 30:5145–50
29. Kuimelis RG, McLaughlin LW. 1996. Ribozyme-mediated cleavage of a substrate analogue containing an internucleotide-bridging 5'-phosphorothioate: evidence for the single-metal model. *Biochemistry* 35:5308–17
30. Long DM, LaRiviere FJ, Uhlenbeck OC. 1995. Divalent metal ions and the internal equilibrium of the hammerhead ribozyme. *Biochemistry* 34:14435–40
31. McKay DB. 1996. Structure and function of a hammerhead ribozyme: an unfinished story. *RNA* 2:395–403
32. Michel F, Ellington AD, Couture S, Szostak JW. 1990. Phylogenetic and genetic evidence for base-triples in the catalytic domain of group I introns. *Nature* 347:578–80
33. Moras D, Comarmond MB, Fischer J, Weiss R, Thierry JC, et al. 1980. Crystal structure of yeast tRNA^{Asp}. *Nature* 288:669–74
34. Pecoraro V, Hermes JD, Cleland WW. 1984. Stability constants of Mg(II) and Cd(II) complexes of adenine nucleotides and thionucleotides and rate constants for formation and dissociation of MgATP and MgADP. *Biochemistry* 23:5262–71
35. Peracchi A, Beigelman L, Scott EC, Uhlenbeck OC, Herschlag D. 1997. Involvement of a specific metal ion in the transition of the hammerhead ribozyme to its catalytic conformation. *J. Biol. Chem.* 272:26822–26
36. Pley HW, Flaherty KM, McKay DB. 1994. Model for an RNA tertiary interaction from the structure of an intermolecular complex between a GAAA tetraloop and an RNA helix. *Nature* 372:111–13

37. Pley HW, Flaherty KM, McKay DB. 1994. Three-dimensional structure of a hammerhead ribozyme. *Nature* 372:68–74
38. Pley HW, Lindes DS, DeLuca FC, McKay DB. 1993. Crystals of a hammerhead ribozyme. *J. Biol. Chem.* 268:19656–58
39. Pontius BW, Lott WB, von Hippel PH. 1997. Observations on catalysis by hammerhead ribozymes are consistent with a two-divalent-metal-ion mechanism. *Proc. Natl. Acad. Sci. USA* 94:2290–94
40. Prody GA, Bakos JT, Buzayan JM, Schneider IR, Bruening G. 1986. Autolytic processing of dimeric plant virus satellite RNA. *Science* 231:1577–80
41. Quigley GJ, Rich A. 1976. Structural domains of transfer RNA molecules. *Science* 194:796–806
42. Ruffner DE, Stormo GD, Uhlenbeck OC. 1990. Sequence requirements of the hammerhead RNA self-cleavage reaction. *Biochemistry* 29:10695–702
43. Ruffner DE, Uhlenbeck OC. 1990. Thiophosphate interference experiments locate phosphates important for the hammerhead RNA self-cleavage reaction. *Nucl. Acids Res.* 18:6025–29
44. Saenger W. 1984. *Principles of Nucleic Acid Structure.* New York: Springer-Verlag
45. SantaLucia J, Kierzek R, Turner DH. 1990. Effects of GA mismatches on the structure and thermodynamics of RNA internal loops. *Biochemistry* 29:8813–19
46. SantaLucia JJ, Turner DH. 1993. Structure of (rGGCGAGCC)₂ in solution from NMR and restrained molecular dynamics. *Biochemistry* 32:12612–23
47. Sawata S, Komiyama M, Taira K. 1995. Kinetic evidence based on solvent isotope effects for the nonexistence of a proton-transfer process in reactions catalyzed by the hammerhead ribozyme—implications to the double-metal-ion mechanism of catalysis. *J. Am. Chem. Soc.* 117:2357–58
48. Scott WG, Finch JT, Klug A. 1995. The crystal structure of an all-RNA hammerhead ribozyme: a proposed mechanism for RNA catalytic cleavage. *Cell* 81:991–1002
49. Scott WG, Murray JB, Arnold J, Stoddard BL, Klug A. 1996. Capturing the structure of a catalytic RNA intermediate: the hammerhead ribozyme. *Science* 274:2065–69
50. Sheldon CC, Symons RH. 1989. Mutagenesis analysis of a self-cleaving RNA. *Nucl. Acids Res.* 17:5679–85
51. Sigurdsson ST, Tuschl T, Eckstein F. 1995. Probing RNA tertiary structure: interhelical crosslinking of the hammerhead ribozyme. *RNA* 1:575–83
52. Slim G, Gait MJ. 1991. Configurationally defined phosphorothioate-containing oligoribonucleotides in the study of the mechanism of cleavage of hammerhead ribozymes. *Nucl. Acids Res.* 19:1183–88
53. Slim G, Pritchard C, Biala E, Asseline U, Gait MJ. 1991. Synthesis of site-specifically modified oligoribonucleotides for studies of the recognition of TAR RNA by HIV–1 tat protein and studies of hammerhead ribozymes. *Nucl. Acids Symp. Ser.* 1991, pp. 55–58
54. Tuschl T, Eckstein F. 1993. Hammerhead ribozymes: importance of stem-loop II for activity. *Proc. Natl. Acad. Sci. USA* 90:6991–94
55. Tuschl T, Gohlke C, Jovin TM, Westhof E, Eckstein F. 1994. A three-dimensional model for the hammerhead ribozyme based on fluorescence measurements. *Science* 266:785–89
56. Uhlenbeck OC. 1987. A small catalytic oligoribonucleotide. *Nature* 328:596–600
57. van Tol H, Buzayan JM, Feldstein PA, Eckstein F, Bruening G. 1990. Two autolytic processing reactions of a satellite RNA proceed with inversion of configuration. *Nucl. Acids Res.* 18:1971–75
58. Woese CR, Winker S, Gutell RR. 1990. Architecture of ribosomal RNA: constraints on the sequence of "tetra-loops". *Proc. Natl. Acad. Sci. USA* 87:8467–71
59. Wu M, SantaLucia J, Turner DH. 1997. Solution structure of (rGGCAGGCC)₂ by two-dimensional NMR and the iterative relaxation matrix approach. *Biochemistry* 36:4449–60
60. Zhou D-H, Kumar PKR, Zhang L-H, Taira K. 1996. Ribozyme mechanism revisited: evidence against direct combination of a Mg²⁺ ion with the *pro*-R oxygen of the scissile phosphate in the transition state of a hammerhead ribozyme catalyzed reaction. *J. Am. Chem. Soc.* 118:8969–70
61. Zhou D-H, Usman N, Wincott FE, Matulic-Adamic J, Orita M, et al. 1996. Evidence for the rate eliminating departure of the 5′-oxygen in non-enzymatic and hammerhead ribozyme-catalysed reactions. *J. Am. Chem. Soc.* 118:5862–66

Annu. Rev. Biophys. Biomol. Struct. 1998. 27:503–28

PLECKSTRIN HOMOLOGY DOMAINS: A Common Fold with Diverse Functions

M. J. Rebecchi[1,2] and S. Scarlata[2]

Departments of [1]Anesthesiology and [2]Physiology and Biophysics, State University of New York at Stony Brook, Stony Brook, NY 11794;
e-mail: rebecchi@epo.hsc.sunysb.edu; suzanne@physiology.pnb.sunysb.edu

KEY WORDS: protein motifs, protein modules, membrane binding, phosphoinositides, G proteins

DEDICATION

This review is dedicated to the memory of Gregorio Weber, a pioneer in the study of the physical properties of proteins.

ABSTRACT

Pleckstrin homology (PH) motifs are approximately 100 amino-acid residues long and have been identified in nearly 100 different eukaryotic proteins, many of which participate in cell signaling and cytoskeletal regulation. Despite minimal sequence homology, the three-dimensional structures are remarkably conserved. This review gives an overview of the PH domain architecture and examines the best-studied examples in an attempt to understand their function.

CONTENTS

1056-8700/98/0610-0503$08.00

INTRODUCTION

In 1993, researchers recognized a novel protein motif of approximately 100 amino acid residues, repeated twice in *p*latelet and *l*eukocyte *C* kinase sub*str*ate prote*in* (pleckstrin), in a number of signal-transducing proteins, suggesting the existence of a modular domain (38, 65). Within one year of these reports, three-dimensional structures of pleckstrin homology (PH) domains appeared. Currently, the structures of the PH domains of pleckstrin (*N*-terminal) (103), β-spectrin (42, 62), dynamin (21, 30, 84), *p*hospho*l*ipase *C*-δ_1 (PLC-δ_1) (22), *S*on *o*f *s*evenless (Sos) (52), and *B*ruton's *t*yrosine *k*inase (Btk) (43) have been determined to high resolution; in two cases, PLC-δ_1 and β-spectrin, the domains are bound to a putative ligand, the polar head group of phosphatidylinositol 4,5-bisphosphate [PI(4,5)P$_2$]. Since the first reports of their existence, nearly 100 different eukaryotic proteins with pleckstrin homology domains have been identified, many involved in receiving and transmitting signals at the interface between the membrane and cytosol. Several different functions have been proposed. Here, we review these proposed functions using several examples to try to develop general conclusions.

A Common Structure

PH domains lack primary sequence similarity; only with newly developed computer programs have so many been identifed (78). At this low level of similarity, structural homology cannot be assured (12). Yet the known structures show a remarkable conservation of three-dimensional organization. The PLC-δ_1 PH domain can serve as an example (Figure 1*a*, color insert) (22). The core structure consists of a pair of nearly orthogonal beta sheets of four and three antiparallel strands resembling a collapsed β-barrel. The amino and carboxy-termini are located on the same side of the protein, but protrude in opposite directions. In all PH domains, the long C-terminal alpha helix packs against one edge of the β-sheet structure, stabilizing the entire fold. When their structures were first determined, the domains were compared to the family of up/down β barrels exemplified by retinol binding protein (103). The β-sheets of PH domains are closely packed, however, with no space for a comparable hydrophobic ligand.

Sequence alignment of the domains that have defined three-dimensional structure reveals few conserved amino acids, with the exception of a handful of hydrophobic residues in the core (Figure 2). The minimal secondary structure elements consist of seven β-strands and one C-terminal α-helix. Three of the six loops connecting the β-strands have hypervariable sequences: β1/β2, β3/β4,

```
Dyn    513 RKGWLTINNI |G........IMKGG|SK.EYWFVLT|AE|NLSWY|KDDEE.....|.........KE|KKYMLS
PLCδ1   23 LKGSQLLKVK |S..........SSW|RR.ERFYKLQ|ED|CKTIW|QESRKVMRTP|ESQLFSIEDIQ|EVRMGH
PLCβ2   22 SQGERFIKWD |D.........ETT|VA.SPV.ILR|VD|PKGYY|LYWTYQS..K|EMEFLDITSIR|DTRFGF
Plec1    7 REGYLVKKG. |.........SVFNT|WKPMWVVLL.|ED|GIEFY|KKKSDNS...|..........|PKGMIP
βSpec 2199 MEGFLNRKHE |WEAHNKK.ASSRS|WH.NVYCVIN|NQ|EMGFY|KDAKSAASGI|PY........H|SEVPVS
Btk      6 LESIFLKRSQ |Q.....KKKTSPL|NFKKRLFLLT|VH|KLSYY|EYDFERGRR.|...GS..KKG|SIDVEK
           |---β1---|  |---L---|   |--β2---|      |-L-|    |--β3--|          |-L-|  |--β4--|


Dyn    558 VDN|LKLRDVE|KGFMS|SKHIF...|ALF|NTE..QR|NVYKDY|RQLELAC|ET|QEEVDSWKASFLRAG
PLCδ1   80 RT.|EGLEKFA|RDVPE|DRCFSI..|.VF|K......|...DQR|NTLDLIA|PS|PADAQHWVLGLHKII
PLCβ2   73 AKi|DVFNMii|DNSFL|LKTLTV..|.VS|G......|...PDM|iFHNFVS|YK|ENVGKAWAEDVLALV
Plec1   51 LKG|STLTSPC|QDFGK|RMFVF...|KIT|T......|...TKQ|QDHFFQA|AF|LEERDAWVRDINKAI
βSpec 2256 LKE|.AICEVA|LDYKK|KKHVE...|KLR|L......|...SD|GNEYFQA|KD|DEEMNTWIQAISSA.
Btk     61 ITC|VETVVPE|KNPii|IERFPY..|.PF|QVV....|...YDE|GPLYVFS|PT|EELRKRWIHQLKNVI
           |-L-|  |--β5--|     |--L--|  |--β6--|        |---L---|   |--β7---|  |-L-|  |-----α-----|
```

Figure 2   Sequence alignment of several representative PH domains. Residues of PLC-δ1 and β-spectrin PH domains that specifically interact with ligand are in *bold* and *italics*; R → C mutation in Btk found in Xid mice (64) is underlined. *dyn*, dynamin; *plec1*, N-terminal PH domain in pleckstrin; *β-spec*, βIIΣ2 spectrin; *i*, insertions; *L*, loop; *heavy bars* under sequences, secondary structural elements that define PH domains. (Modified from 22, 76).

and $\beta6/\beta7$ (loops 1, 3, and 6 of the core structure), that tolerate large insertions; for example, one of the two PH motifs of PLC-γ is split at the $\beta3/\beta4$ loop by three src homology (SH) domains! Even though the sequence similarities are extremely low, the core backbones are nearly superimposable, leading to the conclusion that this is a modular domain whose structure is retained within the contexts of a diverse collection of host proteins.

An interesting feature of PH domains is their distribution of charged residues (Figure 1b, color insert). Typically, lysines, arginines, and histidines, some of which are located in the hypervariable loops, form a positively charged surface on one side of the domain, while the protein's opposite face, containing the C-terminal α-helix, is populated by acidic residues. A possible ligand binding site is located at the center of the positively charged surface. As will be seen in the examples to follow, this highly dipolar structure could help direct the host proteins to charged ligands located on target membranes.

The family of PH domain-related proteins has been expanded with the discovery of another modular domain that recognizes and binds to phosphotyrosines in the consensus sequence L/IXNPXpY. Known as phosphotyrosine-binding (PTB) domains, the motifs are found in adaptor proteins such as Shc, and function, like SH2 domains, to link their host proteins to specific phosphotyrosine sites (106). Despite a lack of sequence similarity, PH and PTB domains have a core backbone structure that is superimposable (rms < 2 Å) (56, 106). This extensive structural similarity argues in favor of a common evolutionary ancestor. Their function, however, may be more narrowly circumscribed than either PH or SH2 domains.

Plausible Functions

The number and variety of host proteins with PH motifs are staggering (over 100 at last count). Most can be grouped by function into a few classes: Ser/Thr protein kinases, Tyr protein kinases, small G-protein regulators, endocytic GTPases, adaptors, phosphoinositide metabolizing enzymes, and cytoskeletal associated proteins (79). Many contain a catalytic domain (e.g. kinase) and other adaptor domains (e.g. SH2 or SH3) as well. Some host proteins also contain the Dbl homology motif found in proteins with guanine nucleotide exchange factor (GEF) activity for Rac/Rho family members. Because PH domains lack any obvious catalytic properties and are often found in proteins tied in some way to the membrane, it was suggested that these domains function as membrane adaptors or tethers, linking their host proteins to the membrane surface (23). Although this idea has received some experimental support, the identity of the membrane binding partners (lipid or protein or both) is often controversial.

In this review, we give a brief summary of those PH domains and their host proteins that are best understood. We focus on two principal binding partners for PH domains: polyphosphoinositides and WD-40 proteins (motifs containing Trp-Asp $\sim$ every 40 residues), exemplified by G-protein β subunits. Most examples are chosen because they illustrate plausible functions that are supported by structural information. We apologize to the reader for leaving out other interesting PH domain proteins, and instead refer to other reviews that have appeared on this subject (56, 79).

SPECIFIC EXAMPLES

Phospholipase C-δ_1

PLC-δ_1 is a member of the phosphoinositide-specific PLC family of isozymes (designated β, γ, or δ) that cleave the phosphodiester bond of PI(4,5)P$_2$, releasing two intracellular second messenger molecules, inositol(1,4,5)trisphosphate [Ins(1,4,5)P$_3$] and diacylglycerol. All eukaryotic PI-PLCs are multidomain enzymes, containing at least one PH domain located near the amino terminus (except PLC-β_4) that is followed by two pairs of EF-hand motifs, an X and Y catalytic region, and a C-2 domain.

Each of the three mammalian forms of PLC has its own distinct mode of regulation (20, 55, 99). The δ isozymes, which are smallest ($\sim$85 kDa), are activated by a G-protein (G$_h$), a rho-GAP isoform, and calcium. Interestingly, δ_4 is localized to the nucleus where the level of expression varies with cell cycle. The γ isozymes, regulated by tyrosine protein kinases, have a long insertion between the X and Y regions encompassing an additional PH domain split by a pair of SH2 and a single SH3 domain. The PLC-β isozymes, which have a long C-terminal extension, are coupled to cell surface receptors by heterotrimeric GTP binding-proteins.

Like many other phospholipases, the PLC isozymes are soluble proteins that bind to the membrane/solution interface where they operate by a two-dimensional "scooting" mechanism, hydrolyzing numerous substrate molecules before returning to the bulk solution (33). There is substantial evidence that the PH domain contributes to this kinetic behavior. PLC-δ_1 (70, 75), and PLC-β isolated from turkey erythrocytes (45), bind strongly to PI(4,5)P$_2$ through a site that is not catalytic. Their PI(4,5)P$_2$ hydrolytic activities are consistent with a bisubstrate model in which at least one high-affinity PI(4,5)P$_2$ binding site, located in the PH domain, tethers the low-affinity catalytic site to the membrane surface (8, 13, 45, 60, 94). Studies of PLC-δ_1 directly support this idea. Deletion of the amino terminal 60 amino acids, comprising part of the PH domain, or specific amino acid substitutions therein, abolishes high-affinity PI(4,5)P$_2$ binding and scooting behavior, although the catalytic site remains functional (8, 13, 45, 60, 101). Identification of the PH domain as the sole high-affinity site is further supported by the observation that only the PH domain of the native enzyme is labeled by photoreactive analogs of Ins(1,4,5)P$_3$ or PI(4,5)P$_2$ (83).

Isolated recombinant δ_1 PH domain binds D-Ins(1,4,5)P$_3$ and PI(4,5)P$_2$ with high affinity (K$_d$s $\sim$ 0.2 and 1.2–5 μM, respectively) (31, 57, 83). Other inositol polyphosphates bind 15- to 62-fold less strongly and the L-stereoisomer of Ins(1,4,5)P$_3$ is 42-fold weaker than the D-isomer (57). Relative binding affinities of the native enzyme and its PH domain for phosphoinositides are PI(3,4,5)P$_3$ > PI(4,5)P$_2$ > PI(3,4)P$_2$ > PI(4)P $\gg$ PI (31). Curiously, the binding of the δ_1 PH domain to Ins(1,4,5)P$_3$ is at least fivefold stronger than that of PI(4,5)P$_2$ (57).

A high-resolution crystallographic structure of PLC-δ_1 PH domain complexed to Ins(1,4,5)P$_3$ (22) has been determined (Figure 1, panels a–c, color insert). As in other PH domains, the core structure is well conserved. Besides the normal complement of secondary structures, a short α-helix is found near the amino-terminus and another in the loop connecting β-strands 5 and 6. The whole structure is highly dipolar, with the positively charged surface surrounding the Ins(1,4,5)P$_3$ binding site formed by β strands 1 and 2 and loops 1, 3, and 6 (connecting β strands 1/2, 3/4, and 6/7). Most of the specific contacts involve hydrogen bonds to the 4- and 5-position phosphates contributed by 9 amino acids: K30, K32, R40, S55, R56, and K57 (Figure 1c, see color insert). Remarkably, 7 of the 12 bonds formed in the complex are contributed by 6 amino acids that participate in contacts with the 5-position phosphomonoester group: K30, R40, E54 (through a water molecule), S55, R56 (main chain amide), and K57. The 4-position phosphate is hydrogen-bonded to four amino acids: K30, K32, K57, and T107 (through a backbone carbonyl). The indole ring of W36 and a portion of K32 form van der Waals contacts with the inositol ring itself. This structure provides a molecular explanation for the binding specificity and affinities previously observed.

It is instructive to compare the three-dimensional structure of the PLC-δ_1 catalytic core (18, 19) to its own PH domain. Within the low-affinity catalytic site, a network of hydrogen bonds and salt-bridges ligate inositol ring substituents. K438, K440, S522, and R549, which are conserved in PLC-β and γ isozymes, bond with the 4- and 5-position phosphates, although the distribution of contacts does not favor the 5 position, as in the PH domain, and there are far fewer. The active site cannot accommodate a 3-position phosphomonoester, whereas the PH domain can, which is consistent with the observation that D-3 phosphoinositides are not substrates but can strongly bind the δ_1 PH domain in bilayer membranes (31) or as inositol polyphosphates (57). The structures of the catalytic region of PLC-δ and its PH domain explain the binding and enzymatic behavior and suggest the very simple idea that the δ_1 PH domain serves as a membrane tether for a processive catalyst, directing the enzyme to membrane surfaces enriched in its substrate. Indeed, the PH domain is required to localize PLC-δ_1 to the plasma membrane in living cells (69) and measurements of the cellular levels of PI(4,5)P_2 suggest that there is enough of this rare lipid to bind up all the intracellular PLC-δ_1 (9, 75). Because this isozyme also has a high affinity for Ins(1,4,5)P_3, it is likely that a dynamic equilibrium exists between PLC-δ_1 bound to PI(4,5)P_2 on the membrane surface, and bound to its soluble polar head group in the cytosol (57). This may have important functional implications that have yet to be addressed. For example, PLC-δ_1, responding to changes in calcium and Ins(1,4,5)P_3, could drive oscillations in PI(4,5)P_2 levels that are, like calcium, highly localized, thereby regulating the extent and frequency of other processes dependent on this lipid.

Although the function of this PH domain seemed settled, recent observations suggest a more complex role. Lomasney's group (8) discovered a single amino acid substitution in the PH domain (E54K) that enhances both K_s (twofold) and V_{max} (sixfold) of PLC-δ_1. The glutamate side chain at this position is normally linked through a water molecule to the 5-phosphomonoester in the δ_1 PH domain/Ins(1,4,5)P_3 complex. The simplest interpretation is that the catalytic core is altered, becoming more active by V_{max} allostery rather than merely enhanced affinity for PI(4,5)P_2. It is worth noting that the corresponding glutamic acid residue in Btk is subject to a gain-of-function mutation, E41K, that results in constitutive activation of Btk (58). As yet, there is no evidence of an interface between the PH module and the multidomain catalytic core. It is possible, however, that the PH domain once bound to the membrane surface forms stable contacts with the rest of the protein. Occupancy of the PH domain by PI(4,5)P_2, in conjunction with other activators such as calcium, could transmit information to the multidomain core through a concerted conformational change.

β-Spectrin

Spectrins are essential proteins and main structural components of the mesh-like cytoskeletal network beneath the membranes of mature erythrocytes. This submembrane framework is linked to transmembrane polypeptides via other peripheral proteins, such as ankyrin and band 4.1 (93). β- (∼220-kDa) and α- (240-kDa) spectrins consist of multiple domains strung together like beads on a string. Most information on higher-order structures come from the study of erythroid spectrin, which consists of α/β heterodimers (∼200 nm in length) with each polypeptide arranged in an antiparallel configuration wound together with its partner. The heterodimers are further arranged head to head. Five or six of these tetramers bind through their tail ends to a junctional complex, consisting of filamentous actin and band 4.1. Additional interactions with the membrane occur through the β chain amino-terminal region and ankyrin that binds to the band-3 anion channel. Many of the details of this cytoarchitecture are probably unique to erythroid cells, which are subjected to enormous stresses during their sojourn through narrow capillaries.

In nonerythroid cells, portions of the spectrin molecule may interact directly with the membrane surface, perhaps through a domain with pleckstrin homology. Longer forms of spectrin, βI and II (fodrin), which are found in abundance in the CNS, contain an approximately 200-amino acid long C-terminal region that includes a 110-amino acid PH domain (79, 96). Although membrane attachment, per se, is not dependent on the presence of this domain, it has been shown that the PH domain of the human $\beta I\Sigma 2$ isoform binds to protein-depleted membranes containing $PI(4,5)P_2$ and to $Ins(1,4,5)P_3$ in solution (96). Moreover, this domain localizes to the plasma membranes of COS7 cells expressing the $\beta I\Sigma 2$-spectrin PH domain attached to a green fluorescent protein from *Aequoria victoria* (95).

An X-ray crystallographic structure of $Ins(1,4,5)P_3$ bound to mouse $\beta II\Sigma 2$ spectrin was determined at high resolution (42). Additionally, NMR solution structures of the PH domains of mouse brain (62) and *Drosophila* β-spectrins (104) were also determined. Besides the typical core structure, both mouse and *Drosophila* β-spectrins contain a short α-helix in the loop connecting β-strands 3 and 4, which is not seen in the PLC-δ_1 structure. Like other PH domains, the protein is electrically polarized.

$\beta II\Sigma 2$-spectrin PH domain binds $Ins(1,4,5)P_3$ in a shallow groove formed by loops 1 and 5 connecting β-strands 1/2 and 5/6, and located in the center of a positively charged surface (42). Salt bridges and several hydrogen bonds are contributed by K8, R21, W23, and Y69 to the 4- and 5-position phosphates of $Ins(1,4,5)P_3$. S22 contributes a single hydrogen bond to the 1-phosphomonoester. Binding of $Ins(1,4,5)P_3$ is stereoselective for the natural D-stereoisomer of the $PI(4,5)P_2$ polar headgroup. The K_d of binding to the PH domain is ~40 μM, as measured by circular dichroism (CD), while mutation of K8 or R21 to N abolishes binding. There is no indication that a phosphomonoester group at the 3 position would enhance binding, which agrees with the relatively low-affinity of this domain for $Ins(1,3,4)P_3$.

As in the N-terminal pleckstrin PH domain (35; see below) and the mouse-brain form of β-spectrin (42), $Ins(1,4,5)P_3$ binding perturbs residues located in or near loop 1 of the *Drosophila* spectrin PH domain (104). Somewhat smaller chemical shifts are noted for residues in loop 5. Other residues perturbed in the *Drosophila* spectrin are near, but do not coincide with, those identified as the ligating residues in mouse spectrin. Although there is significant sequence similarity between *Drosophila* and mouse spectrin PH domains, only K17, corresponding to K8 in the mouse sequence of β-strand 1, was perturbed upon binding. Interestingly, K8 (mouse) and K17 (*Drosophila*) correspond to a lysine residue conserved in many PH domains known to bind polyphosphoinositides (Figure 2).

Unlike the PH domain of PLC-δ_1, the binding site of β-spectrin has no elaborate hydrogen bonding network and the inositol ring has no specific contacts with the protein. The binding site resembles a groove in the positively charged surface rather than the binding pocket of the PLC domain. Moreover, spectrin does not bind Ins(1,4,5)P$_3$ on the same face as PLC-δ_1, whose binding pocket is located on the other side of the protein bounded by loops 1 and 3 (22). Despite these differences, a few similarities are found. Position K8 in spectrin is equivalent to K30 of PLC-δ_1. Both ligate the 4- and 5-position phosphates. W23 in spectrin hydrogen bonds to the 4-position phosphate, while W36 of PLC-δ_1 ligates the 1-phosphomonoester.

The substantial differences between the spectrin and the δ_1 PI(4,5)P$_2$ binding sites explain the very large difference in binding constants (the K_d of spectrin is about 100-fold greater). It appears that the PH domain of spectrin falls into a class of PH domains with moderate affinity for the polyphosphoinositides. In cells, this polarized domain may direct a few spectrin isoforms to PI(4,5)P$_2$-enriched sites such as caveoli (71) or focal adhesions (10), where other determinants of membrane association are likely to play an equal or more dominant role in stabilizing attachment.

Pleckstrin

Pleckstrin, an abundant soluble protein found in cells of hematopoietic origin, is the major protein kinase C (PKC) substrate in thrombin-stimulated platelets (91). The protein contains N-terminal and C-terminal repeats of approximately 100 amino acids, which are the namesake for pleckstrin homology (38, 65). They are separated by a peptide of ~150 amino acids containing a number of PKC consensus phosphorylation sites.

Although the function of pleckstrin is not entirely clear, it is believed to regulate phosphoinositide/Ca^{2+} signaling. Pleckstrin down-regulates PLC-β activity by a mechanism that requires an intact N-terminal PH domain (1, 3). This inhibition of PLC-β is weakened by mutations of the PKC phosphoacceptor sites S113, T114, and S117 of pleckstrin; conversely, a mutant containing glutamates at each of these positions down-modulates signaling constitutively (3).

The amino-terminal pleckstrin PH domain, one of the first PH structures solved (103), binds polyphosphoinositides with modest affinity. Harlan and coworkers (35) found that the N- and C-terminal PH domains of pleckstrin along with others (T-cell specific tyrosine kinase, ras GTPase activating protein, and the β-adrenergic receptor kinase) bind to phospholipid vesicles that contain either PI(4,5)P$_2$ or PI(4)P with moderate affinity ($K_d \sim 50~\mu$M), but weakly to vesicles composed of other acidic lipids, phosphatidylserine (PS), and phosphatidic acid (PA).

The polyphosphoinositide binding site was identified by heteronuclear NMR experiments (35), which indicated that binding of the pleckstrin amino-terminal domain to $PI(4,5)P_2$, dissolved in a zwitterionic detergent, perturbs residues located in the positively charged cleft formed by β strands 1 and 2, and loop 1, as well as strands 3 and 4; of the residues perturbed, K14, T20, and W21, are well conserved among other PH domains that bind polyphosphoinositides with moderate or high affinity (β-spectrin and PLC-δ_1; see Figure 2). The appearent K_d, determined by an NMR perturbation assay, is approximately 30 μM (assuming a 1:1 binding stoichiometry). This is similar to the binding constant reported for β-spectrin (42). $PI(3,4)P_2$ and $PI(4)P$ binding is also detected, but appears to be weaker. Binding of $Ins(1,4,5)P_3$ to the pleckstrin N-terminal domain is apparently quite weak ($K_d \sim 500$ μM) in phosphate-buffered saline (36, 57), but may be stronger if measured in MES-buffered saline (36). Mutations of loop 1 lysines to glutamines, lowered the affinity for $PI(4,5)P_2$ in bilayers by $\sim$10-fold (36). As the authors point out, the $\Delta\Delta G$ of binding for each mutation was $\sim$1.4 kcal/mol, similar to the change in ΔG for removal of a Lys from model peptides binding to bilayers composed of acidic lipids (46). The results suggest a strong, but relatively nonspecific electrostatic component to the binding energy that appears to be typical of PH domains with a moderate affinity for polyphosphoinositides. Interestingly, the same mutations (K13N, K14N) in pleckstrin block plasma membrane association in living cells (61), suggesting that $PI(4,5)P_2$-binding is essential.

The recruitment of pleckstrin to membranes requires additional factors, including PKC, D-3 phosphoinositides, and G-$\beta\gamma$ subunits. The amino and carboxy-terminal PH domains bind $\beta\gamma$ subunits in vitro (4), with the later binding more strongly. The region involved was localized by truncation experiments to the first 30 amino acids overlapping the $PI(4,5)P_2$ binding site. This would suggest that $\beta\gamma$ interacts with pleckstrin through a site that is distinct from those proposed for β-adrenergic receptor kinase (β-ARK) or Bruton's tyrosine kinase (Btk) (see below). Moreover, unlike β-ARK, binding to $\beta\gamma$ subunits is not reversed by the addition of excess G-α subunits, suggesting the binding sites on G-$\beta\gamma$ subunits for this PH domain and G-α do not overlap, which is not typical.

Stable plasma membrane binding of pleckstrin in vivo requires phosphorylation of the PKC sites, as well as an intact amino-terminal PH domain (61). Other PH domains, including β-ARK fail to substitute for the amino terminal domain of pleckstrin, suggesting that this domain contains unique determinants. The interactions with phosphoinositides and G-$\beta\gamma$ subunits suggest a model in which pleckstrin functions as a down-modulator of phosphoinositide/Ca^{2+}

signaling through a feedback loop involving phosphorylation by activated PKC, and adsorption of G protein $\beta\gamma$ subunits released by receptor activation (2). Here, $PI(4,5)P_2$ and $\beta\gamma$ subunits serve as membrane tethering sites for pleckstrin. Isoforms of PKC, or other kinases, dependent on DAG or a localized D-3 phosphoinositide signal generated by PI-3 kinase, are recruited to the same membrane site, bringing together the protein kinases and pleckstrin. Phosphorylation of pleckstrin further stabilizes its binding, thereby promoting the sequestration of G-protein subunits and shutting down PLC. An additional level of autoregulation may be involved, since an isoform of PI-3 kinase, $PI3K\gamma$, is itself activated by $\beta\gamma$-subunits and phosphopleckstrin specifically inhibits this stimulation (2).

Dynamin

Dynamin is a 100-kDa GTPase that associates with endocytic vesicles (92). All dynamins contain a single PH domain, a C-terminal proline-rich region (SH3 binding motif), and an amino-terminal GTPase domain. In mammals, dynamin II is thought to participate in clathrin-mediated endocytosis and is ubiquitous. Dynamin I is predominantly expressed in brain, and is required for the rapid endocytosis of synaptic vesicles. Dynamin I molecules coat the necks of forming vesicles. The subsequent pinching off of these vesicles requires activation of the dynamin GTPase and clathrin (82). Microtubules, acidic phospholipids, synaptic vesicles, and SH3 domains bind to and increase the GTPase activity of dynamin (34, 89, 90). Activation by vesicles appears to involve oligomerization of dynamin and formation of GTP-independent helical filaments (40). Presumably, the dynamin GTPase activity is required to tighten the helical noose and pinch off the membrane. Phosphorylation by PKC stimulates dynamin GTPase activity by generating a soluble GTP-hydrolyzing form of dynamin, whereas dephosphorylation by calcineurin, stimulated by the rise in cytoplasmic calcium, results in membrane binding (59).

Dynamin GTPase activity is also stimulated by $PI(4,5)P_2$ and $Ins(1,4,5)P_3$, by a mechanism that requires an intact PH domain (77). $PI(3,4,5)P_3$ fails to activate, suggesting that binding to the 3-position phosphate is excluded. Binding is also stereospecific since D-$Ins(1,4,5)P_3$ binds ($K_d = 1.2$ mM) and stimulates catalysis, but the L-isomer does not. Although initial studies failed to find any evidence of high-affinity binding of phosphoinositides (21), Salim and coworkers, using a BIA core sensor chip, reported that the dynamin PH domain binds specifically to vesicles composed of phosphatidyl choline (PC), PE, PS, SPM, cholesterol, and $PI(4,5)P_2$, and to a lesser extent to $PI(4)P$, in agreement with their GTPase activation assay (77). Curiously, binding required micromolar calcium or millimolar magnesium chloride. The role of the divalent cations is unknown. In a separate study, binding to SDS-solubilized phospholipids was measured by the quenching of intrinsic tryptophan fluorescence (105). Binding in this study was in the order PI(4)P > PI(4,5)P$_2$ > PI. How these lipids affect membrane binding or control dynamin GTPase activity in vivo is unknown. Nonetheless, the results obtained with purified protein and artificial membranes suggest an important role.

Crystallographic (21) and NMR solution structures (30) of the dynamin PH domain have been determined. Charged amino acids are arranged on the surface to give an electrically polarized structure as is seen with other PH domains, although the calculated positive field potentials have a bilobal distribution. In addition, dynamin contains several solvent-exposed hydrophobic patches, which could accommodate an extended hydrophobic group such as the acyl chain of a phospholipid.

The Ins(1,4,5)P$_3$ binding site has been localized by perturbation of the 2-D (^{15}N-^{1}H) heteronuclear single quantum correlation NMR signals (77). The residues most perturbed were located in loops 1 and 3. Single amino acid substitution experiments identified residues essential for PI(4,5)P$_2$-specific membrane binding in loops 1, 3, and 6. Binding sites were explored theoretically using manual docking and energy minimization methods. Of the two possibilities, the site bounded by loops 1 and 3 is best supported by the mutagenesis work. Interestingly, mutations in loop 1 of the dynamin PH domain blocks rapid endocytosis (7).

In a separate study (105), a similar NMR methodology was used to locate the binding site for glycerophosphoinositol 4,5-bisphosphate (GPIP$_2$). Some of the residues were in the same or similar positions to those perturbed by Ins(1,4,5)P$_3$. According to these authors, the floor of the binding site, which accommodates GPIP$_2$ quite well, consists of the β-sheet formed by strands 1-4. Residues of loop 3 form one boundary. A hydrophobic patch on the surface of dynamin that extends away from the polar head group site could interact with the acyl chains of the glyceryophospholipids, explaining the observed high affinity for polyphosphoinositides in detergent/phospholipid mixed micelles. By contrast, Salim and coworkers (77) reported additional perturbations in loop 1 residues (^{1}H-^{1}H TOCSY and NOESY experiments). Their mutagenesis experiments further support their contention that the binding site is bounded by basic residues of loops 1 and 3 on the opposite face of the protein! Where this would leave any acyl chain interaction is not clear.

The low affinity of dynamin PH domain for Ins(1,4,5)P$_3$ suggests that additional interactions with the lipids are required, but these need not involve acyl chain binding. The affinity for polyphosphoinositides undoubtedly has a strong electrostatic component, not encountered in binding to the soluble polar head group, that should orient the binding site of this polarized domain toward the negatively charged membrane surface, thereby favoring adsorption.

Electrostatics alone, however, cannot explain the specificity for polyphospho-inositides. The key to understanding the source of the specificity may be the flexibility found in the hypervariable loops. NMR relaxation studies of the dynamin PH domain in solution show that loops 1 and 5 have extraordinary motion, on the nanosecond time scale, compared to the rest of the protein (29). By contrast, loops 3 and 6 are somewhat mobile, but on a much slower time scale (microseconds to milliseconds). It seems likely that loop 1, which inter-acts with the polar head group and undergoes large scale rapid motion, would be constrained when concentrated in the layer of solution above the membrane surface. This would present a limited ensemble of isoenergetic conformers to the interface. All that may be needed to further fix the loop and select the correct conformation are a few hydrogen bonds or salt bridges between the loop, the polyphosphoinositide, and the rest of the PH domain. At this stage divalent cations may also play a role. Thus, the difference in equilib-rium constants of approximately three orders of magnitude between binding to inositolpolyphosphates in solution and the comparable inositol lipid could represent the restriction in loop mobility provided by the interface and paid for by a favorable electrostatic attraction.

Son of Sevenless (Sos)

Sos is a ras guanine nucleotide exchange factor, catalyzing the exchange of GTP for bound GDP on ras (66). It is $\sim$150 kDa, has a Dbl homology motif, a PH domain, and a proline-rich region that binds the SH3 domain of Grb2. Sos is normally cytosolic and must be translocated to the membrane for ras activation (6). Grb2 recruits it to the membrane in response to receptor tyrosine kinase (RTK) stimulation. Alternately, translocation can occur without Grb2, and under these circumstances the PH domain of Sos appears to be essential to ras activation and may serve as the principal plasma membrane tether (98).

Polyphosphoinositides have been considered as possible ligands for the PH domain of Sos and some evidence of polyphosphoinositide-specific binding has been obtained. Murine Sos1 (mSos1) binds strongly to PC bilayers containing 5% $PI(4,5)P_2$, weakly to $PI(4)P$ and undetectably to $PI(3,4,5)P_3$ or PS (5 or 20%) (53). The isolated PH domain of mSos1 binds to $PI(4,5)P_2$ with a K_d of 1.8 μM (assuming a 1:1 complex). Chen and coworkers (11) have reported that human Sos1 (hSos1) PH domain binds to bilayers composed of PC:PE:PS $(1:1:1) + 2\%$ $PI(4,5)P_2$ with a comparable affinity. Curiously, intact mSos1 and the Sos1/Grb2 complex have much lower affinities for $PI(4,5)P_2$ ($K_d \sim 50$ μM) than the isolated PH domain (53).

The solution structure of mSos1 was determined by multidimensional NMR (52). In addition to the standard structural elements, this PH domain contains a short amino-terminal α-helix. Like other PH domains, it is electrically polarized with positive charges grouped on the surface opposite the C-terminal α-helix. Loop 3, which is unusually long, contains inserts unique to Sos. $Ins(1,4,5)P_3$ binding perturbs several of the residues located in loops 1 and 3, but the apparent equilibrium constant (K_d is $\sim$1.6 mM) is much weaker than that determined for $PI(4,5)P_2$, suggesting that high-affinity binding only occurs on the membrane surface. Interestingly, loop 3, like loop 1 in dynamin, is highly mobile in solution.

In vivo studies of hSos1 PH domain indicate that $PI(4,5)P_2$ binding is not the sole determinant of membrane localization or function. Chen and coworkers (11) reported that a mutation which disrupts the binding of hSos1 PH domain to $PI(4,5)P_2$, in vitro, does not affect its localization in living cells or its ability to serve as a dominant negative inhibitor of ras activation. By contrast, the PH domains of PLC-δ_1 and pleckstrin (61) are required for appropriate membrane localization of their host proteins; mutant forms of PLC-δ_1 lacking one of the $Ins(1,4,5)P_3$ loops remain diffusely cytoplasmic (69). Interestingly, other PH domains that bind $PI(4,5)P_2$ with high affinity (including PLC-δ_1) cannot substitute for hSos1 PH domain in stimulating ras to induce germinal vesicle breakdown in oocytes (16). These observations imply the presence of unique functional determinants in Sos1 PH domain that are unrelated to $PI(4,5)P_2$ binding.

Bruton's Tyrosine Kinase (Btk)

BTK, a member of the Tec kinase family, is found only in hematopoietic cells and plays a critical role in B-cell development and proliferation (64). It has received prominent attention because mutations found in Btk are responsible for human X-linked agammaglobulinemia (XLA), and murine X-linked immunodeficiency (Xid). From C to N terminus, it contains SH1(catalytic), SH2 (pTyr adaptor), and SH3 (proline-rich sequence adaptor) domains, a Tec homology region, which encompasses a proline-rich region and Btk motif, and a single PH domain. Although XLA mutations have been identified throughout the Btk gene, a cluster of mutations is found in the PH domain itself.

Btk is rapidly phosphorylated and activated following B-cell stimulation. Although this reaction presumably takes place at the plasma membrane, what links Btk there is not clear. Unlike Src, Btk and other Tec kinases lack a myristoylation site. One possibility is that the PH domain functions as a membrane tether. So far, G-protein $\beta\gamma$ subunits, PKC, D-3 phosphoinositides, and inositolpolyphosphates have been identified as possible binding partners that could mediate or affect membrane adsorption, perhaps through the PH domain.

The Btk PH domain binds $\beta\gamma$ subunits in vitro (88). Like β-ARK, however, sequences beyond the domain may be required for high-affinity binding (see below). Autophosphorylation of Btk, as well as phosphorylation of an exogenous substrate, are stimulated by G-$\beta\gamma$ subunits (54); $\beta_1\gamma_3$ is the most potent heterodimer tested. In living cells, overexpression of the Btk PH domain reduces the extent of phosphoinositide hydrolysis stimulated by $\beta\gamma$ subunits (88), suggesting some connection to G protein–coupled receptors.

The Btk PH domain also binds the calcium-dependent isoforms of protein kinase C (α, βI, βII), as well as the calcium-independent isoforms (ϵ, ζ) (102). Association with θ or η PKC is not detected. In mast cells, only a small fraction (<0.2%) of Btk is recovered in immunoprecipitates with PKC βI, but not other isoforms. The relevance of these observations to Btk function remains elusive.

Recent binding measurements of the Btk PH domain to D-3 phosphoinositides and their corresponding inositol polyphosphates have drawn considerable attention. The Btk PH domain binds inositolpolyphosphates with high affinity (K_d for Ins(1,3,4,5)P_4 ~40 nM) in the order: Ins(1,3,4,5)P_4 $\geq$ InsP$_6$ > Ins(1,3,4,5,6)P_5 > Ins(1,4,5)P_3 (27, 50). Itk and Tec, and two ras-GAP proteins with highly related PH domain sequences, GAP1 and IP4BP, also exhibit similar affinities for Ins(1,3,4,5)P_4 (14, 28). The exceedingly strong binding may be caused by the relatively low ionic strength of the binding buffer (50 mM HEPES-KOH, pH 7.2). At physiologic ionic strength the apparent K_d's are likely to shift upwards five- to tenfold, perhaps revealing a greater degree of specificity. Nevertheless, tenfold weaker binding constants would still fall into the physiologic range of inositolpolyphosphate concentrations (9). Interestingly, single amino acid substitutions corresponding to the mutations found in XLA, including R28C, greatly weaken inositolpolyphosphate binding, whereas the activating mutation E41K enhances binding to InsP$_6$ (twofold). Btk also binds the D-3 phosphoinositide, PI(3,4,5)P_3, but not PI(4,5)P_2, PI(4)P or PI (77), in qualitative agreement with the inositolpolyphosphate binding studies; lipid binding can also be abolished by the mutation R28Y. Binding to PI(3,4,5)P_3, however, requires divalent cations, whereas no such requirement was reported for inositolpolyphosphate binding.

Given the high affinity of Btk PH domain for Ins(1,3,4,5)P_4, it seems likely that a dynamic equilibrium exists between soluble Btk bound to Ins(1,3,4,5)P_4 and the membrane-associated fraction bound to PI(3,4,5)P_3. In cells, the concentration of InsP$_4$ (a mixture of different isomers) is 2–6 μM (9), while the concentration of PI(3,4,5)P_3, generated at the peak of cell stimulation, is comparable (assuming that this D-3 phosphoinositide is ~5% of the PI(4,5)P_2 pool). How this situation affects Btk signaling is unclear. For further discussion of related models of Btk regulation see Fukuda & Mikoshiba (28).

A high-resolution crystallographic structure of a mutant form of Btk PH domain (Xid: R28C), including a 56-amino-acid extension, the Btk motif, was recently reported (43). The PH core structure is typical, except for a long, partly disordered insertion in loop 5, which includes a short α-helix. Loop 1 is also somewhat disordered. The putative inositolpolyphosphate binding site, which in some ways is similar to that of PLC-δ_1, is formed by residues contributed by loop 1 and β strands 1, 2, 3, and 4. Interestingly, Xid and XLA mutations R28C or H and S14F, found within this binding site, do not affect domain stability, yet substantially weaken Ins(1,3,4,5)P$_4$ binding (27, 50).

The Btk motif consists of a globular structure whose fold is stabilized by the coordination of a single zinc ion by H143, C154, C155, and C165. This motif, which may contribute a portion of the binding surface recognized by G-protein $\beta\gamma$-subunits connects to the C terminus of the PH domain by an 8-residue peptide and forms an extensive interface with β-strands 5 through 7 of the PH domain. F146 of the Btk motif lies in a hydrophobic crevice formed by amino acids from several different regions of the PH domain. The observation that this PH domain has intimate contact with a neighboring sequence (Btk motif) suggests a route for transmitting allosteric signals to other regions of this multidomain enzyme. In this scenario, the PH domain senses the appearance of G-$\beta\gamma$ and inositolpolyphosphates, triggering a kinase response.

Akt

Akt (also known as PKB) protooncogenes constitute a subfamily of three related serine-threonine protein kinases, α, β, and γ, whose activity is dependent on activation of PI-3 kinase and membrane binding (39). These enzymes consist of an amino terminal PH domain, a central kinase region, and a carboxy-terminal region containing critical serine and threonine phosphoacceptor sites. Akt participates in growth-factor regulation of cell survival through a protein-kinase cascade in which Akt is activated by upstream protein kinases, such as PI(3,4,5)P$_2$-dependent protein kinase (PDK1) (5); downstream phosphorylation regulates other protein kinases, providing input for the cell's decision to undergo proliferation or apoptosis.

The D-3 phosphoinositides figure prominently in the regulation of Akt. PI(3,4)P$_2$ stimulates Akt kinase activity 50-fold, in vivo, and two- to sixfold in vitro (24, 25, 48). For a notable exception, see James et al (44). PI(4,5)P$_2$ is less effective than PI(3,4)P$_2$, and PI(3,4,5)P$_3$ is slightly inhibitory. An intact PH domain is required for activation. While it is clear that the Akt PH domain binds polyphosphoinositides in vitro (24, 25, 44, 48), more direct biophysical studies are needed to establish the molecular basis for D-3 phosphoinositide specificity, as well as the mechanism of Akt kinase activation, in vivo.

GRP1 and Cytohesin

A PI(3,4,5)P$_3$-specific binding protein, designated GRP1 (general receptor for phosphoinositides), has been cloned by a novel expression-screening method using radiolabeled phosphoinositides (47). Binding of GRP1 and cytohesin to PI(3,4,5)P$_3$ is specifically competed by Ins(1,3,4,5)P$_4$ (K$_i \sim 8$ μM), but not other inositolpolyphosphates such as Ins(1,3,4)P$_3$ or Ins(1,4,5)P$_3$. So far, no direct structural information is available. GRP1 is related in sequence to cytohesin 1, which is found in natural killer-T lymphocytes and contains a region that binds the carboxy-terminal cytoplasmic region of intergrin $\beta2$ (51).

In the current model proposed by Klarlund et al (47), PI(3,4,5)P$_3$ generated from PI(4,5)P$_2$ by PI-3 kinase provides the pivotal link between tyrosine kinase receptors and signal transmission from the inside of the cell through intergrin to the extracellular matrix. Activation of tyrosine kinase receptors stimulates PI-3 kinase, which in turn generates PI(3,4,5)P$_3$. PI(3,4,5)P$_3$ then recruits GRP1 or cytohesin-1 to the membrane surface, facilitating their binding to the cytoplasmic domain of intergrin $\beta2$.

Phospholipase C-β

Phospholipase C-β (PLC-β), like PLC-δ, hydrolyzes PI(4,5)P$_2$. Three of the four PLC-β isoforms, -β_1, -β_2, and -β_3, have PH domains at their N terminus in a similar arrangement to PLC-δ_1 (99). The β isozymes are regulated by heterotrimeric G proteins, with PLC-β_1 being preferentially activated by α subunits of the G$_q$ family, β_2 by G-$\beta\gamma$ subunits, and β_3 by both (20). Unlike PLC-δ_1, the PH domains of the three PLC-β isozymes do not function as PI(4,5)P$_2$-specific binding anchors. PLC-β_1 and -β_2 bind strongly to membranes regardless of the presence of PI(4,5)P$_2$, other acidic lipids, or calcium ions (76). Moreover, PLC-β_1, -β_2, and -β_3 fail to bind Ins(1,4,5)P$_3$ with high affinity or to photolabel with various inositol polyphosphate and polyphosphoinositide analogs (83). Of the nine amino acid residues that ligate Ins(1,4,5)P$_3$ in the δ_1 PH domain, only K30 of the δ_1 binding site is conserved (Figure 2). It is worth noting that turkey erythrocyte PLC, which has comparable amino-acid replacements as PLC-β_2, also shows specific binding to PI(4,5)P$_2$ (45), raising the question of whether other PI(4,5)P$_2$-specific binding regions, in addition to the catalytic site, could reside in the erythrocyte isozyme.

Activation of PLC-β_2 by G-$\beta\gamma$ subunits does not occur by recruitment of the enzyme to the membrane surface analogous to the mechanism proposed for β-ARK (see below). The presence of G-$\beta\gamma$ subunits activates PLC-β_2 catalytic activity several fold, but does not significantly alter the binding affinity of PLC-β_2 for artificial membrane bilayers (76). Under conditions where nearly all the enzyme is bound to the membrane interface, the increment of G-$\beta\gamma$ activation of PLC still depends on its surface concentration, implying a lateral association between this isozyme and G-$\beta\gamma$. Whether PH domains mediate this interaction is currently under investigation, but it is likely that additional regions of the β isozymes are involved [for example, see Wu et al (100)].

β-Adrenergic Receptor Kinases (β-ARKs)

β-adrenergic receptors are part of a larger family of G protein–coupled receptors. Agonist binding to the receptor stimulates exchange of GDP for GTP on the

α subunits of heterotrimeric G proteins, triggering the dissociation of α-GTP and $\beta\gamma$ subunits, and activating downstream effector proteins like adenylyl cyclase. Receptor-induced signaling rapidly wanes, however, because of phosphorylation of the receptor, which uncouples it from further G-protein activation. Phosphorylation can occur either by second messenger kinases (e.g. PKC and PKA), in an agonist-independent manner, or by a unique set of serine/threonine kinases, β-ARKs or G protein–coupled Receptor Kinases 2 and 3 (GRK-2 and -3). These later kinases only recognize the activated form of the β-adrenergic receptor and are thus agonist dependent (26, 74). Numerous GRKs (types 1–6) have been identified (81), but only GRK-2 and -3 (β-ARK for this discussion), lack palmitoylation or isoprenylation sites, and use G-$\beta\gamma$ subunits to facilitate membrane binding.

Stoffel and coworkers have investigated how β-ARK is recruited to the membrane surface where it phosphorylates β-adrenergic receptors (81). A key observation is the increase in rate and extent of agonist-dependent phosphorylation of the receptor by β-ARK, when free G-$\beta\gamma$ subunits are present in the membranes (72). Their studies indicated that the presence of G-$\beta\gamma$ increases β-ARK binding, which led these authors to reason that G-$\beta\gamma$ subunits activate β-ARK by recruiting the enzyme to the membrane surface, where it is in close proximity to its substrate. In addition to the G-protein subunits, acidic lipids—PI(4,5)P$_2$, in particular—are required for strong membrane association and receptor phosphorylation (17, 73). It is worth noting that β-ARK can be found constitutively associated with microsomal fractions, suggesting that additional factors control its binding to membranes (32, 67).

The site of interaction on β-ARK responsible for G-$\beta\gamma$ binding localizes to the C-terminal region of the protein (49) and encompasses the PH domain along with an $\sim$20 residue extension (86). Recognition that the PH domain participates in G-$\beta\gamma$ binding led to the suggestion that these domains anchor their host proteins to the membrane through G-$\beta\gamma$. Support for this idea comes from reports that many other proteins containing the PH motif are controlled by or regulate GTP-binding proteins (79).

Before discussing further β-ARK/G-$\beta\gamma$ association, it is worthwhile to consider the methods used in assessing G-$\beta\gamma$ binding affinity. The most common approach involves expressing the PH domain as a fusion protein with glutathione S-transferase (GST) in a bacterial system, which allows for a simple, affinity chromatography-based purification (49). The GST-fusion proteins are immobilized on glutathione S-sepharose beads. Binding is assessed by allowing the detergent-solubilized G-$\beta\gamma$ subunits to equilibrate with the resin, which is subsequently washed to remove unbound material. Bound proteins are then eluted and G-$\beta\gamma$ subunits are detected by immunoblotting. The source of G-$\beta\gamma$ is typically a mixture of isoforms from bovine brain or an impure mixture from cell lysates, but recent experiments utilized purified recombinant proteins (15). Binding is also assayed by measuring the ability of the GST-PH domains to compete for $\beta\gamma$-dependent receptor phosphorylation of membrane bound substrates by β-ARK (87).

Using these fusion protein assays, it has been shown that the β-ARK PH domain interacts strongly with G-$\beta\gamma$ subunits. Converting the central trypto-phan residue of the C-terminal α-helix to Ala, a destabilizing mutation, results in a protein that no longer interferes with G-$\beta\gamma$ activation (73). Further in-vestigation of β-ARK and G-$\beta\gamma$ binding showed that the C-terminal region of the β-ARK PH domain interacts with the WD40 region of G-$\beta\gamma$ (37, 87). The idea that this type of interaction may be general comes from studies indicating that many different PH domains (Dbl, ras-GRF, ras-GAP, PLC-γ_1, Atk, OSBP, Akt, β-spectrin, and IRS-1) also bind to G-$\beta\gamma$, but much more weakly and to a smaller extent (63, 87). In parallel studies, it was found that β-ARK, as well as several other PH domains, bind to another WD40 protein, the *Lis1* gene prod-uct, which is unrelated to G-β (97). These observations imply that binding to WD40 motifs is a general property of PH domains and that other determinants in the PH domain or its WD40 protein binding partner are required for speci-ficity. Indeed, intact β-ARK shows a preference for G-β_1 and β_2 over β_3 (15). It is important to note that the G-$\beta\gamma$ interaction site of GRK-2 spans some 20 residues beyond the PH domain, and elimination of these extra residues greatly reduces the extent of binding (63, 87).

The association of GST-PH domains to β-ARK, ras-GRF, ras-GAP, PLC-γ, Atk, OSBP, Rac b, β-spectrin, and IRS-1 PH domains to G-$\beta\gamma$ are all reversed with addition of G-α_o (86, 87). See Abrams et al (4) for a notable exception. These results imply that the site on G-$\beta\gamma$ bound by an α subunit overlaps the binding site for PH domains. It was suggested that the PH domain C-terminal region, including the α-helix, binds to G-β in a manner analogous to the G-α subunit switch-II region, which is responsible for the change in conformation upon GTP-GDP exchange (80). The crystallographic structure of G-β shows the first 20 residues are helical, followed by 7 repeats of the WD40 motif. The motifs are composed of β-sheets arranged in a ring to give a propeller-like structure. The small γ subunit forms a helical coiled-coil with the N terminus of the β-subunit that juts away from the center of the propeller. The switch II region, which is coordinated in a tunnel formed by the G-$\beta\gamma$ propeller region, may be displaced by the PH domain. Presently, more structural information is needed to determine whether PH domains, and their coextensive sequences, actually bind G-$\beta\gamma$ subunits in this manner.

G-$\beta\gamma$ and inositol lipids appear to bind opposite sides of the PH domain, suggesting that these domains bind both simultaneously. Indeed, $\beta\gamma$-subunits and negatively charged lipids, including PI(4,5)P$_2$, activate β-ARK (17, 73).

While Pitcher et al (73) presented evidence for synergistic activation of β-ARK by PI(4,5)P$_2$ and G-$\beta\gamma$, DebBurman et al (17) found that activation by PI(4,5)P$_2$ and G-$\beta\gamma$ at short times was additive, and at longer times, the kinase activity in the presence of both activators was close to the activity in the presence of only one. This result led to the conclusion that under some conditions acidic lipids may act competitively with G-$\beta\gamma$.

CONCLUSIONS AND PERSPECTIVES

From the limited set considered, it is clear that PH domains bind polyphospho-inositides, but their affinities and selectivities vary widely. Compare PLC-δ_1, β-spectrin, and the mammalian PLC-β. In PLC-δ_1, PI(4,5)P$_2$ binds with high affinity to a pocket lined by numerous specific contacts, whereas in β-spectrin, the binding site is a shallow groove where electrostatic attraction dominates, yielding only modest affinity. The mammalian β isozymes show no specific binding whatsoever. Furthermore, some PH domains, such as those of Btk, GRP1, or Atk, bind preferentially to D-3 phosphoinositides. These observations imply that some, but not all, PH domains serve as phosphoinositide-selective membrane tethers and that they have evolved quite distinct specificities and affinities.

The three-dimensional organization can help explain how the diversity of phosphoinositide binding affinities arose. Three hypervariable loops have been identified (1, 3, and 6) that tolerate enormous diversity, including the insertion of other secondary structures without upsetting the core fold. These loops form the positive face of the PH domain and contribute most of the side chains for phosphoinositide binding. Another source of variation is the flexibility of these loops in solution (Sos1, Btk, and dynamin). Their rapid motions, especially in loop 1, permit the adoption of numerous binding conformations, a few of which may be selected when these highly dipolar domains adsorb to negatively charged membrane surfaces. Hence, PH domains had a great deal of freedom to evolve distinct binding specificities independently of their host proteins and their own core structure, which may explain their current prevalence.

Those PH domains with moderate or high affinities for Ins(1,4,5)P$_3$ and PI(4,5)P$_2$ (β-spectrin and PLC-δ_1) appear to have well-ordered loop regions. Especially striking is PLC-δ_1, where the affinity for Ins(1,4,5)P$_3$ exceeds that for PI(4,5)P$_2$. In living cells, lipid and inositolpolyphosphates may compete for the same site in these domains, with important consequences for their host proteins. At the other extreme, dynamin and Sos1 have moderate affinities for polyphosphoinositides, but relatively poor affinities for the soluble inosi-tolpolyphosphates. Here, the flexibility of the binding loop may be functionally important. By avoiding competition from the soluble polar head groups, these domains may bind polyphosphoinositides on the membrane surface without interference. The situation, however, is clearly more complicated, considering that the PH domains of dynamin and Sos1, unlike PLC-δ_1, interact with additional unidentified binding partners that strongly influence both cellular localization and function (56).

WD-40 proteins, including G-protein $\beta\gamma$ subunits, may serve as binding partners for PH domains. High-affinity binding is localized to the C-terminal half of the PH domain, but requires additional sequence (see β-ARK discussion above). The short C-terminal stretch, necessary for strong binding to β-ARK, is not conserved in other proteins that bind $\beta\gamma$ subunits. For example, the BTK motif, which comprises the C-terminal extension of the Btk PH domain, is stabilized by a single zinc ion and folds back onto the β-sheet of the core structure. The corresponding sequence in β-ARK is unlikely to bind zinc or adopt a similar conformation. How or where PH domains interact with G-β subunits or other WD-40 proteins is currently unclear. Obviously, more structural information is needed to determine the nature of this binding site in β-ARK, Btk, PLC-β, and other PH domain proteins.

Most proteins with PH motifs also contain other adaptor modules, such as SH2 or SH3 domains, and are often the targets for protein kinases. This suggests the possibility that multiple different adaptor modules permit the simultaneous binding to different membrane partners or separate sites on the same macromolecule. Thus, in the absence of one partner (Tyr phosphorylation or generation of D-3 phosphoinositides), the other signal may not suffice. If distinct signals or combinations of signals are required to recruit each adaptor, then the binding between host protein and its membrane-anchored partner could be a mechanism for coincidence detection and signal integration, filtering out noise and summing the information from disparate pathways. If a catalytic moiety is attached, the host protein may amplify the input it receives and transmit a new, integrated signal. For example, by binding selectively to different polyphosphoinositides, host proteins containing PH and SH2 domains, like Btk, could detect and integrate the signals emanating from phosphoinositide and protein tyrosine kinase pathways.

The impression that PH domains only function as tethering devices is probably wrong. Current models imply that the PH domain is like a ball attached to the rest of the protein by a string, but there is not sufficient structural information to support this idea. The full-length PLC-δ_1 protein containing a single amino-acid substitution in its PH domain, analogous to the gain-of-function mutation in Btk, directly activates the catalytic core (8). Moreover, the structure of the Btk PH domain and its adjacent motif shows that they form a well-packed interface, suggesting a possible route, perhaps through loop 1, for transmitting an allosteric signal. This could place PH domains beyond the simple tethering model.

ACKNOWLEDGMENTS

We wish to thank Drs. Fukuda and Mikoshiba for sharing unpublished information and providing copies of manuscripts prior to publication; Dr. Diana Murray for preparation of the color molecular graphics; and Drs. Srinivas Pentyala, Edward Tall, and Loren Runnels for critical reading of the manuscript. Finally, we apologize to the many investigators whose work could not be cited or discussed only because of the breadth of this field and limited space. MJR and SS are supported by grants from the National Institutes of Health (GM-43422 and GM-53132, respectively).

Visit the *Annual Reviews home page* at
http://www.AnnualReviews.org.

Literature Cited

1. Abrams CS, Wu H, Zhao W, Belmonte E, White D, Brass LF. 1995. Pleckstrin inhibits phosphoinositide hydrolysis initiated by G-protein–coupled and growth factor receptors. A role for pleckstrin's PH domains. *J. Biol. Chem.* 270:14485–92
2. Abrams CS, Zhang J, Downes CP, Tang X, Zhao W, Rittenhouse SE. 1996. Phosphopleckstrin inhibits G-$\beta\gamma$-activable platelet phosphatidylinositol-4,5-bisphosphate 3-kinase. *J. Biol. Chem.* 271:25192–97
3. Abrams CS, Zhao W, Belmonte E, Brass LF. 1995. Protein kinase C regulates pleckstrin by phosphorylation of sites adjacent to the N-terminal PH domain. *J. Biol. Chem.* 270:23317–21
4. Abrams CS, Zhao W, Brass LF. 1996. A site of interaction between pleckstrin's PH domains and G-$\beta\gamma$. *Biochim. Biophys. Acta* 1314:233–38
5. Alessi DR, James SR, Downes CP, Holmes AB, Gaffney PR, et al. 1997. Characterization of a 3-phosphoinositide-dependent protein kinase which phosphorylates and activates protein kinase B-α. *Curr. Biol.* 7:261–69
6. Aronheim A, Engelberg D, Li N, al-Alawi N, Schlessinger J, Karin M. 1994. Membrane targeting of the nucleotide exchange factor Sos is sufficient for activating the Ras signaling pathway. *Cell* 78:949–61
7. Artalejo CR, Lemmon MA, Schlessinger J, Palfrey HC. 1997. Specific role for the PH domain of dynamin-1 in the regulation of rapid endocytosis in adrenal chromaffin cells. *EMBO J.* 16:1565–74
8. Bromann PA, Boetticher EE, Lomasney JW. 1997. A single amino acid substitution in the pleckstrin homology domain of phospholipase C-δ1 enhances the rate of substrate hydrolysis. *J. Biol. Chem.* 272:16240–46
9. Bunce CM, French PJ, Allen P, Mountford JC, Moor B, et al. 1993. Comparison of the levels of inositol metabolites in transformed hemopoietic cells and their normal counterparts. *Biochem. J.* 289:667–73
10. Burridge K, Chrzanowska-Wodnicka M. 1996. Focal adhesions, contractility, and signaling. *Annu. Rev. Cell Dev. Biol.* 12:463–518
11. Chen RH, Corbalan-Garcia S, Bar-Sagi D. 1997. The role of the PH domain in the signal-dependent membrane targeting of Sos. *EMBO J.* 16:1351–59
12. Chothia C, Lesk AM. 1986. The relationship between divergence of sequence and structure in proteins. *EMBO J.* 5:823–26
13. Cifuentes ME, Honkanen L, Rebecchi MJ. 1993. Proteolytic fragments of phosphoinositide-specific phospholipase C-δ_1: catalytic and membrane binding properties. *J. Biol. Chem.* 268:11586–93
14. Cullen PJ, Dawson AP, Irvine RF. 1995. Purification and characterization of an Ins(1,3,4,5)P$_4$ binding protein from pig platelets: possible identification of a novel non-neuronal Ins(1,3,4,5)P$_4$ receptor. *Biochem. J.* 305:139–43
15. Daaka Y, Pitcher JA, Richardson M, Stoffel RH, Robishaw JD, Lefkowitz RJ. 1997. Receptor and G-$\beta\gamma$ isoform-

specific interactions with G-protein-coupled receptor kinases. *Proc. Natl. Acad. Sci. USA* 94:2180–85

16. de Mora JF, Guerrero C, Mahadevan D, Coque JJR, Rojas JM, et al. 1996. Isolated Sos1 PH domain exhibits germinal vesicle breakdown-inducing activity in *Xenopus* oocytes. *J. Biol. Chem.* 271:18272–76

17. DebBurman SK, Ptasienski J, Boetticher E, Lomasney JW, Benovic JL, Hosey MM. 1995. Lipid-mediated regulation of G protein–coupled receptor kinases 2 and 3. *J. Biol. Chem.* 270:5742–47

18. Essen LO, Perisic O, Cheung R, Katan M, Williams RL. 1996. Crystal structure of a mammalian phosphoinositide-specific phospholipase C-δ. *Nature* 380:595–602

19. Essen LO, Perisic O, Katan M, Wu Y, Roberts MF, Williams RL. 1997. Structural mapping of the catalytic mechanism for a mammalian phosphoinositide-specific phospholipase C. *Biochemistry* 36:1704–18

20. Exton JH. 1996. Regulation of phosphoinositide phospholipases by hormones, neurotransmitters, and other agonists linked to G proteins. *Annu. Rev. Pharmacol. Toxicol.* 36:481–509

21. Ferguson KM, Lemmon MA, Schlessinger J, Sigler PB. 1994. Crystal structure at 2.2 Å resolution of the pleckstrin homology domain from human dynamin. *Cell* 79:199–209

22. Ferguson KM, Lemmon MA, Schlessinger J, Sigler PB. 1995. Structure of the high affinity complex of inositol trisphosphate with a phospholipase C pleckstrin homology domain. *Cell* 83:1037–46

23. Ferguson KM, Lemmon MA, Sigler PB, Schlessinger J. 1995. Scratching the surface with the PH domain. *Nat. Struct. Biol.* 2:715–18

24. Franke TF, Kaplan DR, Cantley LC, Toker A. 1997. Direct regulation of the Akt proto-oncogene product by phosphatidylinositol-3,4-bisphosphate. *Science* 275:665–68

25. Frech M, Andjelkovic M, Ingley E, Reddy KK, Falck JR, Hemmings BA. 1997. High affinity binding of inositol phosphates and phosphoinositides to the pleckstrin homology domain of rac protein kinase b and their influence on kinase activity. *J. Biol. Chem.* 272:8474–81

26. Freedman NJ, Lefkowitz RJ. 1996. Desensitization of G protein-coupled receptors. *Recent Prog. Horm. Res.* 51:319–53

27. Fukuda M, Kojima T, Kabayama H,

Mikoshiba K. 1996. Mutation of the pleckstrin homology domain of Bruton's tyrosine kinase in immunodeficiency impaired inositol 1,3,4,5-tetrakisphosphate binding capacity. *J. Biol. Chem.* 271:30303–6

28. Fukuda M, Mikoshiba K. 1997. The function of inositol high polyphosphate binding proteins. *BioEssays* 19:1–11

29. Fushman D, Cahill S, Cowburn D. 1997. The main-chain dynamics of the dynamin pleckstrin homology (PH) domain in solution: analysis of 15N relaxation with monomer/dimer equilibration. *J. Mol. Biol.* 266:173–94

30. Fushman D, Cahill S, Lemmon MA, Schlessinger J, Cowburn D. 1995. Solution structure of pleckstrin homology domain of dynamin by heteronuclear NMR spectroscopy. *Proc. Natl. Acad. Sci. USA* 92:816–20

31. Garcia P, Gupta R, Shah S, Morris AJ, Rudge SA, et al. 1995. The pleckstrin homology domain of phospholipase C-δ1 binds with high affinity to phosphatidylinositol 4,5-bisphosphate in bilayer membranes. *Biochemistry* 34:16228–34

32. Garcia-Higuera I, Penela P, Murga C, Egea G, Bonay P, et al. 1994. Association of the regulatory beta-adrenergic receptor kinase with rat liver microsomal membranes. *J. Biol. Chem.* 269:1348–55

33. Gelb MH, Jain MK, Hanel AM, Berg OG. 1995. Interfacial enzymology of glycerolipid hydrolases: lessons from secreted phospholipases A2. *Annu. Rev. Biochem.* 64:653–88

34. Gout I, Dhand R, Hiles ID, Fry MJ, Panayotou G, et al. 1993. The GTPase dynamin binds to and is activated by a subset of SH3 domains. *Cell* 75:25–36

35. Harlan JE, Hajduk PJ, Yoon HS, Fesik SW. 1994. Pleckstrin homology domains bind to phosphatidylinositol-4,5-bisphosphate. *Nature* 371:168–70

36. Harlan JE, Yoon HS, Hajduk PJ, Fesik SW. 1995. Structural characterization of the interaction between a pleckstrin homology domain and phosphatidylinositol 4,5-bisphosphate. *Biochemistry* 34:9859–64

37. Haske TN, DeBlasi A, LeVine H. 1996. An intact N terminus of the gamma subunit is required for the G-$\beta\gamma$ stimulation of rhodopsin phosphorylation by human beta-adrenergic receptor kinase-1 but not for kinase binding. *J. Biol. Chem.* 271:2941–48

38. Haslam RJ, Koide HB, Hemmings BA. 1993. Pleckstrin domain homology. *Nature* 363:309–10

39. Hemmings BA. 1997. PH domains—a universal membrane adapter. *Science* 275:1899

40. Hinshaw JE, Schmid SL. 1995. Dynamin self-assembles into rings suggesting a mechanism for coated vesicle budding. *Nature* 374:190–92

41. Huang CC, Pettersen EF, Klein TE, Ferrin TE, Langridge R. 1991. Conic: a fast renderer for space-filling molecules with shadows. *J. Mol. Graphics* 9:230–36, 242

42. Hyvonen M, Macias MJ, Nilges M, Oschkinat H, Saraste M, Wilmanns M. 1995. Structure of the binding site for inositol phosphates in a PH domain. *EMBO J.* 14:4676–85

43. Hyvonen M, Saraste M. 1997. Structure of the PH domain and BTK motif from Bruton's tyrosine kinase: molecular explanations for X-linked agammaglobulinaemia. *EMBO J.* 16:3396–404

44. James SR, Downes CP, Gigg R, Grove SJ, Holmes AB, Alessi DR. 1996. Specific binding of the Akt-1 protein kinase to phosphatidylinositol 3,4,5-trisphosphate without subsequent activation. *Biochem. J.* 315:709–13

45. James SR, Paterson A, Harden TK, Downes CP. 1995. Kinetic analysis of phospholipase C beta isoforms using phospholipid-detergent mixed micelles: evidence for interfacial catalysis involving distinct micelle binding and catalytic steps. *J. Biol. Chem.* 270:11872–81

46. Kim J, Mosior M, Chung LA, Wu H, McLaughlin S. 1991. Binding of peptides with basic residues to membranes containing acidic phospholipids. *Biophys. J.* 60:135–48

47. Klarlund JK, Guilherme A, Holik JJ, Virbasius JV, Chawla A, Czech MP. 1997. Signaling by phosphoinositide-3,4,5-trisphosphate through proteins containing pleckstrin and Sec7 homology domains. *Science* 275:1927–30

48. Klippel A, Kavanaugh WM, Pot D, Williams LT. 1997. A specific product of phosphatidylinositol 3-kinase directly activates the protein kinase Akt through its pleckstrin homology domain. *Mol. Cell. Biol.* 17:338–44

49. Koch WJ, Inglese J, Stone WC, Lefkowitz RJ. 1993. The binding site for the $\beta\gamma$-subunits of heterotrimeric G proteins on the beta-adrenergic receptor kinase. *J. Biol. Chem.* 268:8256–60

50. Kojima T, Fukuda M, Wantabe Y, Hamazato F, Mikoshiba K. 1997. Characterization of the pleckstrin homology domain of Btk, an inositol polyphosphate and phosphoinositide binding protein. *Biochem. Biophys. Res. Commun.* 236:333–39

51. Kolanus W, Nagel W, Schiller B, Zeitlmann L, Godar S, et al. 1996. Alpha L beta 2 integrin/LFA-1 binding to ICAM-1 induced by cytohesin-1, a cytoplasmic regulatory molecule. *Cell* 86:233–42

52. Koshiba S, Kigawa T, Kim J-H, Shirouzu M, Bowtell D, Yokoyama S. 1997. The solution structure of the pleckstrin homology domain of mouse son of sevenless (mSos)1. *J. Mol. Biol.* 269:579–91

53. Kubiseski TJ, Chook YM, Parris WE, Rozakis-Adcock M, Pawson T. 1997. High-affinity binding of the pleckstrin homology domain of mSos1 to phosphatidylinositol (4,5)-bisphosphate. *J. Biol. Chem.* 272:1799–804

54. Langhans-Rajasekaran SA, Wan Y, Huang XY. 1995. Activation of Tsk and Btk tyrosine kinases by G protein $\beta\gamma$-subunits. *Proc. Natl. Acad. Sci. USA* 92:8601–5

55. Lee SB, Rhee SG. 1995. Significance of PIP2 hydrolysis and regulation of phospholipase C isozymes. *Curr. Opin. Cell Biol.* 7:183–9

56. Lemmon MA, Falasca M, Ferguson KM, Schlessinger J. 1997. Regulatory recruitment of signaling molecules to the cell membrane by pleckstrin-homology domains. *Trends Cell Biol.* 7:237–42

57. Lemmon MA, Ferguson KM, O'Brien R, Sigler PB, Schlessinger J. 1995. Specific and high-affinity binding of inositol phosphates to an isolated pleckstrin homology domain. *Proc. Natl. Acad. Sci. USA* 92:10472–76

58. Li T, Tsukada S, Satterthwaite A, Havlik MH, Park H, et al. 1995. Activation of Bruton's tyrosine kinase (BTK) by a point mutation in its pleckstrin homology (PH) domain. *Immunity* 2:451–60

59. Liu JP, Sim AT, Robinson PJ. 1994. Calcineurin inhibition of dynamin I GTPase activity coupled to nerve terminal depolarization. *Science* 265:970–73

60. Lomasney JW, Cheng HF, Wang LP, Kuan Y, Liu S, et al. 1996. Phosphatidylinositol 4,5-bisphosphate binding to the pleckstrin homology domain of phospholipase C-δ_1 enhances enzyme activity. *J. Biol. Chem.* 271:25316–26

61. Ma AD, Brass LF, Abrams CS. 1997. Pleckstrin associates with plasma membranes and induces the formation of membrane projections: requirements for phosphorylation and the NH2-terminal PH domain. *J. Cell Biol.* 136:1071–79

62. Macias MJ, Musacchio A, Ponstingl H, Nilges M, Saraste M, Oschkinat H.

1994. Structure of the pleckstrin homology domain from beta-spectrin. *Nature* 369:675–77
63. Mahadevan D, Thanki N, Singh J, Mc-Phie P, Zangrilli D, et al. 1995. Structural studies on the PH domains of Dbl, Sos1, IRS-1, and beta ARK1 and their differential binding to G beta gamma subunits. *Biochemistry* 34:9111–17
64. Mattsson PT, Vihinen M, Smith CI. 1996. X-linked agammaglobulinemia (XLA): a genetic tyrosine kinase (Btk) disease. *BioEssays* 18:825–34
65. Mayer BJ, Ren R, Clark KL, Baltimore D. 1993. A putative modular domain present in diverse signaling proteins. *Cell* 73:629–30
66. McCormick F. 1994. Activators and effectors of ras P21 proteins. *Curr. Opin. Genet. Dev.* 4:71–76
67. Murga C, Esteban N, Ruiz-Gomez A, Mayor F Jr. 1997. The basal subcellular distribution of beta-adrenergic receptor kinase is independent of G-protein beta gamma subunits. *FEBS Lett.* 409:24–28
68. Nicholls A, Sharp KA, Honig B. 1991. Protein folding and association: insights from the interfacial and thermodynamic properties of hydrocarbons. *Proteins* 11: 281–96
69. Paterson HF, Savopoulos JW, Perisic O, Cheung R, Ellis MV, et al. 1995. Phospholipase C-δ_1 requires a pleckstrin homology domain for interaction with the plasma membrane. *Biochem. J.* 312:661–66
70. Pawelczyk T, Lowenstein JM. 1993. Binding of phospholipase C-δ_1 to phospholipid vesicles. *Biochem. J.* 291:693–96
71. Pike LJ, Casey L. 1996. Localization and turnover of phosphatidylinositol 4,5-bisphosphate in caveolin-enriched membrane domains. *J. Biol. Chem.* 271: 26453–56
72. Pitcher JA, Inglese J, Higgins JB, Arriza JL, Casey PJ, et al. 1992. Role of the beta-gamma subunits in targeting of the beta-adrenergic receptor kinase to membrane-bound receptors. *Science* 257:1264–67
73. Pitcher JA, Touhara K, Payne ES, Lefkowitz RJ. 1995. Pleckstrin homology domain-mediated membrane association and activation of the beta-adrenergic receptor kinase requires coordinate interaction with G beta gamma subunits and lipid. *J. Biol. Chem.* 270:11707–10
74. Premont RT, Inglese J, Lefkowitz RJ. 1995. Protein kinases that phosphorylate activated G protein-coupled receptors. *FASEB J.* 9:175–82

75. Rebecchi M, Peterson A, McLaughlin S. 1992. Phosphoinositide-specific phospholipase C-δ_1 binds with high affinity to phospholipid vesicles containing phosphatidylinositol 4,5-bisphosphate. *Biochemistry* 31:12742–47
76. Runnels LW, Jenco J, Morris A, Scarlata S. 1996. Membrane binding of phospholipases C-β 1 and C-β 2 is independent of phosphatidylinositol 4,5-bisphosphate and the alpha and beta gamma subunits of G proteins. *Biochemistry* 35:16824–32
77. Salim K, Bottomley MJ, Querfurth E, Zvelebil MJ, Gout I, et al. 1996. Distinct specificity in the recognition of phosphoinositides by the pleckstrin homology domains of dynamin and Bruton's tyrosine kinase. *EMBO J.* 15:6241–50
78. Saraste M, Hyvonen M. 1995. Pleckstrin homology domains: a fact file. *Curr. Opin. Struct. Biol.* 5:403–8
79. Shaw G. 1996. The pleckstrin homology domain: an intriguing multifunctional protein module. *BioEssays* 18:35–46
80. Srinivasan V, Waterfield MD, Blundell TL. 1996. Comparative analysis of the regions binding beta gamma-subunits in G alpha and PH domains. *Biochem. Biophys. Res. Commun.* 220:697–702
81. Stoffel RH, Pitcher JA, Lefkowitz RJ. 1997. Targeting G-protein-coupled receptor kinases to their receptor substrates. *J. Membr. Biol.* 157:1–8
82. Takel K, McPherson PS, Schmid SL, De Camilli P. 1995. Tubular membrane invaginations coated by dynamin rings are induced by GTP-γ S in nerve terminals. *Nature* 374:186–90
83. Tall E, Dorman G, Garcia P, Runnels L, Shah S, et al. 1997. Phosphoinositide binding specificity among phospholipase C isozymes as determined by photo-cross-linking to novel substrate and products analogs. *Biochemistry* 36:7239–48
84. Timm D, Salim K, Gout I, Guruprasad L, Waterfield M, Blundell T. 1994. Crystal structure of the pleckstrin homology domain from dynamin. *Nat. Struct. Biol.* 1:782–88
85. Touhara K, Hawes BE, van Biesen T, Lefkowitz RJ. 1995. G-protein $\beta\gamma$ subunits stimulate phosphorylation of Shc adapter protein. *Proc. Natl. Acad. Sci. USA* 92:9284–87
86. Touhara K, Inglese J, Pitcher JA, Shaw G, Lefkowitz RJ. 1994. Binding of G protein beta gamma-subunits to pleckstrin homology domains. *J. Biol. Chem.* 269:10217–20

87. Touhara K, Koch WJ, Hawes BE, Lefkowitz RJ. 1995. Mutational analysis of the pleckstrin homology domain of the beta-adrenergic receptor kinase: differential effects on G-$\beta\gamma$ and phosphatidylinositol 4,5-bisphosphate binding. *J. Biol. Chem.* 270:17000–5

88. Tsukada S, Simon MI, Witte ON, Katz A. 1994. Binding of $\beta\gamma$-subunits of heterotrimeric G-proteins to the PH domain of Bruton tyrosine kinase. *Proc. Natl. Acad. Sci. USA* 91:11256–60

89. Tuma PL, Collins CA. 1994. Activation of dynamin GTPase is a result of positive cooperativity. *J. Biol. Chem.* 269:30842–47

90. Tuma PL, Stachniak MC, Collins CA. 1993. Activation of dynamin GTPase by acidic phospholipids and endogenous rat brain vesicles. *J. Biol. Chem.* 268:17240–46

91. Tyers M, Rachubinski RA, Stewart MI, Varrichio AM, Shorr RG, et al. 1988. Molecular cloning and expression of the major protein kinase C substrate of platelets. *Nature* 333:470–73

92. Urrutia R, Henley JR, Cook T, McNiven MA. 1997. The dynamins: redundant or distinct functions for an expanding family of related GTPases? *Proc. Natl. Acad. Sci. USA* 94:377–84

93. Viel A, Branton D. 1996. Spectrin: on the path from structure to function. *Curr. Opin. Cell Biol.* 8:49–55

94. Wahl MI, Jones GA, Nishibe S, Rhee SG, Carpenter G. 1992. Growth factor stimulation of phospholipase C-γ_1 activity: comparative properties of control and activated enzymes. *J. Biol. Chem.* 267:10447–56

95. Wang DS, Miller R, Shaw R, Shaw G. 1996. The pleckstrin homology domain of human $\beta I\Sigma 2$ spectrin is targeted to the plasma membrane in vivo. *Biochem. Biophys. Res. Commun.* 225:420–26

96. Wang DS, Shaw G. 1995. The association of the C-terminal region of $\beta I\Sigma 2$ spectrin to brain membranes is mediated by a PH domain, does not require membrane proteins, and coincides with a inositol-1,4,5 triphosphate binding site. *Biochem. Biophys. Res. Commun.* 217:608–15

97. Wang DS, Shaw R, Winkelmann JC, Shaw G. 1994. Binding of PH domains of beta-adrenergic receptor kinase and beta-spectrin to WD40/beta-transducin repeat containing regions of the beta-subunit of trimeric G-proteins. *Biochem. Biophys. Res. Commun.* 203:29–35

98. Wang W, Fisher EM, Jia Q, Dunn JM, Porfiri E, et al. 1995. The Grb2 binding domain of mSos1 is not required for downstream signal transduction. *Nat. Genet.* 10:294–300

99. Williams RL, Katan M. 1996. Structural views of phosphoinositide-specific phospholipase C: signalling the way ahead. *Structure* 4:1387–94

100. Wu Y, Kuang Y, Smrcka A, Jiang H, Wu D. 1996. Identification of a phospholipase CB$_2$ region that interacts with G-$\beta\gamma$. *Proc. Natl. Acad. Sci. USA* 93:2964–68

101. Yagisawa H, Hirata M, Kanematsu T, Watanabe Y, Ozaki S, et al. 1994. Expression and characterization of an inositol 1,4,5-trisphosphate binding domain of phosphatidylinositol-specific phospholipase C-γ_1. *J. Biol. Chem.* 269:20179–88

102. Yao L, Kawakami Y, Kawakami T. 1994. The pleckstrin homology domain of Bruton tyrosine kinase interacts with protein kinase C. *Proc. Natl. Acad. Sci. USA* 91:9175–79

103. Yoon HS, Hajduk PJ, Petros AM, Olejniczak ET, Meadows RP, Fesik SW. 1994. Solution structure of a pleckstrin-homology domain. *Nature* 369:672–75

104. Zhang P, Talluri S, Deng H, Branton D, Wagner G. 1995. Solution structure of the pleckstrin homology domain of *Drosophila* beta-spectrin. *Structure* 3:1185–95

105. Zheng J, Cahill SM, Lemmon MA, Fushman D, Schlessinger J, Cowburn D. 1996. Identification of the binding site for acidic phospholipids on the pH domain of dynamin: implications for stimulation of GTPase activity. *J. Mol. Biol.* 255:14–21

106. Zhou MM, Ravichandran KS, Olejniczak EF, Petros AM, Meadows RP, et al. 1995. Structure and ligand recognition of the phosphotyrosine-binding domain of Shc. *Nature* 378:584–92

SUBJECT INDEX

A

A-74704
  HIV-1 protease inhibitors and, 267
A-75925
  HIV-1 protease inhibitors and, 267
A-77003
  HIV-1 protease inhibitors and, 267
A-80897
  HIV-1 protease inhibitors and, 267
ABT-38, see Ritonavir
Acidity
  cooperative effects in hemoglobin and, 16
  three-dimensionality of ribosome structure and, 47
Acquired immunodeficiency syndrome (AIDS)
  HIV-1 protease inhibitors and, 249–50, 276
Acridine orange
  spatio-temporal resolution of exocytosis from individual cells and, 80
Actin
  pleckstrin homology domains and, 509
  signaling complexes and, 67–68
Active invasion models
  chromatin and, 311
Acylphosphatase
  RNP recognition of RNA and, 422
Adair constants
  cooperative effects in hemoglobin and, 6, 12–13
Adaptors
  pleckstrin homology domains and, 506, 516
  signaling complexes and, 59, 65–66
Adenosine triphosphate (ATP)
  chromatin and, 312
  cytochrome c oxidase and, 330, 342
  signaling complexes and, 70–71
Adenylate cyclase
  signaling complexes and, 70
β-Adrenergic receptor kinases
  pleckstrin homology domains and, 511, 519–22

Advanced chemical synthesis
  HIV-1 protease inhibitors and, 249
Aequoria victoria
  pleckstrin homology domains and, 510
Aerobic bacteria
  cytochrome c oxidase and, 329
Affinity labeling
  three-dimensionality of ribosome structure and, 46
AG-1002
  HIV-1 protease inhibitors and, 270
AG-1004
  HIV-1 protease inhibitors and, 270
AG-1343, see Nelfinavir
AKAP79 protein
  signaling complexes and, 65
Alanine
  minor groove-binding architectural proteins and, 111
  multidimensional NMR and, 366–67, 371, 388, 390
  protein phosphatases and, 153
Algae
  multidimensional NMR and, 358, 363, 365
Alkalinity
  cooperative effects in hemoglobin and, 1, 3–4, 16, 27–30, 32
Allostery
  cooperative effects in hemoglobin and, 1–4, 19–20, 24, 27, 31–32
  pleckstrin homology domains and, 518
  protein phosphatases and, 135
Amino acids
  chromatin and, 288
  cytochrome c oxidase and, 334–40, 348–49
  cooperative effects in hemoglobin and, 1, 3–5, 15–17, 23–24, 26–30
  fMRI of brain and, 460
  HIV-1 protease inhibitors and, 255–60, 264, 269, 272, 275, 277
  minor groove-binding architectural proteins and, 111–14, 117–20, 122–28

multidimensional NMR and, 363–71, 381–82, 387–89, 392, 398
  pleckstrin homology domains and, 503, 506, 509–12, 514, 516–18, 520–21, 523
  protein phosphatases and, 133, 136–59
  RNP recognition of RNA and, 409–11, 420–21, 424–35
  signaling complexes and, 59–60, 62, 64
  spatio-temporal resolution of exocytosis from individual cells and, 82, 92
Aminoglycosides
  three-dimensionality of ribosome structure and, 45
Amperometry
  spatio-temporal resolution of exocytosis from individual cells and, 77, 86–90, 99
Anchors
  pleckstrin homology domains and, 519
  signaling complexes and, 59, 65–66
Anisotropy
  multidimensional NMR and, 393–95
Ankyrin
  pleckstrin homology domains and, 509
Antibiotics
  three-dimensionality of ribosome structure and, 45
Antibodies
  three-dimensionality of ribosome structure and, 39, 47
Antigens
  signaling complexes and, 66
Apoptosis
  pleckstrin homology domains and, 518
Arabidopsis thaliana
  minor groove-binding architectural proteins and, 108, 110, 113
  protein phosphatases and, 146–47
Archaebacteria
  three-dimensionality of ribosome structure and, 47

exocytosis from individual
cells and, 77, 84–88
Cysteine
cytochrome *c* oxidase and,
334–36
protein phosphatases and, 138,
140–41, 150–53, 155
Cysteinyl phosphate intermediate
protein phosphatases and, 133,
154
Cytochrome *c* oxidase
coupling of electron transfer
and proton motion, 347–48
ferryl species, 345–47
high-resolution structures
additional subunits, 337–38
electron-transfer pathways,
338–39
overall structure, 331–38
oxygen channels, 340
prosthetic groups, 331–38
protein subunits, 331–38
proton-transfer pathways,
339–40
subunit I, 334–37
subunit II, 334–36
subunit III, 332, 334
water channels, 340
hydroxy species, 345–47
introduction, 330–31
oxygen reduction and its
coupling to proton
movement, 341
electron transfer and oxygen
intermediates in mixed
valence enzyme, 344
ferrous-oxy species, 342–44
oxygen reduction in
fully-reduced enzyme, 345
proton-binding groups, 348–50
proton pumping pathways,
348–50
Cytohesin
pleckstrin homology domains
and, 518–19
Cytoplasm
three-dimensionality of
ribosome structure and, 37
Cytoskeleton
pleckstrin homology domains
and, 503, 506

D

DBD2 domain
minor groove-binding
architectural proteins and,
123
Denoising
fMRI of brain and, 463

Dephosphorylation
protein phosphatases and, 133,
147
RNP recognition of RNA and,
418
Deuteration
multidimensional NMR and,
358–72, 379, 381–98
Developmental switches
prokaryotic genetic circuit
simulation and, 209–11,
217
Diabetes
spatio-temporal resolution of
exocytosis from individual
cells and, 94
Diacylglycerol
pleckstrin homology domains
and, 513
Dictyostelium discoideum
prokaryotic genetic circuit
simulation and, 210
Diffraction patterns
three-dimensionality of
ribosome structure and, 35,
53
Diffusion
multidimensional NMR and,
393–94
signaling complexes and, 59,
61, 68–71, 73
spatio-temporal resolution of
exocytosis from individual
cells and, 85
Dihedral angle restraints
multidimensional NMR and,
392–93
Dimerization
chromatin and, 288, 292,
302–3, 319
cooperative effects in
hemoglobin and, 7–8,
10–11, 14–16
cytochrome *c* oxidase and,
338
HIV-1 protease inhibitors and,
254, 266, 276
minor groove-binding
architectural proteins and,
119
pleckstrin homology domains
and, 520
prokaryotic genetic circuit
simulation and, 217
protein phosphatases and, 156,
158–159
signaling complexes and, 60,
62, 65
Dinucleosomes
chromatin and, 297–98
2,3-Diphosphoglycerate

cooperative effects in
hemoglobin and, 2, 6–7, 9
Dipolar couplings
multidimensional NMR and,
393–94
Directional binding
minor groove-binding
architectural proteins and,
125–28
Disproportionation
cooperative effects in
hemoglobin and, 14
Distal pocket effects
cytochrome *c* oxidase and, 344
Distance restraints
multidimensional NMR and,
387–92
Diversity
pleckstrin homology domains
and, 503–23
protein phosphatases and, 133
DMP-323
HIV-1 protease inhibitors and,
259, 273–74
DMP-450
HIV-1 protease inhibitors and,
265
DNA-based computing
DNA nanotechnology and, 225,
239, 243
DNA nanotechnology
DNA geometrical object
construction
components of DNA
geometrical shapes,
229–30, 232
cube construction, 230, 232
solid-support methodology,
232–33
topology, 230–31
truncated octahgedron
construction, 233
double-crossover molecules,
239–41
networks of DNA
DNA-based computing, 243
periodic designs, 242–43
rigidity, 241–42
overview, 226–29
perspectives, 226–29
topological constructions
Borromean rings, 239
catenanes, 233–38
knots, 233–38
RNA topoisomerase,
238–39
DNA networks
DNA nanotechnology and,
241–44
DNA polymerases
chromatin and, 319

CUMULATIVE INDEXES

CONTRIBUTING AUTHORS, VOLUMES 23–27

549

CHAPTER TITLES, VOLUMES 23–27

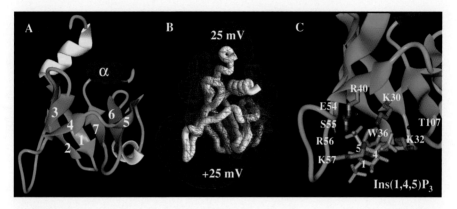

Figure 1   (*a*) Crystal structure of the PH domain of PLC-δ_1 solved by Ferguson and coworkers (22) as represented using MIDAS (41). *Green*, β sheets, and *purple*, α helix, characterize PH domains; *blue*, variable loop regions; *yellow*, helical insertions. (*b*) Electronic structure of PH-PLC-δ_1 in the same orientation as (*a*) in which the voltages have been calculated using GRASP (68). (*c*) Enlargement of the specific contacts made between the negatively charged bound ligand [Ins(1,4,5)P$_3$], *orange*, and residues in the PH domain of PLC-δ_1 (22). *Small pink circles*, water molecules that bridge ligand-protein hydrogen bonds.

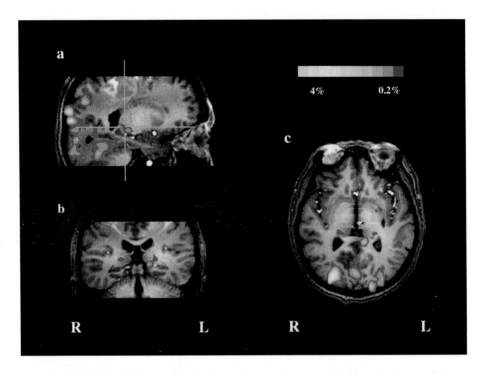

Figure 5 · The fMRI maps (in color) superimposed on anatomical images (gray scale) from a single individual during the photic stimulation task illustrating the activation in LGN and V1 areas in the (a) sagittal, (b) coronal and (c) axial image orientations. The cross-point of the two orthogonal lines in (a) identifies the LGN location in this sagittal plane. The two lines define the plane of images in (b) and (c) relative to each other and relative to the sagittal image shown in (a). The LGN activation is shown bilaterally in (b) and (c). (from Chen et al. (14))

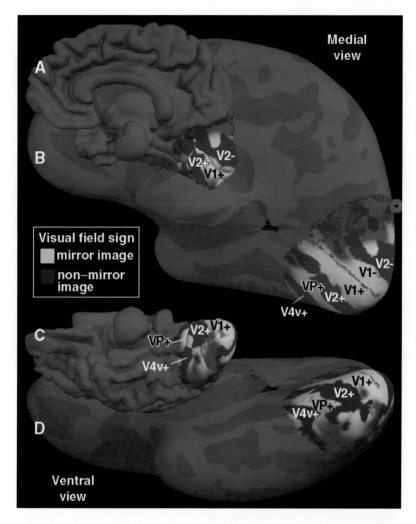

Figure 6   Visual areas V1, V2, V4 and VP in the human visual cortex identified using retinotopic mapping and the mirror versus non-mirror image representation of the visual field. Visual area maps presented either in the normal brain (A and C), or after "unfolding" the various convolutions of the cortical surface so as to generate a flat surface (B and D) for the medial view (A and B) and ventral view (C and D). (from Sereno et al. (83))